HIGH POLYMERS

Vol. I: Collected Papers of W. H. Carothers on High Polymeric Substances
               Edited by H. Mark and G. S. Whitby
Vol. II: Physical Chemistry of High Polymeric Systems
               Second Edition. By H. Mark and A. V. Tobolsky
Vol. III: Mechanism of Polymer Reactions
               By G. M. Burnett
Vol. V: Cellulose and Cellulose Derivatives (in three parts)
               Second Edition. Edited by Emil Ott, H. M. Spurlin, and M. W. Grafflin
Vol. VI: Mechanical Behavior of High Polymers
               By Turner Alfrey, Jr.
Vol. VII: Phenoplasts: Their Structure, Properties, and Chemical Technology
               By T. S. Carswell
Vol. IX: Emulsion Polymerization
               By F. A. Bovey, I. M. Kolthoff, A. I. Medalia, and E. J. Meehan
Vol. X: Polymer Processes
               Edited by Calvin E. Schildknecht
Vol. XII: Analytical Chemistry of Polymers (in three parts)
               Edited by Gordon M. Kline
Vol. XIII: Polyethers (in three parts)
               Edited by Norman G. Gaylord
Vol. XIV: Polyesters (in two parts)
               Edited by Norman G. Gaylord
Vol. XV: Radiation Chemistry of Polymeric Systems
               By Adolphe Chapiro
Vol. XVI: Polyurethanes: Chemistry and Technology (in two parts)
               By J. H. Saunders and K. C. Frisch
Vol. XVII: Configurational Statistics of Polymeric Chains
               By M. V. Volkenstein. Translated by Serge N. Timasheff and M. J. Timasheff
Vol. XVIII: Copolymerization
               Edited by George E. Ham
Vol. XIX: Chemical Reactions of Polymers
               Edited by E. M. Fettes
Vol. XX: Crystalline Olefin Polymers (in two parts)
               Edited by R. A. V. Raff and K. W. Doak
Vol. XXI: Macromolecules in Solution
               By Herbert Morawetz
Vol. XXII: Conformation of Macromolecules
               By T. Birshtein and O. Ptitsyn. Translated by Serge N. Timasheff and M. J. Timasheff

HIGH POLYMERS

A SERIES OF MONOGRAPHS ON THE CHEMISTRY, PHYSICS, AND

TECHNOLOGY OF HIGH POLYMERIC SUBSTANCES

VOLUME XXI

MACROMOLECULES IN SOLUTION

HERBERT MORAWETZ

Polytechnic Institute of Brooklyn
Brooklyn, New York

INTERSCIENCE PUBLISHERS

a division of John Wiley & Sons
NEW YORK • LONDON • SYDNEY

SECOND PRINTING, OCTOBER, 1966

PRINTED IN THE UNITED STATES OF AMERICA

To my father

Richard Morawetz

who first introduced me to the enjoyment of science

PREFACE

In submitting this book to the public, I should like to formulate briefly the motivations which guided me in the selection of the material and the manner in which I tried to present it. I have tried to impress the reader with the variety of phenomena which can be observed in solutions of macromolecules. This richness of the field was my main inspiration. Not all the phenomena observed are clearly understood and I made a conscious effort to avoid the common tendency to exclude the mention of observations for which there is currently no satisfactory interpretation. This, it is hoped, will have the result that the reader is not left with the impression that all that remains to be done are minor additions to the work of the great masters, but will stimulate him to search for exciting new discoveries yet to be made.

Since Flory's classical book on Polymer Chemistry was published in 1953, two revolutionary developments have had a profound impact on the field. The first was the discovery of techniques for the synthesis of stereoregular vinyl polymers. This development broadened the field of the study of solution properties of macromolecules with an increase of emphasis on techniques which might characterize the stereoregularity of a sample. It also had the effect of stimulating a more careful theoretical analysis of the conformations of chain molecules. The second major development was the discovery of the existence of systems in which chain molecules assume in solution precisely defined helical conformations. The study of helix-random coil transitions in isolated chain molecules was recognized as a one-dimensional analog of a melting process with a theoretical significance transcending macromolecular chemistry. This discovery also had another important effect: with the realization that macromolecules which retain in solution precisely defined conformations are not confined to the realm of biological macromolecules, the *de facto* separation of the fields of natural and synthetic macromolecules became an absurdity and a serious impediment to progress. This book was written, therefore, with the idea of drawing the exciting facts of modern protein and nucleic acid research to the attention of the chemist, whose work is mostly concerned with synthetic macromolecules. It tries to pose questions such as whether it is not possible that synthetic polymers with specific affinities for small molecules or with the ability to act as highly specific catalysts might one day be prepared.

Every author is faced with the difficult problem of defining for himself the public for which he is writing. This book had its origins in a set of lecture notes for a course in "Solution Properties of High Polymers" given at the Polytechnic Institute of Brooklyn and the graduate students attending this course influenced, without doubt, my image of the potential reader. More than half of the chemists specializing in high polymers are organic chemists; they have an increasing need to use physicochemical techniques based on difficult theoretical concepts, but a qualitative comprehension of the manner in which theoretical results were obtained coupled with a feeling for their physical significance are usually quite adequate. At any rate, a book dealing with such a vast subject has to restrict its scope in some manner, and it seemed wise to refer the reader to detailed treatments of theoretical developments written by specialists in those fields.

I imagine that it is always difficult for the author of a scientific treatise to find dedicated friends who will read his manuscript and offer constructive criticism. I was most fortunate in obtaining such help, particularly from my colleagues, J. E. Mark, who read the text "cover-to-cover" and Murray Goodman, who spent with me many hours patiently suggesting corrections and improvements. Others who read one or more chapters and helped me greatly with their criticism include F. A. Bovey, J. J. Hermans, G. Oster, and U. P. Strauss. A. Silberberg read the original outline of Chapter VI and offered many valuable suggestions. I am grateful to Mrs. Dorothy Luyster for her patience and skill in typing the text from a near-illegible manuscript and to my daughter Pegeen for checking the literature references. I also want to thank sincerely a number of my associates at the Polytechnic Institute of Brooklyn who spotted numerous mistakes and misprints. I am particularly indebted to M. Yamamoto; others who contributed substantially include R. Abbott, M. S. M. Alger, C. R. Earle, J. R. Earle, J. Falcetta, W. J. McGahren, E. Macchi, E. P. Mark, and G. Niu. All these friends have been most generous and helpful and I can only hope that they are fully aware of my gratitude. Finally, I want to thank C. G. Overberger and F. M. Beringer, who headed the Chemistry Department at the Polytechnic Institute of Brooklyn during the three years when this book was written, for helping me concentrate on this project by a reduction of my normal teaching assignment.

HERBERT MORAWETZ

CONTENTS

Glossary of Symbols   xiii

I. General Considerations   1

   A. Comparison of Methods Used for the Study of Small and Large Molecules   2
     1. Methods More Applicable to Small than to Large Molecules   3
     2. Methods Specifically Suited to Macromolecules   6
     3. Motivation Characteristic of the Study of Macromolecules   8
   B. Distribution Functions of Chain Lengths and Composition   12
     1. The "Most Probable Distribution" of Chain Lengths   13
     2. Chain Length Distribution in Vinyl Polymerization Terminated by
       Radical Recombination   16
     3. The Poisson Distribution   17
     4. Molecular Weight Averages   19
     5. Real Distributions and Generalized Molecular Weight Distribution
       Functions   21
     6. The Distribution of Copolymer Composition   23
   C. Relation of the Study of Macromolecules in Solution and in Bulk . . .   25
     1. Molecular Weight and Polydispersity   25
     2. The Shape of Macromolecules   26
     3. Relation of Solution Properties to Technologically Important Charac-
       teristics   30

II. The Solubility of Macromolecules   33

   A. Formation of Solutions from Species of Low Molecular Weight   33
     1. Thermodynamic Considerations.   33
     2. The Ideal Solution   37
     3. The Heat of Mixing.   39
     4. Regular Solutions.   43
     5. The Free Energy of Mixing in Real Systems   44
     6. The Solvent Properties of Water   47
     7. Phase Equilibria . . . . , ...   51
     8. Solubility of Crystalline Solids   54
   B. Binary Systems Containing Macromolecules   55
     1. Deviation of Polymer Solutions from Ideal Solution Behavior . . .   55
     2. Phase Equilibrium in Systems of a Polymer and Poor Solvents . . .   62
     3. The Consolute Point   63
     4. Phase Separation in Solutions of Stiff Elongated Macromolecules . .   68
     5. Some Typical Examples of Polymer-Solvent Interaction   69
     6. The Solubility of Crystalline Chain Polymers.   74

7. Thermally Reversible Gelation 76
8. Application of the Concept of "Solution" to Extremely Large Molecules 77
C. Three-Component and Multicomponent Systems Containing Macromolecules. 79
1. The Effect of Polydispersity on Polymer Solubility 79
2. Solubility of Polymers in Mixed Organic Solvents. 80
3. Solubility in Aqueous Electrolyte Solutions. 81
4. Incompatibility of Polymer Solutions 85
5. Ternary Systems with Strongly Interacting Polymers 86

III. Configuration and Conformation of Chain Molecules 91

A. The Stereoisomerism of Chain Molecules 93
B. Geometry of Flexible Chains 99
1. The Flexibility of Molecular Chains. 99
2. Statistics of Random Flight Chains 112
3. Model Chains with Restricted Flexibility 117
4. Random Flight Models of Branched Chain Molecules 121
5. Effect of Long Range Interactions on the Shape of Flexible Chains . 122
C. Specific Conformations. 132
1. Helical Conformations of Synthetic Polypeptides 132
2. The Double Helix of DNA. 139
3. Ordered Structures in Solutions of RNA and Synthetic Polyribonucleotides 145
4. Theoretical Treatments of Helix-coil Transitions 149
5. The Tertiary Structure of Proteins 153

IV. Equilibrium Properties of Dilute Solutions. 161

A. The Colligative Properties 161
1. Raoult's Law as a Limiting Law 161
2. Relation of Solvent Activity to Measurable Quantities. 162
a. Vapor Pressure. 163
b. Cryoscopy and Ebulliometry. 163
c. Osmotic Pressure. 164
3. The Scope of the Methods 164
4. Deviations from Raoult's Law in Dilute Solutions. 167
5. Osmotic Measurements with Partially Selective Membranes 175
6. Surface Pressure 178
B. Equilibrium Centrifugation 181
1. Methods for Determining Solute Distribution in the Ultracentrifuge Cell. 182
2. Ultracentrifuge Equilibrium in a Two-Component System 183
3. Equilibrium Centrifugation of a Polydisperse Polymer Solution . . . 185
4. Time Required for Approach to Equilibrium 188
5. Equilibrium Sedimentation in a Density Gradient. 189

V. Spectroscopy, Optical Activity, and the Scattering of Light and X-Ray . 197

A. Absorption Spectroscopy 199

1. Ultraviolet Spectra 200
2. Infrared Spectra 206
3. NMR Spectra 209
4. Fluorescence Spectra 219
B. Optical Activity. 221
1. General Considerations 221
2. Proteins and Synthetic Polypeptides. 229
3. Vinyl Polymers and Polyethers. 238
C. Light Scattering. 243
1. Scattering by Gases 243
2. Scattering from Solutions of Molecules much Smaller than the Wavelength of Light 246
3. Estimation of the Size and Shape of Macromolecules from the Angular
   Dependence of the Scattered Light Intensity 249
4. Light Scattering from Solutions in Mixed Solvent Media. 258
5. Light Scattering from Solutions of Polymers with a Variable Chemical
   Composition 260
D. X-Ray Scattering 262

VI. Frictional Properties of Dissolved Macromolecules 269

A. Linear Translation. 270
1. The Frictional Coefficient of Rigid Particles 270
2. Frictional Coefficients of Chain Molecules 273
3. Diffusion. 275
4. Sedimentation Velocity 278
5. Mobility of Small Molecules and Ions in Polymer Solutions 283
B. Rotary Diffusion 284
1. Rotary Diffusion Coefficient of Rigid Particles 284
2. Rotary Diffusion of Chain Molecules 286
3. Flow Birefringence 287
4. Disorientation of Oriented Solutions. 296
5. Depolarization of Fluorescence 297
C. Solution Viscosity 298
1. Viscosity of Solutions of Rigid Molecules 298
2. Viscosity of Solutions of Flexible Chain Molecules. 303
3. Interpretation of Intrinsic Viscosity in Conjunction with Other Solution Properties 312

VII. Polyelectrolytes 315

A. The Expansion of Flexible Polyions 320
1. Theories in Which the Chain Character of the Polyion is Taken Fully
   into Account. 321
2. Models Using Spherically Symmetrical Continuous Charge Distributions 325
3. Critique of Theories of Polyion Expansion 328

4. Experimental Evidence for Polyion Expansion 330
B. The Distribution of Counterions. 334
   1. Long-Range Electrostatic Interactions. 334
   2. Site-Binding of Counterions 339
C. Thermodynamic Properties 340
   1. Dialysis Equilibrium 340
   2. Ionic Activity Coefficients 342
   3. Osmotic Pressure 346
   4. Ionization Equilibria 348
D. Transport Properties. 356
   1. Electrophoresis 356
   2. Conductance 361
   3. Diffusion and Sedimentation 363

VIII. Molecular Association. 367

A. Association of Macromolecules with Low Molecular Weight Species . . 369
   1. Ion Binding by Flexible Polyion Chains 369
   2. Association of Small Molecules and Ions with Uncharged Chain Molecules 377
   3. Binding of Small Molecules and Ions to Globular Proteins 383
B. Molecular Aggregation of Macromolecules 392
   1. Aggregation of Flexible Chain Molecules. 392
   2. Association of Globular Proteins with other Macromolecules 395
   3. Dissociation and Association of Protein Molecules. 398
   4. The Antigen–Antibody Reaction 403
   5. The Tobacco Mosaic Virus Particle 407

IX. The Reactivity of Macromolecular Solutions 409

A. Reactions of Polymers with Small Molecules and Ions 410
   1. Effects of Conformation of Globular Proteins on their Reactivity . . 410
   2. Isotopic Exchange 412
   3. Electrostatic Effects on the Reactivity of Polyions 414
B. Intramolecular Interaction Effects on Polymer Reactivity. 422
   1. Neighboring Group Effects on the Reactivity of Chain Molecules . . 422
   2. Statistical Analysis of the Kinetic Pattern 427
   3. Bifunctional Catalysis 430
   4. Effects of Non-neighboring Groups 432
C. Reactions of Two Low Molecular Weight Species in the Presence of Polyions 434
D. Behavior of Solutions Containing Reactive and Catalytically Active Macromolecules 437

References 441

Author Index 469

Subject Index. 485

GLOSSARY OF SYMBOLS

a	activity
a_1	semiaxis of revolution of ellipsoidal particle
a_2	equatorial radius of ellipsoidal particle
A_2, A_3	second, third virial coefficient
A_s	surface area
b	length of chain link
b_0	optical rotatory dispersion parameter
b_s	length of statistical chain element
c	concentration (g-cm^{-3})
d	diameter of rod-shaped particle
D	linear diffusion constant
D_r	rotatory diffusion constant
$\mathfrak{D}$	dielectric constant
e	charge of electron
E	energy
$\mathcal{E}$	electromotive force
f	fugacity
f	frictional coefficient
f	ratio of concentrations of fixed and mobile charges in polyelectrolyte solutions
f^*	functionality of branch point
F	Force
F	Helmholtz free energy
$\mathfrak{F}$	Faraday constant
g	gauche
g	terrestrial gravitational constant
g^*	ratio of the radius of gyration in branched and linear chains
G	Gibbs free energy
h	elevation
h	distance between chain ends of flexible chain molecules
H	enthalpy
J	coupling constant
J	rate of energy dissipation
k	$4\pi \sin(\theta/2)/\lambda'$
k	reaction rate constant
k	Boltzmann constant

l	optical path length
L	length of rod-shaped particle, contour length of chain molecule
L_f	hydrodynamic shielding length
m	mass of particle
m_s, m_s'	molarity of uni-univalent salt
M	molecular weight
n	refractive index
n	number of moles
N	number of molecules
N^*	number of molecules per unit volume
$\boldsymbol{N}$	Avogadro's number
p	axial ratio of ellipsoidal particles
p	vapor pressure
P	degree of polymerization
P	pressure
$\wp$	factor describing the attenuation of scattered light owing to destructive interference
P_S	surface pressure
q	shear gradient
q_i	charge on the ith polymer chain segment
Q	charge of polyion
r	distance from center of molecular coil or distance from the axis of an ultracentrifuge
r_{ij}	distance between light scattering elements
R_s	radius of sphere
R_t, R_r, R_η	radius of hydrodynamically equivalent sphere
$\boldsymbol{R}$	gas constant
$\mathcal{R}$	Rayleigh ratio
s	radius of gyration
$\boldsymbol{s}$	sedimentation constant
S	entropy
s	selectivity coefficient
t	trans
t	time
T	temperature (°K)
u	velocity
$\bar{u}$	electrophoretic mobility
U	molar excluded volume
v	volume of particle
$\bar{v}$	specific volume

V_i	molar volume of species i
V_e	molar volume of hydrodynamically equivalent spheres
w	weight fraction
$\mathcal{W}$	probability distribution function
x	coordinate
x_i	mole fraction of species i
X	electrical field
y	coordinate
z	coordinate
z	coordination number
$\mathbf{z}$	parameter describing the permeability of molecular coils
z^*	dissymmetry of light scattering
Z	number of chain segments
Z_s	number of statistical chain elements
α	polarizability
α_i	degree of ionization
α_e	linear expansion coefficient
$\boldsymbol{\alpha}$	ratio of shear gradient to rotary diffusion constant
η	viscosity
η_0	viscosity of solvent
$[\eta]$	intrinsic viscosity ($cm^3 \cdot g^{-1}$)
θ	bond angle (Chapter III); scattering angle (Chapter V)
Θ	characteristic temperature for polymer–solvent system
κ	reciprocal of Debye-Hückel shielding length
λ	wavelength
λ'	λ/n
$\langle \lambda \rangle$	ratio of net charge to fixed charges of polyion
ν	number of charges
$\mathbf{v}$	frequency
ξ	extinction angle
Ξ	hydrodynamic permeability parameter
Π	osmotic pressure
ρ	density
ϱ	charge density
σ^*	stereoregularity parameter
δ	standard deviation
τ	relaxation time
ϕ	volume fraction (Chapter II); internal angle of rotation (Chapter III)
φ	orientation angle

Φ'	constant relating the intrinsic viscosity to the molecular weight and the radius of gyration of chain molecules
χ	Flory-Huggins interaction parameter
ψ	electrostatic potential
Ψ	Flory entropy parameter
Ω	element of solid angle
ω	angular velocity

Chapter I

GENERAL CONSIDERATIONS

About forty years have now elapsed since it was clearly recognized that some important materials occurring in nature or synthesized in the laboratory consist of very large molecules. Since then, the field of macromolecular chemistry has grown at a rate which seems spectacular even in our age of scientific and technological revolution. The driving force for this advance has been twofold: On the one hand, scientists learned to understand the relationship between the useful properties of such materials as cotton or Hevea rubber and what they came to call their "molecular architecture." This understanding proved invaluable in "designing" a wide variety of new materials such as synthetic fibers, synthetic rubbers, and plastics which duplicated and frequently surpassed the technically useful properties of materials available in nature. On the other hand, it was recognized that some of the most important constituents of living organisms are macromolecules, most notably perhaps the proteins and nucleic acids. It became increasingly apparent that an understanding of the relation between the molecular properties of these materials and their function in the living cell is one of the most hopeful pathways of advance in biology. The discipline dealing with such relationships came to be called "molecular biology."

The difference in the aims pursued by the "molecular architects" and the "molecular biologists" makes it unfortunately inevitable that they should often go their separate ways, each group knowing relatively little about the activities of the other. This, it might be said, is but another example of the specialization brought about inevitably by the vastness of scientific literature. Yet, when an investigator attempts to answer such questions as those concerning the size and shape of macromolecules, it may make little difference as to the methods he will employ whether the material to be investigated is a nucleic acid whose function it is to transmit the genetic message in successive cell divisions, or a synthetic fiber which is to be used for making socks. Until a few years ago a dividing line appeared to exist, due to the fact that macromolecules important in the life

1

process usually have rather rigorously defined shapes, while synthetic polymers consist generally of flexible chain molecules whose shape, highly dependent on conditions, could be discussed only in statistical terms. It is significant in this connection that the masterly exposition of the physical chemistry of high polymers, published by Flory in 1953, deals mostly with synthetic polymers and exclusively with materials consisting of flexible chain molecules. However, since then it has been demonstrated that the rigid structures characteristic of proteins and nucleic acids can be simulated by synthetic polypeptides and polynucleotides, and this has led to a strengthening of the conceptual unity of the polymer field.

A. COMPARISON OF METHODS USED FOR THE STUDY OF SMALL AND LARGE MOLECULES

In classical physical chemistry, dealing with small molecules, it is well understood that the interpretation of measured properties in terms of the properties of the molecular constituents of a sample is accomplished most easily in the case of very dilute gases and in the case of crystals. Investigations of the gaseous state have the advantage that samples can be easily dealt with under conditions where the effects of molecular interactions are small and can be taken care of by a suitable extrapolation procedure. The macroscopic properties of the gas may then be considered as made up additively from the properties of the individual molecules. At the other extreme, the crystalline state represents a state in which the constituent molecules of a sample are arranged in an almost perfect three-dimensional order and x-ray diffraction analysis methods may be used to define, except for thermal vibrations, the position of every atom in the crystal lattice. The theory of the liquid state is incomparably more difficult. Here the distances of molecules from each other are small, so that effects due to molecular interactions are dominant but are complicated by the absence of a long-range order. Nevertheless, the study of the liquid state, particularly that of dilute solutions, is an important branch of classical physical chemistry. If the solution is so dilute that the solute molecules may be considered to be effectively separated from one another, the property of the individual solute molecule is independent of the number of such molecules in the system and we may then study the molecular properties of the solute by comparing the macroscopic behavior of the solution and the pure solvent. Thus there is an analogy between the study of dilute gases and the study of solutes in dilute solutions. The properties of the solute molecule may be, of course, strongly affected by the nature of the solvent medium.

The basic principles used by physical chemists are equally applicable to large and small molecules.   Nevertheless, there are several considerations which make it convenient to deal with the physical chemistry of high polymers as a separate subject.   We may wish to subdivide these considerations into three categories.   On the one hand, we find that many important techniques widely used in classical physical chemistry are not practical with macromolecules.   Conversely, we shall see that a number of effects are too small to be conveniently measurable with small molecules, but become prominent and most useful when the molecules are large. Finally, there is a significant qualitative difference between the questions to be answered by the physical chemist, depending on whether he concerns himself with substances composed of small molecules or with polymers.

1. Methods More Applicable to Small than to Large Molecules

Many of the methods most useful with small molecules are either experimentally inaccessible with high polymers, or else have to be modified before they can be utilized.   This limitation particularly concerns techniques used in the determination of molecular weights.

It is obvious that it is not possible to study high polymers in the gaseous state.   In Fig. I.1. the equilibrium vapor pressures at 100°C of liquid normal paraffin hydrocarbons are plotted as a function of the number n of carbon atoms in the chain from hexane to hexadecane.   The data correspond closely to the relation $\log p = 5.55 - 0.33n$ where the pressure p is given in millimeters Hg.   On this basis, a normal paraffin with 50 carbon atoms would have a vapor pressure of only 10^{-12} mm Hg at 100°C.   For more polar compounds, the energy to separate a molecule of any given size from its neighbors would be larger and the vapor pressure correspondingly smaller.

When a substance is studied in solution, some characteristic effects, the so-called colligative properties, are proportional in the limit of high dilution to the number of molecules contained in the solute.   As the size of the molecules increases, the number of solute molecules present at any solution concentration is reduced and the effects due to the colligative properties fall off.   We shall deal with this subject more fully in Chap. IV and want to note here only that such classical measurements as those of freezing point depression and boiling point elevation can be applied to polymers only up to moderate molecular weights and require even then the use of special, highly sensitive techniques.

In the case of low molecular weight compounds, it is in general possible to determine molecular weights by analyzing the x-ray diffraction pattern

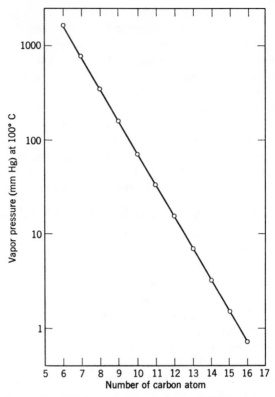

Fig. I.1. Dependence of equilibrium vapor pressure at 100°C on the chain length of normal alkanes.

obtained from crystals of a given substance. With polymers, this approach is feasible only in the exceptional case of crystalline globular proteins in which all the macromolecules are identical and where the individual macromolecules represent the repeating unit of the crystal lattice. This case is shown schematically in Fig. I.2(a). In the vast majority of cases polymers either do not crystallize at all, or else the repeating unit of the crystal lattice bears no relation to the length of chains, whose ends occur randomly dispersed within the lattice structure. Such a case is represented schematically by Fig. I.2(b). The estimation of the molecular weight of insoluble polymers can, therefore, be achieved only by indirect methods. One such case, which has been the subject of numerous studies over many years, is that of cellulose. It is possible to dissolve cellulose in a variety of reagents (such as concentrated phosphoric acid or aqueous cupriammonia

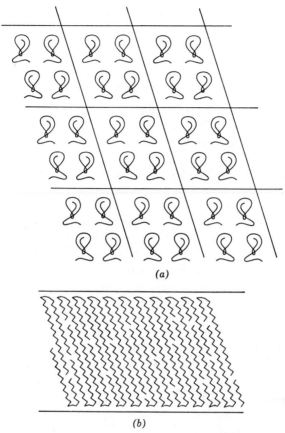

(a)

(b)

Fig. I.2. The nature of macromolecular crystals. (a) Schematic representation of a crystal of a typical globular protein. The unit cell contains several protein molecules. (b) Schematic representation of a crystal of a typical chain polymer. Chain ends are distributed at random within the crystal and the repeat pattern bears no relation to the size of the molecules.

solutions) but the polymer chains tend to degrade in all such solutions (Spurlin, 1955). It is, therefore, best to study the molecular weight of cellulose in the form of an easily soluble derivative, for instance cellulose nitrate, which can be prepared without significant degradation of the chains (Immergut et al., 1953). An even more difficult case is that of Teflon, which is insoluble and cannot be converted into soluble derivatives. Its molecular weight can be estimated by comparing the physical properties of a sample with those of calibration standards prepared with a radioactive chain initiator, so that the number of chain ends may be obtained from a determination of radioactivity (Berry and Peterson, 1951). However, the use of such indirect methods is generally undesirable and should be minimized as much as possible.

2. Methods Specifically Suited to Macromolecules

Just as some experimental techniques become inaccessible with increasing molecular size, other effects tend to become more prominent. The theory underlying the relation between the light scattering of a solution and the molecular weight of the solute, which we shall discuss in Chap. V, is of course equally applicable to large and small solute molecules, but the effects to be expected in solutions of low molecular weight solutes are small and could be studied only by using extreme care. Since the molecular weights of small molecules can be obtained much more conveniently and precisely from the measurement of colligative properties, it is not surprising that the light-scattering method was developed only in the search for new approaches to the characterization of high polymers. A similar point can be made about the equilibrium distribution of small or large molecules in a gravitational field. Again, the same principles hold for molecules of all sizes, but for small molecules the method is generally less convenient and less precise than molecular weight determinations by classical methods.

A different group of phenomena which are peculiarly well suited for the characterization of large molecules in solution are those which reflect the frictional resistance of the medium to the linear translation or rotation of the macromolecule. It is a striking fact that the resistance to the motion of the macromolecular solute through a space occupied by much smaller solvent molecules can be predicted satisfactorily from theories formulated for the motion of macroscopic bodies through a continuous viscous medium. It is obvious that any theory which treats the solute as composed of molecular particles and the solvent as a structureless continuum becomes increasingly unrealistic as the dimensions of the molecules of the two components of a system approach each other.

A polymeric chain molecule may change its shape within wide limits by rotation around the bonds connecting neighboring atoms of the chain backbone. Such changes in molecular shape, to be discussed in Chap. III, are described by organic chemists as molecular "conformations" and we shall use this term consistently in preference to "configuration," which has been used frequently to describe the shape of chain molecules, but which has a different and precise meaning in stereochemistry. The differences in energy corresponding to the transition from one conformation to another are usually rather small, so that even mild effects due to solvent–solute interaction may alter profoundly the probability distribution of the conformations in which the solute can exist. For small molecules these effects are difficult to study and little is known about them, since they have only recently become accessible to quantitative investigation by nuclear magnetic resonance spectroscopy (Bothner-By and Naar-Colin, 1962; Anet, 1962; Siddall and Prohaska, 1962).* In a long chain molecule, on the other hand, a systematic change in the conformation of the large number of bonds constituting the chain backbone will lead to an expansion or contraction of the chain which may be studied conveniently by following changes in the frictional properties of the solution. In addition, we shall see that the characteristic dimensions of large molecules may be estimated from the angular distribution of scattered light.

The measurement of osmotic pressure occupies a peculiar intermediate position between the phenomena discussed in this and the previous section. On the one hand, as one of the colligative properties, osmotic pressure decreases, at constant solution concentration, with the size of the solute molecule and the measurement of osmotic pressure for molecular weight determination becomes impracticable if the solute molecule is too large. On the other hand, it is also true that in classical physical chemistry osmotic pressure was "much talked about but little used" and that for good reason. The phenomenon depends on the existence of a semipermeable membrane which will transmit solvent but not solute and such selectivity can hardly be achieved without a considerable difference in the dimensions of the molecular particles of the two components of the system.

The very large deviations from ideal solution behavior observed in osmotic pressure measurements on polymer solutions were historically one of the serious obstacles to the acceptance of the existence of macromolecules. Later, when Staudinger proved that very large molecules did in fact exist, a need arose to explain on theoretical grounds why their solutions should be so non-ideal. The credit for a quantitative theory of these effects goes largely to Huggins and to Flory and his school. Qualitatively, they are due to the fact that bulk specimens of high polymers composed of flexible chain molecules must have the shapes of neighboring molecules correlated with one another, while this restriction is gradually eliminated when the system is diluted. It is interesting, in retrospect, that an analogous effect was never considered as a possible contributing cause of deviations from solution ideality until data on macromolecules became available.

---

* In the special case of optically active compounds, rotatory dispersion may also be used to demonstrate conformational transitions of small molecules (see Chap. V).

This is perhaps not surprising, since this effect remains rather small unless the chain length of the solute molecules becomes quite large.* Before the advent of polymer chemistry the theory of the excluded volume had been developed specifically for non-ideal gases, in which the molecules may be treated as compact spheres or ellipsoids and where there is no need to consider the behavior of flexible chains.

3. Motivation Characteristic of the Study of Macromolecules

It is, perhaps, not sufficiently emphasized that the questions which a physical chemist dealing with high polymers tries to answer are in general *qualitatively* different from the questions concerning a physical chemist who deals with substances composed of small molecules. Imagine a physical chemist who is being asked to describe the properties of an aqueous solution in which the solute does not consist of a single molecular species, but, for instance, of a mixture of alcohols. These may be not only members of the homologous series of primary alcohols derived from normal paraffin hydrocarbons but may contain also molecules with various numbers of branches and even polyhydric alcohols. Obviously there would be little purpose in describing a mixture of such complexity and since mixtures of small molecules may be fractionated to yield samples containing a single molecular species in a high state of purity, the study of the solution properties of small molecules is generally concerned with systems containing a single or at most two molecular species as solutes. With high polymers, on the other hand, pure molecular species may be isolated only in the case of a restricted group of naturally occurring globular proteins. In the case of synthetic macromolecules and many macromolecular preparations derived from living organisms we have to deal with complex mixtures. It is true that such mixtures may be subdivided by fractional precipitation, fractional extraction or other techniques, but even the sharpest fraction obtained in that manner is far from the ideal of "chemical purity" in the classical sense of consisting of a single molecular species. The task of the physical chemist is then twofold: Not only does he want to *describe* and *explain* the properties of solutions of his complex solute, but he is called upon to *characterize* the solute both in terms of the properties of its "average" molecule and in terms of the variability of these properties.

To obtain a feeling for the magnitude of the problem, let us consider a

* Particularly if the larger species is the dilute component of the solution as would normally be the case in the study of colligative properties.

"simple" polymer, such as polystyrene, whose formula is written schematically as

$$R-(-CH_2-CH-)_P-R'$$

where R and R' may be various end-groups which will make little difference to the properties of the substance if the chain is very long. No means are as yet known by which high molecular weight polystyrene with a uniquely defined degree of polymerization P can be prepared and a precise characterization of a sample requires, therefore, the specification of the distribution function of the molecular weight M. We define the distribution $N(M)$ so that

$$\int_{M_1}^{M_2} N(M)dM$$

is the fraction of chains with molecular weights in the interval $M_1 \leqslant M \leqslant M_2$ and

$$\int_0^\infty N(M)dM = 1$$

For unfractionated polystyrene samples, the form of $N(M)$ will depend on the polymerization conditions in a manner to be considered in the following section.

A further complication arises due to the fact that branched chains can be formed during the polymerization of styrene. The specification of the probability distribution of the various types of polymer molecules now becomes quite unwieldy, unless we introduce certain assumptions, which may be justified by mechanistic and kinetic considerations of the polymerization reaction. For instance, we may assume that the number of branches is proportional to the length of the chain backbone and that the probability of chain termination at every stage of monomer addition is the same in the growing chain backbone and the growing branch. It is important to emphasize that such assumptions do not have general validity but depend on the precise manner in which the branched macromolecules were formed.

In recent years yet another structural variable has become increasingly important in studies of synthetic polymers. We may note that in the chain molecule produced by polymerizing any vinyl or unsymmetrically substituted vinylidene monomer $CH_2{=}CXY$, every second carbon atom is an asymmetric center. Depending on the conditions of the polymerization we may have a completely random sequence of the steric configurations of these centers, or we may produce chains in which long sequences of these centers have either the same or regularly alternating configurations. Such polymers, represented schematically below, are called atactic, isotactic, and syndiotactic.

$$
\begin{array}{cccccc}
X & X & Y & X & Y & Y \\
| & | & | & | & | & | \\
-CH_2-C-CH_2-C-CH_2-C-CH_2-C-CH_2-C-CH_2-C- \\
| & | & | & | & | & | \\
Y & Y & X & Y & X & X
\end{array}
$$

atactic chain

$$
\begin{array}{cccccc}
X & X & X & X & X & X \\
| & | & | & | & | & | \\
-CH_2-C-CH_2-C-CH_2-C-CH_2-C-CH_2-C-CH_2-C- \\
| & | & | & | & | & | \\
Y & Y & Y & Y & Y & Y
\end{array}
$$

isotactic chain

$$
\begin{array}{cccccc}
X & Y & X & Y & X & Y \\
| & | & | & | & | & | \\
-CH_2-C-CH_2-C-CH_2-C-CH_2-C-CH_2-C-CH_2-C- \\
| & | & | & | & | & | \\
Y & X & Y & X & Y & X
\end{array}
$$

syndiotactic chain

Let us note that complete randomness or complete order in the sequence of the asymmetric centers represent extreme cases and that polymers prepared under a given set of conditions may show a systematic bias towards the isotactic or syndiotactic structure without the appearance of long ordered sequences. It would then be most desirable to develop methods for the characterization of the stereoregularity ("tacticity") of polymer chains and considerable effort has been expended in that direction.

The task of defining the nature of a sample becomes even more involved when we deal with copolymers. In that case, a complete characterization requires, in addition to the factors discussed above, a description of the relative frequency of the monomeric units as well as their distribution in the macromolecule. For instance, a copolymer containing an equal number of styrene (X) and p-chlorostyrene (Y) residues may have them distributed in the following ways:

The monomers may form a random sequence in a linear chain:

XYXXYXYYYXYXXYXYXXYXYY

The array in the linear chain may favor an alternation of the two monomer units:

XYXYYXYXYXYXYXXYXYXY

The chain may consist of long "blocks" of the two units (block copolymers):

XXXXXXYYYYYYYYXXXXX

Finally, the chain backbone may consist of units of one type and carry branches consisting of units of the other type ("graft copolymer"):

```
XXXXXXXXXXXXXXXX
   Y        Y        Y
   Y        Y        Y
   Y        Y        Y
   Y        Y        Y
   Y                 Y
   Y
   Y
```

Moreover, just as a sample of homopolymer does not consist of identical molecules but should be described by distribution functions of chain lengths, degrees of branching and stereoregularity, so the compositional variables of a copolymer will also cover a range described by probability distribution functions. This presents the polymer chemist with a particularly difficult problem, since fractionation procedures are generally more or less sensitive to all these variables. For instance, the solubility of polyethylene tends to increase both with increasing branching and decreasing molecular weight, or the solubility of cellulose acetate tends to increase both with increasing degree of acetylation and decreasing chain length. Methods which can be used to study compositional variation in isolation from chain length variation are particularly valuable. We shall see in Chapters IV and V how the study of ultracentrifugation and light scattering can contribute to the solution of these problems.

We have already touched on another class of molecular properties which are of special interest to the student of macromolecules—namely, the study of molecular shape. In a typical synthetic chain molecule whose "backbone" contains a sequence of a large number of single bonds, the possibility of rotation around these bonds enables the molecule to assume a large number of conformations. It is then obvious that we cannot deal with "a shape" of the molecular chain, but must consider a distribution function of such shapes or some particular average values. The average extension of a chain molecule in solution gives us an important insight into the relative energy of the available conformations and into interactions of the polymer with the solvent medium. In addition it is possible to gain information about the height of the energy barriers for rotation around the bonds of the chain backbone from data reflecting the behavior of the molecular coil when it is subjected to an alternating stress.

The aims of the physical chemist dealing with macromolecular solutions are somewhat different if he deals with materials of biological origin which may contain a single kind of macromolecule or a relatively small number of chemical species. Such materials may be highly complex chemically— for instance, proteins may consist of a sequence of up to twenty different amino acids constituting the building blocks of the chain. However, the molecules of a given species are uniquely defined, not only with respect to the exact sequence of these amino acid units along the chain, but even with respect to the conformation of the chain backbone. This precise definition of the molecular shape may be dealt with by the experimentalist on two levels: The historically older approach deals with the "overall shape" of the molecule in which its intricate form is approximated by an "equivalent ellipsoid of revolution." This is the type of information obtainable, in principle, from a study of the frictional properties of the solutions of rigid macromolecules. On the other hand, methods have become available more recently for studying the formation of helical sections in the chain backbone, which result from the ordered sequence of certain preferred conformations. This is the subject discussed in Chaps. III and V.

If the solution contains several well-defined macromolecular species, then it is most desirable to have a method by which the system may be analyzed quantitatively without the need of separating the macromolecular constituents from each other. This may be accomplished by the use of ultracentrifugation or by electrophoresis and this application provided, in fact, much of the stimulus for the development of these methods. Both methods may be adapted to serve as tools for the isolation of pure constituents from complex mixtures, but we shall not concern ourselves in this book with such developments.

B. DISTRIBUTION FUNCTIONS OF CHAIN LENGTHS AND COMPOSITION

We have seen in the previous section that the characterization of a polymer sample may involve not only the evaluation of a number of parameters but also distribution functions for the values of these parameters. A rigorous solution of this problem for a given sample is extremely difficult if not impossible. On the other hand, the interpretation of data obtained from measurements of the solution properties of the sample may be greatly assisted by knowledge of the manner in which the sample was prepared. With this additional information, we may use kinetic arguments to assume that we are dealing with certain *types of distributions* and our task is then simplified to the evaluation of a small number of parameters by which these distributions are characterized. We shall first discuss the nature and the origin of some simple distributions and consider later the causes for more complex distribution functions.

1. The "Most Probable Distribution" of Chain Lengths

A very frequently assumed distribution of chain length in a sample of linear macromolecules is commonly referred to as "the most probable distribution" (alternatively, this is referred to as a "normal" distribution). It would be obtained if we joined all the monomer units in the system into a single linear chain and cut subsequently at random a fraction ϵ of the links. The fraction of chains containing P units will then be proportional to the probability that in proceeding from one cut to the next we shall find P monomer units linked together, while the next link is broken. This probability is

$$N(P) = A(1 - \epsilon)^{P-1}\epsilon \tag{1.1}$$

For long average lengths of the chain $\epsilon \ll 1$ and we may approximate (1.1) by a continuous distribution function

$$N(P)dP = A\epsilon e^{-\epsilon P}dP \tag{1.2}$$

Moreover, since

$$\int_0^\infty \epsilon e^{-\epsilon P}dP = 1,$$

the normalization constant A must be equal to unity, so that

$$N(P)dP = \epsilon e^{-\epsilon P}dP \tag{1.3}$$

This distribution function is applicable to several cases of practical importance. Consider, for instance, a typical polycondensation reaction of two bifunctional reagents, such as a polyesterification

$$\underset{\parallel}{\overset{}{HOC}}\!\!-\!\!(-CH_2-)_n\!\!-\!\!\underset{O}{\overset{}{COH}} + HO\!-\!(-CH_2-)_m\!-\!OH \rightarrow$$
$$\qquad O$$

$$\underset{O}{\overset{}{HOC}}\!\!-\!\!(-CH_2-)_n\!\!-\!\!\underset{O}{\overset{}{CO}}\!\!-\!\!(-CH_2)_m\!\!-\!\!OH \rightarrow$$

$$HOC\!\!-\!\!\left[-(CH_2)_n\!\!-\!\!CO\!\!-\!\!(-CH_2)_m-\right]\!\!-\!\!OH \tag{1.4}$$

Since it has been shown that the reactivity of the hydroxyl or carboxyl groups does not depend on the length of the chain to which they are attached (Flory, 1939, 1940b), the reasoning leading to the distribution function (1.3) will describe the product of a polyesterification. The parameter ϵ will then have the significance of the fraction of the total number of carboxyl and hydroxyl groups which have remained unaltered at a given stage of the reaction if the two reactive groups were originally present in equivalent amounts.

The same type of distribution may be obtained in polymerization processes in which a single monomer at a time is added to the growing chain, provided the length of the chain is determined by a termination step, that this termination does not involve the coupling of two chains, and that the polymerization conditions remain constant during the preparation of the sample. Among numerous examples of such processes we may cite the following:

(a) The free radical polymerization of a vinyl monomer such as styrene in the presence of sufficient concentrations of chain transfer agents, *e.g.*, mercaptans, to ensure that chain transfer controls the length of the macromolecules:

$$R-(CH_2CH)_n-CH_2-\overset{\cdot}{C}H \;+\; CH_2{=}CH \xrightarrow{k_p} R-(CH_2CH-)_{n+1}-CH_2\overset{\cdot}{C}H \quad (1.5a)$$

$$R-(CH_2CH)_n-CH_2-\overset{\cdot}{C}H \;+\; R'SH \xrightarrow{k_{tr}}$$

$$R-(CH_2CH-)_n-CH_2CH_2 \;+\; R'S\cdot \quad (1.5b)$$

$$R'S\cdot \;+\; CH_2{=}CH \xrightarrow{k_p} R'SCH_2\overset{\cdot}{C}H \quad (1.5c)$$

(b) The ionic polymerization of formaldehyde with water acting as chain transfer agent:

$$HO-(CH_2O)_n-CH_2O^- + CH_2O \xrightarrow{k_p} HO-(CH_2O)_{n+1}-CH_2O^- \quad (1.6a)$$

$$HO-(CH_2O)_n-CH_2O^- + H_2O \xrightarrow{k_{tr}} HO-(CH_2O)_n-CH_2OH + OH^- \quad (1.6b)$$

$$OH^- + CH_2O \xrightarrow{k_i} HOCH_2O^- \quad (1.6c)$$

For both the processes (1.5) and (1.6), the parameter ϵ governing the chain length distribution function is given by

$$\epsilon = k_{tr} \, (S)/[k_{tr} \, (S) + k_p \, (M)] \tag{1.7}$$

where (S) and (M) are concentrations of chain transfer agent and monomer, respectively.

(c) Ionic polymerizations in which ion recombination terminates the chain:

$$\text{H}-(\text{CH}_2\text{CH})_n-\text{CH}_2\overset{+}{\text{CH}}\ldots\text{X}^- + \text{CH}_2{=}\text{CH} \xrightarrow{k_p} \text{H}-(\text{CH}_2\text{CH})_{n+1}-\text{CH}_2\overset{+}{\text{CH}}\ldots\text{X}^-$$

(1.8a)

$$\text{H}-(\text{CH}_2\text{CH})_n-\text{CH}_2\overset{+}{\text{CH}}\ldots\text{X}^- \xrightarrow{k_t}$$

$$\text{H}-(\text{CH}_2\text{CH})_n-\text{CH}{=}\text{CH} + \text{HX} \tag{1.8b}$$

In this case ϵ is given by

$$\epsilon = k_t/[k_t + k_p(M)] \tag{1.9}$$

(d) Free radical polymerization terminated by radical disproportionation:

$$\text{R(CH}_2\text{CH})_n-\text{CH}-\overset{\cdot}{\text{CH}} + \text{R(CH}_2\text{CH})_m-\text{CH}_2\overset{\cdot}{\text{CH}} \xrightarrow{k_t}$$
$$\qquad\qquad |\quad\quad\; | \qquad\qquad\qquad |\quad\quad |$$
$$\qquad\qquad \text{X}\quad\;\; \text{X} \qquad\qquad\qquad \text{X}\quad\; \text{X}$$

$$\text{R(CH}_2\text{CH})_n\text{CH}_2\text{CH}_2 + \text{R(CH}_2\text{CH})_m\text{CH}{=}\text{CH} \tag{1.10}$$
$$\quad\; |\quad\quad\quad\quad\quad\quad |\qquad\qquad |$$
$$\quad\; \text{X}\quad\quad\quad\quad\quad\;\; \text{X}\qquad\qquad \text{X}$$

For this case the characteristic parameter of the distribution function is

$$\epsilon = k_t(\text{R}\cdot)/[k_p(M) + k_t(\text{R}\cdot)] \tag{1.11}$$

when $(\text{R}\cdot)$ is the radical concentration.   If we assume steady-state conditions with the rate of chain initiation I equal to the chain termination rate, then we can express (1.11) as

$$\epsilon = (Ik_t)^{1/2}/[k_p(M) + (Ik_t)^{1/2}] \tag{1.12}$$

The most probable distribution is also obtained if a very long chain molecule is degraded under conditions such that all the links between the monomer residues have an equal probability of being broken. This condition is most likely to be met in various solvolytic degradations, although complications may arise from a slight difference between the reactivity of linkages close to the chain end and in the interior of the chain (Freudenberg and Blomquist, 1935).

Finally it should be pointed out that this type of chain length distribution corresponds to a state of maximum entropy with respect to the distribution of monomer units among a fixed number of macromolecules. Since the transfer of a monomer residue from one chain to a chain of different length does not involve any energy change, the "most probable distribution" of chain lengths is characteristic of a state of chemical equilibrium. This will be attained, for instance, if a polyester sample is heated with a transesterification catalyst or if a vinyl polymer is heated with a source of free radicals which will catalyze both polymerization and depolymerization.

2. Chain Length Distribution in Vinyl Polymerization Terminated by Radical Recombination

If free-radical-catalyzed vinyl polymerizations are carried out under conditions such that chain transfer is negligible, the chain termination may involve a disproportionation reaction as represented by (1.10) or a combination of two chain radicals:

$$R(CH_2CH)_{P'}—CH_2\dot{C}H + R(CH_2CH)_{P-P'}—CH_2\dot{C}H \xrightarrow{k_t}$$
$$\underset{X}{\mid} \qquad \underset{X}{\mid} \qquad \underset{X}{\mid} \qquad \underset{X}{\mid}$$

$$R(CH_2CH)_{P'}CH_2CHCHCH_2(CHCH_2)_{P-P'}R$$
$$\underset{X}{\mid} \qquad \underset{X}{\mid}\underset{X}{\mid} \qquad \underset{X}{\mid}$$

In this case a chain with a degree of polymerization P will form whenever two chains combine which contain P' and $P - P'$ monomer units, respectively. The fraction of such chains will be, therefore,

$$N(P) = A' \sum_{P'=1}^{P'=P-1} (1 - \epsilon)^{P'} \epsilon (1 - \epsilon)^{P-P'} \epsilon$$

$$= A' \sum_{P'=1}^{P'=P-1} (1 - \epsilon)^{P} \epsilon^2 \qquad (1.12)$$

Since all values of P′ are equally probable and the normalization constant $A' = 1$, the continuous distribution function becomes

$$N(P)dP = P\epsilon^2 e^{-\epsilon P}dP \qquad (1.13)$$

It is qualitatively obvious that this distribution is narrower than the "most probable distribution." This may be seen most easily by comparing a free radical polymerization in which chain termination takes place by recombination with one which occurs by the disproportionation of two chain radicals. If the recombination always involved two chains of equal length, the chain length would be merely doubled and the two distributions would be similar. Since, however, the chain combination may involve chains of different length, an averaging process is superimposed on the chain doubling and the chain length distribution is narrowed.

3. The Poisson Distribution

Much narrower chain length distributions are obtained if a fixed number of chains is allowed to add for the same period one monomer unit at a time in the absence of any chain termination process.* This case was first analyzed by Flory (1940a) for the polymerization of ethylene oxide. The methoxide catalyzed reaction would now be represented by

$$CH_3O^- + \overset{O}{\overset{/\backslash}{CH_2\!-\!CH_2}} \rightarrow CH_3OCH_2CH_2O^- \qquad (1.14a)$$

$$CH_3(OCH_2CH_2)_n\!-\!O^- + \overset{O}{\overset{/\backslash}{CH_2\!-\!CH_2}} \rightarrow CH_3(OCH_2CH_2)_{n+1}\!-\!O^- \qquad (1.14b)$$

and it would be assumed that (1.14a) is at least as fast as the subsequent steps. This type of kinetics leads to a Poisson distribution of chain lengths

$$N(P) = e^{-r}r^{P-1}/(P-1)! \qquad (1.15)$$

where r is the ratio of the number of molecules of monomer consumed to the number of growing polymer chains. For large values of r this distribution is extremely narrow and a high polymer sample with this distribution would be indistinguishable, with the available experimental precision, from a unique chemical species.

---

* The nature of this distribution may be visualized as follows: Let us select a time τ such that there is a 50% chance that a growing chain will add a unit. The fractional probability $N(P)$ that P units are added at time t is then equivalent to the probability of obtaining P "heads" in t/τ tosses of a true coin.

Another case in which a stepwise addition of monomer to growing polymer chains can take place without chain termination is the polymerization of N-carboxy-α-amino acid anhydrides to polypeptides

$$
\text{RH} + \underset{\underset{\displaystyle O}{\overset{\displaystyle \|}{\underset{HN}{\diagdown}}}{\overset{\displaystyle R'}{\underset{\displaystyle |}{HC}}}\!\!\!\!\underset{\displaystyle C}{\!\!-\!\!}\!\!\underset{\displaystyle O}{\diagup}\!\!\!CO \longrightarrow \underset{\displaystyle O}{\overset{\displaystyle R'}{\underset{\displaystyle \|}{RC}}}\!\!-\!CHNH_2 + CO_2 \qquad (1.16a)
$$

$$
R{-}(\underset{\underset{\displaystyle O \;\; H}{}}{-CCHN-})_n{-}H + \underset{\underset{\displaystyle O}{}}{\overset{\displaystyle R'}{HC}}\!\!-\!CO \longrightarrow R{-}(-CCHN-)_{n+1}{-}H + CO_2 \quad (1.16b)
$$

More recently, it has been pointed out (Waack et al., 1957) that anion-catalyzed vinyl polymerization can, in principle, be carried out under conditions under which the chains do not terminate and that such processes could, therefore, lead to a product with a narrow Poisson distribution. These processes are initiated by the product of an electron transfer from metallic alkali to an aromatic hydrocarbon D (such as naphthalene) in a suitable solvent medium,

$$
\text{Na} + \text{D} \rightarrow \text{Na}^+ + \text{D}^{\overline{\;}} \qquad (1.17a)
$$

On addition of a monomer such as styrene, the subsequent reaction steps are presumably

$$
\text{D}^{\overline{\;}} + CH_2{=}CH \rightleftarrows D + \dot{C}H_2{-}\bar{C}H \qquad (1.17b)
$$

$$
2\dot{C}H_2{-}\bar{C}H \rightarrow \bar{C}HCH_2CH_2\bar{C}H \qquad (1.17c)
$$

followed by monomer addition to the dianion. Wenger (1960a,b) has emphasized that the attainment of a Poisson distribution requires that (1.17b) reach completion before the onset of chain propagation and has outlined procedures to assure this result.

A very interesting method by which a Poisson distribution may be approached in free-radical-catalyzed vinyl polymerization was suggested by Bianchi et al. (1957). The monomer is dispersed in an emulsion and exposed to intense light flashes at fixed time intervals. Each flash produces radicals which may initiate polymerization in small particles of polymer swollen with monomer. Since these particles are very small, the radicals contained in them will tend to combine rapidly so that within a short time all radicals will have disappeared except for those contained in particles carrying a single radical. Such radicals cannot react with each other, since they are separated by the aqueous phase, and they will continue to add monomer until they are terminated by new radicals produced in the next light flash.

4. Molecular Weight Averages

When a procedure suitable for the determination of molecular weights is applied to a sample containing molecules of different sizes, it will yield a value which we may call the "average molecular weight." The nature of the averaging process depends on the property which is being measured and the magnitude of the average molecular weight will tend to increase with increasing sensitivity of the measured effects to the weight of a molecule.

In the determination of molecular weights by the colligative properties of solutions, each molecule, large or small, makes the same contribution to the observed effect. This effect would then remain unchanged if the total weight were shared equally among the molecules of the system, a procedure leading to the *number average* molecular weight $\bar{M}_n$. If

$$\int_{M_1}^{M_2} N(M)dM$$

is the fraction of molecules with molecular weights in the range $M_1 \leqslant M \leqslant M_2$, then

$$\bar{M}_n = \int_0^\infty MN(M)dM \bigg/ \int_0^\infty N(M)dM \tag{1.18}$$

On the other hand, we may be interested in an effect which, for a given solution concentration, is proportional to the molecular weight of the solute. The effect obtained with a polydisperse solute will then depend on its *weight average* molecular weight $\bar{M}_w$ defined by

$$\bar{M}_w = \int_0^\infty MW(M)dM \tag{1.19}$$

where the distribution function $W(M)$ is defined so that

$$\int_{M_1}^{M_2} W(M)dM$$

is the weight fraction of material with molecular weights in the range $M_1 \leqslant M \leqslant M_2$. Since $W(M)$ is related to $N(M)$ by

$$W(M)dM = MN(M)dM \Big/ \int_0^\infty MN(M)dM \qquad (1.20)$$

we may express $\bar{M}_w$ as

$$\bar{M}_w = \int_0^\infty M^2 N(M)dM \Big/ \int_0^\infty MN(M)dM \qquad (1.21)$$

A comparison of (1.21) with (1.18) shows that the large species are weighted more heavily in the weight average than in the number average, so that for any polydisperse sample $\bar{M}_w > \bar{M}_n$. In fact, in the absence of precise information on the molecular weight distribution function, the ratio $\bar{M}_w/\bar{M}_n$ is frequently used to characterize the "polydispersity" of a sample. In Germany it has become customary to use in a similar manner the parameter U ("Uneinheitlichkeit") defined by U = $(\bar{M}_w/\bar{M}_n) - 1$.

Another average which plays a role in the interpretation of the behavior of polymer solutions is the so-called "z-average" defined by

$$\bar{M}_z = \int_0^\infty M^3 N(M)dM \Big/ \int_0^\infty M^2 N(M)dM \qquad (1.22)$$

It is influenced by the high molecular weight species even more than the weight average.

Whenever we are justified in assuming that the molecular weight distribution has a form derived from the simple kinetic patterns discussed in Sec. B1, B2, and B3, a single molecular weight average will define the complete molecular weight distribution function. For the "most probable distribution" the molecular weight averages are related to the parameter ϵ and to M_0, the molecular weight of the monomer, by

$$\epsilon = M_0/\bar{M}_n = 2M_0/\bar{M}_w = 3M_0/\bar{M}_z \qquad (1.23)$$
$$\text{(most probable distribution)}$$

For radical polymerization with termination by recombination of chain radicals

$$\epsilon = 2M_0/\bar{M}_n = 3M_0/\bar{M}_w = 4M_0/\bar{M}_z \qquad (1.24)$$
$$\text{(termination by recombination)}$$

For the Poisson distribution, the characteristic parameter is r, the ratio of monomer moles consumed to moles of chains initiated.   It is obvious that $r = \bar{M}_n$.   The ratio of $\bar{M}_w$ to $\bar{M}_n$ is given by

$$\bar{M}_w/\bar{M}_n = 1 + [r/(r + 1)^2] \tag{1.25}$$

Thus, even for chains of no more than 100 units, $\bar{M}_w$ is only 1% larger than $\bar{M}_n$, well within the experimental error of molecular weight determinations.

5. Real Distributions and Generalized Molecular Weight Distribution Functions

In the preceding sections we have considered chain length distributions predicted on the basis of kinetic considerations that apply under idealized conditions.   In practice these distributions will be modified by a number of complicating factors.   For instance, if the polymerization of a vinyl monomer is carried to an appreciable conversion, the ratio of the chain propagation and chain termination rates will gradually change and produce a drift in the value of the parameter ϵ.   As a result, the polymer will be characterized by a superposition of the normal distributions of chain lengths obtained at any given time and the actual distribution will be broader than predicted from eq. (1.3) or (1.13).   A similar broadening may be obtained even for the polydispersity of the polymer obtained at a given time, if reaction conditions vary from point to point within the polymerizing system.   This may happen if the polymerization is carried out in a viscous medium, so that temperature is subject to significant fluctuations, a condition not uncommon in industrial processes.   Very often, several chain terminating mechanisms, for which different forms of molecular weight distribution functions are predicted, may occur in the same system.   For instance, the termination of methyl methacrylate chains occurs partly by chain disproportionation and partly by chain combination (Bevington et al., 1954).   Such superposition of several chain terminating mechanisms will have a particularly drastic effect on polymerizations which should, under ideal conditions, yield the very narrow Poisson distribution of molecular weights.   For instance, Sela and Berger (1953) have shown that a N-carboxy-α-amino acid anhydride unit need not always add to a growing polypeptide chain as indicated in eq. (1.16b), but may also add in a manner such as to produce a species

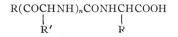

which will not add any further monomer. Such a monomer addition represents, therefore, a chain termination step and if it occurs with sufficient frequency, the polymer will be characterized by a normal, rather than a Poisson distribution of chain lengths. Another factor which will lead to a broadening of the polydispersity in polymers for which a Poisson distribution is expected is a relatively low rate of the chain initiation process. For instance, Becker and Stahmann (1952) have shown that the initiation of N-carboxy-α-amino acid anhydride polymerizations by water is slow compared to the subsequent rate of chain growth. In the electron transfer initiated polymerizations of vinyl monomers represented in eq. (1.17) we may have complications arising not only from chain termination by impurities and an insufficiently rapid initiation rate, but also due to the reversibility of the addition of monomer to the growing chain (Wenger, 1960a,b). An approach to the ideal of a Poisson distribution can, therefore, be realized only if the experimental conditions are very carefully chosen and controlled.

We shall then be frequently faced with the need to take account of the polydispersity of a polymer in the theoretical interpretation of its solution properties, without being able to rely on the applicability of a form of the distribution function based on kinetic considerations. It is, therefore, advantageous to use *generalized* molecular weight distribution functions in which the breadth of the distribution is characterized by an adjustable parameter. Such a function was proposed by Schulz (1939) and applied by Zimm (1948) to the treatment of light scattering from a solution of a polydisperse polymer. It has the form

$$N(P) = [y^z/\Gamma(z)]P^{z-1}\exp(-yP) \qquad (1.26)$$

where Γ is the gamma function and the number, weight, and z-average molecular weights are related to the parameters y and z by

$$\bar{M}_n = M_0(z/y)$$

$$\bar{M}_w = M_0(z+1)/y \qquad (1.27)$$

$$\bar{M}_z = M_0(z+2)/y$$

We may note that $z = 1$ corresponds to the "most probable" distribution, while $z = 2$ represents the case of vinyl polymerization terminated by radical recombination. The polydispersity decreases with increasing values of z.

It should, however, be strongly emphasized that a limited number of parameters cannot define uniquely a molecular weight distribution. The

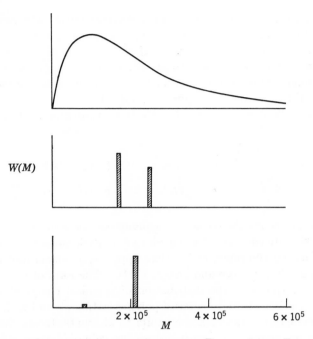

$W(M)$

2×10^5 4×10^5 6×10^5

M

Fig. I.3. Three molecular weight distributions with $\bar{M}_n = 10^5$ and $\bar{M}_w = 2 \times 10^5$

point is illustrated in Fig. I.3, where two systems containing two sharp fractions are shown, which have the same number average and weight average molecular weight as the normal distribution shown on top. A ratio of $\bar{M}_w/\bar{M}_n = 2$ does not, by itself, guarantee that we are dealing with a normal distribution. On the other hand, if the conditions under which a polymer sample was prepared are such that a distribution function with two maxima ("bimodal distribution") seems unlikely, the generalized distribution function (1.26) is likely to be a close approximation to the real distribution of chain lengths.

6. The Distribution of Copolymer Composition

When we deal with copolymers, we must consider the heterogeneity of the sample with respect to chemical composition as well as the polydispersity of molecular weights. This problem may be divided into two parts, considering first the distribution in the composition of chains produced at any given time during a copolymerization and treating subsequently the drift of copolymer composition with polymerization time.

The first problem was solved by Stockmayer (1945) who considered the case of a vinyl copolymerization leading to a normal distribution of polymer chain lengths (such as would result if chain termination is by disproportionation or if the chain lengths are governed by chain transfer). If the two comonomers have the same molecular weight, x is the mole fraction of one of the monomers in a given polymer chain and Δ is the deviation of x from its bulk average value, then the weight distribution function of Δ is given by

$$W(\Delta)d\Delta = [3\sqrt{A}/4(1 + A\Delta)^{5/2}]d\Delta$$
$$A = \bar{P}_n/2x(1 - x)[1 - 4x(1 - x)(1 - r_1r_2)]^{1/2} \tag{1.28}$$

where r_1 and r_2 are the so-called copolymerization reactivity ratios giving the relative rate constants for the addition of each monomer to a chain end terminating by the same, rather than opposite, monomer unit (Alfrey and Goldfinger, 1944; Mayo and Lewis, 1944). The form of eq. (1.28) shows that the sharpness of the distribution of chemical composition increases with the number average degree of polymerization $\bar{P}_n$ and with an increase of the tendency of the monomer units to alternate during the growth of the polymer chains (i.e., with decreasing values of r_1r_2). The extreme sharpness of the distribution corresponding to very long copolymer chains may be exemplified by a copolymer containing equal concentrations of the two comonomers, with the monomer units distributed at random (i.e., $r_1r_2 = 1$). If $\bar{P}_n = 1000$, the probability of finding chains deviating by as little as 1% from the average composition is 2000 times smaller than for chains in which the composition corresponds to the bulk average. However, the ratio of these probabilities drops to 17 if the chains contain, on the average, only 100 monomer units.

Copolymer samples with which we have to deal in practice will have generally much broader distributions than those indicated above. This is due to the fact that the comonomers usually differ in their reactivity, so that the more reactive one is depleted more rapidly in the course of the polymerization. The drift in the composition of the monomer mixture will then lead to a corresponding drift in the composition of the copolymer. This effect has been dealt with quantitatively in a theory due to Skeist (1946) (see also Alfrey et al., 1952a). We shall not concern ourselves here with the details of this development but we should note that in some cases the distribution function of chemical compositions obtained when copolymerization is carried to high conversions may have two maxima.

C. RELATION OF THE STUDY OF MACROMOLECULES IN SOLUTION AND IN BULK

At the outset of a discussion of the properties of macromolecules in solution it is helpful to gain perspective by considering the relation of the studies of solution properties and studies of the properties of macromolecules in bulk.   There is, first of all, the obvious fact that the possibilities of studying a polymer which cannot be brought into solution are very severely limited.   All fractionation procedures, whether designed to separate materials of varying molecular weight or varying composition require a prior dissolution of the sample.   Also, dissolution of the polymer is required for the preparation of single crystals of polymeric substances and for the preparation of specimens in which the individual macromolecules are deposited, separated from each other, on some suitable surface for study by electron microscopy.   It is no exaggeration to say that the very existence of substances of very high molecular weight could not have been demonstrated conclusively if these substances could not have been dissolved.

1. Molecular Weight and Polydispersity

One of the important aims in the study of polymer solutions was the development of a number of techniques for the determination of the mean molecular weight of the sample.   It is also possible to characterize the distribution of molecular weights by measurements carried out on a solution of a polydisperse sample without resort to a tedious and time-consuming fractionation procedure.   Similar analyses can be carried out to characterize either samples with a continuous distribution of chemical composition (such as may occur in synthetic copolymers) or samples containing several well-defined macromolecular species (characteristic of specimens of biological origin).

We have already alluded in Sec. A.1. to the possibility of determining molecular weights of macromolecules from information obtained by x-ray crystallography for the very restricted class of high molecular weight substances represented by the crystalline globular proteins.   Even in this case, this alternative to molecular weight determination is only of academic interest, since the crystallographic studies require a tremendous effort as compared with that needed for a conventional molecular weight determination of a dissolved polymer.   Of greater practical interest is the possibility of deriving molecular weights from measurements on the images obtained with the electron microscope (Hall, 1960).   However, in using this method one has to exercise special care in the preparation of specimens to avoid artifacts due particularly to molecular aggregation (Hayes et al., 1959). The limits of resolution obtainable with the electron microscope seem to limit this method, for the present, to the molecules of globular proteins and to helically coiled molecular particles, such as those of nucleic acid. Hall and Doty (1958) have shown that electron micrographs may be evaluated in terms of the distribution of molecular weights. However secure we may feel in the use of the theoretical interpretation of data obtained on polymer solutions, the old adage "seeing is believing" is still applicable to some extent and it is, therefore, comforting that we should be in a position where measurements on images representing the individual molecules are in agreement with results obtained in a seemingly less direct manner.

2. The Shape of Macromolecules

All of our knowledge concerning the shapes of macromolecules was derived, up to very recent times, from a study of these substances in dilute solution. The methods for obtaining such information constitute one of the main subjects of this book. Nevertheless, knowledge obtained in studies of polymers in bulk has been helpful in a variety of ways and has originated several concepts necessary in the interpretation of solution properties. When we shall consider the behavior of polymer chains which may be represented by flexible coils (Chap. III) we shall see that the treatment of the resistance to an expansion of the coil by osmotic forces is exactly analogous to the resistance of a rubber to elongation by an applied mechanical stress. Here again, observations of measurable retractive forces on rubber samples which we can see give us added confidence in reasoning about the behavior of chain molecules, which we can deduce only indirectly. Moreover, the detailed consideration of the conformations of linear chain polymers which exist in solution as "random coils" owes much to the crystallographic determination of the conformations assumed by these or similar chains when they are packed in a crystal lattice.

A much more important contribution to the understanding of the behavior of dissolved macromolecules has been made by crystallography in connection with the phenomenon of "helix-coil transitions" of synthetic polypeptides and polynucleotides which we shall discuss in Chap. III. These phenomena introduce an entirely new concept of "one-dimensional crystallization" into physical chemistry and it is doubtful whether a detailed understanding of them could have been hoped for if detailed descriptions of the helical conformation of the chain backbone in crystalline globular proteins (Pauling et al., 1951) and synthetic polypeptides (Pauling and Corey, 1951) had not been established on the basis of x-ray diffraction

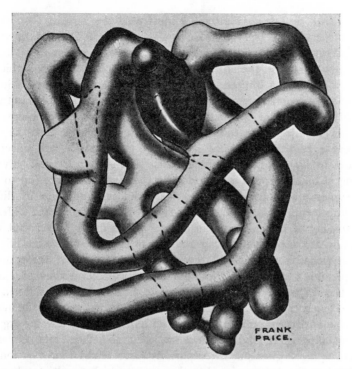

Fig. I.4.   The folding of the polypeptide chain in a molecule of myoglobin.   (Courtesy
of Prof. J. C. Kendrew.)

data, to be followed by the proposal of the double helix for deoxyribose
nucleic acid (Watson and Crick, 1954) on the basis of x-ray diffraction data
from DNA fibers.

The spectacular progress achieved in recent years in applying the technique of x-ray crystallography to single crystals composed of the large
molecules of globular proteins has made it possible to derive the detailed
shape of these molecules.   At the time of this writing such detailed analyses
have been published for myoglobin (Bodo et al., 1959; Kendrew et al.,
1960, 1961), hemoglobin (Perutz et al., 1960), chymotrypsinogen
(Kraut et al., 1962), and lysozyme (Blake et al., 1965), substances with
molecular weights of 17,000, 68,000, 25,000, and 13,000, respectively.
The resolution of the myoglobin structure is already at such a high
level of refinement that positions of amino acid residues in the polypeptide chain may be identified and it seems probable that a definition of the
molecular shape to a similar level of precision will soon be achieved for

several other proteins. Figure I.4 illustrates the general shape of the myoglobin molecule emerging from these studies. The details of even this representation at relatively low resolution far surpass anything that can be hoped for in the study of macromolecular solutions, which can yield at best only a limited number of parameters characterizing the shape of the dissolved particle. Nevertheless, this does not mean that the study of the shapes of globular proteins by the use of various solution techniques is now antiquated. First of all, it is probable that the shapes of globular protein molecules in their crystal lattice are affected to some extent by the mutual interactions of these molecules. Evidence pointing in that direction is provided by the large difference (up to 50%) in the volume containing one chymotrypsinogen molecule in different crystalline forms (Kraut et al., 1962) suggesting significant differences in the folding of the polypeptide chain.* It is to be hoped that in the next few years a complete x-ray analysis of two crystalline modifications of some globular protein will become available, so that the magnitude of the possible variations in the molecular shape can be assessed. At any rate, if the shape of the protein molecule in dilute solution is different from that in a given crystal lattice, we must regard the property of the molecule in solution as more significant in terms of its function in a living organism. The crystallographic and solution methods, therefore, complement one another, with one giving us incomparably more detailed information while the other is more closely related to the system which we ultimately wish to understand. There is, however, a second reason why we cannot abandon the study of solution properties even in the case of globular crystallizable proteins: In the foreseeable future the solution of a protein crystal structure from x-ray diffraction data will represent a formidable undertaking (requiring the efforts of large research teams over several years) and there is as yet no assurance that the task can be accomplished in every case. By comparison, the task involved in the measurement of solution properties and an analysis of the data is relatively minor and well worth while for whatever information it may yield.

The use of electron microscopy, mentioned briefly in the previous section, can also contribute to our knowledge of molecular shapes. However, it is important to realize that surface tension may result in serious distortions of molecular shapes during the drying of a solution, which must necessarily precede electron microscopic observation. Nevertheless, the technique has been refined to the point where reliable results can be obtained in careful

* These differences in volume reflect the differences in the amount of solvent incorporated into different crystalline forms of chymotrypsinogen.

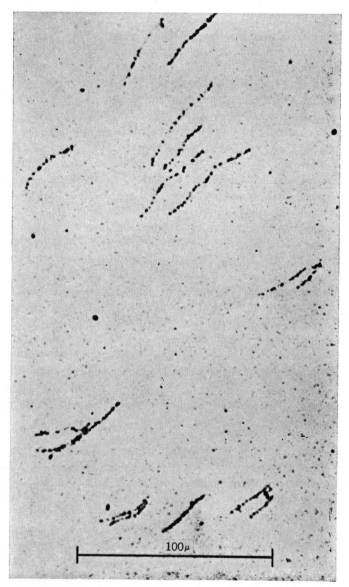

Fig. I.5. Autoradiograph of DNA from T2 bacteriophages labeled with tritiated thymine (11.2 curies/mmole). The autoradiographic exposure was 63 days. Courtesy of Dr. J. Cairns.

work and such phenomena as the helix-coil transformations of nucleic acid can be observed on electron micrographs (Kisselev et al., 1961). Another technique which permits us to visualize, to some extent, the shape of extremely large macromolecules is that of autoradiography. Here the sample is labeled with a radioactive isotope and a very dilute solution is dried on a support which is brought into intimate contact with a photographic emulsion. If sufficient time is allowed so that a large number of radioactive atoms in every molecule of the sample has decomposed, if the molecule is stretched out and if its dimensions are large compared to the resolving power of the emulsion, the images of the disintegrating atoms will outline the shape of the molecule. The beautiful picture of a deoxyribose nucleic acid (DNA) preparation obtained by Cairns (1961) with the use of this method is shown in Fig. I.5. Here only the length of the molecule (52 μ) can be measured from the image, since the thickness is obviously well below the resolving power of the method. More recent work by the same author (Cairns, 1962) has shown that the DNA molecules occurring in a bacterial virus are much larger than even Fig. I.5 would indicate, since the long molecular chains are inevitably broken in any handling of their solutions (Hershey and Burgi, 1960; Levinthal and Davison, 1961). It is, however, possible to disintegrate the wall of the virus particle chemically, allowing the DNA molecules to settle onto a membrane, which can then be dried and studied by autoradiography. This seems to be the most reliable method for the determination of the molecular weight of such fragile species.

3. Relation of Solution Properties to Technologically Important Characteristics

In the practical utilization of synthetic high polymers a control of the molecular chain length of the product is of crucial importance. The mechanical strength of rubbers, plastics, and fiber-forming polymers generally falls off sharply below a molecular weight of 20,000–30,000. For very high molecular weights, the mechanical properties tend to approach an asymptotic limit and become independent of a further chain length extension, but such high molecular weight materials are extremely viscous at the elevated temperatures at which polymers are being processed into useful shapes. The industrial polymer chemist must, therefore, control the molecular weight of his material both with a view to its properties under the conditions of its technological utilization and its processability characteristics. He will aim at as close a reproducibility of polymer chain length as he can obtain. With a sample polydisperse with respect to molecular weight, useful properties depend often, to a first approximation, on the weight average molecular weight. Nevertheless, other molecular weight averages will be useful indices for the purposes of quality control, since for samples prepared by any given procedure the shape of the molecular weight distribution function is fixed, so that various averages are related by a constant ratio.

The details of the molecular weight distribution function are of less importance to the mechanical characteristics of a polymer in bulk, but they do affect these characteristics to some extent (Ferry, 1961a). As for copolymers, it is generally desirable that they should be as homogeneous with respect to chemical composition as possible, since variations in chemical composition may lead to a tendency towards phase separation resulting in mechanical weakness.

We should realize, however, that some properties of crucial importance to the behavior of polymers in bulk have little or no relation to their behavior in solution. For instance, although it is possible in principle to assess the height of the potential energy barriers which have to be overcome if a dissolved chain molecule is to change its shape, effects due to this "internal viscosity" are not particularly prominent. Therefore, it would, not be easy to predict, on the basis of solution behavior alone, that polyisoprene is a highly extensible rubber, while poly(methyl acrylate) is not. Another example of inherent limitations in solution methods is their inability to predict the striking phenomena associated with the crystallization of polymers. Let us consider, for instance, poly(hexamethylene adipamide) (the commercial nylon 66) and a polyamide resulting from a condensation of adipic acid with a mixture of pentamethylene diamine and heptamethylene diamine. The properties of the dissolved polyamides will be probably indistinguishable, but the behavior of the two materials in bulk will be strikingly different, since the regular spacing of the amide linkages in nylon 66 will lead to a highly crystalline product, while the random distribution of these linkages in the copolymer renders crystallization impossible.

In the case of vinyl polymers, a high degree of stereoregularity is a precondition to crystallizability. Most solution properties are rather insensitive to differences in "tacticity." Even though in later discussions nuclear magnetic resonance spectroscopy of polymer solutions will be shown to be, in some cases, the most powerful currently available method for the quantitative evaluation of tacticity, we must bear in mind that a stereoregular structure does not in itself insure that a given polymer will crystallize.

These examples are merely offered as typical of the limits of the information which may be obtained when macromolecules are studied in solution—

and usually in highly dilute solution. Such studies aim mainly at the definition of the properties of the isolated macromolecule and cannot be expected to predict phenomena which are dominated by the enormous viscosity of high polymers in bulk, which frequently prevents the system from attaining a state of thermodynamic equilibrium. They can also not be expected to reveal the geometric possibilities of packing chain molecules into a crystal lattice which may result in large differences between the bulk properties of crystalline and amorphous polymers.

Chapter II

THE SOLUBILITY OF MACROMOLECULES

Most high polymers occurring in nature or synthesized in the laboratory are soluble under some conditions. Insoluble polymers are crosslinked structures (such as lignin, vulcanized rubber, "cured" phenolic resins, etc.) and a few highly crystalline materials such as polytetrafluoroethylene (Teflon) or poly(p-phenylenediamine terephthalamide). The insolubility of these substances may be a technical advantage in some applications but it certainly sets severe limits to their physico-chemical study.

Before discussing the special problems encountered in the solubility of high molecular weight solutes, it will be convenient to consider briefly the conditions governing the formation of a solution in binary systems whose components consist of molecules of comparable size. We shall then discuss solubility in binary systems containing a polymeric species and a low molecular weight solvent and finally turn to a description of the solubility properties of polymers in multi-component systems.

A. FORMATION OF SOLUTIONS FROM SPECIES OF LOW MOLECULAR WEIGHT

1. Thermodynamic Considerations

For a system at constant temperature T and constant pressure P the equilibrium state is represented by the state of minimum free energy. The Gibbs free energy function G is defined by

$$G = H - TS = E + PV - TS \qquad (2.1)$$

where H is the enthalpy, E the internal energy, V the volume, and S the entropy of the system. If we consider a system of several components in two phases, then the condition of equilibrium requires that the free energy remain unchanged if an infinitesimal number of moles δn_i of component i is transferred from phase I to phase II.

$$[-(\partial G/\partial n_i)^{\mathrm{I}}_{T,P,n_j \neq n_i} + (\partial G/\partial n_i)^{\mathrm{II}}_{T,P,n_j \neq n_i}] \, \delta n_i = 0 \qquad (2.2)$$

where the superscripts I and II refer to quantities evaluated in phases I and II, respectively. Using for partial quantities the notation $\bar{X}_i \equiv (\partial X/\partial n_i)_{T,P,n_j \neq n_i}$, we may state that equilibrium between two phases requires

$$\bar{G}_i^I = \bar{G}_i^{II} \qquad (2.3)$$

The partial molar free energies $\bar{G}_i$ are customarily referred to as the "chemical potentials." The activity of species i denoted by a_i is defined by

$$\Delta \bar{G}_i \equiv \bar{G}_i - \bar{G}_i^0 = RT \ln a_i \qquad (2.4)$$

$$\overline{\Delta G_i} = \overline{\Delta H_i} - T \overline{\Delta S_i}$$

$$\overline{\Delta H_i} \equiv \bar{H}_i - \bar{H}_i^0$$

$$\overline{\Delta S_i} \equiv \bar{S}_i - \bar{S}_i^0 \qquad (2.5)$$

where R is the gas constant and the superscript ^{0} refers to an arbitrarily chosen standard state. When dealing with non-electrolytes, we shall invariably use the pure component as its standard state. The activity a_i is related to the "escaping tendency" of component i as measured by its fugacity f_i according to

$$a_i = f_i/f_i^0 \qquad (2.6)$$

The fugacity is equal to the partial vapor pressure P_i in the limit of low pressures, but for finite pressures f_i/P_i deviates from unity in a manner depending on the deviation of the vapor from ideal gas behavior. Specifically, if we represent the equation of state of the vapor by $PV = RT + A_{2g}/V + A_{3g}/V^2 + ...$, where A_{2g}, A_{3g}, etc., are the second, third, and higher virial coefficients, we obtain from

$$RT \ln (f_2/f_1) = \int_{P_1}^{P_2} V dP$$

the relation

$$f/P = \exp [A_{2g}P/(RT)^2] + ... \qquad (2.7)$$

For the vapors of liquids below their normal boiling points the deviation of f from P is generally quite small. As an example, we may consider carbon tetrachloride for which $A_{2g} = -17$ l²-atm-moles^{-2} at 25°C, where the saturated vapor pressure is 0.15 atm. Under these conditions, $f/P = 0.996$.

It is convenient to interpret the thermodynamic behavior of non-electrolyte solutions by comparing them with *ideal solutions* in which the activities of all components a_i are equal to their mole fractions x_i. The a_i values found in real solutions are then expressed by

$$a_i = \gamma_i x_i \tag{2.8}$$

where γ_i is referred to as the activity coefficient. We may then rewrite (2.4) as

$$\overline{\Delta G_i} = RT \ln x_i + RT \ln \gamma_i \tag{2.9}$$

where the second term on the right represents the contribution to the chemical potential due to the nonideality of the solution. It was suggested by Scatchard (1931) that the results of thermodynamic measurements should generally be expressed in terms of the deviation of thermodynamic functions from the values corresponding to ideal solutions. Defining an "excess function" as $X^E \equiv X - X_{\text{ideal}}$, the excess chemical potential ΔG_i^E is given by

$$\overline{\Delta G_i^E} = RT \ln \gamma_i \tag{2.10}$$

and the excess free energy, enthalpy, and entropy of mixing in a binary system are related to the partial molar excess functions by

$$\Delta G_M^E = n_1 \overline{\Delta G_1^E} + n_2 \overline{\Delta G_2^E}$$

$$\Delta H_M^E = n_1 \overline{\Delta H_1^E} + n_2 \overline{\Delta H_2^E}$$

$$\Delta S_M^E = n_1 \overline{\Delta S_1^E} + n_2 \overline{\Delta S_2^E} \tag{2.11}$$

Since the ideal solution is, by definition, formed from its components without any heat effect, $\Delta H_M^E = \Delta H_M$ and $\overline{\Delta H_i^E} = \overline{\Delta H_i}$. As for the excess entropy of mixing, its meaning will be clarified when we consider later in more detail the theory of ideal solutions.

Utilizing with eq. (2.9) the Gibbs–Helmholtz relation

$$\left[\frac{\partial}{\partial T} \left(\frac{\Delta G}{T} \right) \right]_P = - \frac{\Delta H}{T^2} \tag{2.12}$$

we obtain for the temperature dependence of the activity coefficient

$$(\partial \ln \gamma_i / \partial T)_{P,\, n_j \neq n_i} = - \overline{\Delta H_i} / RT^2 \tag{2.13}$$

It may be noted that increasing values of γ_i indicate a decreasing tendency of component i to remain in solution, so that relation (2.13) may be regarded as a quantitative statement of Le Chatelier's principle which predicts that exothermic dissolution should be hindered and endothermic dissolution favored by an increase in temperature.

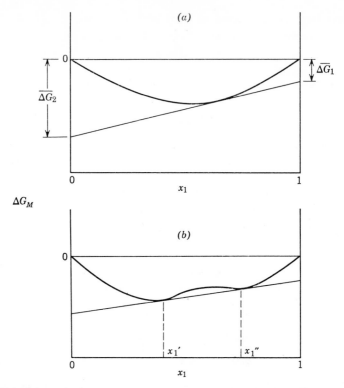

Fig. II.1. Schematic representation of the free energy of mixing. (a) System of two components miscible in all proportions. (b) A system of two components with limited miscibility.

In the representation of thermodynamic quantities of binary systems it is convenient to use plots referring to a total of one mole. Figure II.1 shows two typical plots of the free energy of mixing ΔG_M which may be easily shown to be related to the chemical potentials of the components by

$$\Delta G_M = n_1 \overline{\Delta G_1} + n_2 \overline{\Delta G_2} \qquad (2.14)$$

In Fig. II.1(a) the ΔG_M curve has no inflection points and any system represented by two coexisting phases corresponds to a higher free energy than the single phase formed when the two phases merge. This diagram is then typical of binary systems which form solutions in all proportions. On the other hand, Fig. II.1(b) shows a ΔG_M curve, two points of which have a common tangent. The two phases characterized by x_1' and x_1'' have identical values for $\overline{\Delta G_1}$ and $\overline{\Delta G_2}$, so that they are in equilibrium with each

other. It is clear that points representing any one phase system intermediate between x_1' and x_1'' correspond to a state of higher free energy
than the corresponding point representing a two-phase system with the
same overall composition, and any such single phase is, therefore, thermodynamically unstable.

The temperature dependence of the composition of two coexisting phases
of a binary system may be obtained from eq. (2.4) and (2.12) as

$$\left(\frac{\partial \ln a_1}{\partial x_1}\right)'_{T,P} \frac{dx_1'}{dT} - \left(\frac{\partial \ln a_1}{\partial x_1}\right)''_{T,P} \frac{dx_1''}{dT} = \frac{-(\overline{\Delta H_1})' + (\overline{\Delta H_1})''}{RT^2} \quad (2.15)$$

where ( )′ and ( )″ symbolize quantities evaluated at the compositions x_1'
and x_1'', respectively. For the special case of a binary system in which
one phase is the pure component 2 at all temperatures (e.g., a crystalline solid
which does not form solid solutions with the solvent), eq. (2.15) reduces to

$$dx_2/dT = (\overline{\Delta H_2})'/RT^2(\partial \ln a_2/\partial x_2)'_{T,P} \quad (2.16a)$$

or,

$$d \ln x_2/dT = (\overline{\Delta H_2})'/RT^2 \ [1 + (\partial \ln \gamma_2/\partial \ln x_2)'_{T,P}] \quad (2.16b)$$

2. The Ideal Solution

Ideal solutions are defined as solutions in which the activity is equal to
the mole fraction

$$a_i = x_i \quad (2.17)$$

for all components and all compositions of the system (Raoult's law).
It was once believed that any multicomponent system in which forces
between like and unlike molecules are equal (and for which, therefore, the
solution process is athermal) will lead to an ideal solution, but we shall see
later that the mixing of molecules of different size may lead to deviations
from ideal solution behavior even if no heat effect accompanies the formation of the solution. We shall, therefore, begin with a consideration of
binary systems in which both the molecular size and the forces exerted by
the molecules are the same for both components.

The entropy of the pure components may be considered to be the sum of
contributions due to molecular translation, rotation, and vibration. When
the components are mixed to form an ideal solution, these entropy contributions may be considered to remain unchanged since molecular interactions have a relatively small effect on translational, vibrational and
rotational motions of the individual molecules. However, a configurational

term S_{conf} will now make a contribution to the entropy of the systems, since the solution may contain a large number of distinguishable arrangements of the molecules of the two components. We have, therefore, in good approximation

$$\Delta S_M = S_{conf} \tag{2.18}$$

The evaluation of S_{conf} is most easily carried out by placing the molecules onto a lattice. If we have N_1 molecules of type 1 and N_2 of type 2, the number of distinguishable arrangements on $N_1 + N_2$ lattice points is

$$\mathfrak{W} = (N_1 + N_2)!/N_1!N_2! \tag{2.19}$$

and since all of these configurations represent states of equal energy, the configurational entropy is

$$S_{conf} = k \ln \mathfrak{W} \tag{2.20}$$

where k is the Boltzmann constant and $\mathfrak{W}$ is the multiplicity of statistical states. Approximating the factorials in eq. (2.19) by Stirling's approximation formula

$$y! = (y/e)^y \tag{2.21}$$

we obtain from eq. (2.18), (2.19), and (2.20) for the ideal entropy of mixing

$$\Delta S_M^i = k \left[N_1 \ln \left(\frac{N_1 + N_2}{N_1} \right) + N_2 \ln \left(\frac{N_1 + N_2}{N_2} \right) \right] \tag{2.22a}$$

or

$$\Delta S_M^i = -R \left[n_1 \ln x_1 + n_2 \ln x_2 \right] \tag{2.22b}$$

The ideal partial molar entropy is then obtained by differentiation with respect to n_1 or n_2

$$\overline{\Delta S_1^i} = -R \ln x_1; \quad \overline{\Delta S_2^i} = -R \ln x_2 \tag{2.23}$$

and since the solution is athermal, so that $\overline{\Delta H_1} = \overline{\Delta H_2} = 0$, we have for the ideal free energy of mixing

$$\Delta G_M^i = -T\Delta S_M^i = RT \left[n_1 \ln x_1 + n_2 \ln x_2 \right] \tag{2.24}$$

yielding for the chemical potentials of the two components in an ideal solution

$$\overline{\Delta G_1^i} = RT \ln x_1; \quad \overline{\Delta G_2^i} = RT \ln x_2 \tag{2.25}$$

Comparison with eq. (2.4) shows that the activities are equal to the mole fractions. This proves the validity of the ideal solution law under the special conditions which we have considered.

We may note that just as the *excess* chemical potential is defined in eq. (2.10) as the difference between the value of the chemical potential of a component in a real solution and in ideal solution (as given in eq. 2.25), so the excess entropy of mixing is given by

$$\Delta S_M^E = \Delta S_M + R \sum n_i \ln x_i \qquad (2.26)$$

and the excess partial molar entropies are

$$\overline{\Delta S_j^E} = \overline{\Delta S_i} + R \ln x_i \qquad (2.27)$$

3. The Heat of Mixing

When a solution is formed from two pure liquids, similar molecules are separated from each other and contact points are created between dissimilar molecules. It is then qualitatively obvious that the direction of heat flow in the mixing of two components at constant temperature will depend on the relative magnitude of forces operating between like and unlike molecules. A quantitative theory of the energy of mixing is derived most simply for two substances consisting of molecules of equal size which are placed into the cells of a three-dimensional lattice. Let each molecule have z nearest neighbors and let the energetic interactions, restricted to nearest neighbors, be characterized by an energy w_{ij} required for the separation of a mole of pairs of molecules of species i and j. If we then transfer one mole of a species A into a large volume of a species B (so that all molecules of A are completely surrounded by molecules of B), the required energy will be

$$(\Delta E_M)_A^\infty = z[(w_{AA}/2) + (w_{BB}/2) - w_{AB}] \equiv z\Delta w \qquad (2.28)$$

We see then that such transfers would be athermal if w_{AB} were the arithmetic mean of w_{AA} and w_{BB}. It was, however, pointed out by van Laar and Lorenz (1925) that forces between two dissimilar particles are more usually equal to the *geometric mean* of the forces which each of the particles would exert on a second particle of its own kind, so that we should expect for the energetic interaction of dissimilar molecules

$$w_{AB} = \sqrt{w_{AA}w_{BB}} \lessgtr (w_{AA} + w_{BB})/2 \qquad (2.29)$$

Hildebrand and Scott (1950) have analyzed in detail the physical basis for the assumption expressed in (2.29) and they have pointed out that the "postulate of the geometric mean" accurately expresses interactions of permanent dipoles and is a close approximation to energetic interactions due to London dispersion forces. It is definitely unsatisfactory for the description of forces between permanent and induced dipoles, but this type of interaction usually makes only a small contribution to the total of cohesive forces between molecules. They concluded, therefore, that the van Laar postulate is justified when considering the mixing of relatively nonpolar molecules. Combining (2.28) and (2.29), it is then predicted that such mixing will be generally endothermic. Since the molar energy of vaporization of species i is given by $\Delta E_i^v = z w_{ii}/2$, we obtain, by combining (2.28) and (2.29)

$$(\Delta E_M)_A^\infty = \Delta E_A^v + \Delta E_B^v - 2\sqrt{\Delta E_A^v \, \Delta E_B^v} = [(\Delta E_A^v)^{1/2} - (\Delta E_B^v)^{1/2}]^2 \quad (2.30)$$

In the general case, where mixing leads to solutions which are not highly dilute, we have to estimate the relative number of A. . .A, B. . .B, and A. . .B nearest neighbor pairs. This problem may be treated approximately as a "quasichemical equilibrium" (Guggenheim, 1935; Fowler and Guggenheim, 1939), so that

$$A. . .A + B. . .B \rightleftharpoons 2A. . .B$$

$$\frac{(A. . .B)^2}{(A. . .A)(B. . .B)} = \frac{1}{4} \exp(-\Delta w/RT) \quad (2.31)$$

In many cases $\Delta w \ll RT$ and we may obtain a reasonable approximation with the assumption that the occupancy of a given lattice cell is independent of the nature of the species occupying neighboring cells. This leads, for the mixing of n_A moles of species A with n_B moles of species B, to the energy of mixing

$$\Delta E_M = z \left\{ (n_A w_{AA}/2) + (n_B w_{BB}/2) \right.$$
$$\left. - (n_A^2 w_{AA} + n_B^2 w_{BB} + 2n_A n_B w_{AB})/(2n_A + n_B) \right\} \quad (2.32)$$

or, using the identity of the right-hand side of (2.28) and (2.30),

$$\Delta E_M = [n_A n_B/(n_A + n_B)][(\Delta E_A^v)^{1/2} - (\Delta E_L^v)^{1/2}]^2 \quad (2.33)$$

We may extend the lattice model to a mixture of molecules of different volumes, where each molecule may occupy one or several adjoining lattice cells. If it is assumed that the number of neighboring lattice cells with which a given molecule engages in energetic interactions is proportional to the molecular volume (i.e., that the "molecular surface-to-volume ratio" is the same for all molecular species) then a treatment analogous to that outlined above leads to

$$\Delta E_M = V\phi_A\phi_B \left[(\Delta E_A^v/V_A)^{1/2} - (\Delta E_B^v/V_B)^{1/2}\right]^2 = V\phi_A\phi_B (\delta_A - \delta_B)^2 \quad (2.34)$$

where ϕ_A, ϕ_B are the volume fractions of the two components. The energy of vaporization per unit volume of a liquid, $\Delta E_i^v/V_i$ is often referred to as the "cohesive energy density" and its square root δ_i as the "Hildebrand solubility parameter." Relation (2.34) may also be obtained by applying to the liquids the van der Waals equation for non-ideal gases or by integrating the intermolecular potentials between pairs throughout the liquid with use of a continuous distribution function (Hildebrand and Scott, 1950, 1962). We see then that within the limitations of this treatment the heat of mixing is predictable from the values of a single parameter assigned to each constituent of the solution. Some typical values for the δ parameter are listed in Table II.1.

TABLE II.1
Hildebrand Solubility Parameters for Some Typical Solvents

Solvent	$\delta(cal^{1/2} cm^{-3/2})$ (at 25°C)
n-Pentane	7.1
n-Hexane	7.3
n-Heptane	7.4
n-Octane	7.5
2,2,4-Trimethylpentane	6.9
Cyclohexane	8.2
Benzene	9.2
Toluene	8.9
Methylene chloride	9.8
Chloroform	9.2
Carbon tetrachloride	8.6
Pyridine	10.7
Chlorobenzene	9.5
Nitrobenzene	10.0
Carbon disulfide	10.0
Diethyl ether	7.4
Dioxane	10.0

Hildebrand and Scott have discussed in detail the various factors which limit the scope of the van Laar treatment. We may first note that this treatment applies to constant volume processes (i.e., the volume of the solution is the sum of the volumes of its components before mixing) while in practice the solution process is carried out at constant pressure and leads generally to changes in volume. This factor may be taken into account by the relation

$$(\Delta H_M)_P = (\Delta E_M)_V + T \ (\partial P/\partial T)_V (\Delta V_M)_P + \ldots \qquad (2.35)$$

where $(\Delta V_M)_P$ is the volume change on mixing at constant pressure. Although ΔV_M is in most cases less than 1% of the volume of the system, the large values of $T(\partial P/\partial T)_V$ (typically of the order of about 3000 atm) frequently produce a significant difference between ΔH_M and ΔE_M. For the system benzene–cyclohexane with 0.5 mole of each component, $\Delta V_M = 0.65$ cc, $\Delta H_M = 182$ cal, and $\Delta E_M = 131$ cal (Goates et al., 1959). In most cases ΔV_M has the same sign as ΔH_M, as would be expected, since strong energetic interactions between the components of a mixture should lead both to heat evolution and volume contraction. However, there are some interesting exceptions such as the carbon tetrachloride–neopentane system (Mathot and Desmyter, 1953) and mixtures of aliphatic hydrocarbons (Desmyter and van der Waals, 1958), in which mixing leads to positive ΔE_M but negative ΔV_M values. Such phenomena are obviously related to changes in the efficiency of molecular packing when the components of a solution are mixed. A much more serious limitation arises because of the different nature of forces between molecules. It turns out that whenever relatively polar substances are involved in the mixing process, an athermal solution is no longer assured if the two components have equal cohesive energy densities, but the dipole–dipole forces and the dispersion forces of the components must each separately be equal. If this factor is neglected, the heats of mixing calculated from latent heats of vaporization will, in general, be too small (Hildebrand and Scott, 1950). Yet another complication may arise because of molecular geometry, which may favor energetic interactions between like or unlike molecules, so that the dependence of ΔE_M on the composition of the solution may deviate from the symmetry suggested by eq. (2.33). Better fits may sometimes be obtained if the volume fractions are based on empirically chosen "effective molar volumes."

It is a characteristic feature of the van Laar treatment that it can explain only athermal or endothermic mixing, but cannot account for processes in which solution results in an *evolution* of heat. Such a result is in most cases a consequence of specific forces between unlike molecules, which may make w_{AB} much larger than the geometric mean of w_{AA} and w_{BB}. A well known example is provided by the system chloroform–acetone (Staveley et al. 1955), where the heat evolved on mixing may be accounted for by hydrogen bond formation. Exothermic solution may be generally expected when the mixing involves a Lewis acid and a Lewis base.   Other types of exothermic solution process will be considered when we discuss the special solvent properties of water and certain solutions of hydrocarbon chain molecules in paraffins of low molecular weight.

4. Regular Solutions

The concept of a "regular solution" was introduced by Hildebrand (1929) and defined as a solution in which the partial molar entropies of the components are those to be expected from the ideal solution law.   From this definition it follows that any deviation from ideal solution behavior in a regular solution is entirely accounted for by the heat of mixing.   However, it is obvious that any difference in the forces between similar and dissimilar molecules in a solution (such as will cause the mixing process to be accompanied by the evolution or absorption of heat) should lead also to a deviation from a random distribution of the interacting molecules, i.e., to ΔS_M values lower than those predicted for an ideal solution.   The concept of a regular solution will, therefore, be a valid approximation only as long as the ordering forces are insufficient to prevent Brownian motion from disorienting the system almost as much as if the ordering forces were eliminated.   In practice this condition is reasonably well satisfied in many cases.   Using again the example of a solution containing 0.5 mole of benzene and 0.5 mole of cyclohexane at 25°C we see that the $(\Delta H_M)_P$ value of 182 cal is small compared to RT, so that the error introduced in neglecting differences of the energy corresponding to different configurations in the computation of the configurational entropy of the solution would be expected to be minor.

When Hildebrand first formulated the concept of regular solutions, he assumed that athermal solutions would necessarily follow the ideal solution law.   Much later, when the physical chemistry of solutions of high molecular weight substances was subjected to a detailed investigation, it became obvious that differences in the molecular size of solute and solvent may lead to a very large deviation from solution ideality even if no heat effect accompanies the formation of the solution.   The proposal was, therefore, made (Hildebrand, 1953) to reformulate the definition of a regular solution as "one in which thermal agitation is sufficient to give practically complete randomness."   This means that the entropy of mixing of a regular solution, defined in this manner, need not be ideal and we shall see later that it may deviate very far from ideality in systems containing polymeric solutes.   The definition has the advantage that a theoretical interpretation of the thermodynamic behavior of a solution may be treated by considering *separately* the entropy of mixing, based on a count of distinguishable configurations and the heat of solution, based on the assumption of random mixing.

5. The Free Energy of Mixing in Real Systems

As we have already noted above, the approximation involved in the concept of the "regular solution" has to break down when the forces operating between unlike molecules are very different from those characterizing interactions between molecules of the same species. Fortunately, there is a strong tendency for the "regular solution" treatment to lead to predictions of the free energy of mixing which are a good approximation to physical reality, even if the entropy of mixing deviates from the value expected for athermal solutions. This peculiar paradox of a theory giving satisfactory results in spite of the inadequacy of its underlying assumptions, may be explained as follows:

Consider a solution which is formed with absorption of heat. Since energy has to be supplied to induce the components to mix, there will be a tendency for like species to form aggregates more frequently than would be predicted by the assumption of random mixing. As a consequence, ΔS_M will have a lower value than predicted for the regular solution. But ΔH_M will also be lower than predicted, since the formation of aggregates of like molecules reduces the energy requirement for the endothermic mixing process. The free energy of mixing, $\Delta G_M = \Delta H_M - T\Delta S_M$ will, therefore, be predicted *more precisely than either* ΔH_M *or* $T\Delta S_M$. A similar argument holds for exothermic solution processes. Here, the tendency will be for dissimilar molecules to lie next to each other more frequently than predicted by chance. Again, ΔS_M will be lower because of this deviation from randomness. Since more contacts between dissimilar molecules are created than expected, more heat will be evolved. As a result, there will again be a tendency for the errors in the assumed ΔH_M and $T\Delta S_M$ to be in the same direction, so that they will tend to compensate one another in the calculation of the free energy of mixing. A similar point may be made with regard to effects produced by volume changes on the thermodynamic relationships. We have seen that such changes may make an appreciable contribution to the heat of mixing [see eq. (2.35)] but Scatchard (1937) has shown that the effect produced by a volume change on $T\Delta S_M$ is, to a first approximation, the same, so that the relative error involved in neglecting volume changes in the estimation of ΔG_M is much smaller than for ΔH_M and ΔS_M.

The heat effects produced by the mixing of pairs of liquids to which the van Laar theory would be expected to apply are rather small and a rather high degree of experimental precision is required to test the validity

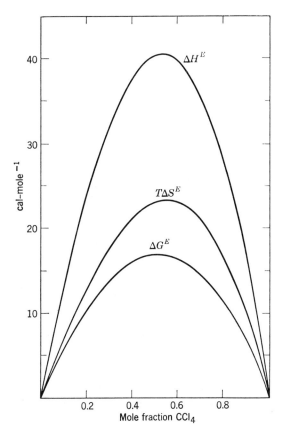

Fig. II.2. Excess thermodynamic functions for the carbon tetrachloride–cyclohexane system at 25°C.

of the treatment. Nevertheless, it appears that the theory is less satisfactory than might be expected. In particular, it is surprising that the mixing of nonpolar liquids is typically characterized by a positive value of ΔS_M^E, as shown, for example, in a plot of the excess functions for the carbon tetrachloride–cyclohexane system (Goates et al. 1959) reproduced in Fig. II.2. A similar observation was first made by Scatchard et al. (1939), who pointed out that an entropy of mixing at constant volume larger than the ideal value could be explained only by postulating that at least one of the components is, in the pure state, characterized by an ordered array of the molecules, which is destroyed by the mixing process. These investigators studied the benzene–cyclohexane system and it seemed reasonable to

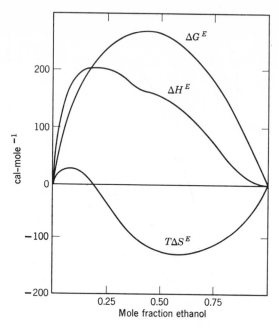

Fig. II.3. Excess thermodynamic functions for the carbon tetrachloride–ethanol system at 45°C.

assume that the high symmetry of benzene molecules gives rise, in the pure liquid, to some elements of the structure characterizing the lattice of benzene crystals. A similar conclusion was reached by van der Waals and Hermans (1950), who found that ΔS_M^E was about twice as large in the mixing of n-hexadecane with the highly branched 2,2,4-trimethylpentane as when n-hexadecane was mixed with the straight chain molecules of n-heptane. However, positive values of the excess entropy of mixing are very frequent even in cases where the constituents of the mixture cannot be said to consist of highly symmetrical molecules. Although many investigators fail to allow for volume changes, which could partly account for the phenomenon, other causes must undoubtedly contribute to the increase of the entropy of mixing. It has been suggested that such an effect may accompany the mixing of molecules if the forces exerted by them are strongly directional (Rowlinson and Sutton, 1955; Dyke et al., 1959). In such cases the forces between dissimilar nearest neighbors may, apparently, be even weaker than one would be led to expect on the basis of the rule of the geometric mean [eq. (2.29)]. Discrepancies between measured heats of mixing and values predicted from simplified models have been listed for a considerable number of systems by Brown et al. (1955) and by Mathieson and Thynne (1956), who have pointed out that ΔE_M is generally higher than predicted from the δ values given by Hildebrand and Scott (1950) and this even in cases when dipole–dipole interactions would not be expected to make themselves felt. Moreover, Brown et al. showed that it is impossible to assign a single parameter to each liquid in a manner such that the heat of mixing of any pair could be predicted.

When the energetics of the mixing process are determined by such highly specific interactions as hydrogen bonding and the association of electron donor and acceptor molecules, the dependence of the thermodynamic functions on the composition of the system may become very complex. Typical of such complex situations is the system carbon tetrachloride–ethanol (Barker et al., 1953), whose behavior is shown in Fig. II.3. The symmetrical curve representing the excess free energy is here quite deceptive in hiding a very complex behavior of both ΔH_M^E and $T\Delta S_M^E$. This complexity is hardly surprising since the alcohol molecules may interact with each other to form a series of open-chain or cyclic association complexes, each species behaving differently on dilution. Also, the strength of the hydrogen bond is not the same in all these species; for instance, the cyclic tetramers are believed to be characterized by stronger hydrogen bonds than the open chain polymers (Kuhn and Bowman, 1961). It is much more difficult to account for the complex behavior of the benzene-diphenylmethane system studied by Everett and Swinton (1963). In this case the solutions show a positive deviation from ideal solution behavior when they are rich in benzene, but a negative deviation from ideality when they are rich in diphenylmethane. These results probably reflect a change in the efficiency of molecular packing and it would be difficult to predict such an effect.

6. The Solvent Properties of Water

Water is a liquid with many unique properties which are reflected in various ways in its characteristics as a solvent medium. The most striking anomaly in the behavior of water is the contraction observed when the liquid is warmed from its freezing point of 0 to 4°C and attempts to interpret this phenomenon have been made for many years. The classical contribution in this field is due to Bernal and Fowler (1933). They found that the angular dependence of the intensity of x-rays scattered from water indicates a distance of 1.38 Å for neighboring oxygen atoms and they pointed out that this would correspond to a density of 1.84 if

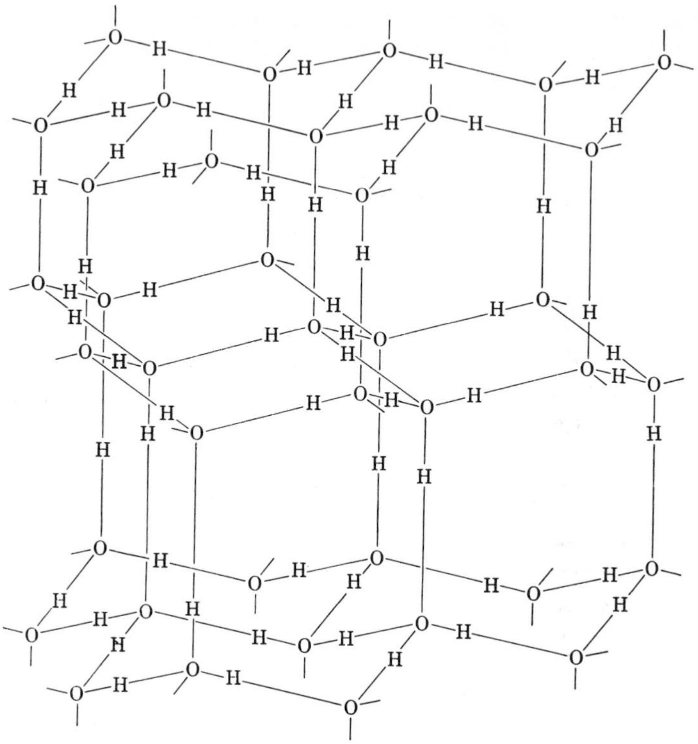

Fig. II.4. The crystal structure of ice.

water consisted of spherical molecules arranged in a close packed array. We must then account for the very much larger volume which liquid water in fact occupies. This tendency to take up a very large volume for each water molecule is even more pronounced in ice, which has the structure shown on Fig. II.4. In this structure each oxygen is surrounded tetrahedrally by four hydrogen atoms—two with which it forms a covalent bond and two belonging to neighboring water molecules to which it is hydrogen-bonded. The quantum mechanical requirement that a hydrogen bond can form between two neighboring water molecules only if a hydrogen is located close to the line connecting their oxygen atoms is responsible for preventing the molecules from packing as efficiently as they would if their interactions were due solely to dispersion forces and dipole–dipole interactions. According to Bernal and Fowler, liquid water retains to some extent molecular aggregates with the open ice-like structure and this accounts for its low density. This representation is also in good quantitative agreement with the angular distribution of the intensity of scattered x-rays. As the temperature of the liquid is raised, the tendency for ice-like aggregates to "melt" contributes a volume contraction which is superimposed on the expansion due to thermal agitation. This concept was considered in greater detail by Frank and Wen (1957) who pointed out that the partial charge transfer accompanying the formation of a hydrogen bond

$$\begin{array}{cc} \text{H} & \text{H} \\ {}^{-\delta}| & {}^{+\delta}| \\ \text{—O—H} & \text{....O—H} \end{array}$$

makes the acceptor molecule a stronger hydrogen bond donor, while the donor molecule becomes a stronger hydrogen bond acceptor. As a result there will be a tendency for hydrogen bonds to reinforce one another, favoring the formation of relatively large "flickering clusters" which form and dissolve as a result of local energy fluctuations. Recently, Némethy and Scheraga (1962a) have presented a detailed statistical mechanical treatment of water based on similar ideas. The parameters which they chose for the best representation of the thermodynamic properties of water give ice-like clusters with an average of 91, 57, and 38 water molecules and a fraction of 0.53, 0.46, and 0.41 unbroken hydrogen bonds at 0, 20, and 40°C, respectively.

When organic compounds containing nonpolar residues are introduced into an aqueous solution, large positive deviations from ideality are observed. However, whereas poor solvent properties are normally caused by an unfavorable heat of mixing, the solution of materials such as aliphatic hydrocarbons in water has frequently been found to be exothermic. We are then left with the conclusion that the poor solubility of nonpolar solutes in water is a consequence of a large negative excess entropy of mixing. A detailed consideration of these findings was first undertaken in a pioneering investigation of Frank and Evans (1945). They pointed out that the negative ΔH_M and the negative ΔS_M^E may be rationalized by assuming that an ice-like structure is stabilized in the neighborhood of nonpolar solutes—thus the heat evolved may be thought of as due to the latent heat of freezing of "icebergs" which represent regions of crystalline order and whose formation, therefore, leads to a loss of entropy. The tendency of nonpolar solutes to aggregate in aqueous media reduces the number of water molecules in their immediate vicinity and leads to "iceberg melting." This provides the driving force towards such aggregation and has been referred to as the "hydrophobic bond" (Kauzmann, 1959). Frank and Evans noted that the solution of nonpolar hydrocarbons in water leads generally to a volume contraction, in contrast to the expansion observed when water freezes to ice. They interpreted this discrepancy by assuming that the "icebergs" may be characterized by a structure which is more efficiently packed than the usual low-pressure modification of ice. (Crystalline forms of ice stable

TABLE II.2

Thermodynamic Parameters for the Solution of Liquid Hydrocarbons in Water at 25°C

Substance	$\Delta G°$ (kcal/mole)	$\Delta H°$ (kcal/mole)	$\Delta S°$ (cal-deg^{-1}-mole^{-1})	$\Delta \bar{C}_p$	$\Delta V°$ (cm^3-mole^{-1})
Propane	+4.9	−1.8	−22	90	−22.7
Butane	+5.9	−0.8	−22	99	
Benzene	+4.6	+0.6	−13	73	−6.5
Toluene	+5.3	+0.6	−16	85	

under high pressure are denser than water.) However, Nemethy and Scheraga (1962b) have pointed out that the volume contraction is consistent with ice-like water aggregates packed in the manner of the low-pressure ice modification, since the solute molecules can be accommodated in the

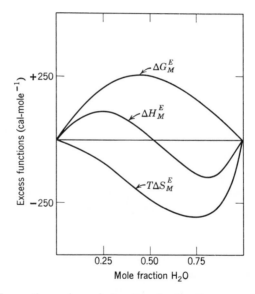

Fig. II.5. Excess thermodynamic functions for the dioxane–water system.

large vacancies typical of this structure.   Some of the data compiled by these authors are shown in Table II.2.   We may note that for benzene and toluene ΔH for transfer to the aqueous medium has a small positive value, which is interpreted as due to special effects produced by interactions with the π-electrons of the aromatic ring.   The increase in the partial molar heat capacities $\overline{\Delta C_p}$ of the hydrocarbons is a consequence of the additional heat required to melt the "icebergs" formed around them.

When a substance dissolved in the aqueous medium contains not only nonpolar residues but also functional groups which may participate in hydrogen bonding, the situation becomes much more complex and is apparently governed to a considerable extent by geometric factors. We may consider as typical examples the systems water–ethanol (Mitchell and Wynne-Jones, 1953) and water–dioxane (Malcolm and Rowlinson, 1957) for which the excess thermodynamic functions are plotted in Fig. II.5. For both systems there is a positive deviation from ideal solution behavior and a negative ΔS_M^E over the entire concentration range. However, the heat of mixing data for the dioxane–water system show an interesting inversion of sign, which apparently signifies that exothermic iceberg formation is the dominant effect only in water-rich media, whereas the endothermic mixing for systems of high dioxane concentration follows the normal pattern for the mixing of two liquids of different cohesive energy density.

7. Phase Equilibria

Limited solubility of liquids in liquids may be the result of an unfavorable heat of mixing or of a large negative value of the excess entropy characterizing the solution process. The first is by far the more frequent case. We may then inquire, what is the magnitude of ΔH_M which will lead in a binary system to the coexistence of two liquid phases. Hildebrand and Scott (1950) have considered this problem for a regular solution in which the molar volumes are similar for the two components. For such a solution it is reasonable to expect the heat of mixing to be proportional to the product of the concentrations of the two components, so that for a total of one mole

$$\Delta G_M = RT(x_1 \ln x_1 + x_2 \ln x_2) + Bx_1 x_2 \qquad (2.36a)$$

and for n_1 and n_2 moles of the two components

$$\Delta G_M = RT \left[n_1 \ln \left(\frac{n_1}{n_1 + n_2} \right) + n_2 \ln \left(\frac{n_2}{n_1 + n_2} \right) \right] + Bn_1 n_2 / (n_1 + n_2)$$

$$(2.36b)$$

We have seen in Fig. II.1(a) and II.1(b) that ΔG_M curves corresponding to systems which exhibit limited miscibility have two inflection points. These will coalesce in the limiting case of the consolute point, at which the two components become miscible in all proportions. This point will, therefore, be characterized by the conditions (Tompa, 1956):

$$(\partial^2 \Delta G_M / \partial x_1^2)_{T,P} = 0 \qquad (\partial^2 \Delta G_M / \partial x_2^2)_{T,P} = 0$$
$$(\partial^3 \Delta G_M / \partial x_1^3)_{T,P} = 0 \qquad (\partial^3 \Delta G_M / \partial x_2^3)_{T,P} = 0 \qquad (2.37)$$

It can be shown that these conditions correspond to $x_1 = x_2 = 1/2$ and $B = 2RT_c$, where T_c is the consolute temperature, so that at the consulate point the mixing is endothermic to the extent of $RT_c/2$ per mole. If we use the van Laar theory for estimating the heat of mixing from eq. (2.34), then for liquids with a molar volume of 100 ml a critical miscibility temperature T_c of 300°K requires that the solubility parameters δ of the two components differ from each other by 3.5 units. Inspection of Table II.1 will show that such large differences in the δ parameters are rare. Nonpolar systems of low-molecular-weight organic liquids, therefore, generally do not exhibit phase separation, unless one of the components is a fluorocarbon (with very low δ values of 5.6 to 6.1) or the strongly hydrogen-bonded methanol. Other systems with incomplete miscibility at room temperature are formed by aniline, nitrobenzene or phenol with normal aliphatic hydrocarbons.

If the mixing process is endothermic, solubility will increase with rising temperature and the critical point will lie at an "upper consolute temperature" above which the components of the system are miscible in all proportions. An example of such a system (Hildebrand, 1953) is given in Fig. II.6(a). It is much more unusual to have a binary system with complete miscibility below a "lower consolute temperature" and separation into two phases above it. The conditions leading to phase diagrams of this type have been discussed by Copp and Everett (1953). A lower consolute temperature can only occur if mixing is exothermic and the excess entropy of mixing has a large negative value, so that ΔG_M^E attains the value required for phase separation. These conditions are satisfied in some aqueous solutions due to the "iceberg" formation discussed in the previous section and Fig. II.6(b) representing the phase diagram of the N-methylpiperidine–water system (Flaschner, 1908) is a typical example of this case. Finally, it is possible for a binary system to have both an upper and a lower consolute temperature, so that coexistence of two liquid phases is observed only in a limited temperature range and the phase diagram is characterized by a closed loop. The thermodynamic requirement for this phenomenon is a change of sign of ΔH_M from a negative value at the lower critical solution temperature to a positive value at the upper critical solution temperature. This requires that $d\Delta H_M / dT = \Delta C_p$ have a large positive value, a condition

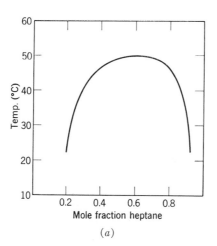

(a)

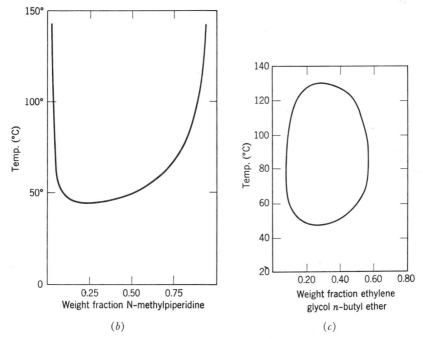

(b)   (c)

Fig. II.6 Typical phase diagrams of binary liquid systems. (a) Heptane–perfluoro-heptane. (b) Water–N-methylpiperidine. (c) Water–ethylene glycol mono-n-butyl ether.

which is fulfilled, as we have seen in Table II.2, for solutions of "iceberg-forming" solutes in water. Barker and Fock (1953) have pointed out that phase diagrams with a closed loop might be expected, in general, for systems in which interaction between unlike molecules are repulsive for most relative orientations but attractive for a few. A typical phase diagram of this type, that for the system ethylene glycol monobutyl ether–water shown on Fig. II.6(c), was studied by Cox and Cretcher (1926) who have listed a number of other systems with similar behavior.

8. Solubility of Crystalline Solids

The general relation for the solubility of a crystalline solute was given in eq. (2.16b). Here the partial molar heat of solution $(\overline{\Delta H_2})'$ may be considered as the sum of the latent heat of melting and the ΔH corresponding to the mixing of one mole of the molten solute with a large volume of an almost saturated solution. If the molten solute forms an ideal solution with the solvent, this heat of mixing vanishes as does also the term $(\partial \ln \gamma_2/\partial x_2)_{T,P}$. We may then integrate eq. (2.16b) from any temperature T to the melting temperature T_m, and disregarding the variation of the latent heat of melting ΔH_m with T, we obtain an estimate of the "ideal solubility"

$$\ln x_2 = -(\Delta H_m/R)(T_m - T)/T_m T \tag{2.38}$$

We see then that the ideal solubility of a crystal is related to its melting point and its latent heat of melting. But these two quantities are not independent of each other, since T_m is the ratio of the heat to the entropy of melting, so that T_m usually increases with an increase in ΔH_m. For similar compounds, ΔH_m depends on the efficiency of packing in the crystal lattice and tends to rise with an increasing symmetry of the molecule. This is the cause, for instance, of the general rule that *para*-disubstituted benzenes have higher melting points and lower solubilities than their *ortho* and *meta* isomers. Data typifying this effect are listed in Table II.3

TABLE II.3

Thermodynamic Data for the Melting of the Isomeric Dinitrobenzenes and Their Ideal Solubility

	ortho	*meta*	*para*
ΔH_m(cal-mole^{-1})	5,430	4,150	6,720
ΔS_m(cal-deg^{-1}-mole^{-1}	13.9	11.4	15.0
T_m(°K)	390	363	447
Ideal solubility (x_2) at 303°K	0.136	0.319	0.027

for the isomeric dinitrobenzenes. The entropy of melting of organic compounds depends on many factors such as the number of accessible conformations in the liquid state, imperfect ordering of the crystals, and partial ordering of the liquids. As a characteristic example we may cite the wide variation in ΔS_m (in cal-deg^{-1}-mole^{-1}) of some C_6 hydrocarbons i.e., 1.32 for 2,3-dimethylbutane, 2.29 for cyclohexane, 8.46 for benzene, and 17.6 for n-hexane (Westrum and McCullough, 1963).

B. BINARY SYSTEMS CONTAINING MACROMOLECULES

1. Deviation of Polymer Solutions from Ideal Solution Behavior

In classical treatments of the thermodynamic behavior of solutions it was generally assumed—implicitly or explicitly—that deviations from ideal solution behavior must be associated with a finite heat of solution. However, when physical chemists began to deal intensively with the properties of systems containing high molecular weight components, it soon became obvious that such systems showed extremely large deviations from the behavior to be expected of ideal solutions, even in cases when the heat of mixing of a polymer with a low molecular weight solvent was negligible. We may use as an extreme example the case of a vulcanized automobile tire swollen with one gram of benzene. By the classical definition, the tire is a single molecule, since any two atoms in it are connected by a series of covalent bonds. We have then a system containing one rubber molecule and 8×10^{21} benzene molecules. Since the heat of mixing of rubber and benzene is extremely small, the system might have been expected to behave ideally, so that the vapor pressure of the benzene swelling the tire should have been indistinguishable from that of pure benzene. We know, of course, that this is far from being the case and that the vapor pressure of the benzene under the conditions described will be very small indeed.

In studying the thermodynamic behavior of a binary system containing a polymeric and a low molecular weight component, it is most convenient to focus attention on the thermodynamic activity of the small molecules. The large negative deviations from ideal solution behavior imply a large negative value of $\overline{\Delta G}_1^E$, and since this is found even when the enthalpy of dilution is zero or positive, we must conclude that polymer solutions are characterized by large positive excess entropies of dilution. A theory of this effect may be developed by the methods of statistical mechanics, but before we discuss the results obtained in this manner, we shall try to obtain a qualitative feeling for the origins of the effect.

Most polymer molecules may be represented as flexible chains. If such chains are sufficiently long, the shape of their backbones may be likened to the random flight path of a particle undergoing Brownian motion and it is then commonly referred to as a "random coil." At extreme dilutions, each one of these chains can assume a large number of shapes (conformations) and the probability that any one chain exists at a given time in a given shape will be independent of the shapes assumed by all the other chains. In the pure amorphous polymer the chain molecules are just as flexible as in solution and may be assumed to be able to exist in a similar number of conformations. However, it is obvious that now these molecular shapes are not independent of each other, but the shape of each molecular chain must be correlated with the shape assumed by its neighbors so as to fill the available space. It is this restraint which is eliminated when a molecular chain is transferred from the pure polymer phase to a dilute solution and this accounts for the characteristic positive ΔS_M^E values of solutions of chain molecules. In considering the problem more closely, we shall be led to distinguish two ranges of concentration in systems containing chain molecules. In relatively dilute solution, the loose molecular coils will only occasionally interpenetrate and the frequency of such interference will depend on the size of the individual coil. In this range we may, therefore, suspect that ΔS_M^E is sensitive to the polymer chain length. At higher concentrations the total available volume is much less than the sum of the volumes enclosed by the twisting chain molecules and the molecular chains must, therefore, necessarily become heavily intertwined. In this range we might suspect that the interference with the shape of a given chain, due to the presence of other chain molecules, will depend on the fraction of the volume occupied by these chains. It should be rather independent of the occasional occurrence of chain ends—which means that it should not depend significantly on the molecular weight of the polymer.

A quantitative theory of this effect was formulated by Flory (1942) and Huggins (1942a,b,c,) who evaluated the number of distinguishable ways in which N_1 solvent molecules with a molar volume V_1 and N_2 polymer chains with a molar volume V_2 could be placed on a lattice so that each lattice site is occupied either by a solvent molecule or one of the V_2/V_1 segments of a polymer chain. The crucial point in the calculation is the assumption that, in placing a given chain segment on the lattice which already contains previously placed chains, the probability of occupancy of a lattice site may be approximated by the overall fraction of occupied sites. This approximation is clearly untenable in very dilute solutions, where molecular coils, representing high local concentrations of chain segments, are separated by

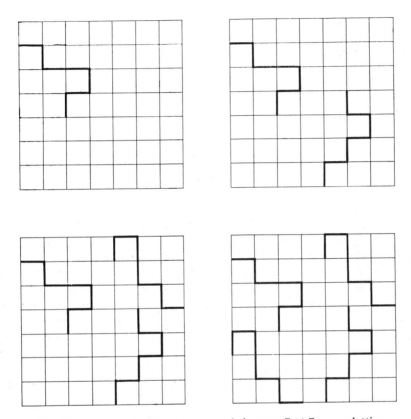

Fig. II.7. Placement of seven-segment chains on a 7 × 7 square lattice.

regions of pure solvent. However, the assumption of the Flory–Huggins theory is reasonable in the concentration range in which the chains interpenetrate each other, so that the density of chain segments is uniform, on the molecular scale, throughout the system and it is in this range that the theory has been eminently successful. Figure II.7 is a schematic representation of the successive placement of four chains, each containing seven segments, on a lattice of 49 sites. It is apparent that a large number of shapes can be chosen for the first chain, but that the choice of any one of them imposes restrictions on the second chain and that this effect becomes more pronounced with each successive chain. (In fact, a fifth chain cannot be added without rearranging the previous four.)

Denoting by W_1 the number of distinguishable ways in which the N_2 polymer chains may be placed on a lattice of $N_2 V_2 / V_1$ sites (corresponding to the pure disordered polymer) and by $\mathcal{W}_2$ the number of distinguishable ways in which they can be placed on the $N_1 + N_2(V_2/V_1)$ lattice sites corresponding to the solution, we can obtain the configurational entropy of mixing as

$$(\Delta S_M)_{con} = k \ln (\mathcal{W}_2/\mathcal{W}_1) \tag{2.39}$$

In Flory's and Huggins' evaluation of the statistical problem, the result becomes

$$(\Delta S_M)_{conf} = -k[N_1 \ln \phi_1 + N_2 \ln \phi_2]$$
$$= -R[n_1 \ln \phi_1 + n_2 \ln \phi_2] \tag{2.40}$$

where n_1 and n_2 are the numbers of moles of solvent and polymer, respectively, while ϕ_1 and ϕ_2 are their volume fractions. It may at first seem surprising that this result does not contain parameters characterizing the lattice used in the model or the flexibility of the chain molecule. It is, of course, obvious that the increase in the number of distinguishable patterns will increase more sharply during the mixing process if the coordination number of the lattice (the number of nearest neighbors to each lattice site) and the chain flexibility are increased. However, the entropy gain depends on the *ratio* of possible arrangements in the initial and final state and it can be shown that this does not change appreciably when the character of the lattice or the chain stiffness are altered.*

For athermal solutions the Flory–Huggins theory leads to solvent activities given by

$$\ln a_1 = -(1/R)[\partial(\Delta S)_{conf}/\partial n_1]_{n_2}$$
$$= \ln \phi_1 + [1 - (V_1/V_2)]\phi_2$$
$$= -\phi_2(V_1/V_2) - \phi_2^2/2 - \phi_2^3/3 - \ldots \tag{2.41}$$

which may be compared to the value for dilute ideal solutions in which $x_2 \approx \phi_2(V_1/V_2)$ so that

$$\ln a_1^i = \ln (1 - x_2)$$
$$= -\phi_2(V_1/V_2) - (^1/_2)(\phi_2 V_1/V_2)^2 - (^1/_3)(\phi_2 V_1/V_2)^3 \ldots \tag{2.42}$$

In classical physical chemistry, thermodynamic measurements on solutions usually emphasized the determination of the molecular weight

---

* It has been assumed that the chain remains sufficiently flexible to correspond to a relatively large number of "statistical chain elements" (see Chap. III, Sect. B.3.). For a discussion of very stiff chains, see Flory (1956).

from colligative properties of dilute solutions, where the effect observed is proportional to $\ln a_1$. A comparison of (2.41) and (2.42) shows that at a typical solute concentration $\phi_2 = 0.01$ the value of $\ln a_1$ differs from its ideal value by factors of only 1.01, and 1.10 for $V_2/V_1 = 2$ and 20, respectively, so that it is not surprising that effects due to an excess configurational entropy of dilution should have been missed until solutions of very long chain molecules became the subjects of investigation. On the other hand, it may be noted that deviations from solution ideality, observable as reduced vapor pressures of the solvent, become very obvious in the range of composition where most of the volume is occupied by the larger molecules even if V_2/V_1 has relatively low values. For instance, at $\phi_2 = 0.99$ the Flory–Huggins theory predicts a decrease of a_1 below the ideal solution value by factors of 1.2, 2.2, and 6.4 for $V_2/V_1 = 2$, 5, and 20, respectively.

In addition to the deviation from ideality caused by the chain-like character of the solute molecules, we have to consider contributions to ΔH_M and ΔS_M^E due to solute–solvent contacts. These effects are short-range in character (except in the case of long-range Coulombic interactions in solutions of polyelectrolytes) and should, therefore, be proportional to the "number of contact points" between solute and solvent. The concentration dependence of this somewhat nebulous quantity should not be altered appreciably when chain segments are joined together to a macromolecule and we may assume that the contribution to ΔG_M^E due to nearest neighbor contacts is approximately proportional to $V\phi_1\phi_2$. We have seen [eq. (2.34)] that this is the form predicted by the van Laar theory for ΔE_M and in binary systems of small molecules, in which molecular interactions are governed largely by dispersion forces, a similar concentration dependence holds also for ΔS_M^E (see the carbon tetrachloride–cyclohexane system, Fig. II.2). However, inspection of Fig. II.3 and especially Fig. II.5 shows that ΔG_M^E approaches the predicted parabolic behavior even in systems with very complex interactions which lead to striking deviations from this concentration dependence for ΔH_M^E and ΔS_M^E.

Using the concept of a regular solution, we may treat the free energy of mixing as being made up additively from contributions due to configurational probability and a free energy characterizing nearest-neighbor interactions. Assuming the nearest-neighbor interaction term to be proportional to the product of the volume fractions of the components,

$$\Delta G_M = -T(\Delta S_M)_{\text{conf}} + BV\phi_1\phi_2 \qquad (2.43)$$

or, substituting from (2.40) and using the conventional notation of the Flory–Huggins theory,

$$\Delta G_M = RT[n_1 \ln \phi_1 + n_2 \ln \phi_2 + n_1 \chi \phi_2]$$

$$\chi = B V_1 / RT \tag{2.44}$$

where χ is referred to as the "Flory–Huggins interaction parameter."[*] We obtain then for the activity of the solvent:

$$\ln a_1 = \overline{\Delta G_1}/RT = \ln \phi_1 + [1 - (V_1/V_2)]\phi_2 + \chi \phi_2^2 \tag{2.45}$$

which yields, on expansion of the $\ln \phi_1 = \ln (1 - \phi_2)$ term,

$$\ln a_1 = -\phi_2 V_1 / V_2 - (1/2 - \chi)\phi_2^2 - 1/3 \phi_2^3 - \ldots \tag{2.46}$$

It is instructive to compare this result with one which would be obtained if the entropy of dilution had the ideal value given in eq. (2.23). The solvent activity would then be given by

$$\ln a_1 = -\phi_2 V_1 / V_2 - (1/2)(\phi_2 V_1 / V_2)^2 - (1/3)(\phi_2 V_1 / V_2)^3 \ldots + \chi \phi_2^2 \tag{2.47}$$

It is clear that in this case a large value of V_2/V_1 would make mixing impossible if χ had an appreciable positive value. We may then conclude that endothermic mixing of high molecular weight polymers with solvents is possible only because of the configuration entropy gained by flexible chain molecules in the process of dilution.

Sometimes it is erroneously assumed that the negative deviations from ideality, characteristic of the solutions of long chain molecules, are a necessary consequence of the large ratio of the molar volumes of solute and solvent. However, Zimm (1946) and Huggins (1948) have pointed out that athermal solutions of large molecules behaving as rigid spheres may show a negligible deviation from solution ideality. Calculations of the excluded volume effect in such systems lead to a solvent activity given, for athermal solutions, by

$$\ln a_1 = -\phi_2 V_1 / V_2 - 4(V_1/V_2)\phi_2^2 - 10(V_1/V_2)\phi_2^3 - \ldots \tag{2.48}$$

so that the relative magnitudes of the leading term and the terms depending on the higher powers of solute concentration remain unchanged as the molecular volume of the solute is increased. For ellipsoidal particles the coefficient of ϕ_2^2 increases with particle asymmetry, but it is still inversely proportional to V_2/V_1 (Isihara, 1950a). However, for very long, rigid, rod-like solute particles of length L and diameter d, Zimm (1946) obtained

---

[*] This parameter specifies, in units of kT, the excess free energy for the transfer of a solvent molecule from the pure solvent to the pure polymer phase.

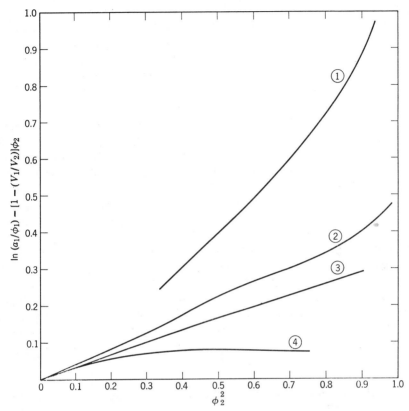

Fig. II.8. Comparison of Flory-Huggins theory with experimental data. (1) Polyiso-butene–benzene. (2) Hevea rubber–benzene. (3) Polybutadiene–benzene. (4) Poly-styrene–chloroform.

for the coefficient of the ϕ_2^2 term the value $LV_1/V_2 d$, so that for rods of a fixed diameter, where L/V_2 has a constant value, this coefficient is independent of the length of the rod. We see then that the term proportional to the square of the solute concentration becomes increasingly important in determining the solvent activity as the asymmetry of the solute particle is increased. Some of the consequences of this situation will be considered further in Sect. B.4.

A test of the validity of the Flory–Huggins theory for solutions of flexible chain molecules may be carried out by plotting $\ln (a_1/\phi_1) - [1 - (V_1/V_2)]\phi_2$ against ϕ_2^2. According to (2.45) such a plot should be linear and have a slope χ. In Fig. II.8 experimental data obtained for four typical systems are plotted in this manner. For Hevea rubber in benzene (Gee and Treloar, 1942) and polybutadiene in benzene (Jessup, 1958), two systems in which mixing is nearly athermal, the predicted linearity of the plot is in fairly good agreement with experiment. For polyisobutene in benzene, which is a poor solvent for this polymer (Jessup, 1958), the plot has an upward curvature, a feature which seems to be typical of very poor solvents in general (Booth et al., 1957). On the other hand, the plot for the polystyrene–chloroform system (Bawn and Wajid, 1956) is characterized by a strong downward curvature. This is a system in which one would expect exothermic mixing as a result of hydrogen bonding of the acidic hydrogen of chloroform with the aromatic nuclei of polystyrene (Creswell and Allred, 1962) in systems rich in polystyrene. Once the hydrogen acceptor capacity of the polymer has been saturated, further chloroform addition should be characterized by much weaker energetic interactions. A similar principle may account for the rapid decrease of the χ values with increasing polymer content in the acetone–cellulose nitrate system (Takenaka, 1957). It is, of course, possible to improve agreement of an analytical expression for ln a_1 with experimental results by increasing the number of adjustable parameters, for instance, by introducing a second interaction parameter to be used as a coefficient of the ϕ_2^3 term in eq. (2.46). Krigbaum and Geymer (1959) showed that this coefficient [unlike the coefficient of $1/3$ in eq. (2.46)] is temperature dependent in the polystyrene–cyclohexane system. It is, however, doubtful whether this coefficient can be given a clear physical interpretation.

2. Phase Equilibrium in Systems of a Polymer and Poor Solvents

The general theory of phase equilibria in systems containing long chain molecules and low molecular weight solvents is rather complex and it is questionable whether a theoretical model lending itself to mathematical analysis can take account of all the factors involved. It is much simpler to consider the limiting case of a two-component system in which the mutual solubility of the components is very low, so that each of the phases contains one of the components in highly dilute solution, while the other component is virtually in its standard state. The condition for equilibrium is then

$$\bar{G}_i^0 = \bar{G}_i^0 + RT \ln x_i + \bar{G}_i^E$$

$$x_i = \exp\left[-\bar{G}_i^E/RT\right] \tag{2.49}$$

The $\bar{G}_1^E$ value characterizing solvent molecules in very slightly swollen polymer will be due to nearest neighbor interaction effects between solvent molecules and polymer segments. The chain length of the polymer will affect this quantity only insofar as the medium will have different properties in the immediate vicinity of chain ends. For high polymers the concentration of chain ends will be very low and $\bar{G}_1^E$ will approach the limiting value characteristic of solvent molecules in polymer of infinite molecular weight. We may, therefore, conclude that the equilibrium swelling of polymers with small solvent molecules will not depend appreciably on the chain length of the polymer.

The situation is quite different with $\bar{G}_2^E$, characterizing the chain molecules in dilute solution. This quantity contains not only contributions from nearest-neighbor interactions of solvent molecules with polymer segments, but also a contribution resulting from the increase of configurational entropy accompanying the separation of flexible chains from each other. But both contributions should be proportional to chain length, so that the solubility of polymers in poor solvents should fall off with their molecular weight in a manner indicated by

$$x_2 = \exp\left[-AM_2\right] \qquad (2.50)$$

when A is a characteristic constant.

Results based on the Flory–Huggins theory are in agreement with these qualitative considerations. Setting $\ln a_1 = 0$ and $\phi_2 \rightarrow 1$ in eq. (2.45) we obtain for the volume fraction of solvent contained in the swollen polymer in equilibrium with a poor swelling agent

$$\phi_1 = \exp\left[-1 - \chi + (V_1/V_2)\right] \qquad (2.51)$$

Similarly, from the activity of the polymeric species

$$\ln a_2 = (1/RT)(\partial G_M/\partial n_2)_{n_1} = \ln \phi_2 + \left[1 - (V_2/V_1)\right]\phi_1 + (V_2/V_1)\chi\phi_1^2 \qquad (2.52)$$

we obtain, by setting $\ln a_2 = 0$, $\phi_1 \rightarrow 1$, for the volume fraction of polymer in a solution phase which is in equilibrium with very slightly swollen polymer

$$\phi_2 = \exp\left\{-(V_2/V_1)\left[\chi + (V_1/V_2) - 1\right]\right\} \qquad (2.53)$$

This expression has the form postulated in (2.50).

3. The Consolute Point

In our previous discussion of the mutual solubility of liquids (Sec. A-7) we saw that the consolute point (at which the difference between two coexisting phases vanishes) requires $(\partial^2 \Delta G_M/\partial x_1^2)_{T,P} = 0$ and

$(\partial^3 \Delta G_M / \partial x_1^3)_{T,P} = 0$. We may write these conditions in the form $\partial \ln a_1 / \partial \phi_2 = 0$, $\partial^2 \ln a_1 / \partial \phi_2^2 = 0$ and use for $\ln a_1$, the expression given in (2.45). This leads to the prediction that the critical point is characterized (Flory, 1942) by

$$(\phi_2)_{\text{crit}} = 1 / [1 + \sqrt{V_2/V_1}] \tag{2.54}$$

$$\chi_{\text{crit}} = (^1/_2) + \sqrt{V_1/V_2} + V_1/2V_2 \tag{2.55}$$

It should be noted that this result depends on the applicability of the Flory–Huggins expression for the free energy of mixing at the relatively high dilution corresponding to the consolute point of high polymer solutions. We shall see later (Chap. IV) that a different approach becomes necessary when dealing with systems in which the polymer coils occupy discrete regions of space. However, it seems reasonable to assume that at the critical point the chains will interpenetrate sufficiently to justify the assumption of the uniform concentration of chain segments, on which the Flory–Huggins theory is based. On the other hand, it can be shown that the results (2.54) and (2.55) are quite sensitive to the dependence of $\ln a_1$ on ϕ_2^3. In the Flory–Huggins theory this dependence is constant for all solvent media [see eq. (2.46)] but Krigbaum and Geymer (1959) have shown that the coefficient of ϕ_2^3 tends to vanish at the consolute point and this should introduce an error in the theory of the critical point as outlined above. This applies particularly to the predicted value of $(\phi_2)_{\text{crit}}$, which is found experimentally to be appreciably higher than predicted (Shultz and Flory, 1952).

The relations (2.54) and (2.55) have two features which should be noted. First, the critical polymer concentration, for high molecular weight solutes, occurs at $\phi_2 \approx \sqrt{V_1/V_2}$, i.e., the consolute point will occur in a very dilute system if the polymer chains are very long. This means that a slight variation in the quality of the solvent may result in a shift from complete miscibility to a very low equilibrium solubility of the polymer. Also, since even the more concentrated of the two phases in equilibrium close to the consolute point may be highly dilute, it may separate as a viscous liquid, rather than as a gel. This phenomenon, termed coacervation by Bungenberg de Jong and Kruyt (1930) is fairly common in ternary systems but has also been observed in systems containing only one polymer and one solvent (Dobry, 1945). Secondly, the critical value of the interaction parameter, χ, approaches a limiting value of $^1/_2$ as V_2/V_1 becomes very large. The consolute point corresponding to an infinite V_2/V_1 has been designated by Flory as the Θ-point. If the solvent medium is variable, the

Θ-point corresponds to a "Θ-solvent," if temperature is varied for a constant solvent composition, the Θ-point is reached at the "Θ-temperature." The meaning of these concepts will be explored further in Chap. IV.

The interaction parameter, χ, which characterizes the contribution to the excess free energy of mixing from binary nearest-neighbor interactions is composed, in general, of an energy and an entropy term, as we have seen in our discussion of mixtures of small molecules. We may, therefore, write (2.55) in the form

$$\chi_{\text{crit}} = \frac{\overline{\Delta H_1^*}}{RT_c\phi_2^2} - \frac{\overline{\Delta S_1^*}}{R\phi_2^2} = {}^1\!/_2 + \sqrt{V_1/V_2} + V_1/2V_2 \qquad (2.56a)$$

where T_c is the consolute temperature and the stars denote excess thermodynamic quantities due to binary nearest-neighbor interactions. For $V_2/V_1 \rightarrow \infty$, $T_c = \Theta$ and

$$\frac{\overline{\Delta H_1^*}}{R\Theta\phi_2^2} = {}^1\!/_2 + \frac{\overline{\Delta S_1^*}}{R\phi_2^2} \equiv \Psi \qquad (2.56b)$$

so that

$$\frac{1}{T_c} = \frac{1}{\Theta}\left[1 + \frac{1}{\Psi}\left(\sqrt{V_1/V_2} + V_1/2V_2\right)\right] \qquad (2.56c)$$

This relation was derived by Shultz and Flory (1952, 1953) who subjected it to extensive experimental testing. They found that plots of $1/T_c$ against $\sqrt{V_1/V_2} + V_1/2V_2$ are indeed linear, as predicted, defining

TABLE II.4
Thermodynamic Data for Polymer–Solvent Systems from the
Dependence of the Consolute Temperature on the Polymer Chain Length

Polymer	Solvent	$\Theta(°K)$	Ψ
Polystyrene	Octadecanol	474	1.30
Polystyrene	Cyclohexanol	358.4	1.51
Polystyrene	Cyclohexane	307.2	1.056
Polystyrene	Ethylcyclohexane	343.2	0.875
Polyethylene	Nitrobenzene	503	1.09
Polyisobutene	Diisobutyl ketone	331.1	0.65
Poly(methyl methacrylate)	Heptanone-4	305	0.61
Polydimethylsiloxane	Phenetole	358	0.69
Polydimethylsiloxane	Butanone	298.2	0.43
Cellulose tricaprylate	Dimethylformamide	413	0.39
Cellulose tricaprylate	3-Phenylpropanol-1	323	0.21
Poly(acrylic acid)	Dioxane	302.2	−0.31
Polymethacrylonitrile	Butanone	279	−0.63

the two characteristic parameters Θ and Ψ.   Their values for these parameters for a number of systems are listed in Table II.4.   It may be noted that for two of the systems, poly(acrylic acid) in dioxane and polymethacrylonitrile in butanone, the value of Ψ is negative.   This makes the polymer dilution an exothermic process and the solubility must then decrease with rising temperature.   In these cases Θ represents, therefore, the *highest* temperature at which very high molecular weight polymer and solvent are miscible in all proportions.   Such behavior is particularly common with polymer solutions in water, for reasons which we have discussed in connection with aqueous solutions of low molecular weight solutes (Sect. A6).   In the case of the poly(ethylene oxide)–water system, Malcolm and Rowlinson (1957) found that the composition–temperature phase diagram was characterized by a closed loop similar to that shown in Fig. II.6(c). Since this implies an upper and a lower consolute temperature, Ψ must increase with rising temperature, changing from a negative to a positive value. It is clear that in such a complex situation the Shultz–Flory analysis cannot be expected to apply, since it depends on the assumption that the excess entropy of mixing is independent of temperature.   In view of the increase in the partial molar heat capacities, characteristic of the formation of aqueous solutions (Table II.2), a positive temperature coefficient of Ψ is probably far from exceptional for aqueous polymer solutions.

Another type of system, exhibiting quite unexpectedly the phenomenon of a lower consolute temperature, was discovered by Freeman and Rowlinson (1959), who found that polyisobutene solutions in short-chain aliphatic hydrocarbons precipitate on heating.   The consolute temperature increased with the chain length of the solvent.   They interpreted their findings as reflecting the difference in the thermal expansion coefficient of the solvent and the polymer, which tends to widen the difference between their cohesive energy densities as the temperature is raised.   In thermodynamic terms, a lower consolute temperature implies exothermic mixing, which cannot be understood for systems of two nonpolar components in terms of the simple van Laar–Lorenz treatment.   However, Bellemans and Colin–Naar (1955) who treated the statistical thermodynamics of chain molecules by the deformable lattice model of Prigogine et al. (1952) have shown that the mixing of molecules with similar polarity may be exothermic if they differ sufficiently in their thermal coefficients of expansion.   Such differences would be predicted when comparing chain polymers with their low molecular weight analogs, since the bond length between chain segments will be almost temperature independent, while the weak van der Waals interactions between molecules will allow substantial separation with an increase of temperature.   The introduction of the less expanded polymer chains into the solvent produces an improvement in the efficiency of packing which manifests itself as a volume contraction and an evolution of heat. As would be expected, it is found in polymer–solvent systems which exhibit phase separation on heating that the lower consolute temperature tends to decrease with an increasing polymer chain length (Kinsinger and Ballard, 1964).

On the basis of eq. (2.56b) it may be shown that the excess enthalpy and excess entropy due to nearest-neighbor interaction are related to the parameters Θ and Ψ by

$$\Delta H^* = n_1 R \Theta \Psi \phi_2 \qquad (2.57a)$$

$$\Delta S^* = n_1 R (\Psi - 1/2) \phi_2 \qquad (2.57b)$$

We may then use the Θ and Ψ values obtained by the Shultz–Flory treatment for polymer–solvent systems and compare the magnitudes of ΔH^* and ΔS^* with experimental data of the excess functions in binary mixtures of small molecules, where nearest-neighbor interactions may be assumed to account substantially for deviations from ideality.   This would lead, with the values of Θ and Ψ in Table II.4, for a system comparable to that of polystyrene–cyclohexane to a maximum of $\Delta H^E = 160$ cal and ΔS^* of 0.28 cal-deg^{-1} for a mole of mixed liquids.   Experimentally, the toluene–cyclohexane system (Rowlinson, 1959) was found to have at 20°C maximum values of $\Delta H^E = 140$ cal-mole^{-1} and $\Delta S^E = 0.16$ cal-deg^{-1}-mole^{-1}.   It is doubtful that the agreement will be as good as in this case when solvent and solute are more dissimilar, leading to more powerful effects as a result of nearest-neighbor interactions.   We have seen in Sec. B-1 that the thermodynamic behavior of such systems often cannot be described by a single value of χ.   In addition, the parabolic behavior of the nearest-neighbor interaction term assumed in (2.43) is often valid for the free energy when it does not apply to the heat and entropy terms separately.   We have seen a striking example of this phenomenon in Fig. II.5.

In recent years, some attempts have been made to correlate the Θ and Ψ parameters with the stereoregularity of vinyl polymers.   Although significant differences have been detected, the method is not particularly sensitive.   Kinsinger and Wessling (1959) have studied the critical miscibility temperature of polypropylene in phenyl ether and found $\Theta = 419.4°K$, $\Psi = 1.414$ for the isotactic species as against $\Theta = 426.5$, $\Psi = 0.986$ for the atactic polymer.   These data suggest, rather surprisingly, that for polypropylene the isotactic species should be less soluble only for low molecular weights, while for sufficiently long chains the atactic form is less soluble. Krigbaum et al. (1961) carried out similar studies on poly-(1-butene) in anisole and reported $\Theta = 362.3$ °K, $\Psi = 0.956$ for the isotactic and $\Theta = 359.4$ °K, $\Psi = 0.740$ for the atactic polymer. Thus, a lower solubility of the isotactic species is indicated in this case for all molecular weights. Finally, we should note results reported by Schulz et al. (1964) on poly(methyl methacrylate), which may be obtained in essentially pure isotactic and syndiotactic form. The Θ-temperature was lower for the isotactic polymer in butyl chloride solution, but higher if the solvent was a mixture of butanone and isopropanol.

4. Phase Separation in Solutions of Stiff Elongated Macromolecules

If a solution contains solute molecules, which may be represented by stiff elongated rods, significant deviations from a random orientation of the rod-like particles will persist even at high dilution. In that case the solute particle will have a very large excluded volume and yet the entropy gained in transferring it from an ordered to a disordered phase will be

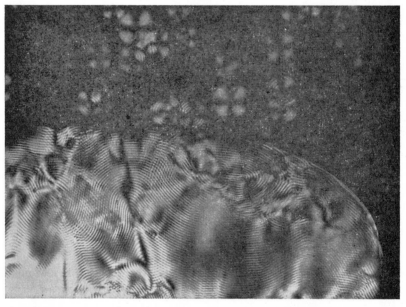

Fig II.9. Appearance of poly(γ-L-benzyl glutamate) solution in methylene chloride under crossed nicols. Solution concentration, 12 g/100 ml; molecular weight of polymer, 70,000. The spacing of the dark lines in the anisotropic phase is 14 μ. Courtesy of Dr. C. Robinson.

relatively small. Under these circumstances it may happen that the transfer of a solute molecule from a dilute to a more concentrated phase results in a net increase of entropy, so that the system will separate into two phases even if mixing is athermal (Onsager, 1949; Flory, 1956). The more concentrated phase should contain partially oriented solute molecules, and may be expected to exhibit optical anisotropy. Such a phenomenon was, in fact, observed by Bernal and Fankuchen (1941) and by Oster (1950) with solutions of tobacco mosaic virus, where the solute is a cylindrical particle of 150 Å diameter and 3000 Å length. The appearance of the anisotropic phase occurs in this case at a solution concentration of about 2% and if the virus particles vary in length, the longer ones will be accumulated in the concentrated phase. The interpretation of the data on tobacco mosaic virus solutions is undoubtedly complicated by the fact that the rods bear ionic charges, and the same difficulty arises in the interpretation of the formation of an anisotropic phase in solutions of ribonucleic acid (Spencer et al., 1962). It is, therefore, of special interest that the phenomenon of the separation of a highly birefringent concentrated phase may also be observed in certain solutions of synthetic polypeptides in organic solvent media in which the polymer molecules exist in the form of rigid helices (Robinson, 1956; Robinson et al., 1958). The appearance of a solution of poly (γ-benzyl-L-glutamate) in dioxane under polarized light is shown in Fig. II.9.

5. Some Typical Examples of Polymer–Solvent Interaction

The simplest cases of molecular interactions in polymer-solvent systems are those in which the components are relatively nonpolar so that their interactions may be described reasonably well by the theory of van Laar and Lorenz (1925). In that case the heat of mixing may be estimated from eq. (2.34), using for the solvents δ parameters such as those listed in Table II.1, if a suitable method can be found by which δ values can be estimated for the polymer, for which an energy of vaporization is obviously not obtainable. A variety of methods have been suggested towards that objective. It can, for instance, be assumed that the swelling of lightly crosslinked rubber (Gee, 1942; Scott and Magat, 1949) or polystyrene (Boyer and Spencer, 1948) with a series of solvents involves only nonspecific interactions, so that ΔH for the process is either zero or positive. In that case the maximum swelling would correspond to athermal mixing and to equal values of δ for the two components of the system. This approach works well enough with rubber, but in the case of polystyrene a number of anomalies have been observed. The same assumption that an athermal solvent is the best solvent is the basis for the method of Alfrey et al. (1950) in which the maximum on a plot of intrinsic viscosities (see Chap. VI) as a function of the cohesive energy density of the solvent is assumed to indicate that solvent and polymer have identical CED values. Walker (1952) estimated the δ value of polyacrylonitrile from that of a group of its low molecular weight analogs and Small (1953) assumed that $\delta_i V_i$ is made up additively from contributions characteristic of various groups contained in a molecule. The contribution to $T\Delta S_M^E$ from nearest-neighbor interactions is in these cases generally positive but considerably smaller than ΔH_M, so that the van Laar treatment gives us an approximate measure of the contribution to ΔG_M^E due to interactions of nearest neighbors. To this approximation, a comparison of (2.34), (2.44), and (2.55) shows that at the critical point for polymers of very long chain length

$$V_1(\delta_2 - \delta_1)^2 = RT_c/2 \qquad (2.58)$$

This relation indicates that for a typical solvent with a molar volume $V_1 = 100$ cc, polymer–solvent systems will be miscible in all proportions around room temperature if the difference in the δ parameters is less than about 1.7. We see that the large gain in configurational entropy, characterizing the dilution of flexible chains, permits the mixing to be endothermic to a considerable extent before the onset of phase separation. We should also note that the maximum value of $\delta_2 - \delta_1$ which will allow complete miscibility is inversely proportional to the square root of the molar volume of the solvent.

The van Laar theory would lead us to expect that mixing would be always endothermic in the absence of specific group interactions. Yet, a number of cases have been reported where the solution of nonpolar polymers in nonpolar solvent media led to an *evolution* of heat. We have to be careful in interpreting such data because polymers in the glassy state have a volume larger than that which would correspond to a thermodynamic equilibrium state and the contraction which becomes possible with the decrease in viscosity during the swelling and dissolution is an exothermic process (Hellfritz, 1951; Schulz et al., 1955). On the other hand, an evolution of heat was measured by Walters et al. (1960), Baker et al. (1962), and Delmas et al. (1962a,b) for the dissolution of polyisobutene in low molecular weight hydrocarbons, although the polymer was far above its glass transition temperature ($-70°C$) in these experiments, so that significant deviations from its equilibrium state seemed unlikely. Moreover, Tompa (1952) has measured an evolution of heat on diluting polystyrene solutions in benzene or toluene where there could be no doubt that the initial and final states represented thermodynamic equilibrium. These effects can be explained as we have already noted in Sec., B-3 of this chapter, by Prigogine's deformable lattice theory. This theory takes account of the obvious fact that two lattice sites containing segments of a chain molecule joined by a covalent bond will separate on heating much less than two sites containing species attracted to one another by relatively weak van der Waals forces. The resulting calculations lead to a contribution from binary nearest neighbor interactions to ΔG_M (rather than ΔE_M) of the form of eq. (2.34), while ΔH_M, ΔS_M, and ΔV_M are all more negative than predicted earlier. Delmas et al. have used this theory for the limiting case of the dissolution of a very high polymer in homologous series of solvents. They found that ΔH_M contained, as predicted, a negative term inversely proportional to the square of the chain length of the solvent. A detailed theoretical analysis of the behavior of mixtures of aliphatic hydrocarbons (Flory et al., 1964) led to the conclusion that ΔH_M is determined mainly by a positive term, arising from the difference in free volume per chain segment in the two pure components, and a negative term which is a consequence of the shrinkage which typically accompanies the mixing of paraffins of different chain length. The theory predicts, in accord with experiment, that the relative importance of the negative excess volume increases with rising temperature, so that the mixing becomes eventually exothermic.

When we pass to a consideration of polymers carrying highly polar, strongly interacting groups, the problem of interpreting solubility behavior becomes much more complex. Schuerch (1952) studied the solubility properties of lignin and pointed out that solvents characterized by the same value of the Hildebrand solubility parameter δ may differ widely in their solvent power. He correlated such differences with the ability of the solvent to accept a hydrogen bond. The question then arises how such hydrogen bonding capabilities should be characterized in a quantitative manner. Badger and Bauer (1937) proposed that the O—H stretching frequency should be a linear decreasing function of the strength of the hydrogen bond and Schuerch found that he could make a reliable prediction of lignin solubility on the basis of the δ parameter of the solvent combined with its ability to shift the O–D stretching frequency of CH_3OD (Gordy, 1941). In the case of polyacrylonitrile, solubility does not correlate with cohesive energy density (Walker, 1952) and it does not appear to be related to hydrogen-bonding (since the C–H group is a very poor hydrogen-bond donor) but rather to very strong dipole–dipole interaction (Phibbs, 1955). A group of "active" solvents, which are frequently effective in dissolving such strongly interacting polymers, include dimethyl-formamide, m-cresol, dichloroacetic acid, dimethyl sulfoxide, cyclic tetra-methylene sulfone, and ethylene carbonate. All of these have very high dipole moments. Phibbs points out the significant fact that succinic anhydride, with a dipole moment of 4.2 D, is a solvent for polyacrylonitrile while the closely related acetic anhydride, with a dipole moment of 2.5 D is a nonsolvent. The other cyclic molecules among the active solvents, such as tetramethylene sulfone, ethylene carbonate, and γ-butyrolactone, have probably also dipole moments much higher than their linear analogs.

Whenever the dissolution of a polymer is exothermic, the driving force towards the dissolution will decrease with rising temperature. If the solution process is characterized by a negative excess entropy (as a result of solvent orientation in the neighborhood of the macromolecule) the polymer may precipitate when its solution is heated. Although such behavior is most typical of aqueous solutions (to be discussed below) it has also been reported for some polymer solutions in organic solvents. For instance, cellulose nitrate solutions in a number of alkyl acetates will precipitate on heating (Doolittle, 1946) and poly(acrylic acid) solutions in dioxane behave in a similar fashion (Newman et al., 1956). We should note, however, that the enthalpy of dilution may change sign as the composition of the system is altered. Such behavior was reported by Moore and Shuttleworth (1963) for the cellulose acetate–acetone system, which was found to be characterized by an endothermic dilution when the polymer content was low, while the dilution of concentrated solutions led to a large evolution of heat. This behavior may be related to the tendency of cellulose acetate to form a molecular complex with acetone which has been observed as a distinct crystalline phase (Katz and Weidinger, 1932).

The special properties of water as a solvent medium are due in part to the effect of the solute on the structure of the solvent. We have already discussed the tendency towards "iceberg formation" when nonpolar solutes are introduced into water, resulting in heat evolution but a large negative excess entropy (Sec. A-6). These effects manifest themselves frequently in a reduction of the solvent power of water with rising temperature such as was observed e.g., for poly(methacrylic acid) (Silberberg et al., 1957). Sometimes the aqueous polymer solution will precipitate on heating. This has been observed with vinyl alcohol–acetate copolymers (Nord et al., 1951), methylcellulose (Heymann, 1935; Uda and Meyerhoff, 1961), and other water-soluble polymers. However, the solvent power of water does not always decrease with rising temperature. In the case of polyacrylamide, for instance, Silberberg et al. (1957) found that water became a thermodynamically better solvent as the temperature was raised. In any case, we have to remember that the interaction of water molecules with macromolecular solutes will be strongly localized at specific sites, so that the solvent–solute interaction parameter would be expected to vary widely with the composition of the system. To cite an extreme case: nylon has an extremely high affinity for water as long as the water concentration is very low (Starkweather, 1959), yet the solubility of water in the polymer is quite limited and the solubility of nylon in water is too low to be detected. It is obvious that in a case such as this we have to consider separately the interaction of the water with the highly polar amide groups and with the nonpolar portions of the polymer solute.

Another property of water which is of crucial importance in its characteristics as a solvent is its ability to provide an ionizing medium of high dielectric constant. This accounts for its striking solvent power for polymeric electrolytes. We may note, for instance, that materials such as poly(sodium acrylate) or poly(vinylpyridinium chloride), which have a high affinity for water and are miscible with it in all proportions, are highly insoluble (and little swollen) even by methanol, which would appear rather similar to water. We must assume that the lowering of the dielectric constant results in almost complete association of the fixed charges of the polymer with the counter-ions and that the mutual interactions of the ion pairs are too strong to be disrupted by the forces of solvation. The same point may be made with respect to the mutual interactions of the dipoles in polymeric ampholytes, particularly proteins (Cohn and Edsall, 1943), although hydrazine, ethylene diamine (Rees and Singer, 1956), and anhydrous hydrogen fluoride (Katz, 1954), among others, have been shown in recent years to be active protein solvents (for a review see Singer, 1962). With synthetic amphoteric polymers it must be remembered that the dipolar ion structure will make a large contribution only if the uncharged base has a higher hydrogen-ion affinity than the anionic base. For instance, in a copolymer of vinylpyridine and methacrylic acid the equilibrium

$$-CH_2-CH-CH_2-\underset{\substack{| \\ C=O \\ | \\ OH}}{\overset{\substack{CH_3 \\ |}}{C}}- \quad \rightleftharpoons \quad -CH_2-CH-CH_2-\underset{\substack{| \\ O=C \\ | \\ O \\ \ominus}}{\overset{\substack{CH_3 \\ |}}{C}}-$$

favors the uncharged species while in a methacrylic acid copolymer with
dimethylaminoethyl methacrylate

the dipolar ion form predominates. Alfrey and Morawetz (1952) and
Alfrey et al. (1952b) found that the first copolymer was insoluble in pure
water, while the second dissolved easily. They assigned this difference to
the different extent of ionization of the two substances in their isoelectric
forms.

6. The Solubility of Crystalline Chain Polymers

We have seen in Sec. A-8 that the solubility of crystalline solutes is
intimately related to their melting point. For crystalline chain molecules,
the melting point $T_m = \Delta H_m / \Delta S_m$ approaches a limiting value for samples
of very high molecular weight (Flory and Vrij, 1963). This value increases with the magnitude of the energetic interactions between the
chains (which increases ΔH_m) and with increasing chain stiffness (which
reduces ΔS_m). It should be noted, however, that ΔH_m is also quite sensitive to the efficiency with which the chains are packed in the crystal lattice.
Thus, isotactic polypropylene has $\Delta H_m = 2.37$ kcal/mole of monomer units,
appreciably higher than the value of 1.84 kcal/mole reported for polyethylene (Miller and Nielsen, 1961).

In considering the phase equilibrium between a crystalline polymer and
its saturated solution, we may assume in first approximation that the effect
of the swelling of the polymer phase may be neglected. Spontaneous
transfer of the chain molecules from the crystallite to the solution requires
then that the sum of the free energies, corresponding to melting and the
dilution of the melt by the solvent, be negative. If we neglect the temperature dependence of the latent heat of fusion in applying the Gibbs–Helmholtz relation to the free energy of fusion and if we use eq. (2.51) for the
activity of the polymeric species, referred to the melt as the standard state,
the condition which must be met, (Huggins, 1942c) becomes

$$\Delta H_m \, (T_m - T)/T_m + RT\{\ln \phi_2 + [1 - (V_2/V_1)]\phi_1 + (V_2/V_1)\chi\phi_1^2\} \lessgtr 0$$

$$(2.59)$$

Although this relation predicts for $\chi = 0$ much higher solubilities than the "ideal solubilities" given by eq. (2.38) (due to the excess configurational entropy of dilution), these solubilities still become extremely low for very long chains. It is instructive to illustrate the consequences of eq. (2.59) on a typical example. For isotactic polystyrene $\Delta H_m = 2.15$ kcal/mole of monomer residues and $T_m = 513°K$ (Miller and Nielsen, 1960). If a solvent has the same molecular volume as a unit of the polymer chain and if the mixing of the solvent with the molten polymer is athermal, chains containing as few as twenty monomer units would give saturated solutions at $300°K$ with only 10^{-6} volume-% polymer.* It is clear that for long polymer chains an appreciable solubility can be expected at a substantial temperature interval below the melting point only if the mixing of molten polymer and solvent is sufficiently exothermic to compensate for the heat absorbed in the melting process. With a material such as polyethylene, the specific solute–solvent interactions required for a strongly exothermic mixing cannot be achieved and it is not surprising that this crystalline polymer is insoluble at low temperatures in all solvent media. On the other hand, it is reasonable that crystalline polymers in which hydrogen bonding contributes a large fraction of the energy of the crystal lattice (e.g., polyamides and polypeptides) should be soluble in media which are known to be strong hydrogen bond acceptors (e.g., dimethylformamide) or hydrogen bond donors (e.g., cresol). A recent compilation of ΔH values for hydrogen bonds formed by phenol (Joesten and Drago, 1962) gives -3.2 kcal/mole for ethyl acetate, acetone, or acetonitrile as the acceptors, -5.0 kcal/mole for diethyl ether, -6.1 kcal/mole for dimethylformamide, and -9.2 kcal/mole for triethylamine. The heat of melting for nylon 66 is 11 kcal/mole of the repeat unit (Miller and Nielsen, 1960); it may then be concluded that this polymer will be soluble only if the repeat unit can participate in at least two more hydrogen bonds in solution than in the crystal lattice. This condition is apparently satisfied when nylon 66 is dissolved in solvents such as m-cresol, formic acid, or fluorinated alcohols (Middleton and Lindsey, 1964).

In practice, there are several factors which may increase the solubility of crystalline polymers above the values predicted by the considerations discussed above, which apply to relatively large perfectly formed crystals. It is well known that the solubility of all crystalline substances increases with their degree of subdivision, and with high polymers crystallized in bulk, the crystallites are usually very small. Moreover, a variety of

* In this estimate we have neglected the difference between T_m for a low polymer and the limiting T_m value for very high polymers.

"molecular imperfections" will tend to reduce the crystal stability. We may cite two examples of such an effect: (1) Isotactic vinyl polymers probably never attain perfect stereoregularity and a relatively small content of chain segments with the "wrong" steric configuration will weaken considerably the stability of the crystal lattice; (2) Branched polyethylene, as produced in the oxygen-catalyzed high-pressure process, precipitates from solution at a substantially lower temperature (Myers, 1954) than the linear polymer (Griffith and Rånby, 1959). Finally, we should realize that many crystalline polymers are very easily supercooled from the melt to an amorphous product, which may be quite easily dissolved to yield solutions which are metastable with respect to the crystalline polymer. The polymer will eventually precipitate from such systems, but since nucleation of a polymer crystal is a slow process, the metastable solutions may persist over extended periods of time. Isotactic polystyrene and poly(vinylidene chloride) are typical examples of crystalline polymers which behave in this manner.

7. Thermally Reversible Gelation

When the solvent power of the medium in which a polymer is dissolved is reduced (e.g., by a change in temperature) the precipitation of the polymeric species may be prevented by the formation of a gel. The rheological behavior of such gels suggests that the polymeric chains form, at widely separated points, association complexes which link them into a continuous network structure extending throughout the volume of the system (Ferry, 1961b). The association producing the "quasi-crosslinkages" is a reversible process, so that the gel may be liquefied and reset many times without any change in the nature of the macromolecules. The nature of the linkage is rather imperfectly understood but the phenomenon of thermally reversible gelation is usually encountered with more or less crystalline chain molecules and gelation is sometimes associated with the appearance of a sharp x-ray diffraction pattern, which disappears at the "melting point" of the gel. Such observations have been made on aqueous solutions of gelatin (Herrmann et al., 1930; Katz et al. 1931; Gerngross et al., 1932), agar–agar (Katz and Derksen, 1932), starch (Derksen and Katz, 1932), and on polyacrylonitrile in dimethylformamide (Jost, 1958) and they suggest that the crosslinkages are related to the formation of microcrystallites. Other observations of gel formation during the cooling of polymer solutions include those of Bisschops (1954, 1955) on polyacrylonitrile in dimethylformamide, Walter (1954) on poly(vinyl chloride) solutions, and Van Amerongen (1951) on solutions of gutta percha. The most detailed studies have been carried out on gelatin gelation because of the enormous technological importance of the phenomenon. The ability of dilute gelatin solutions to set to a gel is not affected appreciably by modifications of various functional groups (hydroxyl, carboxyl, amino, guanidino) carried by the polypeptide chain of gelatin, but even slight modifications of the peptide linkage will inhibit gelation (Bello and Vinograd, 1958; Bello et al., 1962). These observations would seem to support Ferry's (1948) view that certain sequences in the polypeptide chain are easily packed into crystallites and that these provide the cross-linkages of the gel.

In cases where the solvent power of a medium decreases with rising temperature, a polymer solution may gel on warming. Such behavior has been reported for cellulose nitrate in ethanol (Newman et al., 1956), for poly(vinyl alcohol) in dimethylformamide (Jones, 1962), and for aqueous solutions of methylcellulose (Heymann, 1935).

In some cases, gels exhibit syneresis, i.e., they tend to contract with separation of pure solvent on prolonged standing. In other cases they appear to be stable; nevertheless, since they can be prepared only by changing the temperature of a solution and not by interaction of solvent and solute at constant temperature, we cannot be certain whether they represent states of thermodynamic equilibrium.

8. Application of the Concept of "Solution" to Extremely Large Molecules

The question may arise whether there is an upper limit to the size of a particle which may be considered to be in "true solution." A generation ago a rather arbitrary dividing line was drawn between solutions in the classical sense and "colloid solutions" comprising systems in which the disperse phase had characteristic dimensions between about 0.01 and 1 μ. Such systems could be of various types, comprising solutions of macromolecules, solutions in which a number of the solute molecules associated into micellar aggregates, and finally "sols" of metals, sulfur, etc., in which the size of the particles held in suspension bore no relation to the size of their constituent molecules. In recent years the emphasis has been increasingly on the essential unity of physical chemistry and on the interpretation of "colloid phenomena" in terms of general physico-chemical principles. From that point of view we may define a solution as a system of several components forming a single phase. A phase is defined, in turn, as a physically and chemically distinct, mechanically separable portion of the system. However, here we are facing an obvious ambiguity in trying to decide what constitutes "mechanical separability." If passage of a liquid through a filter paper results in the separation of suspended particles, we should have no doubt in considering them a separate phase. Yet, membranes of various pore dimensions are known, which make it possible to separate a liquid first from "dissolved" macromolecules and eventually even from solutes with molecules as small as that of sucrose. In considering a series of filtrations through increasingly tight filters, we shall find it very difficult, or impossible, to define a demarcation line between suspensions and solutions, which will not appear to be arbitrary.

A possible pragmatic criterion could be based on the extent to which the components of a system will be separated from each other at equilibrium by the gravitational field of the earth. If a particle of mass m_2 and density ρ_2 is suspended in a liquid of density ρ_1, the gravitational pull on it will be, after allowing for the buoyancy effect, $m_2 g (\rho_2 - \rho_1)/\rho_2$, where g is the acceleration due to the gravitational field. The ratio of the concentrations of the particles at two heights, h_1 and h_2, will then be given by the Boltzmann distribution law as

$$c_2/c_1 = \exp\ [-m_2 g (\rho_2 - \rho_1)\ (h_2 - h_1)/\rho_2 k T] \tag{2.60}$$

If we then allow some limiting value for c_2/c_1 as being compatible with the concept of a "solution," the weight of the particle considered to be dissolved will depend critically on an arbitrary choice of the dimensions of the system and will be highly sensitive to the relative densities of solute and solvent, so that a definition of "solutions" based on such a criterion cannot be considered to have any fundamental significance. With $h_2 - h_1 = 10$ cm, $(\rho_2 - \rho_1)/\rho_2 = 0.2$, and $T = 300°$K, a particle weight corresponding to a molecular weight of 10^6 would be sufficient to produce a 10% concentration difference, while a solute with a molecular weight of 30×10^6 would be, at equilibrium, ten times as concentrated at the bottom as at the top of the system. Such a situation would hardly seem to be compatible with the classical concept of a "phase," unless we define it so as to include portions of a system with continuously varying properties. It should be noted, however, that solutions such as those discussed above would appear much more homogeneous in practice, since approach to an equilibrium distribution of the solute in the gravitational field of the earth would be extremely slow.

Whatever the nomenclature which we may want to adopt, it is significant that the same experimental methods used for the study of solutions of macromolecules may be adopted, for instance, for aqueous systems containing virus particles, which we might hesitate to describe as "dissolved."

In the field of synthetic polymers, spherical particles with dimensions in the range of 0.1 to 1 μ may be prepared by emulsion polymerization in the presence of a crosslinking agent and sols of these "microgels" may also be studied by techniques similar to those employed in the investigation of linear polymers in solution (Shashoua and Beaman, 1958).

C. THREE-COMPONENT AND MULTICOMPONENT SYSTEMS CONTAINING MACROMOLECULES

1. The Effect of Polydispersity on Polymer Solubility

The phase rule requires that in a two-component system with two condensed phases the composition of the phases should be uniquely determined at a given temperature and pressure. This means, in particular, that the phase composition should be unaffected by any variation in the relative volume of the coexisting phases. When we deal with a polymer which is a single molecular species, this principle is valid and the concentration of a solution in equilibrium with the polymer phase does not increase as more undissolved polymer is added. As would be expected, such behavior represents an exacting test of the molecular homogeneity of the solute species; it has been demonstrated with high polymeric solutes only in the case of carefully purified preparations of globular proteins. Typical data are those of Butler (1940) showing that with chymotrypsinogen a well defined solubility can be attained after extensive purification of the material. The situation will be quite different in a two phase system containing macromolecules of varying chain length, such as are obtained in the preparation of synthetic polymers. We may then apply the expression for the activity of the polymeric species (eq. 2.52) to the distribution of chains of any given length between the polymer gel phase and the solution phase. Denoting by ϕ_i and ϕ_i' the concentrations of species i in solution and in the gel, respectively, and setting $\ln a_1 = \ln a_1'$ we obtain

$$\ln (\phi_i/\phi_i') = [1 - (V_i/V_1)] (\phi_1' - \phi_1) + (V_i/V_1)\chi[(\phi_1')^2 - \phi_1^2]$$
$$\approx (V_i/V_1)[(\phi_1 - \phi_1') - \chi\{\phi_1^2 - (\phi_1')^2\}] \quad (2.61)$$

so that the distribution coefficient is an exponentially decreasing function of the chain length as would be expected from the general considerations discussed in Sec. B-2.

The molecular heterogeneity of the solute affects also the theory of the critical miscibility point. The use of relations (2.37) for the location of the critical point from analytical expressions describing the free energy of mixing of binary systems is not justified for systems containing polydisperse polymers, since the molecular weight distribution of the polymeric component will, in general, be different in the two coexisting phases. The problem has been analyzed by Stockmayer (1949) who concluded that the location of the critical point should depend on an average lying in general between the weight average and the z-average molecular weight of the solute. For most molecular weight distributions encountered in practice, Stockmayer expects $\bar{M}_w$ to be the controlling factor. This conclusion is consistent with the experimental data of Shultz and Flory (1952).

2. Solubility of Polymers in Mixed Organic Solvents

It is frequently found that a polymer is more soluble in a mixture of two liquids than in either component of the mixture. A systematic study of this phenomenon was first undertaken by Gee (1944) who pointed out that it is possible to match the cohesive energy density (or the Hildebrand δ parameter) of a polymer by mixing in suitable proportions solvents characterized by high and low δ values. For instance, a styrene–butadiene copolymer with $\delta = 8.1$ is insoluble both in pentane ($\delta = 7.1$) and in ethyl acetate ($\delta = 9.1$) but it will dissolve in a 1:1 mixture of the two solvents. However, the behavior of mixed solvents frequently cannot be accounted for in this manner. For instance, it is often found that small concentrations of a liquid, which is decidedly a nonsolvent for a polymer, will solubilize it in a second nonsolvent because the cosolvent can satisfy hydrogen-bonding requirements of functional groups carried by the polymer. It has been observed, for example, in the author's laboratory that styrene copolymers with carboxylic acid comonomers may be insoluble in typical polystyrene solvents unless a small amount of an alcohol or an amine is added to the solvent medium. Another well known example of cosolvent action is the solubility of cellulosenitrate in ethanol–ether mixtures. Finally, we may cite the case of a 2-vinylpyridine–methacrylic acid copolymer, which was insoluble in methanol but dissolved in methanol mixtures containing either benzene or water (Alfrey and Morawetz, 1952). Since benzene is less polar and water more polar than methanol, it is clear that cosolvent action must be of a highly specific type in this case.

The relative importance of cohesive energy density and specific solvation is illustrated in an interesting manner in the studies of cellulosenitrate solubility carried out by Doolittle (1944, 1946). He dissolved polymer samples in a homologous series of solvents and titrated with a nonsolvent, noting the solvent concentration at the precipitation point corresponding to an arbitrarily chosen polymer concentration. Some typical results are re-

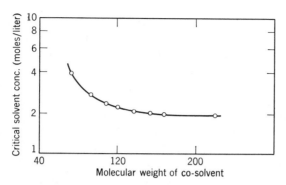

Fig. II.10. Concentration of *n*-alkyl acetate cosolvents required to dissolve cellulose nitrate in toluene.   Polymer concentration 0.5 g/100 ml.

produced in Fig. II.10 and they show that the concentration of the solvating groups required to hold the nitrocellulose in solution approaches a limiting value for the higher members of the homologous series of solvents.   For low molecular weight solvents the required concentration of solvating groups increases.   This effect may be understood by considering separately the paraffinic "tail" and the polar "head" of the solvent molecule which may be thought of as more or less firmly attached to the macromolecular solute.   As the paraffinic portion is shortened, the concentration of end groups is increased, leading to a decrease in the cohesive energy density of the medium provided for the solvated polymer molecules.

Gee (1944) cites an interesting case where a polymer will precipitate when two of its solutions in different solvent media are mixed.   This is the case with cellulose acetate, which will dissolve both in aniline and in glacial acetic acid but not in a mixture of these two solvents.   This phenomenon is clearly due to the fact that the mutual interactions of the acidic and the basic solvent is much stronger than the interaction of either of them with the polymeric species.

3. Solubility in Aqueous Electrolyte Solutions

It is well known that the solubility of organic non-electrolytes in water is usually reduced by the addition of neutral salts.   This "salting-out" was once thought to result from the formation of the hydration shells of the ions leading to a reduction of the number of water molecules available for the solvation of non-electrolyte solutes.   However, the phenomenon is obviously more complex, since the relative "salting-out efficiency" of different salts varies widely with the non-electrolyte solute (Long and

McDevit, 1952). Polymeric non-electrolytes behave in a manner similar to that of low molecular weight solutes and their water solubility is frequently reduced sharply by salt addition. Occasionally, systems containing polymeric non-electrolytes, water and salt separate into two solution phases, one containing most of the polymer and the other most of the salt (Albertsson, 1958).

There exist, however, some important cases where water-insoluble polymers dissolve in aqueous solutions of electrolytes. It has been known for a long time that cellulose is soluble in solutions of Cu(II)–ammonia or Cu(II)–amine salts (Stamm, 1952) and more recently ferric ammonium tartrate (Jayme and Lang, 1955) and salts containing the cadmium–ethylene diamine complex (Jayme and Neuschäffer, 1957) have been described as cellulose solvents. In the case of the cupric ammonia solutions, the solvation of the cellulose has been accounted for by the formation of cupric complexes with the glucose residues (Reeves, 1949) and an analogous mechanism is undoubtedly responsible for the solvent properties of the ferric and cadmium salts. Similar complexation appears to be involved with concentrated solutions of strong acids, which dissolve cellulose (Stamm, 1952) and polyacrylonitrile (Binder, 1960). The existence of the cellulose–nitric acid and the cellulose–perchloric acid complex has been proven crystallographically (Andress, 1928; Andress and Reinhardt, 1930).

The characteristic ability of strong (> 55 wt.-%) aqueous solutions of certain neutral salts of metals such as lithium and calcium (which do not have a particularly strong tendency to form complex ions) to dissolve such water-insoluble polymers as cellulose (Stamm, 1952), silk fibroin (von Weimern, 1926; Ambrose et al., 1951), poly (L-serine) (Bohak and Katchalski, 1963) or polyacrylonitrile (Rein, 1938; Stanton et al., 1953)

TABLE II.5

Aqueous Salt Solutions Dissolving Polyacrylonitrile

(All Cations Associated with Anions at the Same or Higher Level)

Cations	Anions
K^+, Fe^{3+}, Pb^{2+}	
NH_4^+, Cd^{2+}, Al^{3+}	SCN^-
Na^+, Ba^{2+}	I^-
Ca^{2+}, Li^+, Mg^{2+}	Br^-
Ga^{3+}, Sb^{3+}, In^{3+}, Tl^{3+}, Sn^{4+}	Cl^-
Zn^{2+}, Ag^+, Ni^{2+}, Co^{2+}, Mn^{2+}	NO_3^-
	$SO_4^=$

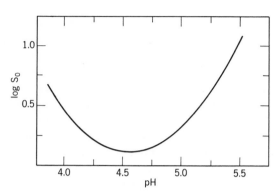

Fig. II.11. Solubility of egg albumin at zero ionic strength and 25°C as a function of pH. S_0 is in grams per liter.

seems to fall into a different category. The solvent power of the salts depends strongly on both cation and anion, increasing with the polarizability of the anion. Stanton et al. give the data reproduced in Table II.5, where the cations increase and the anions decrease in solvent power from the top to the bottom of the table. A salt is a solvent for polyacrylonitrile if the anion is placed at least as high as the cation; thus all salts containing K^+, Fe^{3+}, Pb^{2+}, or $SO_4^=$ are nonsolvents. It may be noted that simple organic compounds form fairly frequently crystalline adducts with some of these "solvent salts" and that a cellulose–lithium thiocyanate complex has been characterized by x-ray diffraction (Katz and Derksen, 1931).

With ionizable polymers, water solubility generally increases with the net charge density of the polymeric species. For instance, poly(2-vinylpyridine) or isotactic poly(acrylic acid) are water-insoluble in the unionized state, but dissolve on partial neutralization. With amphoteric polyelectrolytes, particularly proteins, the solubility is generally a minimum when the polymer is isoelectric and increases on addition of acid or base. A typical example of this behavior is illustrated in Fig. II.11.

The effect of electrolyte addition on the solubility of proteins has been dealt with in detail in the monograph by Cohn and Edsall (1943) and may be understood by an extension of the theory formulated by Kirkwood (1934) for dipolar ions. Even though these species carry no net charge, they will tend to attract one another because of the tendency of their dipoles to assume a mutual orientation such as to minimize the potential energy of the system. A second reason for the mutual attraction of amphoteric species in isoelectric solution is to be found in the fact that the state of ionization of the individual molecules is subject to fluctuations which are not independent of one another but tend to place, at any given time, net charges of opposite sign on neighboring ampholytes (Kirkwood and Shumaker, 1952). Both the dipole (or multipole) interaction and the charge fluctuation theory predict the logarithm of the solubility to increase linearly with the square root of the ionic strength. It should be noted that the magnitude of the effect would be expected to be quite sensitive to the distribution of the ionizable groups on the surface of the protein molecule. Some proteins, traditionally designated as globulins, have extremely low solubilities in water in the absence of simple electrolytes. Protein solubilities in water are also increased by addition of dipolar ions, which may raise substantially the dielectric constant of the medium and in this way suppress electrostatic interactions between solute molecules. The magnitude of this effect varies within rather wide limits. For instance, the addition of glycine increases the solubility of lactoglobulin by a much larger factor than that of hemoglobin (Cohn and Ferry, 1943).

At high electrolyte concentration, addition of salts tends to reduce protein solubility ("salting-out") in a manner similar to that observed with non-electrolyte solutes. The protein solubility S may be represented at high values of the ionic strength, Γ, by the relation

$$\log S = \log S_0 - K_S \Gamma \tag{2.62}$$

where the "salting-out constant" K_S varies in the range 0.6–1.5 for sodium or ammonium sulfate and in the range 1–2 for alkali phosphates. The variation of K_S values characteristic of different proteins is frequently employed in protein fractionation procedures.

A strange finding, which has not found an adequate interpretation, was reported by Pinner and Alfrey (1952) who studied the salting-out of poly-(methacrylic acid) with ammonium chloride or potassium chloride as a function of pH. Very surprisingly, they found that the polymeric acid was salted out most easily around pH 4, while much higher salt concentrations were required both at higher and at lower pH. It behaved, therefore, in a manner which would be expected for an amphoteric polyelectrolyte.

Addition of a salt to an aqueous polyelectrolyte solution may also lead to the formation of two liquid phases, one of which contains most of the polyelectrolyte. This phenomenon was studied in great detail by Bungenberg de Jong (1937) who described the separation of a viscous, protein-rich liquid phase when salt was added to certain aqueous protein solutions. More recently, systems comprising alkali polyvinylsulfonates with alkali halides have been studied by Eisenberg and Mohan (1959). If the system

contains two different cations, one will tend to be enriched in the polyelectrolyte solution, so that the system may be considered a "liquid ion exchanger."
With polyvinylsulfonate the polymer phase concentrates potassium over
sodium or ammonium ions.

4. Incompatibility of Polymer Solutions

More than half a century ago, the strange observation was reported that
dilute aqueous solutions of gelatin and agar would not mix but would form
two coexisting phases (Beijerinck, 1910). Each of these phases was found
to contain almost exclusively one of the polymeric solutes. A similar
phenomenon was later demonstrated on a large number of ternary systems
(Dobry and Boyer-Kawenoki, 1947; Dobry, 1948; Kern and Slocombe,
1955; Kern, 1956; Albertsson, 1958). In fact, of the 35 pairs of polymers tested by Dobry and Boyer-Kawenoki, only four could be dissolved
together to yield a one phase system. A typical phase diagram of two
incompatible polymers and a common solvent is that determined by Kern
for the polystyrene–poly(p-chlorostyrene)–benzene system shown in Fig.
II.12. It may be seen that benzene, which is miscible in all proportions

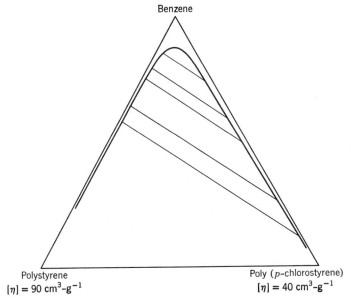

Benzene

Polystyrene
$[\eta] = 90$ cm^3-g^{-1}

Poly (p-chlorostyrene)
$[\eta] = 40$ cm^3-g^{-1}

Fig. II.12. Ternary phase diagram benzene–polystyrene–poly(p-chlorostyrene) at
25°C. The intrinsic viscosities were measured in benzene solution.

with either polymer alone, can dissolve only slightly more than 2% of a mixture of equal weights of the two polymers without phase separation. Poly(p-chlorostyrene) has a negligible solubility in a phase containing 4% of polystyrene. It may be noted that Kern used a polystyrene sample with a substantially longer chain length than that of the poly(p-chlorostyrene) and this accounts for the asymmetry of the phase diagram. It is generally found that the mutual incompatibility of polymers increases rapidly with an increase in their molecular weight.

The thermodynamic causes of this phase separation phenomenon are not difficult to visualize. If two dilute solutions of low molecular weight solutes A and B in the same solvent medium are mixed, the system forms a single phase, since the gain in entropy will outweigh even an unfavorable energy of mixing. However, if the solutions contain initially long chain molecules composed of a large number of A or B units, respectively, the entropy of mixing per unit weight becomes negligible while the energy of mixing per unit weight, depending on the number of contact points between dissimilar chain segments, remains nearly the same as for the low molecular weight analog. The solutions of the chain molecules will, therefore, resist mixing, if contacts between dissimilar chain segments involve an expenditure of energy. Kern (1958) has shown how sensitive the phase separation phenomenon is to small changes in the structure of the polymers: poly(vinyl chloride) solutions, which do not mix with solutions of poly(methyl methacrylate), were found to be miscible with solutions of polymers of ethyl, propyl, butyl, and isobutyl methacrylate.

A very interesting application for the coexistence of two dilute polymer solution phases containing the same solvent medium was demonstrated by Albertsson (1958,1960). Although the two solutions are very similar, the transfer of a suspended particle from one phase to the other may be characterized by a significant change of energy and such particles will, therefore, tend to accumulate in one of the two phases. The effect should increase with the interfacial area per particle and the method should, therefore, be particularly suitable for relatively large particles. Its utility has been studied particularly in procedures for the concentration and purification of viruses by equilibration between two aqueous polymer solutions. It should be noted that the similarity of the two phases imparts to the method a high potential degree of selectivity.

5. Ternary Systems with Strongly Interacting Polymers

We have seen in the previous section that even polymers of very similar structure may be highly incompatible, whenever their mixing is endother-

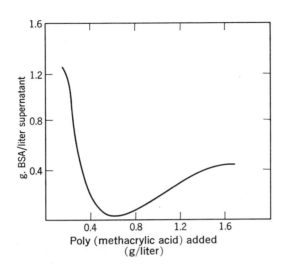

Fig. II.13. Precipitation of bovine serum albumin by poly(methacrylic acid).

mic. The corollary of this situation is the very high affinity of polymers for one another, if their mixing is accompanied by an evolution of heat. In such cases the mixing of two polymer solutions in the same solvent medium will result typically in a separation of a concentrated phase containing both polymers in a ratio such as to maximize their energetic interaction. This behavior is typical, in particular, of systems containing both positively and negatively charged polyions. Fuoss and Sadek (1949) showed that the formation of the association complex between polycations and polyanions may be observed turbidometrically in solutions as dilute as $10^{-6}N$, so that turbidometric titrations provide an unusually sensitive tool for the analytical determination of polyions. Terayama (1952) carried out similar titrations using as the end-point indicator various dyes, such as toluidine blue, which show a striking color change in solutions containing an excess of polyanions over polycations.

When two proteins are contained in a solution at a pH lying between their isoelectric points, one species will bear a positive and the other a negative charge, so that they will tend to precipitate one another. This has long been recognized as an inherent limitation in any protein fractionation and procedures have been developed to take advantage of such interactions for the separation of groups of proteins from complex mixtures. These groups may then be subdivided by refractionation at higher ionic strength or in the presence of dipolar ions, i.e., under conditions which minimize electrostatic interactions between the macromolecular solutes (Cohn et al., 1950). Another approach to the separation of proteins in the interisoelectric range employs a synthetic polymeric acid to displace the anionic species from the complex with the cationic protein (Morawetz and Hughes, 1952; Berdick and Morawetz, 1954). The solubility relations in a system containing a polymeric acid and a protein below its isoelectric point are illustrated in Figure II.13 on the poly(methacrylic acid)–bovine serum albumin system. It may be noted that an excess of the polymeric acid tends to redissolve the precipitate which implies the formation of negatively charged complexes. The solubility curves are independent of the chain length of the polymeric acid, suggesting that the phase equilibrium depends merely on the ratio of the positive and negative charges carried by the two macromolecules. The composition of the precipitate depends on the relative amounts of the cationic and anionic species in the supernatant as was shown both in protein precipitation with synthetic polyacids (Morawetz and Hughes, 1952) and in a detailed study of the precipitation of ovalbumin by nucleic acid (Björnesjö and Teorell, 1945). As would be expected, the solubility of the complex is at a minimum when it is isoelectric (Bungenberg de Jong, 1949).

It is sometimes found that the concentrated phase, forming in systems containing cationic and anionic polymers, does not separate in the form of a flocculent precipitate, but rather as a highly viscous fluid. This phenomenon was termed "complex coacervation" and subjected to extensive studies (Bungenberg de Jong and Kruyt, 1930; Bungenberg de Jong, 1937). Even so, the conditions required for coacervation, rather than the formation of gel-like precipitates, are not clearly understood. It seems that coacervation represents a less intimate interaction of the constituents of the complex, since polyelectrolyte coacervates are generally dissolved on addition of electrolyte. This interpretation is also supported by the finding that serum albumin forms gel-like precipitates with polyacids (which are highly efficient precipitating agents) but coacervates with poly(vinylamine), which interacts with the protein much more weakly (Morawetz and Hughes, 1952). The phenomenon of coacervation is of special interest because of the suggestion that coacervate droplets in the primeval ocean may have been precursors of living cells (Oparin, 1957).

The mutual precipitation of polymers is not restricted to systems containing polyelectrolytes. Smith et al. (1959) demonstrated that the mixing of aqueous solutions of poly(ethylene oxide) and *un-ionized* poly(acrylic acid) results in the separation of a tough, water-insoluble complex of the two polymers. This phenomenon is clearly due to hydrogen bonding of the

carboxyls with the ether oxygens.   It is a remarkable fact that this interaction can be so effective in the presence of water, so that hydrogen bonds
with water have to be broken to form hydrogen bonds between the polymers.   The observation can be explained only in terms of a cooperative
phenomenon, i.e., it is the multiplicity of interacting groups arranged at
corresponding spacings in the two interacting molecular chains which
accounts for the stability of the complex.

More recently, two very striking observations have been reported where
stereoisomeric forms of the same polymer form association complexes
resulting in a sharp reduction of solubility.   Watanabe et al. (1961) found
that the mixing of dilute solutions of isotactic and syndiotactic poly(methyl
methacrylate) in good solvent media resulted in instantaneous gelation.
The gel gave a characteristic sharp x-ray diffraction pattern and had a well-
defined melting point, which was quite insensitive to the ratio in which the
two polymeric components were mixed.   The data suggested that a stoichiometric complex is formed from the two stereoisomeric polymers.   The nature
of this complex has now been clarified by Liquori et al. (1965) and their
results will be discussed in Chapter VIII.   A similar conclusion
must be reached from the report of Yoshida et al. (1962) that the mixing
of dimethylformamide solutions of poly(γ-benzyl-L-glutamate) and poly(γ-
benzyl-D-glutamate) results in the precipitation of an optically inactive
material, whatever the ratio in which the optically active polymers were
mixed.   These results are very important, since they show that complexation based on stereochemical complementariness, so characteristic of specific
interactions of proteins (e.g., the formation of enzyme–substrate and antigen–antibody complexes) is not necessarily restricted to macromolecules
produced in living organisms.

III. CONFIGURATION AND CONFORMATION OF CHAIN MOLECULES

A large proportion of the problems arising in the study of macromolecules involves in one way or another considerations of molecular geometry. This subject may be logically subdivided into two parts. First we have to concern ourselves with the manner in which the atoms constituting the macromolecule are joined together, i.e., in the possibility of chemical isomerism. Secondly, once a chain molecule has been defined in chemical terms, we have to take into consideration its flexibility, which will allow it, in general, to assume a wide variety of shapes. As we shall see later, these two properties may be interdependent to some extent.

Several types of isomerism may be distinguished in chain molecules involving, for instance, the distinction between linear and branched molecular chains, copolymers with different sequential arrangements of the monomer units, and macromolecular stereoisomerism. The subject of stereoisomerism of molecular chains (the "chain configuration") has become particularly inportant in recent years since special techniques for the control of this variable in the production of synthetic polymers were discovered. (For a review see Gaylord and Mark, 1959.) We shall discuss in this chapter the definition and representation of macromolecular stereoisomerism and reserve for later chapters a description of the experimental techniques by which it may be studied in polymer solutions.

The high flexibility of long chain molecules is one of their most characteristic properties. It is reflected in the macroscopic phenomenon of rubber-like elasticity exhibited by polymers above their glass transition temperature, provided the slippage of the chain molecules past one another is prevented by chain entanglements or by chemical crosslinking. Calorimetric experiments have shown that adiabatic extensions of typical rubbers are attended by a temperature rise and thermodynamic analysis of this observation leads to the conclusion that the retractive force of the deformed rubber must be due to a tendency of the chain molecules to return to a state of higher entropy, i.e., an extension of higher probability.

The theoretical and experimental work in this field has been summarized in an excellent monograph by Treloar (1949).

The principles governing the equilibrium extension of a flexible chain molecule in dilute solution are closely analogous to those determining its elastic behavior in bulk. The role of a mechanical stress, which brings about an extension of a bulk specimen, is played by osmotic forces which tend to expand the dissolved chain molecule. In both cases, the forces are being counteracted by the reluctance of the molecular chain to pass from a more probable to a less probable chain extension. An attempt to construct a theory, which would interpret and predict the probability distribution of molecular shapes in a system containing dissolved chain molecules, may be subdivided into three parts. First, the concept of the flexibility of the polymer chain should be defined in terms of its molecular structure. We may then explore the statistical problem of the distribution of shapes in model chains characterized by a given contour length and a flexibility parameter. At this stage the chains are treated as mathematical lines of zero volume. Finally, we have to account for the perturbations in the shapes of the molecules which are brought about by their spatial requirements and by energetic interactions dependent on the nature of the solvent medium, which may favor or hinder contacts of chain segments with each other.

The polymer chains, to which the above remarks apply, may assume a wide variety of "randomly coiled" shapes, none of which is of any special importance. However, a restricted class of linear chain molecules are able, in solution, to assume precisely defined conformations corresponding to helically wound, rod-like structures. This behavior is typical of some proteins, the nucleic acids, and their synthetic analogs. The transition from the random coil form of a chain to the helical conformation may be considered a one-dimensional analog of crystallization and the principles underlying such phenomena transcend, therefore, the specialized interests of the polymer chemist. It appears, moreover, that only large molecules with the precisely defined spatial relationships, such as result from the ordered conformations of proteins and nucleic acids, can exhibit the high degree of specificity of molecular interactions which is indispensable for the existence of the life process. This consideration has undoubtedly been responsible for the massive effort expended in recent years on the detailed understanding of conditions conducive to the stabilization of ordered conformations in solutions of polypeptides and polynucleotides. The additional problem of defining the forces which are responsible for the folding of polypeptide chains consisting of helical and nonhelical sections into the unique "tertiary" structure of native proteins (see Sect. C5) remains a challenge for future investigation.

A. THE STEREOISOMERISM OF CHAIN MOLECULES

During the growth of a typical vinyl polymer, an asymmetric center is created every time a monomer molecule adds to the propagating chain end. This introduces the possibility of stereoisomerism, since the new asymmetric center may have the same or the opposite configuration as the asymmetric center which is its immediate predecessor. For instance, in a growing polystyrene chain, the addition of a monomer unit may take the two alternative routes represented below:

$$- - - -CH_2-\overset{\overset{\phi}{|}}{\underset{\underset{H}{|}}{C}}-CH_2-\overset{H}{\underset{\phi}{C}} + CH_2{=}CH\phi$$

$$\longrightarrow - - -CH_2-\overset{\overset{\phi}{|}}{\underset{\underset{H}{|}}{C}}-CH_2-\overset{\overset{\phi}{|}}{\underset{\underset{H}{|}}{C}}-CH_2\overset{H}{\underset{\phi}{C}}$$

$$\longrightarrow - - -CH_2-\overset{\overset{\phi}{|}}{\underset{\underset{H}{|}}{C}}-CH_2-\overset{\overset{H}{|}}{\underset{\underset{\phi}{|}}{C}}-CH_2-\overset{H}{\underset{\phi}{C}}$$

Since these two alternative modes of monomer addition are available for each monomer unit, a polymer prepared under conditions which do not discriminate between them is composed of a very large number of stereoisomeric forms. This is, in fact, the nature of the product obtained, for instance, when styrene is polymerized in the presence of free radical initiators and the multiplicity of stereoisomeric forms in such polymers has long been regarded as a cause of their inability to crystallize (Flory, 1953a).

In 1955, Natta and his collaborators made the unexpected discovery that it is possible to polymerize such typical vinyl derivatives as propylene, 1-butene, and styrene with special catalyst systems to obtain highly crystalline polymeric products. An analysis of the x-ray diffraction pattern from such polymer samples suggested that the chain backbone must contain long sequences of monomer units in which the carbons carrying the chain substituents have identical steric configurations and such polymer chains were named *isotactic* (Natta et al., 1955). It is most suggestive to represent the steric configuration of a polymer chain by a convention popularized by Natta. In this representation the atoms comprising the chain backbone lie in a plane and form the zig-zag corresponding to maximum chain extension compatible with the bond angles. Such a

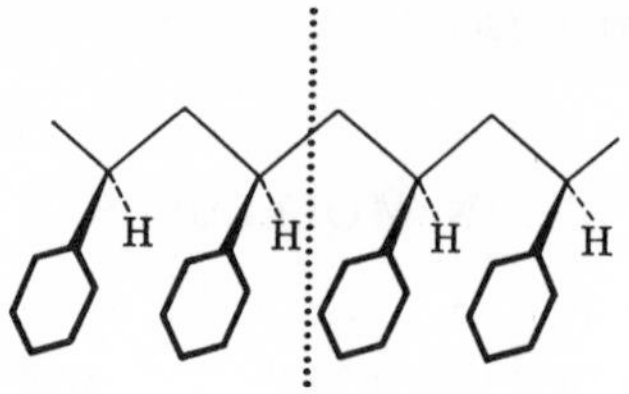

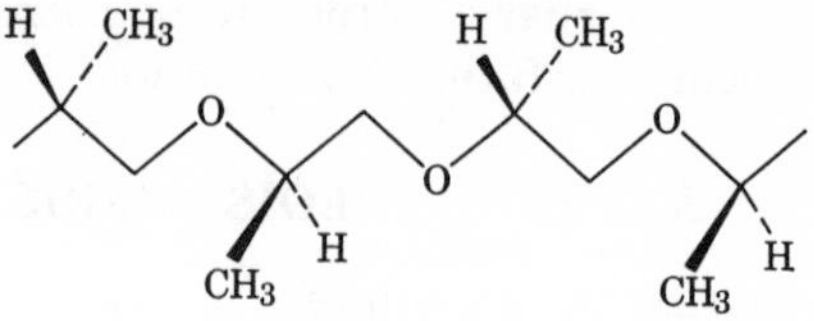

Fig. III.1. Typical isotactic polymers. (a) Isotactic polystyrene. (b) Isotactic poly-(propylene oxide).

representation of a section of an isotactic polystyrene chain is shown in Fig. III.1(a). We should note the following properties of such a chain:

(a) On translation of a monomer unit by a distance equal to its length in the direction of the chain axis, it will be exactly superimposed onto the next monomer unit.

(b) The methylene groups lie in a plane of symmetry, so that the steric relation of two adjoining monomer units is that characteristic of a *meso* structure.

(c) A backbone carbon carrying the chain substituents is not a truly asymmetric carbon, since two of its valences are bound to sections of the polymer backbone which may differ in length but are identical in the neighborhood of the carbon atom under consideration. Such carbon atoms are sometimes called "pseudoasymmetric." We may also note that rotation around the axis represented by the dotted line changes a chain in which the substituents lie above the plane containing the chain backbone to one in which the substituents lie below that plane. We may, therefore, *not* distinguish between d and l isotactic sequences.

When the monomer unit in the chain backbone contains an odd number of atoms, the geometrical relationship in an isotactic sequence is slightly different. A typical case of this kind is isotactic poly(propylene oxide) (Price and Osgan, 1956), represented schematically in Fig. III.1(b). In this case superposition of a monomer unit onto the next one along the polymer chain requires translation by a distance equal to the length of the unit and rotation by 180° around the chain axis. As a result, the chain substituents come to lie alternately above and below the plane containing atoms of the extended chain backbone. It may also be noted that in poly(propylene oxide) the carbons carrying the chain substituents are truly asymmetric, since the chain is joined to them on one side through an oxygen atom and on the other side through a methylene group. We may, for instance, define the configuration of the asymmetric carbons by specify-ing that when viewing the fully extended chain from a direction such that an oxygen precedes the asymmetric center, the direction of the bond to the next methylene carbon has to be rotated clockwise (or counterclockwise) by 120° to be superimposed on the position previously occupied by the methyl group.

Later studies led to the discovery of polymerization conditions leading to a regular alternation of the configuration of the pseudoasymmetric carbon atoms.   This type of stereoregulation was first described by Natta and Corradini (1956) for 1,2-polybutadiene and poly(vinyl chloride), as depicted in Figs. III.2(a) and (b) and the term *syndiotactic* was suggested to

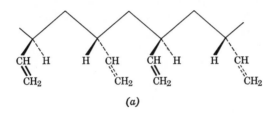

(a)

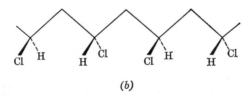

(b)

Fig. III.2. Typical syndiotactic polymers. (a) Syndiotactic 1,2-polybutadiene. (b) Syndiotactic poly(vinyl chloride).

describe it.   In a syndiotactic chain it is impossible to obtain superposition of two nearest-neighbor monomer units by combinations of translations and rotations; such superposition is obtained only onto next-to-nearest neighbors by a translation of the monomer unit.   Specific catalysts leading to syndiotactic polymers seem to be less common than those by which isotactic chains are produced, but they have been reported, e.g., for poly-(methyl methacrylate) (Fox et al., 1958) and for polypropylene (Natta et al., 1962).   In addition it is frequently possible to approach the syndio-tactic structure by carrying out free radical polymerizations at low tem-peratures, since the activation energy involved in chain growth seems to be generally significantly lower if monomers add to the chain so as to produce pseudoasymmetric centers with alternating configurations. This effect has been described for poly(vinyl chloride) (Fordham et al., 1959) and for poly(isopropyl acrylate) (Garrett et al., 1959).

It is doubtful whether the phenomenon of stereoregulation would have been discovered were it not for the striking ability of many stereoregular polymers containing pseudoasymmetric centers to crystallize. Nevertheless, some polymers which are known to be highly stereoregulated cannot be made to crystallize. It was found, for instance, that poly(p-iodostyrene), derived from isotactic polystyrene (Braun, 1959), and poly(vinyl acetate), derived from crystalline poly(vinyl formate) (Fujii et al., 1962), are not crystallizable. In many other cases crystallization of highly stereoregulated polymers is a very slow process and has been achieved only after a long empirical search for suitable experimental conditions. Conversely, in the case of poly(vinyl alcohol) the small size of the hydroxyl substituent enables the polymer to crystallize even if it is not stereoregular. It is then obvious that criteria other than crystallizability are needed to study the phenomena of stereoregulation.

There are still other reasons why such additional techniques for the characterization of polymeric stereoisomerism are required. On one hand, the concept of an isotactic and a syndiotactic chain represents the ideal of perfect stereoregularity which, in practice, can never be quite attained, even under the most favorable conditions. On the other hand, it has been proposed that we describe as *atactic* all polymer samples which "do not possess steric order of the units or possess tacticities of such a complex character that it cannot be understood by a simple intellect" (Natta and Danusso, 1959). Obviously, this definition reflects the lack of interest of the crystallographer in all chains in which the regularity of the distribution of configurations is too low to allow crystallization. This distribution may, in fact, deviate to different extents from perfect randomness and it should be our aim to describe it so that the nature of the distribution of pseudoasymmetric centers would be characterized quantitatively for all cases ranging continuously from perfect order to complete randomness. This problem was discussed for the first time by Coleman (1958) and later by Bovey and Tiers (1960), Miller and Nielsen (1960), and Miller (1962). Using the nomenclature of Bovey and Tiers, the parameter σ^* denotes the probability that an asymmetric (or pseudoasymmetric) center in the chain is followed by another one with the same configuration. Thus, an isotactic polymer would have $\sigma^* = 1$, a syndiotactic polymer $\sigma^* = 0$, while a chain with a perfectly random distribution of the configurations would be characterized by $\sigma^* = 0.5$. Values of σ^* larger or smaller than

0.5 would then denote a varying deviation from randomness with a bias towards syndiotactic or isotactic chain propagation, respectively. However, it is important to stress that a single parameter σ^* can characterize the nature of the stereoregularity of a chain only if the probability of the configuration of an asymmetric center formed in the growth of the chain is determined by the configuration of the immediately preceding asymmetric center. If, for example, the probability of creating an asymmetric center of the same configuration as the preceding one depends on the configuration of the penultimate unit, two independent parameters will be required to describe the stereoregularity of the chain. These parameters may be chosen in various ways. The choice which is most closely related to experimentally observable quantities is that proposed by Bovey and Tiers (1960) in which triads of monomer units are designated as isotactic, syndiotactic, or heterotactic depending on whether their central unit is joined to two units with the same configuration, two units with the opposite configuration, or one unit with the same and one with the opposite configuration. Consider, for instance, a diisotactic chain (Natta et al., 1960; Huggins et al., 1962) of the type

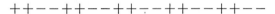

$$+ + - - + + - - + + - - + + - - + + - -$$

where $+$ and $-$ designate the two relative configurations. If we consider only one nearest neighbor of each asymmetric center, then the chain will be characterized by $\sigma^* = 0.5$, although it is obviously quite different from a chain with a random sequence of asymmetric centers. If, on the other hand, we characterize the chain above in terms of triads, then we find that all of them are heterotactic, as distinct from a random chain in which only half of the triad are heterotactic, the remainder being equally divided between isotactic and syndiotactic triads.

Under experimental conditions encountered in practice, more complicated tacticities might occur, which would call for additional parameters for their description. However, it is doubtful whether such theoretical refinements would lend themselves to experimental evaluation. The most important complicating feature is the possibility of the formation of *stereoblock* polymers, consisting either of blocks of regulated and random sequences, or of isotactic and syndiotactic blocks. The latter case represented by

$$+ + + + + + + + + - + - + - + - + - +$$

would be characterized by a high content of isotactic and syndiotactic and a very low content of heterotactic triads. We should note, however, that such a description will be very insensitive to the length of the blocks comprising the stereoblock chain.

When macromolecules are produced in the metabolic processes of living organisms, the chemical stereospecificity of enzymatic catalysis leads typically to perfectly stereoregulated chain molecules. Apart from proteins and nucleic acids, to be discussed more fully in part C of this chapter, this category includes a variety of polysaccharides and the structures of some of them are shown in Fig. III.3. Synthetic macromolecules of a

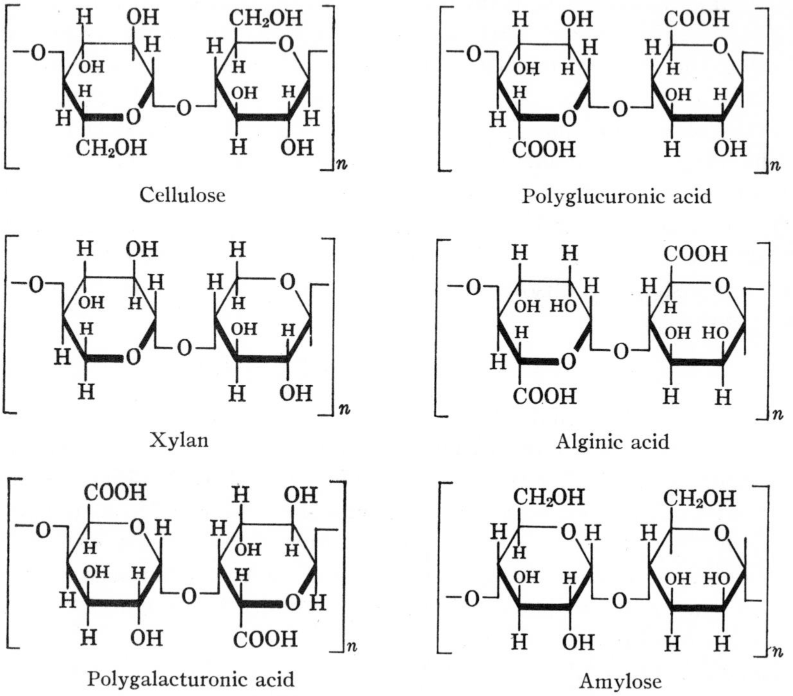

Cellulose

Polyglucuronic acid

Xylan

Alginic acid

Polygalacturonic acid

Amylose

Fig. III.3. Structures of some typical polysaccharides.

uniquely defined steric configuration may be obtained from optically active monomers, if no bond attached to the asymmetric center is involved in the polymerization reaction and no new asymmetric centers are formed in the polymerization. This is the case in the preparation of high molecular weight polypeptides from N-carboxy-α-amino acid anhydrides (Katchalski, 1951; Katchalski et al., 1964),the preparation of polyestersfro m optically active acids (Kleine and Kleine, 1959), polyamides from optically active lactams (Overberger and Jaboner, 1963), etc.

B. GEOMETRY OF FLEXIBLE CHAINS

1. The Flexibility of Molecular Chains

If we want to obtain a feeling for the flexibility of chain molecules, it is best to start by considering the relative rigidity of the carbon skeleton in the homologous series of normal paraffin hydrocarbons. We know from x-ray diffraction studies of hydrocarbon crystals that the equilibrium value of the C–C bond length is about 1.54 Å and that the four carbon valences are distributed symmetrically in space, so that any two of them form a tetrahedral angle of about 109.5°. Any change in the distance between the two carbon atoms of ethane involves a stretching of the C–C bond and spectroscopic data show that an energy of the order of 10^4 to 10^5 cal/mole is required to produce a 10% change in bond length. This value is so high that we may in practice disregard any possibility of extending covalent bonds. In the case of propane the distance between the terminal carbon atoms may be varied by distorting the normal bond angle. The energy required for such distortion may be estimated not only from spectroscopic observations of bending frequencies, but also from heats of combustion of cyclic molecules in which the bond angles deviate significantly from their normal values. For instance, Kaarsemaker and Coops (1952) found that the heat of combustion of gaseous cyclobutane exceeds that of gaseous cyclohexane by 6.6 kcal/mole of methylene residues. This difference should be largely due to the distortion of the tetrahedral angle to an angle of 90°, and if we assume that the energy requirement is proportional to the square of the deviaton from the normal bond angle, we arrive at an estimate of 1.6 kcal/mole for a distortion by 10°. This is a relatively low value and we must then concede that the bond angle may be subject to some variation when strong forces operate on a molecule. However, when we come to a consideration of the carbon skeleton of the next-higher homolog, i.e., n-butane, a much more drastic variation in the shape of the carbon skeleton becomes possible by the rotation of the C_3–C_4 bond around the C_2–C_3 axis (see Fig. III.4). The extremes in the possible separation of the two terminal carbon atoms are represented in Fig. III.5—they correspond to distances of 2.6 Å for the *cis* and 3.8 Å for the *trans* form. The van der Waals radii for methyl groups are of the order of 2 Å, so that the *cis* form represents a situation of high steric strain. As a result we should expect the rotation of the C_3–C_4 bond to be highly hindered. Experimental evidence for such a hindered rotation was first reported by Pitzer (1940), who found that the absolute entropy of gaseous normal paraffins was significantly lower than the value to be expected for a mole-

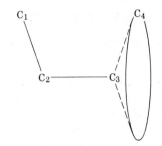

Fig. III.4. Rotation around the C_2—C_3 bond in n-butane.

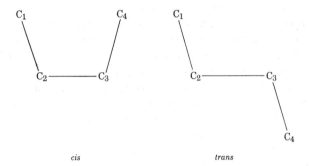

cis   *trans*

Fig. III.5. The *cis* and *trans* conformation of n-butane.

cule with free rotation around all the valence bonds. He showed that the discrepancy can be accounted for if the potential energy barriers hindering the rotation are considered. The variation in the shape of the molecule because of rotation around a covalent bond ("molecular conformation") is visualized most easily by use of the schematic method introduced by Newman (1956). In this representation the second and third carbons of n-butane are symbolized by circles and the bond between them lies in the line of sight. The conformation of the carbon skeleton is then characterized by an "internal angle of rotation," ϕ, by which the bond is rotated from the *trans* conformation. Figure III.6 shows the three "eclipsed" forms corresponding to ϕ values of $+60°$, $-60°$, and $180°$ in which steric strain is maximized by close approach of the terminal carbons to each other or to a hydrogen atom attached to the next-to-nearest carbon atom. Also shown are the three staggered conformations, the *gauche* (g and g') forms $\phi = 120°$ and $\phi = -120°$ and the *trans* (t) form, $\phi = 0°$. The *trans* conformation, corresponding to a maximum separation of the bulky methyl groups, would be expected to be the lowest energy form. Pitzer

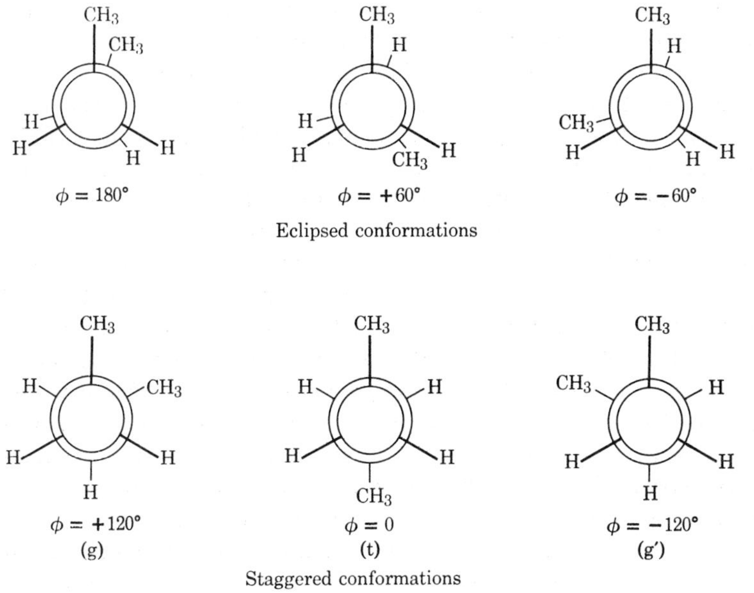

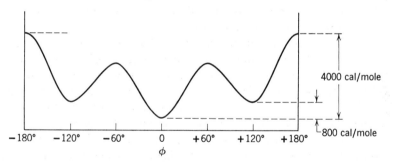

$\phi = 180°$

$\phi = +60°$

$\phi = -60°$

Eclipsed conformations

$\phi = +120°$
(g)

$\phi = 0$
(t)

$\phi = -120°$
(g')

Staggered conformations

Fig. III.6. Newman projections of *n*-butane conformations.

-180°   -120°   -60°   0   +60°   +120°   +180°

ϕ

4000 cal/mole

800 cal/mole

Fig. III.7. The dependence of the energy of *n*-butane on the internal angle of rotation ϕ.

(1940) and Ito (1953) have estimated that the energies of the t and g minima differ by about 800 cal/mole and that the potential energy maximum at $\phi = 180°$ lies about 4000 cal/mole above the energy of the *trans* conformation. Figure III.7 shows the dependence of the energy of the molecule on ϕ. The potential energy barriers are low enough to allow rapid interconversion of the *gauche* and *trans* conformations. On the other hand, this interconversion is slow compared to the time scale of molecular vibrations so that it is possible to observe in vibrational spectra separate absorption lines characteristic of the *trans* and the *gauche* forms.* Under these conditions it seems reasonable to represent the molecule as a system in which the three "rotational isomers," with ϕ values centered at $0°$, $+120°$, and $-120°$, are treated as separate chemical species in equilibrium with each other, while the eclipsed conformations are transition states in the conversion of one rotational isomer into another. This point of view, in which hindered rotation is taken into account in terms of discrete rotational isomers, has been introduced into the study of chain molecules with most fruitful results by the Leningrad school of investigators, whose work has been summarized by Volkenstein (1963). It is instructive, as Volkenstein (1963a) points out, to compare rotational isomerism in saturated paraffins with the *cis–trans* isomerism of 1,2-disubstituted ethylenes. In the latter case rotation around the double bond is much more difficult (with an energy barrier of the order of 40,000 cal/mole) and interconversion of the isomers is, therefore, sufficiently slow to allow their isolation as pure chemical entities. But the difference between rotation around single and double bonds is only a quantitative one which appears to be more important because of our common experimental time scale. There is no reason why the short-lived rotational isomers of molecules containing single bonds only should not be treated in the same manner in which we would naturally treat equilibrium mixtures of the *cis–trans* isomers of 1,2-disubstituted ethylene derivatives.

Yet another principle emerges in the consideration of the possible conformations of the next member of the homologous series, *n*-pentane. A description of the shape of the carbon skeleton now involves the specification of two internal angles of rotation, so that the assignment of the discrete values of $0°$, $+120°$, and $-120°$ to these angles leads to the four distinct molecular shapes tt, tg (equivalent to tg', gt and g't), gg (or g'g'), and g'g (or gg'). These arrangements are represented in Fig. III.8 in a manner such that the central three carbon atoms lie in the plane of the paper, while lines with variable thickness and dashed lines are used to represent bonds pointing towards or away from the observer. The conformation g'g may be seen to result in a very small distance between the terminal carbon atoms (about 2.5 Å) and Taylor (1948) has pointed out that the potential

---

* Kohlrausch (1932) compared the Raman spectra of ethyl halides with those of *n*-propyl halides and observed the doubling of certain absorption lines in the propane derivative, which he interpreted correctly as due to rotational isomerism. His proposal was incorrect in detail, since he thought that the eclipsed *cis* form was one of the conformations contributing to the spectrum.

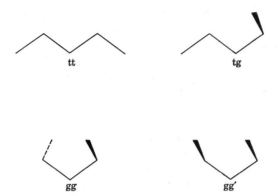

Fig. III.8. Conformations of the carbon skeleton in *n*-pentane.

energy of this form must be extremely high.   Thus, although conformations g and g' were equivalent in butane, conformations gg and g'g in pentane represent a very different potential energy and we may conclude, in general, that the potential energy of a given conformation of a chain molecule may not be evaluated by summing up contributions characteristic of the individual angles of internal rotation.   Extending the principles discussed above to a long polyethylene chain (see Lifson, 1959) one should, in principle, take account of correlations of internal angles of rotation beyond the nearest-neighbor pairs.   However, such a model would lead to prohibitively difficult calculations and it is reasonable to accept an approximate model in which: (a) gg' and g'g sequences are excluded; (b) for all other combinations the difference in the potential energy of a g and a t bond is assumed to be independent of the conformation of the neighboring bonds.   The stiffness of the chain will increase with an increase of the difference in the energy characterizing *gauche* and *trans* bonds and it will decrease with an increase in temperature, which will tend to equalize the occupancy of all accessible chain conformations.

Before passing on to a consideration of more complicated chain molecules, we should point out that considerations of steric interference are occasionally insufficient to account for the relative stability of the various rotational isomers of small molecules.   Volkenstein (1963b) cites spectroscopic data showing that the *gauche* conformation is the low energy form of *n*-propyl chloride and *n*-propyl bromide and similar conclusions were arrived at from electron diffraction studies of gaseous *n*-butyl chloride (Ukaji and Bonham, 1962).   The nature of the forces responsible for the reversal of the usual order of stability in rotational isomers has not been fully clarified.

In cases where the rotational isomers differ appreciably in their dipole moment, the more polar form should be stabilized in the liquid state as compared to the gaseous state because of dipole–dipole interactions of the closely spaced molecules. Thus, Mizushima et al. (1949) estimated from spectroscopic data that gaseous 1,2-dichloroethane at 25°C contains 25% of the *gauche* isomer, while in the liquid state 57% of the molecules are in the *gauche* conformation.

When we proceed to a consideration of chain polymers carrying more or less bulky substituents attached to the chain backbone, the additional steric restrictions become much more difficult to analyze. In tackling this problem it has been an inestimable advantage that the geometry of the molecular chain may be obtained to a high degree of precision by x-ray diffraction analysis of crystalline polymers. Bunn and Holmes (1958) have pointed out that the conformation assumed by the chain molecules in the crystalline state should, in general, be a close approximation of the form corresponding to the lowest energy of the isolated chain, being apparently affected only to a minor extent by intermolecular forces. This principle has been greatly strengthened by the work of de Santis et al. (1963), who calculated the energies of various chain molecules as a function of the internal angles of rotation on the basis of estimated van der Waals repulsion energies of chain substituents. They found striking agreement in a number of cases between the predicted lowest energy form and the conformation assumed by the chain molecule in the crystalline state. Nevertheless, we should note that some exceptions do exist to this broad generalization. For instance, Natta et al. (1959) found quite different conformations for crystalline isotactic polystyrene and for isotactic poly(*p*-fluorostyrene) and this difference must clearly be due to effects produced by a changing chain conformation on the efficiency with which the chains can be packed in the crystal lattice. However, such anomalies are probably rare and molecular chain conformations in crystalline polymers may be used as points of departure in speculations about the preferred shape of these molecules in solution.

Before presenting the crystallographic evidence, let us consider briefly the extent of steric interference to be expected in a chain segment of two monomer units with all possible combinatons of *trans* and *gauche* bonds. The various ways in which two monomer units may be arranged in an isotactic chain are represented schematically on Fig. III.9. It may be seen that the conformational sequence tg is the only one in which neither the methylene groups nor the chain substituents of neighboring monomer units are subjected to steric strain. All other conformations, in which

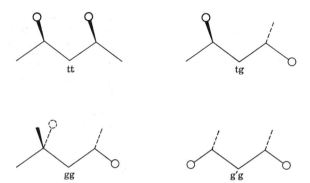

Fig. III.9. Staggered conformations in the chain backbone in a sequence of two monomer residues of an isotactic vinyl polymer. The circles symbolize chain substituents.

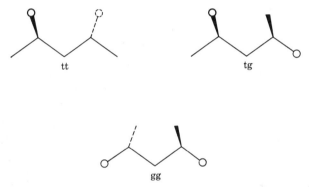

Fig. III.10. Staggered conformations in the chain backbone in a sequence of two monomer residues of a syndiotactic vinyl polymer.

normal bond angles are maintained and in which the internal angle of rotation is restricted to the three values of $0°$, $+120°$, and $-120°$, would seem to represent a highly strained condition. By the same token, a segment of a syndiotactic chain (Fig. III.10) is free of steric strain in the sequences tt and g'g', but is highly strained in all other conformational sequences. Unfortunately our knowledge of the relative potential energies of *sequences of conformations* is much less certain than our knowledge of the energetics of rotational isomerism in molecules such as butane, in which the specification of the conformation of the carbon skeleton involves a single internal angle of rotation. This relative ignorance imposes serious limitations on the quantitative treatment of the conformational isomerism of chain molecules.

In crystalline polyethylene the polymer chains assume the planar zig-zag form of the all-*trans* conformation (Bunn, 1939), which would be expected to correspond to the potential energy minimum.   The crystal structures of a large number of isotactic vinyl polymers have been determined by Natta and his collaborators (Natta, 1957; Natta et al., 1959).   In a number of chains in which the chain substituents have moderate spatial requirements [isotactic $(-CH_2-CHR-)_n$, where R = $-CH_3$, $-C_2H_5$, $-C_3H_7$, $-C_6H_5$, $-OCH_3$, etc.] the stable conformation of the chain backbone has a regular alternation of *trans* and *gauche* bonds ($\phi_1 = 0°$, $\phi_2 =$

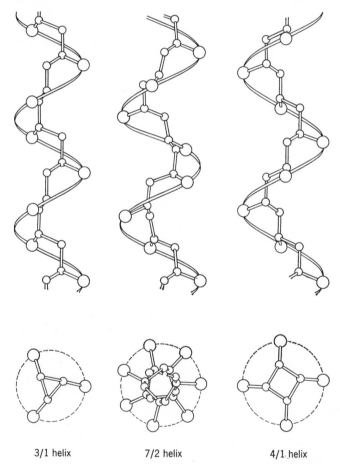

3/1 helix   7/2 helix   4/1 helix

Fig. III.11. Helical conformations of isotactic vinyl polymers in the crystalline state.

120°), generating a helix in which three monomer units are contained in one turn. This conformational sequence is the one predicted as corresponding to the least steric strain on the basis of the crude representations of Fig. III.9. Such steric interference of the chain substituents as is present in these polymers is relieved by expansion of the bond angle joining the backbone carbon atoms from the tetrahedral angle of 109.5° to, e.g., 114.5° in isotactic polypropylene (Bunn and Holmes, 1958) and to 116.5° in isotactic polystyrene (Natta and Corradini, 1955; Bunn and Howells, 1955). When the steric interference of chain substituents becomes more severe, the strain must be relieved by distortion of the internal angles of rotation. If branching of the side chain occurs at the second carbon atom (i.e., R = —CH$_3$CH(CH$_3$)$_2$ or —CH$_3$CH(CH$_3$)C$_2$H$_5$) the internal angles of rotation become, typically, $\phi_1 = -13°$, $\phi_2 - 110°$ and $3^1/_2$ monomer units are accommodated in a turn of the helix; in still more highly hindered chains, such as poly(o-methyl styrene), poly(vinyl cyclohexane) (Natta, 1960), and others (Natta et al., 1959) the distortion of the internal angles of rotation is doubled to $\phi_1 = -26°$, $\phi_2 = 100°$ and the helical chain conformation now contains four monomer units per turn. The three types of helices most commonly found in isotactic polymer crystals are shown on Fig. III.11. With increasing steric hindrance the helix of the chain backbone increases in radius, while the pitch of the helix remains approximately unchanged. We find then that for a chain of a given degree of polymerization the length of the helical structure tends to contract with increasing spatial requirements of the chain substituent. One would naturally expect that right-handed and left-handed helices would form with equal ease in polymers such as isotactic polypropylene or polystyrene. On the other hand, if the side chain of the isotactic polymer contains a center of asymmetry, e.g., in the polymer of a pure optical isomer of 4-methyl-1-hexene

$$
\begin{array}{ccccccc}
-\mathrm{CH_2-CH-} & & -\mathrm{CH_2-} & & -\mathrm{CH-} & & -\mathrm{CH_2-} & & -\mathrm{CH-} \\
| & & & & | & & & & | \\
\mathrm{CH_2} & & & & \mathrm{CH_2} & & & & \mathrm{CH_2} \\
| & & & & | & & & & | \\
\mathrm{CH_3-CH} & & \mathrm{CH_3-CH} & & & & \mathrm{CH_3-CH} \\
| & & | & & & & | \\
\mathrm{C_2H_5} & & \mathrm{C_2H_5} & & & & \mathrm{C_2H_5}
\end{array}
$$

or if the chain backbone contains true centers of asymmetry, as in the isotactic polymer of an optical isomer of propylene oxide

$$
\begin{array}{ccc}
-\mathrm{CH_2-CH-O-CH_2-CH-O-CH_2-CH-O-} \\
| \qquad\quad | \qquad\quad | \\
\mathrm{CH_3} \qquad \mathrm{CH_3} \qquad \mathrm{CH_3}
\end{array}
$$

then a right- or left-handed helix will, in general, be energetically preferred (de Santis et al., 1963). In the case of syndiotactic polymers the qualitative estimates based on the steric relations represented on Fig. III.10 are again found to be a rough guide in predicting correctly that conformations close to the all-*trans* planar structure will be favored (Natta and Corradini, 1956). There is an interesting exception in the case of syndiotactic polypropylene (Natta, 1960) which has usually been found to have a helical conformation in the crystalline state. This is almost certainly due to the efficient packing of such helices. We may assume that the all-*trans* conformation represents a potential energy minimum of the isolated chain also in this case, particularly since a second crystalline modification of polypropylene (Natta et al., 1964) contains chains with this conformation.

For chains with two bulky substituents of the type $(-CH_2-CR_1R_2-)_n$ all conformations represent appreciable strain, so much so, that such molecules would probably be considered impossible from inspection of conventional molecular models. Yet many such polymers do in fact exist and are quite stable, illustrating the limitations of model representations. A typical example is polyisobutene, $(-CH_2-C(CH_3)_2-)_n$, which is crystalline, so that the conformation of its chains can be determined (Liquori, 1955). It corresponds to $\phi_1 = \phi_2 = 82°$ and a bond angle of $114°$. We see then that the severe steric restraints in this molecular chain produce a potential energy minimum for an angle of internal rotation quite far removed from those corresponding to the staggered conformations of normal paraffin chains. In poly(methyl methacrylate), where the asymmetric centers carry two different bulky substituents, the reported crystal structures suggests that the isotactic chain forms a helix with five monomer residues per turn (which could be generated, for instance, by the conformational sequence $\phi_1 = 0°$, $\phi_2 = 72°$), while the syndiotactic chain has an extended form with the conformational sequence $(tgtg')_n$ (Liquori et al., 1965). Another interesting case is that of polyoxymethylene, $(-CH_2-O-)_n$, in which a distorted all-*gauche* conformation is preferred ($\phi = 102.5$), so that the chains assume, in contrast to polyethylene, a helical form (Tadokoro et al., 1960). It has been suggested that this phenomenon may be caused by interactions between the C—O dipoles which would resist conformations in which these dipoles lie parallel to one another (Uchida et al., 1956). However, de Santis et al. (1963) have shown that the helical conformation may be fully accounted for by searching for the form which must be assumed by the chain, so as to minimize van der Waals repulsions of the pairs of methylene hydrogens with each other.

When a chain molecule is transferred from a perfect crystal to a dilute solution, restraints imposed on its shape by factors influencing the efficiency of packing in the crystal lattice are eliminated. This will make it possible for the internal angles of rotation to change to values leading to an irrational number of monomer units in a turn of the helix. There is also no longer a need for the bond angle θ or the internal angles of rotation ϕ to have well-defined values, but they may vary within a range, leading to a flexibility of the macromolecular conformation. Finally, the tendency to increase the entropy of the system will make a number of the bonds in the chain backbone assume conformations of higher energy, leading to "kinks" in the regular arrangement characteristic of the macromolecule in the crystalline state. Figure III.12 shows such a kink produced in an all-*trans* polyethylene chain by the introduction of a single *gauche* bond. In analyzing the conformational correlations in dissolved vinyl or vinylidene chain polymers, Volkenstein (1963c) finds it convenient to subdivide the chain in such a way that a section of the chain backbone between two chain substituents is defined as belonging to one monomer residue. A section of a vinylidene chain is represented in Fig. III.13 with the bonds numbered in such a way that $2j$ and $2j + 1$ refer to the bonds of the jth monomer unit. It may then be easily verified that the mutual approach of neighboring chain substituents will be governed by the internal angles of rotation ϕ_{2j} and

Fig. III.12. Conformation of polyethylene chain backbone with one *gauche* bond.

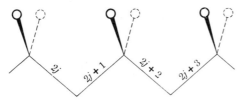

Fig. III.13. Designation of bonds in the chain backbone used in the specification of chain conformations.

ϕ_{2j+1} around the $2j$th and the $(2j+1)$th bond.   In the simplest case, that of a vinylidene polymer of type ($-CH_2CR_2-)_n$, Ptitsyn and Sharonov (1957) have assumed that ϕ may have only one magnitude, either positive or negative.   To avoid interference of neighboring chain substituents, ϕ_{2j} and ϕ_{2j+1} must have the same sign, but the signs of the ω values in adjoining monomer units (e.g., ϕ_{2j}, ϕ_{2j+1} and ϕ_{2j+2}, ϕ_{2j+3}) were assumed to be uncorrelated with one another.   We obtain then a conformational sequence of the type

$$\ldots(+\phi, +\phi)_p(-\phi, -\phi)_q(+\phi, \phi)_r(-\phi, -\phi)_s\ldots$$
$$\text{I}$$

where the sequence lengths $p,q,r,s\ldots$ have a statistical distribution.   The situation is somewhat more complicated in the case of syndiotactic vinyl polymers.   In that case, spatial interference of neighboring chain substituents are minimized if $\phi_{2j}\ \phi_{2j+1}$ are either a tt or a gg sequence, but a gg monomer unit has to be flanked by units with a tt conformation.   The characteristic chain conformation is then

$$\ldots(tt)_p\ (gg)\ (tt)_q\ (gg)\ (tt)_r\ldots$$
$$\text{II}$$

and the number of kinks in the chain will depend on the difference in the energy of a (tt) (tt) and a (tt) (gg) sequence.   The nature of the kinks is most uncertain in an isotactic polymer chain, since all deviations from a regular alternation of *trans* and *gauche* bonds represent states of appreciable steric stress.   Birshtein (1959) and Nagai (1959a) propose conformations of the type

$$\ldots(tg)_p(g't)_q(tg)_r(g't)_s\ldots$$
$$\text{III}$$

but such a sequence contains gg' junctions which, as we have seen, are energetically very unfavorable (Fig. III.8).   It was suggested by Allegra et al. (1963) that this strain can be greatly reduced by substituting for gg' the sequences eg' or ge', where e and e' are eclipsed conformations with the same sense of rotation as g and g', respectively.   In the model which they propose

$$\ldots(tg)_p(e't)\ (g't)_q(tg)_r\ldots$$
$$\text{IV}$$

the eclipsed conformation is such that the close approach is between carbon and hydrogen atoms joined to nearest neighbor carbons of the

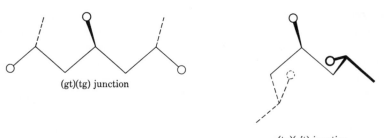

(gt)(tg) junction

(tg)(e′t) junction

Fig. III.14. Proposed conformations for breaks in the helices of isotactic vinyl polymer backbones.

chain backbone. The steric repulsion resulting from this arrangement is estimated to involve an energy increase of 2.7 kcal/mole. Figure III.14 gives a schematic representation of the (gt) (tg′) and the (tg) (e′t) junctions characterizing this model.

It is natural to concentrate our attention on the case of polymers for which a conformational analysis is most accessible. As we have seen, difficult problems have to be overcome even in these cases to gain a complete understanding of chain flexibility, but the situation is even less satisfactory with some other important polymers. We may assume, for instance, that the most stable conformation of cellulose derivatives is similar to that assumed by cellulose in the crystalline state, as depicted on Fig. III.15. Here the anhydroglucose units are in the typical "chair" conformation analogous to that of cyclohexane derivatives and may be considered essentially rigid. However, it is not easy in the case of such a chain, consisting of closely interconnected rings, to estimate the energy requirements for a deviation of the conformation from this low energy form. The actual flexibility of cellulosic chains is so low (Holtzer et al., 1954; Hunt et al., 1956; Levi et al., 1956) that it seems possible that conformational transitions of the chain backbone, such as are assumed in vinyl polymers, are insignificant and that changes in the molecular shape are due to chain bending (because of minor variations in the values of bond angles and the internal angles of rotation) rather than to sharp kinks in the chain.

In concluding this section it should be stressed that we have explored the

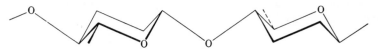

Fig. III.15. Conformation of the cellulose chain in the crystalline state.

question of the flexibility of polymer chains only from the point of view of the accessibility of different shapes, without considering the kinetic problem, i.e., how fast these changes of shape might come about. Thus, we may have a highly sterically hindered chain, such as polyisobutylene, which is still extremely flexible in the thermodynamic sense, since the extent of steric interference of the chain substituents is very similar in alternative chain conformations. This definition of chain flexibility will determine the probability distribution of the shapes of molecular chains in an assembly containing a large number of them, since the potential barriers to be surmounted in the transition of one form to the other will, in general, not be so high as to prevent the rapid attainment of equilibrium conditions. The height of these barriers will, of course, control the kinetics of processes involving conformational transitions. The theoretical and experimental treatment of such phenomena is in a rather unsatisfactory state—we shall touch on it in Chap. V when considering nuclear magnetic resonance spectroscopy of polymer solutions and in Chap. VI in discussing the concept of the "internal viscosity" of chain molecules.

2. Statistics of Random Flight Chains

Having considered the factors which determine the flexibility of molecular chains, we now have to explore the question of the shape which a chain molecule of a given length and flexibility will take up in solution. For a long flexible chain the number of distinguishable shapes will obviously be very large and it is clearly impossible to describe such chain molecules in terms of the probability distribution of the individual conformations in which the position of each atom constituting the chain is specified. Even if such a result could be obtained theoretically, it could not be checked against experimental data which yield one, or at most two, parameters characterizing the average shape of the dissolved macromolecules. A frequently employed parameter is the distance h between the ends of the molecular chains, which is described by a probability distribution function $\mathcal{W}(h)$ defined so that

$$\int_0^\infty \mathcal{W}(h)dh = 1$$

For many purposes, the significant quantity is the mean square end-to-end displacement $\langle h^2 \rangle$ given by

$$\langle h^2 \rangle = \int_0^\infty h^2 \mathcal{W}(h)dh \tag{3.1}$$

Although $\langle h^2 \rangle$ has the advantage of being easily visualized, it should be realized that no rigorous method exists for measuring this quantity. The parameter characterizing the expansion of macromolecules, which may be derived unambiguously from experimental data, is the mean radius of gyration $\langle s^2 \rangle$ defined by

$$\langle s^2 \rangle = \frac{1}{Z} \sum_1^Z \langle r_i^2 \rangle \tag{3.2}$$

where Z is the number of chain elements and $\langle r_i^2 \rangle$ is the mean square distance of the ith element from the center of gravity of the chain. Values of $\langle s^2 \rangle$ are obtained from light scattering measurements (Chap. V)—they are frequently converted into $\langle h^2 \rangle$ by assuming that the two quantities are related by the same factor as in the "random flight" model of the molecular chains. The random flight chain, usually taken as the point of departure in theoretical treatments of the shape of flexible chain molecules, is an idealized model in which links represented by mathematical lines of zero volume are "freely jointed" so that all angles in space between successive links are equally probable (Kuhn, 1934). This implies, of course, that changes in the shape of the chain are not accompanied by any changes in energy. Let us consider first the one-dimensional case, where Z links of length b may be added with equal probability in the positive and negative direction along the x axis of the coordinate system. If Z_+ is the number placed in the positive direction, the probability distribution of Z_+ will be

$$\mathcal{W}(Z_+, Z) = (1/2)^Z Z! / [Z_+! (Z - Z_+)!]$$

Starting at the origin, the coordinate of the chain end will be $x = b(2Z_+ - Z)$ and the probability of a given value of x will be given by

$$\mathcal{W}(x) = (1/2)^Z Z! \Big/ \left[\left(\frac{Z}{2} + \frac{x}{2b} \right)! \left(\frac{Z}{2} - \frac{x}{2b} \right)! \right] \tag{3.3}$$

For large values of Z, the probability of finding Z_+/Z very different from $1/2$ will become very small, so that we need to consider $\mathcal{W}(x)$ only in the range where x is very small compared to Zb the length of the fully extended chain. We may use the Stirling approximation to the factorials, expand the result in powers of x/Zb and retain only the first term of the expansion to obtain the probability distribution function

$$\mathcal{W}(x)dx = \exp(-x^2/2Zb^2)/b\sqrt{2\pi Z} \tag{3.4}$$

If we consider the three-dimensional case of a random flight chain, the reasoning outlined above will be applicable to the probability distribution of the x coordinate of the chain end. The average component of the length of the chain links in the x direction is $b_x = b/\sqrt{3}$, so that the corresponding component of the end-to-end displacement has a probability distribution function

$$\mathcal{W}(h_x)dh_x = \frac{\exp(-3h_x^2/2Zb^2)}{b\sqrt{2\pi Z/3}}\ dh_x \tag{3.5}$$

Since $h^2 = h_x^2 + h_y^2 + h_z^2$, the probability of finding the chain end in a given location of the coordinate system will then be

$$\mathcal{W}(h_x,h_y,h_z)dh_xdh_ydh_z = \frac{\exp[-3h^2/2Zb^2]}{(b\sqrt{2\pi Z/3})^3}\ dh_xdh_ydh_z \tag{3.6}$$

Usually we shall be interested only in the value of the end-to-end displacement h rather than the precise location of the chain ends. If one chain end is at the origin of our coordinate system and the distance to the other end lies between h and $h + dh$, this end will lie within a spherical shell of area $4\pi h^2$ and thickness dh. The probability of such a chain will then be

$$\mathcal{W}(h)dh = \frac{\exp(-3h^2/2Zb^2)}{(b\sqrt{2\pi Z/3})^3}\ 4\pi h^2 dh \tag{3.7}$$

The most probable value of h, corresponding to $d\ln\mathcal{W}(h)/dh = 0$, will be denoted by h^* and its value is given for the distribution function (3.7) by

$$(h^*)^2 = 2Zb^2/3 \tag{3.8}$$

while the mean square chain end displacement obtained by combining (3.1) and (3.7) becomes

$$\langle h^2 \rangle = Zb^2 \tag{3.9}$$

In Fig. III.16 the distribution function (3.7) is represented by a plot of $\langle h^2 \rangle^{1/2}\mathcal{W}(h)$ against $h/\langle h^2 \rangle^{1/2}$. We may note that even for a relatively short chain of 100 segments, h^* is only 8% of the full contour length of the chain. The probabilities of extensions much larger than h^* fall off rapidly to extremely small values. Thus, for instance, $\mathcal{W}(3h^*)/\mathcal{W}(h^*) \approx 10^{-3}$ and $\mathcal{W}(5h^*)/\mathcal{W}(h^*) \approx 10^{-9}$. We see then that for long chains the probabilities become negligible long before the chain end separation approaches the length of the fully extended chain.

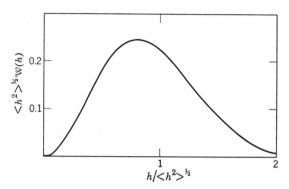

Fig. III.16. Probability distribution of chain end displacements in a random flight chain.

The arguments used to obtain the distribution function of the separation of the chain ends may be used with equal justification for the distance between any given pair of chain elements. Thus, the displacement between the ith and the jth link will be given, provided $|j - i|$ is sufficiently large, by

$$\langle h_{ij}^2 \rangle = b^2 |j - i| \tag{3.10}$$

Such a distribution of chain elements has been shown by Debye (1946) to lead to a mean square radius of gyration

$$\langle s^2 \rangle = Zb^2/6 \tag{3.11}$$

It must be emphasized that the approximations used in the above derivations restrict the validity of the distribution functions (3.6) and (3.7) to chain end separations much smaller than Zb, the length of the fully extended chain. This is apparent from the form of these functions, which give a finite probability for all values of h up to infinity, while values exceeding Zb can have no physical significance. Kuhn and Grün (1942) have tried to overcome this limitation and they have developed a theory for the probability distribution of the chain-end separations for chains which approach their maximum extension. However, such high expansion is now known to involve conformational transitions accompanied by changes of energy which cannot be neglected, so that the application of the Kuhn–Grün theory to the behavior of real polymer chains is questionable.

A very important concept in the theoretical development of the behavior of chain molecules is the distribution of chain segment densities in the space occupied by the molecular coil. We may regard the quantity $(b\sqrt{2\pi Z/3})^{-3} \exp(-3h^2/2Zb^2)$ in eq. (3.6) as a time average concentration of the second chain end at a location with the coordinates x, y, z, if the first chain end is fixed at the origin of the coordinate system. The dependence of this concentration on h is of the form $(\sqrt{\pi\sigma})^{-3/2} \exp(-h^2/\sigma^2)$ characteristic of a Gaussian error function with a variance σ^2 and a similar functional dependence is obtained if we consider the probability of finding the jth segment in a volume element at a distance r from the center of gravity of the chain. The probability of finding this segment within a spherical shell with a radius r is given, according to Isihara (1950b), by

$$\mathcal{W}(j,r)dr = (\pi\sigma_j)^{-3/2} \exp[-r^2/\sigma_j^2]4\pi r^2 dr$$

$$\sigma_j^2 = \frac{2\langle h^2\rangle}{9}\frac{j^3 + (Z-j)^3}{Z^3} \tag{3.12a}$$

The total number of chain segments to be found within the spherical shell is then obtained by integrating $\mathcal{W}(j,r)$ over all j values,

$$\mathcal{W}(r)dr = \int_{j=0}^{j=Z} \mathcal{W}(j,r)djdr \tag{3.12b}$$

This integration was carried out by Debye and Bueche (1952) and their results are compared in Fig. III.17 with the $\mathcal{W}(r)$ corresponding to a

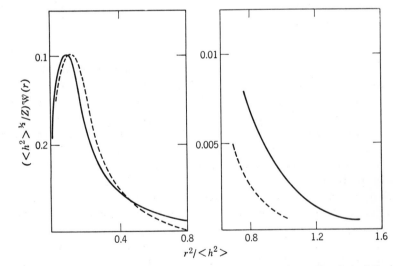

Fig. III.17. Segment distribution in a random flight chain. The dashed line corresponds to a Gaussian distribution of segment densities, the solid line represents the distribution calculated by Debye and Bueche (1952) without consideration of the excluded volume effect.

Gaussian distribution of chain segment densities. The discrepancy is most pronounced at large distances from the center of the coil, where the chain segment density decays much less sharply than would be the case in a Gaussian distribution.* In spite of this difference, mathematical convenience has led many theoreticians to assume a Gaussian distribution of chain segment densities when analyzing the behavior of dissolved chain molecules.

Although the chain segment distribution is spherically symmetrical around the center of gravity of the chain, when averaged over a period of time, no such symmetry would be expected for the instantaneous segment distribution in chains whose end-to-end displacement is oriented in a given direction. Qualitatively, we should expect such chains to occupy an ellipsoidal volume, with the dimension larger in the direction of the chain end displacement than in a direction perpendicular to it. The deviation from spherical symmetry is characterized most conveniently by comparing the mean square radius of gyration around axes running through the center of gravity of the coil parallel to the chain end displacement or at right angles to that direction. According to Kurata et al. (1960) these quantities are given, for moderate deviations of the chain end displacement from its rms value, by

$$\langle s_\parallel^2 \rangle = (Zb^2/36)[1 + (3h^2/Zb^2)]$$
$$\langle s_\perp^2 \rangle = Zb^2/36 \tag{3.13}$$

We see then that, even with h^2 at its average value $h^2 = Zb^2$, the extension of the chain is twice as long in the direction of the chain end displacement than in the direction at right angles to it. The asymmetry of the distribution of the chain segments increases sharply with increasing chain end separation.

3. Model Chains with Restricted Flexibility

To make the random flight model approach more realistically to conditions existing in a chain molecule, we must introduce in some manner the various restrictions to chain flexibility discussed in section (B1). The requirement of a constant bond angle θ was incorporated into the original theory as formulated by Kuhn (1934) and the treatment was further

---

* We shall see later (pp. 129–130) that the spatial interference of chain segments leads to further distortions of the Gaussian distribution.

expanded by Oka (1942) and by Taylor (1947) so as to take account of the unequal probability of the various internal angles of rotation θ. Provided the chain is sufficiently long and is reasonably flexible [i.e., $Z(1 + \cos \theta)$ $\gg 1$; $\langle \cos \phi \rangle$ not too close to unity] and that the probability distribution of internal angles of rotation remains unchanged when the sign of ϕ is reversed, the mean square chain end separation becomes

$$\langle h^2 \rangle = Zb^2 \frac{1 - \cos \theta}{1 + \cos \theta} \cdot \frac{1 + \langle \cos \phi \rangle}{1 - \langle \cos \phi \rangle} \tag{3.14}$$

Comparison with (3.9) will show that the restrictions on chain flexibility have not altered the characteristic proportionality of the chain end displacement on the square root of the number of chain links, they merely modify the effective length of the chain link. For a tetrahedral bond angle, $\cos \theta = -1/3$, so that the bond angle restriction has the effect of doubling $\langle h^2 \rangle$. If a chain with tetrahedral bond angles has a fraction f_t of its bonds in the *trans* conformation, while the remainder is divided equally between g and g', then (3.14) may be expressed by

$$\langle h^2 \rangle = 2Zb^2(1 + 3f_t)/3(1 - f_t) \tag{3.15}$$

as obtained also by Tobolsky (1959) in an analysis of the dimensions of chains placed on a diamond lattice.

The result given in (3.14) was derived on the basis of the assumption that the internal angles of rotation are independent of each other. However, the discussion in Sec. B-1 made it clear that the ϕ values of successive bonds in a polymer backbone are, in fact, governed by complex correlations and these have a pronounced influence on the effective chain flexibility. If we exclude, for instance, the sterically unfavorable gg' sequence in a polyethylene chain, the chain expansion will tend to increase. Hijmans and Holleman (1962) have shown how to treat this case by a modification of Tobolsky's (1959) procedure, referred to above. When we deal with conformational correlations in vinyl chains ($-CH_2-CHR-)_n$ or vinylidene chains ($-CH_2CR_1R_2-)_n$ the problem becomes much more complex, but it can be simplified if we assume that the governing effects are due to mutual steric interference of the bulky chain substituents, while the steric repulsions of the methylene groups of the chain backbone are negligible by comparison. With the symbols introduced in the previous section for the internal angles of rotation, this model leads (Ptitsyn and Sharonov, 1957; Volkenstein, 1963) to a mean-square chain end separation

$$\langle h^2 \rangle = Zb^2 \, \frac{1 - \cos \theta}{1 + \cos \theta} \cdot \frac{1 + \langle \cos \phi \rangle}{1 - \langle \cos \phi \rangle} (1 + \Delta)$$

$$\Delta = \frac{\cos \theta [\langle \cos \phi \rangle^2 - \langle \cos \phi_{2j} \cos \phi_{2j+1} \rangle] + \langle \sin \phi_{2j} \sin \phi_{2j+1} \rangle}{1 - \langle \cos \phi \rangle^2} \qquad (3.16)$$

It may be noted that in the absence of correlations between ϕ_{2j} and ϕ_{2j+1} the quantity Δ vanishes since $\langle \cos^2 \phi \rangle = \langle \cos \phi_{2j} \cos \phi_{2j+1} \rangle$ and $\langle \sin \phi_{2j} \sin \phi_{2j+1} \rangle = 0$, so that (3.16) reduces to (3.14). In the case of polyisobutene, where crystallographic data suggest that $\phi_{2j} = \phi_{2j+1} = \pm 82°$, the model represented by (3.16) leads to a value of $\langle h^2 \rangle$ which is by 45% larger than that predicted without regard for conformational correlations and appears to be in good agreement with estimates based on light scattering and solution viscosity data.

A similar analysis of the extension of isotactic and syndiotactic vinyl polymer chains is somewhat more complex (Birshtein, 1959; Birshtein and Ptitsyn, 1959, 1960; Lifson, 1959; Nagai, 1959b, 1962; Hoeve, 1960; Birshtein et al., 1961). For the syndiotactic chain represented by the conformational sequence II (see p. 110) the chain end displacement depends critically on the frequency of kinks introduced into the all-*trans* form, i.e., the fractional probability q_g that a tt unit will be followed by a monomer with the gg conformation. According to Birshtein and Ptitsyn (1960) and Allegra et al. (1963)

$$\langle h^2 \rangle = 16Zb^2/(1 - q_g)^2 \qquad (3.17)$$

where $q_g = (3 - \sqrt{5})/2$ for the special case when there is no energetic preference between a (tt)(tt) and a (tt)(gg) sequence. In the case of an isotactic chain represented by the conformational sequence IV, (see p. 110). Allegra et al. (1963) obtain for a chain containing a ratio q_i of helical sections to monomer units

$$\langle h^2 \rangle = Zb^2[(16/3q_i) - (8/3)] \qquad (3.18)$$

Here q_i is obviously highly sensitive to the energy required to produce a kink in the helical conformation.

The proportionality of $\langle h^2 \rangle$ and Z is thus preserved even on introduction of conformational correlations. Kuhn (1934) has pointed out in his classical paper that such a relationship must hold quite generally for sufficiently long chains, even if the restrictions to chain flexibility cannot be analyzed in detail. He suggested, therefore, that the real chain with fixed bond angles and various restrictions to rotation around the bonds connecting the atoms of the chain backbone be replaced by an "equivalent chain" of the same contour length L consisting of a smaller number Z_s of "statistical chain elements" with length b_s which are, however, freely jointed without bond angle restrictions.   The value of b_s is chosen so that the equivalent chain, has a mean square displacement equal to that observed in the real chain.   We then have

$$b_s Z_s = L$$

$$b_s^2 Z_s = \langle h^2 \rangle \qquad\qquad (3.19)$$

$$\therefore b_s = \langle h^2 \rangle / L$$

The contour length L of the chain is usually assumed, for chains whose backbones contain carbon atoms only, to correspond to the planar zig-zag of the all-*trans* conformation, with a distance of 2.53 Å between alternate carbon atoms.   We know, however, that the most extended conformation, which is attainable in chains carrying bulky substituents, is frequently considerably shorter, and, since L cannot be measured experimentally, the precise value which one should use for the length of the statistical chain element is subject to some ambiguity.   The probability distribution of chain end displacements of the equivalent chain is, of course, that given in (3.7) with Z replaced by Z_s and b replaced by b_s.   It is generally assumed that this distribution function is also a reasonable representation for real chains of sufficient length in the range of h^2 values which do not deviate too far from $\langle h^2 \rangle$.

Occasionally it is necessary to deal with chains which are so stiff that the contour length of the chain is no longer very large compared to the length of Kuhn's statistical chain element.   In such cases the equivalent random chain with its long rigid links and abrupt kinks leads to faulty conclusions and it may be preferable to use in its place the model of a "worm-like chain" in which the flexibility—characterized by the minimum attainable radius of curvature—has a uniform value at all points.   This model represents the limiting behavior of chains with linear links and a constant angle between adjoining links deviating only slightly from 180° so that the direction of successive links shows a slowly decreasing correlation with the direction of the first link of the chain.   Kratky and Porod (1949) analyzed the mathematical consequences of this model, characterizing this correlation by the average value of the cosine of the angle β subtended by the directions of the first and the last chain segments (or the angle between the direction of the tangents to the two ends in the continuously curving model).

It may be shown that $\langle \cos \beta \rangle$ is an exponentially decreasing function of the chain length

$$\langle \cos \beta \rangle = \exp(-L/a) \qquad (3.20)$$

where a is a characteristic "persistence length" proportional to the minimum attainable radius of curvature of the chain. Kratky and Porod showed that the mean square chain end separation is given by

$$\langle h^2 \rangle = 2a\{L - a[1 - \exp(-L/a)]\} \qquad (3.21)$$

which reduces for very long chains ($L \gg a$) to $\langle h^2 \rangle = 2aL$. This result may be compared with $\langle h^2 \rangle = b_s L$ in eq. (3.19), so that the persistence length is then equal to half the length of the statistical chain element. The representation in terms of the "worm-like chain" is particularly advantageous in the case of cellulose derivatives (Hunt et al., 1956) which, as has been noted in Sec. B-1, consist of unusually stiff chain molecules.

4. Random Flight Models of Branched Chain Molecules

The statistical treatment of the extension of branched chain molecules has been considered in some detail by Zimm and Stockmayer (1949). It is instructive, if we consider first their result for the case of a "star-shaped" molecule which has f^* branches radiating from one point. Macromolecules of this type have been prepared by Schaefgen and Flory (1948) by adding monomer units to a f^*-functional initiator species. Zimm and Stockmayer derived for the mean-square radius of gyration of such structures consisting of freely jointed segments

$$\langle s^2 \rangle = Zb^2 \sum_{i=1}^{i=f^*} \left[\frac{Z_i^2}{2Z^2} - \frac{Z_i^3}{3Z^3} \right] \qquad (3.22)$$

where Z_i is the number of links in the ith chain. For the special case where all the branches are of equal length $Z_b b$, this becomes

$$\langle s^2 \rangle = Z_b b^2 (1/2 - 1/3f^*) \qquad (3.23)$$

Thus, for a constant length of the branches and increasing functionality of the branch point, $\langle s^2 \rangle$ will approach a limiting value. This is physically understandable since the location of the branch point will approach, with increasing functionality, more and more closely to the center of gravity of the structure. If we consider two of the branches as constituting the "chain backbone" then we find that a transformation of this linear structure into a star-shaped one with equal length of branches may increase $\langle s^2 \rangle$ by a factor of as much $3/2$ as f^* becomes large. On the other hand, we may characterize the effect of branching on the radius of gyration by comparing two structures with the same total number of links. If $\langle s^2 \rangle$ refers to the branched chain and $\langle s_u^2 \rangle$ to the unbranched reference chain, then $\langle s^2 \rangle$ must necessarily be smaller than $\langle s_u^2 \rangle$. For the case of a star-shaped molecule with branches of equal lengths $\langle s^2 \rangle / \langle s_u^2 \rangle = (3/f^*) - [2/(f^*)^2]$. We may note that this ratio will increase towards unity as the relative lengths of the branches become more unequal.

Treatment of the general case of branched structures with n^* branchpoints with a functionality f^* is much more complex and any calculation must be based on a specific model which defines the nature of the distribution of branch points and branch lengths. Zimm and Stockmayer used the model of a random distribution of branch points, such as would be obtained in a polycondensation reaction in a mixture of bifunctional and f^*-functional reagents. Defining the parameter $g_{f*}^*(n^*)$ by

$$g_{f*}^*(n^*) = \langle s^2 \rangle / \langle s_u^2 \rangle \tag{3.24}$$

they obtained a result which is approximated for $n^* > 5$ by

$$\begin{aligned} g_3^*(n^*) &\approx (^3/_2)(\pi/n^*)^{1/2} - (5/2n^*) \\ g_4^*(n^*) &\approx (^1/_2)(3\pi/n^*)^{1/2} - (2/3n^*) \end{aligned} \tag{3.25}$$

It should be stressed that the model on which this result is based is not applicable to graft polymers. Any application of statistical analyses of the shapes of branched macromolecules to specific cases must be based on a detailed knowledge of the factors which determine the kinetics of the chain branching process.

5. Effect of Long Range Interactions on the Shape of Flexible Chains

In the statistical treatments discussed so far, the model chains were represented by mathematical lines of zero volume. The spatial requirements of chain substituents were taken into account only insofar as they determine chain flexibility, but no restriction was placed on the return of the chain to a point arbitrarily close to one occupied by a previous chain segment. When we take the spatial interference of chain segments into account, the probability distribution of chain end displacements (or of radii of gyration), arrived at previously, will have to be modified leading generally to an expansion of the molecular coil, since the fraction of conformations which has to be excluded will decrease with an increasing separation of the chain ends. This principle has been referred to customarily as the "excluded volume effect" and has been the subject of intensive theoretical and experimental investigations.

A very revealing procedure for the study of this problem involves the generation of chains on some suitable lattice, rejecting all those in which a lattice point is occupied more than once.   The probability distribution of the end-to-end distances is then analyzed and compared with the distribution which would have been obtained if the self-intersecting chains had not been eliminated.   The method is illustrated in Fig. III.18 on chains

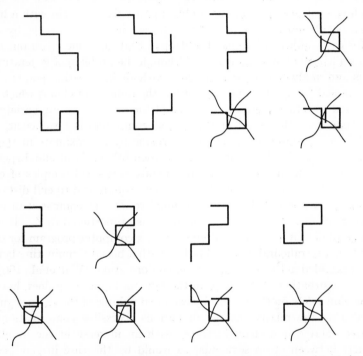

Fig. III.18. Two-dimensional analogy to the excluded volume effect with chains on a square lattice.

of six segments placed on a plane square lattice with the position of the first two segments fixed and the requirement of a right angle between two successive segments.   We see that of the 16 possible chains only 8 are not self-intersecting—if one more segment were added, the fraction of non-intersecting chains would decrease to $^{13}/_{32}$.   If the length of one step is taken as unity, the average end-to-end distance of all the six-segment chains is

2.05—this increases to 3.1 after elimination of the intersecting chains.   The main problem encountered in a study of this type is the rapid decrease in the fraction of nonintersecting chains with increasing Z, the number of chain segments, so that it is difficult to retain a reasonable statistical sample by the time the model chains have grown to a size analogous to the length of the molecular chains of high polymers.   Although the attrition of chains is somewhat less severe in three dimensions than on a plane lattice, Wall et al. (1954) found that the longest nonintersecting chain generated on a cubic lattice in 140,000 trials had only 121 segments.   On a tetrahedral lattice (which is most pertinent to the problem of a polymer chain with a hydro-carbon backbone) the fraction of nonintersecting chains decays by about 4% for each additional segment added, so that only one chain out of 10^7 attains a length of 400 segments.   Although the problem of generating the chains and analyzing the size of those without intersection points can be programmed for an electronic computer, the number of chains which must be started to retain a sufficient sample of the nonintersecting variety is so large that even the speed of the fastest computers is insufficient.   The problem may, however, be largely overcome by approximate methods in which "successful" chains are added to each other; Wall and Erpenbeck (1959) were able in this manner to generate statistical samples of chains up to $Z = 800$.   They found that the mean-square end-to-end distance of the nonintersecting chains is proportional to $Z^{1.18}$ as compared to unper-turbed random walk chains, for which $\langle h^2 \rangle$ is proportional to Z.   It is also possible to design, as an added refinement, a computer program for chains placed on a tetrahedral diamond lattice with a bias discriminating between segments added in the *trans* and *gauche* conformations (Wall et al., 1962).

    The perturbation of the shape of the random flight chain does, however, not depend solely on the physically excluded volume of the chain segments, but also on the relative energy of various accessible conformations.   If the free energy of a chain increases with an increase in the number of contacts between chain segments, as would be the case in good solvent media which favor polymer–solvent over polymer–polymer contacts, the bias against contracted forms of the chain will be increased, leading to an even larger expansion than that predicted in an indifferent solvent medium. On the other hand, we may envisage a thermodynamically poor solvent medium in which chain segments attract one another just enough so that the contraction produced by the preference for contacts between chain seg-ments exactly compensates for the chain expansion which would have been obtained because of the physically occupied volume of the chain.   In that case the excluded volume effect will vanish and the chain should behave, as pointed out by Flory (1949, 1953b), according to the predictions of the random flight theory. However, the elimination of effects of binary interactions between segments of a single chain implies inevitably that binary interactions between solute molecules can make no contribution to the deviation from solution ideality, so that $1/2 - \chi$ in eq. (2.46) must become zero. Solvent media for which this condition is satisfied are called, following Flory, Θ-solvents. They may be found by adjusting the temperature to the consolute point of chains of infinite molecular weight by the extrapolation indicated in eq. (2.56c), or else by an extrapolation of osmotic or light scattering data (see Chaps. IV and V) to a solvent composition or temperature corresponding to the disappearance of the second virial coefficient. A difficulty arises with crystalline polymers soluble only in strongly exothermic solvents which are very far removed from the Θ-condition. A number of approximate equations, reviewed by Kurata and Stockmayer (1963), have been suggested to estimate, from the second virial coefficient, the factor by which such polymers are expanded over their unperturbed dimension. Elias (1961a,b) described the determination of the composition of a solvent-nonsolvent mixture corresponding to a Θ-solvent by a still different procedure. He determined the nonsolvent concentration at incipient precipitation for solutions containing varying polymer concentrations and extrapolated the data on a double logarithmic scale to a 100% concentration of polymer. The theoretical basis for this procedure is doubtful, although it seemed to lead to satisfactory results in a variety of systems.

Since Flory's original definition of the concept, Θ-solvents and unperturbed chain dimensions have been determined for a large number of polymers and the data have recently been tabulated by Peterlin (1961a) and by Kurata and Stockmayer (1963). It is a remarkable fact that the factor by which the unperturbed linear dimensions of forty polymers of vinyl or vinylidene derivatives (listed by Kurata and Stockmayer) are expanded above the value corresponding to free rotation around the tetrahedral bonds of the chain backbone lies in the narrow range from 1.61 for polypropylene to 2.72 for polyacrylamide.

It was pointed out (page 103) that the characteristic flexibility of a chain molecule should, in general, be temperature dependent. The more expanded conformations usually have lower energy, as in polyethylene where *trans* bonds are energetically favored over *gauche* bonds, or in isotactic vinyl polymers, where energy must be expended to produce a kink in the helical conformation. As a consequence, the unperturbed mean square dimensions $\langle h_0^2 \rangle$ and $\langle s_0^2 \rangle$ (obtained, as we shall see later, from light scattering or solution viscosity data) tend to decrease for most polymers with rising temperature. Such an effect has been demonstrated on polyethylene (Flory et al., 1961), polystyrene (Schulz and Baumann, 1963), and polyisobutene (Fox and Flory, 1951). Unfortunately, the experimental determination of the temperature dependence of unperturbed dimensions of dissolved chain molecules suffers from some ambiguity. Since the measurements require the use of a series of solvents with different Θ temperatures, the interpretation of the data involves the explicit assumption that no specific solvent effects are superimposed on the effect of temperature in determining the intrinsic flexibility of the chain. A recent compilation of literature data (Bianchi, 1964) suggests that this assumption has led in the past to many contradictory conclusions; for instance, different workers determined the temperature coefficient of $\langle h_0^2 \rangle$ for poly-(methyl methacrylate) as either positive or negative. It has been suggested that the variation of solvation effects may be eliminated by studying solutions in a homologous series of liquids, e.g., 1-chlorodecane, 1-chloroundecane, and 1-chlorododecane for polystyrene (Orofino and Ciferri, 1964). In any case, the unperturbed dimensions of vinyl polymers change only slowly with changing temperature, the variation being typically of the order of $10^{-3}/^\circ$C. For some polymer chains, the *trans–gauche* conformational transition is clearly attended by a *decrease* of energy and such chains will then tend to expand when the temperature is raised. This is the case, for instance, with polydimethylsiloxane (Mark and Flory, 1964). For cellulose derivatives, the energetic preference for the extended form is particularly pronounced, so that an increase in temperature leads to an unusually rapid contraction of the unperturbed chain dimensions (Flory et al., 1958; Brown et al., 1963).

Since the characteristic dimensions of a polymer in a Θ-solvent are taken as a point of reference in interpreting the expansion of the polymer coil in better solvent media, it is important to ascertain whether these "unperturbed" dimensions are in fact the same in all Θ-solvents at a given temperature. The stiffness of a molecular chain depends, as we have seen, on the relative frequency with which the various accessible rotational isomers occur and it was already pointed out in (page 104) that interactions of low molecular weight species with the solvent medium may affect the rotational isomer distribution. (Such a phenomenon will be described again, pp. 226–227, since optical activity is particularly sensitive to conformational isomerism.) Analogous effects would be expected with polymeric chains (Lifson and Oppenheim, 1960) so that, in principle, the chain flexibility and the "unperturbed dimensions" of polymer chains might depend, even at constant temperature, on the nature of the solvent medium.

Some cases have been uncovered where the "unperturbed" chain dimensions at a given temperature are clearly subject to significant variation. Ivin and Ende (1961) and Ivin et al. (1962) studied the properties of solutions of hexene-1-polysulfone in different Θ-solvents and found a very significant difference of over 20% in the characteristic linear dimensions. They point out that two different types of Θ-solvents should generally exist for polar polymers, since a mutual attraction of chain segments will be favored both when the solvent has too low and too high polarity. It would then not be too surprising to find that the preferred conformations of the chain backbone would be different in the two types of media.

Similar effects were found by Crescenzi and Flory (1964) with polydimethylsiloxane, which was considerably less expanded in a Θ-solvent more polar than the polymer than in a highly nonpolar Θ medium. An analogous situation apparently also exists in solutions of cellulose derivatives, where the chain flexibility is distinctly lower with o-cresol than with chloroform as the solvent medium (Flory et al., 1958).

It is more difficult to account for another effect which has been described by Elias and Etter (1963). These workers studied the behavior of polystyrene in Θ-media consisting of solvent–nonsolvent mixtures at a constant temperature of 25°C. They found very large variations in chain extension, e.g., a rms radius of gyration over 30% larger in the benzene–methanol than in the benzene–cyclohexanol system. A careful study of the behavior of polystyrene in a single solvent at the Θ temperature (Orofino and Mickey, 1963) revealed a much smaller but still significant variation in the unperturbed chain dimensions with the nature of the solvent medium. In view of these findings the flexibility of even nonpolar polymers may be more susceptible to variation in different solvent media than was once believed (see also Bianchi, 1964).

In spite of such effects, which a variation in the solvent medium may have on the intrinsic chain flexibility, the major cause of the increasing dimensions of a polymer coil with increasing solvent power of the medium can generally be assigned to long-range interactions of the chain segments.* If the effective excluded volume of these chain segments is positive, the chain will tend to expand so as to reduce the free energy of mixing G_M of the chain with solvent molecules. On the other hand, the number of conforma-

---

* The behavior of cellulose derivatives seems to be an exception to this generalization (Flory et al., 1958).

tions consistent with a given chain end displacement decreases as h is expanded beyond h^* and the chain therefore resists such expansion. An analogous entropic retractive force is encountered in the elasticity of a rubber network and it is customary to express it in terms of an "elastic free energy" G_{elastic}. The equilibrium expansion of a chain with interacting segments will then correspond to that value of h at which the osmotic swelling force is exactly balanced by the retractive force of the elastic chain. Using as the characteristic parameter the factor $\alpha_e = h^*/h_0^*$, by which the most probable chain end displacement is expanded over the value in the unperturbed random flight chain, the equilibrium extension is characterized by

$$\partial G_M/\partial \alpha_e + \partial G_{\text{elastic}}/\partial \alpha_e = 0 \qquad (3.26)$$

In formulating a theory which would predict the dependence of α_e on chain length, Flory (1949, 1953b) used a model in which the continuous unperturbed chain was substituted by a cloud of unconnected segments whose concentration was spherically symmetrical and was a Gaussian function of the distance from the center of gravity. The value of G_M was estimated from the results of the Flory–Huggins theory [eq. (2.45) and (2.46)], assuming that only the contributions of binary segment interactions to the excess chemical potential of the solvent need be considered. It was, moreover, assumed that the excluded volume effect would expand all chain dimensions by the same factor, so that the Gaussian character of the segment distribution would be maintained. On this basis the elastic retractive force becomes

$$\partial G_{\text{elastic}}/\partial \alpha_e = 3kT(\alpha_e - \alpha_e^{-1}) \qquad (3.27)$$

To simplify the derivation, we shall substitute for the Gaussian chain segment distribution a model in which the chain segments are uniformly distributed within an "equivalent sphere" with a molar volume V_e. The local polymer segment concentration is characterized by the volume fraction $\phi_{2l} = V_2/V_e$ and the number of solvent molecules within an equivalent sphere is $(V_e/V_1)(1 - \phi_{2l}) \approx V_e/V_1$, since the fraction of the volume occupied by the polymer in the region of the swollen molecular coil is rather low. We have then from eq. (2.46)

$$\begin{aligned} G_M &= kT(\tfrac{1}{2} - \chi)\phi_{2l}^2(V_e/V_1) \\ &= kT(\tfrac{1}{2} - \chi)V_2^2/V_1V_e \end{aligned} \qquad (3.28)$$

Since $V_e = V_{e0}\alpha_e^3$ where V_{e0} is the molar volume of the equivalent sphere corresponding to the unperturbed molecular coil,

$$\partial G_M/\partial \alpha_e = -3kT(^1/_2 - \chi)(V_2^2/V_1 V_{e0})/\alpha_e^4 \tag{3.29}$$

Substituting (3.27) and (3.29) into (3.26)

$$3kT(\alpha_e - \alpha_e^{-1}) - 3kT(^1/_2 - \chi)(V_e^2/V_1 V_{e0})/\alpha_e^4 = 0$$
$$\alpha_e^5 - \alpha_e^3 = (^1/_2 - \chi)(V_2^2/V_1 V_{e0}) \tag{3.30}$$

The molar volume of the chain molecule may be represented as $V_2 = V_{s0} Z_{s0}$ where V_{s0} is the molar volume of the statistical segment and Z_{s0} their number in the unperturbed chain. If the equivalent sphere is chosen so as to have the same radius of gyration as the rms radius of gyration of the real chain, then $V_{e0} = N(^4/_3)\pi(^5/_{18})^{3/2}b_{s0}^3 Z_{s0}^{3/2}$, where b_{s0} is the length of the statistical chain element in the unperturbed chain and N is Avogadro's number. Relation (3.30) may then be rewritten as

$$\alpha_e^5 - \alpha_e^3 = 1.63(V_{s0}^2/Nb_{s0}^3 V_1)(^1/_2 - \chi)Z_{s0}^{1/2} \tag{3.31}$$

It may be noted that the result is not very sensitive to the details of the distribution of the segment densities as long as they remain proportional to $1/\alpha_e^3$. With Flory's assumption of a Gaussian distribution, only the numerical coefficient of (3.31) is slightly altered to 1.72. The most important feature of the result is the prediction that the expansion factor α_e increases indefinitely with increasing chain length. For very long chains, where $\alpha_e^5 \gg \alpha_e^3$, we should then expect α_e to be proportional to $Z_{s0}^{0.1}$ so that h would increase as the 0.6 power of the chain length. It is also worth noting that the right side of (3.23) has V_1 in the denominator—thus the excluded volume effect should decrease in importance with an increase in the volume of the solvent molecules. In particular, when a polymer chain is imbedded in a medium of other very large molecules, its expansion should correspond to the unperturbed dimensions observed at high dilution in a θ-solvent medium. This interesting conclusion has been experimentally substantiated (Ciferri et al. (1961)).

The assumption that the swelling of the polymer chain beyond its unperturbed extension can be represented by an increase of all distances by the same factor α_e is equivalent to the replacement of the original random flight chain with Z_{s0} elements of length b_{s0} by a new random flight chain whose elements are expanded to $b_{s0}\alpha_e^2$ and reduced in number to Z_{s0}/α_e^2. This representation has been subjected to a critical analysis by Krigbaum (1955) and by Ptitsyn (1959). They point out that the excluded volume effect must lead to the most pronounced changes in the central region of the molecular coil where the segment density is highest. As a result, the distribution function of chain end displacements tends to become much sharper than in the unperturbed random flight chain. One consequence of this sharpening is a decrease in the ratio $\langle h^2 \rangle / \langle s^2 \rangle$ below the value of 6 [eq. (3.9) and (3.11)] predicted for random flight chains. The modified treatment leads Krigbaum (1955) to conclude that the ratio $(\alpha_e^5 - \alpha_e^3)/M_2^{1/2}$ should not be molecular weight independent, as implied by (3.31), but should pass through a shallow maximum as the chain length is being increased.

Another criticism advanced against Flory's theory of the expansion of molecular coils concerns the assumption of spherical symmetry of chain segment distribution. We have seen [eq. (3.13)] that the coil is, in fact, rather elongated and that an increasing separation of the chain ends increase the coil dimensions in the direction parallel to the chain end displacement, but not the dimensions in a direction perpendicular to it. Kurata et al. (1960) suggested, therefore, a model in which the chain segments are distributed uniformly within an equivalent ellipsoid of revolution, chosen so as to give the same values for the principal radii of gyration as correspond to a Gaussian chain according to eq. (3.13). The volume of such an ellipsoid is proportional to $(1 + 3\alpha_e^2)^{1/2}$ and a treatment analogous to that outlined above for the equivalent sphere model leads to a chain expansion due to the excluded volume effect given, in terms of our notation, by

$$\alpha_e^3 - \alpha_e = 5.4(V_{s0}^2/Nb_{s0}^3 V_1)(1/2 - \chi)Z_{s0}^{1/2}/[1 + (1/3\alpha_e^2)]^{3/2} \qquad (3.32)$$

In comparing (3.32) with (3.31), the most important difference concerns the asymptotic behavior of α_e. While the equivalent sphere model predicts α_e to become proportional to the 0.1 power of the chain length for very long chains, the ellipsoidal model leads asymptotically to α_e proportional to $Z_{s0}^{1/6}$. Okada et al. (1963) report viscosimetric data which suggest that the model of Kurata et al. may, in fact, be more realistic than models assuming spherically symmetrical coils.

The above treatments have in common the assumption that it is legitimate to treat the excluded volume problem with the use of models in which the chain character of the macromolecule is taken into account only in the estimate of the elastic retractive force, while the excess free energy of mixing is approximated by a value to be expected for a cloud of disconnected segments. It is difficult to judge the validity of this assumption and it is, therefore, important that Zimm et al. (1953) and Fixman (1955) were able to treat the excluded volume problem with the use of a "pearl necklace model" in which the chain is represented by spherical beads connected by freely jointed links. They arrived at

$$\alpha_e^2 - 1 = (4/3)\mathbf{z} - [(16/3) - (28\pi/27)]\mathbf{z}^2 + \ldots$$

$$\mathbf{z} = (6\pi)^{3/2}(V_{s0}^2/NV_1b_{s0}^3)(1/2 - \chi)Z_{s0}^{1/2}$$

(3.33)

so that the chain expansion factor depends on the same combination of physical quantities as in the theories based on "smeared out" segment densities. Unfortunately, $(\alpha_e^2 - 1)$ is given by a very slowly converging power series of $\mathbf{z}$, in which only the coefficients of the first two terms are known. As a consequence, the results of this treatment may be considered to apply, in the case of high molecular weight polymers, only in the immediate vicinity of the Θ-point. We may illustrate this by a typical example of a system where the molar volume of the solvent is 80 cc and the polymer contains 1000 statistical chain elements with a length of 7×10^{-8} cm, and a molar volume of 200 cc. In this case $(V_{s0}^2/NV_1b_{s0}^3)Z_{s0}^{1/2} = 74$ so that even with $(1/2 - \chi)$ as low as 0.001 the characteristic parameter $\mathbf{z}$ would have a value of 6, much too large to justify the assumption that terms beyond the first two in the series expansion (3.33) can be neglected. We may then conclude that although the pearl necklace model is more realistic than other models employed in the treatment of the excluded volume effect, the results obtained on its basis are of such restricted applicability that its practical usefulness is severely limited.

In all of the preceding discussion, the expansion of the molecular coils has been treated for an isolated chain molecule without taking account of the consequences of polymer–polymer interactions. The result of theories based on such models should, strictly speaking, be valid only in the limit of infinite dilution of the chain molecules. At finite concentration, the equilibrium coil expansion corresponds to the minimum of free energy which depends on the number of contacts between polymer segments no matter whether these segments belong to the same or to different chains. The expansion of the molecular coil, which reduces the intramolecular interaction of chain segments, increases the probability of interaction of different chain molecules with one another. We should, therefore, expect the driving force toward chain expansion to decrease with an increasing concentration of the chain molecules, so that the molecular coils would tend to shrink as increasing numbers of them are being placed in a given volume. This effect has first been described by Weissberg et al. (1951) and statistical mechanical theories of it have been formulated by Fixman (1960) and by

Grimley (1961). Fixman has pointed out that the concentration dependence of the expansion factor α_e is unfortunately not accessible to unambiguous experimental evaluation.

C. SPECIFIC CONFORMATIONS

1. Helical Conformations of Synthetic Polypeptides

In our discussion of the flexibility of dissolved chain molecules (Sec. B-1) we started with the assumption that the extended or helical conformation assumed by a polymer in the crystalline state represents the lowest energy form of the isolated macromolecule. If rotational isomerism of the chain backbone involves relatively small changes of energy, the entropy gain associated with an increasing number of accessible conformations will lead to the occupancy of a very large number of conformations and the dissolved macromolecules will then be characterized by a high degree of flexibility. On the other hand, as the energy requirement for rotational isomerism of the chain is increased, the molecule will approximate more and more closely to the conformation of lowest energy. Eventually, when the energy needed to produce a kink in the conformation characteristic of the crystalline polymer is very high compared to kT, the probability of finding such a kink in a chain of a given length may become negligible, so that the macromolecules should behave like rigid rods.

This type of behavior has been observed with some synthetic polypeptides. The experimental evidence is of many different kinds, including the estimation of molecular dimensions from light scattering data, frictional properties of the dissolved macromolecules, characteristic spectral shifts, changes in optical activity, and changes in reactivity. The discussion of the applicability of these techniques to the study of the transition from a random coil to a rod-like helical conformation will be left for later chapters. Here we shall concern ourselves only with a consideration of the factors which determine the nature of helical conformations and their stability in solution.

The nature of the helical conformation which would correspond to the state of minimum energy of an isolated polypeptide chain of the type $(\text{—C—CH—N—})_n$ was postulated by Pauling et al. (1951) on the basis of the molecular geometry of amino acids, dipeptides and other low molecular weight analogs which had been subjected to a detailed crystallographic study. These studies led to the conclusion that the characteristic grouping

$$\begin{array}{c} O \\ \| \\ C \qquad C \\ {}_C \diagup \quad \diagdown_N \diagup \\ | \\ H \end{array}$$

had to be planar because of the partial double bond character of the C–N linkage and that the peptide group assumed invariably the *trans* form, with the C=O and N—H bonds extending in opposite directions from the C—N bond.   Thus, only two internal angles of rotation per amino acid residue have to be specified to fix the conformation of the chain backbone.   Pauling et al. chose these angles so that all the C=O and N–H groups would form intramolecular hydrogen bonds with a distance of 2.72 Å between the O and N atoms and so that the N–H $\cdots$ O bond angle would lie close to 180°. These restrictions allow a choice between only two helical conformations with about 3.7 and 5.1 residues per turn of the helix, respectively.   A slight distortion of the 3.7 helix, which is commonly referred to as the α-helix and is characterized by 18 amino acid residues in five turns, was found ·by Pauling and Corey (1951) to describe the conformation of the polymer chains in crystals of poly(γ-methyl-L-glutamate) and poly(γ-benzyl-L-glutamate) (Bamford et al., 1951; Ambrose and Elliott, 1951). It appears now that this helical conformation may be predicted for certain polypeptide chains as the conformation for which van der Waals interactions of nonbonded atoms are minimized, without any need to take into account the stabilizing influence of hydrogen bonds (de Santis et al., 1965). A schematic representation of the α-helix is shown in Fig. III.19.   With a variety of synthetic polypeptides available for study, it was found that their ability to assume a helical conformation depends to some extent on the nature of the side chains carried by the amino acid residues (Blout et al., 1960).   If the β-carbon carries two bulky substituents, steric hindrance apparently prevents formation of the helix.   This may be illustrated by the difference in the behavior of poly(L-valine), which cannot form the α-helix and poly(L-leucine), which does exist in the helical conformation

$$\begin{array}{c} CH_3 \quad CH_3 \\ \diagdown \diagup \\ CH \\ | \\ (-C-CH-N-)_n \\ \| \quad | \\ O \qquad H \end{array}$$

poly(L-valine)

$$\begin{array}{c} CH_3 \quad CH_3 \\ \diagdown \diagup \\ CH \\ | \\ CH_2 \\ | \\ (-C-CH-N-)_n \\ \| \quad | \\ O \qquad H \end{array}$$

poly(L-leucine)

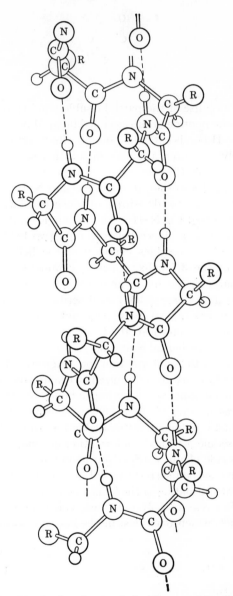

Fig. III.19. The Pauling-Corey α-helix (Corey and Pauling, 1955).

Blout et al. found also that polymers of amino acids which had an oxygen or sulfur atom attached to the β-carbon were unable to exist in the helical form. Such hetero atoms did not impede helix formation if they were further removed from the chain backbone. As an example, we may cite the difference between poly(S-methyl-L-cysteine) which cannot form a helix, while poly(L-methionine) crystallizes readily in the helical form

$$
\begin{array}{cc}
\text{SCH}_3 & \text{SCH}_3 \\
| & | \\
\text{CH}_2 & \text{CH}_2 \\
& | \\
& \text{CH}_2 \\
(-\text{C}-\text{CH}-\text{N}-)_n & (-\text{C}-\text{CH}-\text{N}-)_n \\
\| \quad | & \| \quad | \\
\text{O} \quad \text{H} & \text{O} \quad \text{H} \\
\text{poly}(S\text{-methyl-L-cysteine}) & \text{poly(L-methionine)}
\end{array}
$$

This effect was interpreted by Blout et al. as signifying that oxygen or sulfur atoms placed close to the chain backbone compete with the carbonyl oxygens of the peptide groups as hydrogen bond acceptors.

The existence of rigid helical conformations of synthetic polypeptide molecules in dilute solution was first inferred by Doty et al. (1954) on the basis of viscosimetric data. They found that poly(γ-benzyl-L-glutamate) molecules behaved like rigid rod-like particles if dissolved in chloroform saturated with formamide, while results obtained in dichloroacetic acid solution had the usual pattern compatible with a flexible coil model for the polymer chain. The behavior of poly(γ-benzyl-L-glutamate) in chloroform–formamide (and in other "helix-forming solvents" such as dimethylformamide and m-cresol) was later subjected to detailed analysis based on solution viscosity and light scattering measurements (Doty et al., 1956). From these data the length of the rod-like molecules was calculated to lie close to the value of 1.50 Å per amino acid residue, predicted by Pauling and Corey (1951) for the α-helix. The assignment of the α-helix to the conformation of a variety of synthetic polypeptides in "helix-forming solvent media" has been accepted by most workers, although low-angle x-ray scattering studies have led Luzzati et al. (1961a) to the conclusion that the α-helix is stable only in concentrated solutions and changes on dilution to a more extended helical form with a length of 1.95 Å per amino acid residue.

The helical conformation of dissolved polypeptide molecules can be stable only if the solvent–solute interactions lie within rather narrow, well-defined limits. On the one hand, the solvent must interact sufficiently strongly with the side chains attached to the polypeptide backbone to prevent aggregation of the macromolecules. On the other hand, the solvation of the polypeptide must not be too strong, or else the intramolecular hydrogen bonds, stabilizing the helical conformation, will be disrupted. It is reasonable to assume that the mutual interactions of the side chains attached to the polypeptide backbone will contribute significantly to the stability of the helical form. Variations in helix stability, characteristic of individual polypeptides, may be studied conveniently by following the conformational transitions through a series of solvent media of increasing hydrogen bonding potential (e.g., $CHCl_3 < CHCl_2COOH < CF_3COOH$). In this way Fasman (1962) found that poly(L-leucine) formed the most stable helices, which remained intact in dichloroacetic acid solution and could be completely disrupted only in dichloroacetic–trifluoroacetic acid mixtures containing at least 60% TFA. Since our interest in the conformational transitions of synthetic polypeptides is motivated largely by the analogy in the behavior of these chain molecules and the polypeptide chains in proteins, the stability of helical conformations in an aqueous medium may be considered most significant. As would be expected, the mutual repulsion of ionized groups attached to a polypeptide will tend to disrupt the helical structures. This effect has been observed on poly(α-L-glutamic acid) which is helical in aqueous solution at low pH, but is transformed into random coils when partially neutralized with base (Doty et al., 1957). On the other hand, water-soluble polypeptides may have the stability of their helical form enhanced by the introduction of strongly hydrophobic comonomers such as leucine or methionine (Fasman et al., 1962; Kulkarni and Blout, 1962). In the case of poly(δ-hydroxy-α-L-aminovaleric acid)

$$(-\overset{\overset{\text{O}}{\|}}{C}-\overset{\overset{\text{H}}{|}}{CH}-\overset{|}{N}-)_n$$
$$\underset{\underset{\text{OH}}{|}}{\overset{|}{(CH_2)_3}}$$

the polypeptide is insoluble in water but soluble in aqueous lithium bromide solutions. The chain is randomly coiled if the LiBr concentration is high, but assumes a helical conformation when the salt concentration is reduced so as to arrive at a less solvating medium (Goodman and Felix, 1964).

In the original description of the α-helix by Pauling et al. (1951), the question whether a polypeptide chain composed of L-aminoacid residues would form right-handed or left-handed helices was left open. During the intervening years, the study of optical activity and its dependence on the wavelength of the light used was developed into a powerful method for the study of helical conformations.   This subject will be discussed at some length in Chap. V; here we should only note that it provides an experimental method by which the question of the sense in which the helix is wound may be resolved.   It is found that most of the polypeptides derived from L-aminoacids form right-handed α-helices.   On the other hand, there exist some exceptions to this generalization which provide an interesting insight into the extent to which the mutual interactions of side chains can be the determining factor in the choice between two backbone conformations which differ only slightly in their energy.   While poly(γ-benzyl-L-glutamate) forms right-handed helices, the sense of the helix is reversed in poly(β-benzyl-L-aspartate) in which the ester group is brought closer to the polymer backbone by the elimination of a methylene residue (Karlson et al., 1960; Bradbury et al., 1961).   If, however, poly(β-benzyl-L-aspartate) is substituted by a nitro group in the *para* position of the aromatic residue, the conformation reverts to the right-handed helix (Goodman et al., 1963b).   This case is of particular interest since it shows that even groupings quite remote from the chain backbone may decisively influence the backbone conformation.

poly(γ-benzyl-L-glutamate)   poly(β-benzyl-L-aspartate)   poly(β-*p*-nitrobenzyl-L-aspartate)

The dependence of the stability of the helical conformation on temperature reflects the relative importance of several factors to the heat associated with helix-coil transitions.   In the case of poly(β-benzyl-L-aspartate) in *m*-cresol solution, the stability of the helix is reduced by raising the temperature (Bradbury et al., 1961) indicating that solvation of the peptide groups in the randomly coiled polymer is less exothermic than the formation of the intramolecular hydrogen bonds in the helical conformation. A similar labilization of the helix at higher temperatures was observed with poly(α-L-glutamic acid) in a water–dioxane mixture (Doty et al., 1957), but for poly(γ-benzyl-L-glutamate) in ethylene dichloride–dichloroacetic acid the helix stability increased at elevated temperatures (Doty and Yang, 1956). Helix formation is in this case energetically unfavorable, but it is being brought about by an increase in entropy. This must be caused by the release of dichloroacetic acid accompanying the desolvation of the polypeptide. A more complicated pattern of behavior was observed by Fasman et al. (1962) with copolypeptides of glutamic acid and leucine in aqueous solution, where the helix first melts out and then reforms as the temperature is being raised. These phenomena obviously reflect a reversal in the relative magnitudes of heat effects due to hydrogen bonding and to the formation of "hydrophobic bonds" (cf. Chap. II, Sec. A-6 and B-5).

A particularly interesting case is that of poly(L-proline). This chain may be represented by

$$
\left(-\underset{\underset{O}{\|}}{C}-N-CH-\right)_n
$$

so that the polymer backbone lacks the peptide hydrogens and cannot form intramolecular hydrogen bonds. Nevertheless, poly(L-proline) may exist in rigid helical conformations. In fact, two such conformations with helices wound in the two opposite directions can be stabilized in appropriate solvent media. Downie and Randall (1959) and Katchalski and his collaborators (Steinberg et al., 1960) came to the conclusion that poly(L-proline)I, the form stable in propanol containing 10% acetic acid, contains right-handed helices with the two α-carbons attached to a peptide bond in the *cis*-conformation. In poly(L-proline)II, which is the stable form in most solvent media (water, acetic acid, etc.), the two neighboring α-carbons are believed to lie *trans* to one another and the chains are wound in left-handed helices, which are almost 70% longer than those of form I. Figure III.20 shows the arrangement in a section of the chain, with the coplanar group of atoms in the neighborhood of a peptide bond, as it exists in the two chain conformations. Since the transition of one form into the other involves rotation around the peptide bond which has a partial double bond character, such a transition has a high activation energy and may proceed at a very slow rate (over a period of many hours). In acid media, where the imide group is partially protonated, the double bond character of the C–N linkage is eliminated and the rate of transformation of one helical form into the other is greatly increased.

The case of poly(L-proline) is important in that it proves that stabiliza-

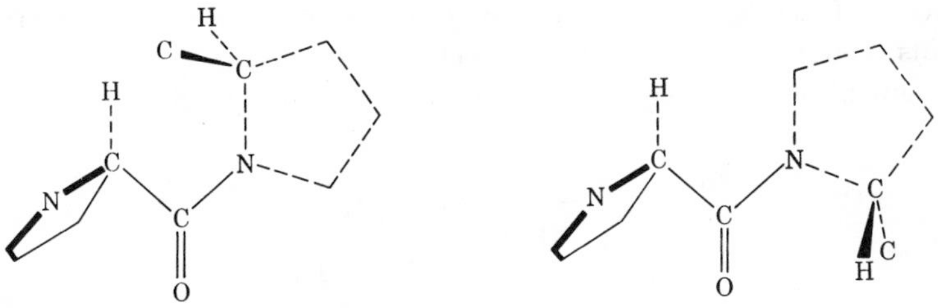

Polyproline I   Polyproline II

Fig. III.20. Conformations of a section of the two helical forms of poly(L-proline).

tion through hydrogen bonding is not a necessary requirement for the existence of stable helical conformations of dissolved chain molecules. While the rigidity of the peptide linkage is an impediment to the interconversion of the conformations, it can affect only the rate of such transitions, not the equilibrium distribution of the conformations. Steinberg et al. (1960) found that the heat content of the two helical forms of poly-(L-proline) is very similar—yet there is a strong tendency for poly(L-proline) to exist at equilibrium either in the pure form I or in the pure form II. This phenomenon suggests that junctions of the two types of helices in any one chain are energetically very unfavorable, presumably because of steric hindrance effects. It seems hard to believe that such behavior should be characteristic only of poly(L-proline) and such closely related substances as poly(hydroxy-L-proline), poly(O-acetylhydroxy-L-proline) (Steinberg et al., 1960), or proline–sarcosine copolypeptides (Fasman and Blout, 1963), but to date no other examples of helix-helix transitions have been discovered.

2. The Double Helix of DNA

We have seen that the results of crystallographic studies were of crucial importance in providing the impetus for a search for helical conformations in dissolved polypeptides. In a similar fashion, it may be said that most of the vast volume of work which has been carried out in recent years on nucleic acid solutions was undertaken under the stimulus of the proposal of a crystal structure for deoxyribose nucleic acid (DNA) by Watson and Crick (1953). Research on the nucleic acids has derived much of its glamor from the crucial role played by these substances in the transmission of hereditary characteristics of living organisms. Beautiful accounts of the dramatic discoveries implicating nucleic acids with some of the central problems of biology were given by Crick (1963), Watson (1963), and Wilkins (1963) in their Nobel prize lectures.

A segment of the molecular chain of DNA is represented by

The chain molecule is a copolymer of four types of units differing in the residues, denoted by Ⓑ, which are selected from the two purine bases, adenine(A) and guanine (G), and the two pyrimidine bases thymine, (T) and cytosine (C). While the overall base composition varies within wide limits in DNA samples derived from different sources, it was found that the adenine content always equals that of thymine and the guanine content that of cytosine (Chargaff, 1950, 1955). This equivalence was of crucial importance in leading Watson and Crick to their DNA model on the basis of rather limited crystallographic data. They pointed out that the hydrogen bonding of A + T and of G + C leads to structures of almost identical dimensions and that the x-ray diffraction pattern of crystalline DNA may be accounted for if two antiparallel, intertwined chains have base sequences such that adenine in one chain is always juxtaposed to thymine in the other chain and guanine is similarly paired with cytosine. The "spiral staircase" model of the resulting double helix is represented in Fig. III.21. Later extensive crystallographic analyses (Langridge et al., 1960a,b) proved the Watson–Crick model to be correct in its essential features. The geometry of the A + T and G + C pairs emerging from this work is depicted in Fig. III.22. The plane of the base pairs is almost perpendicular to the axis of the helix which contains ten base pairs in a repeat distance of 34 Å. It should be noted that the stacking of the conjugated double bond system of the base residues at the short distance of 3.4 Å from each other allows strong interaction of their π-electrons.

In favorable solvent media, DNA exists to a large extent in the double helical conformation. The evidence on which this conclusion is based was reviewed by Steiner and Beers (1961) and by Marmur et al. (1963). The weight per unit length of the scattering particle, deduced from low angle x-ray scattering (Luzzati et al., 1961b) also corresponds to the Watson–Crick model of the double helix. On the other hand, hydrodynamic and light-scattering data show that the chain extension does not increase quite

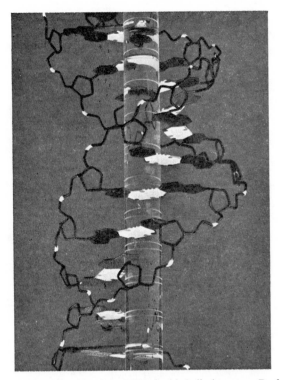

Fig. III.21. Model representation of the DNA double helix (courtesy Prof. N. Davidson).

in proportion to the molecular weight of the particle.   This could be inter-preted by assuming that the double-helical structure is interrupted, at long intervals, by randomly coiled sequences as represented schematically in Fig. III.23.   However, Hearst and Stockmayer (1962) have shown that the hydrodynamic behavior of DNA samples of varying chain lengths is better fitted by the wormlike chain model (with a persistence length of 360 Å), so that it appears that all of the DNA has the double-helical struc-ture, but that this structure is characterized by a slight flexibility.   This picture is also in accord with the appearance of DNA images obtained by electron microscopy.   Transitions between this largely ordered conforma-tion and the isolated chains in the randomly coiled form leads to altered molecular dimensions which are manifested by changes in light scattering or the frictional properties of the macromolecules.   Changes in the ap-parent density and the halving of the apparent molecular weight of the DNA brought about by the dissociation of the double helix may be followed

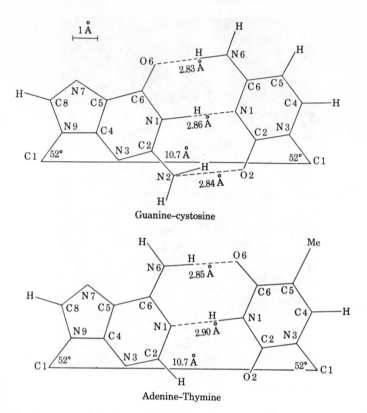

Fig. III.22. Geometry of the hydrogen-bonded guanine–cytosine and adenine–thymine pairs.

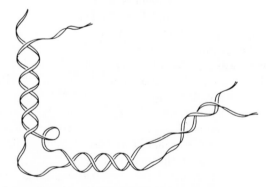

Fig. III.23. Schematic representation of a partially disrupted DNA double helix.

by ultracentrifugation in a density gradient (to be described in Chap. IV). The most convenient indication of helix-coil transition phenomena in DNA is provided by a striking change in the ultraviolet absorption spectrum (see Chap. V).   In addition to these physico-chemical methods, a unique criterion of the integrity of the native helical structure is provided by the biological activity of certain DNA preparations.   Avery et al. (1944) discovered that contact of certain bacteria with DNA solutions may lead to the transformation of the hereditary characteristics of the microorganisms. This "transforming activity," which is lost by any "denaturation" of the nucleic acid, may be used as a most sensitive tool for the determination of the fraction of molecules which are present in intact double helices (Marmur and Lane, 1960; Dove and Davidson, 1962b).

Numerous factors affect the stability of the double helix in solution. Formation of the ordered structure is exothermic, so that the helices tend to "melt" when the temperature of DNA solutions is raised.   Among the forces stabilizing the native form, hydrogen bonds and dipole-dipole interactions between the purine and pyrimidine residues stacked up in the double helix (De Voe and Tinoco, 1962) should lead to evolution of heat, while hydrophobic bonding would be expected to be endothermic.   The importance of hydrophobic bonding is illustrated by the tendency of aqueous DNA solutions to be denatured on addition of organic solvents with large nonpolar residues (Herskovits, 1962).   As would be expected, the high charge density due to the ionized phosphate residues along the DNA chain is a source of instability for the helical conformation.   As a result, the addition of moderate concentrations of electrolytes should stabilize the native form of DNA and this has been found to be the case with such salts as the halides of the alkali and the alkali earth metals (Dove and Davidson, 1962a; Schildkraut and Lifson, 1965).   If we define the "melting temperature" T_m as the temperature at which half of the spectral change characterizing the denaturation has taken place, then T_m appears to be approximately linear in the logarithm of the concentration of alkali metal cations.   In a typical case T_m is raised from 36 to 82°C by increasing the concentration of sodium ions from 0.0003 to $0.1N$ and an increasing salt concentration tends also to narrow the temperature range for the helix-coil transition.   Some divalent ions, which form specific complexes with the phosphate groups of the DNA backbone (e.g., Mg^{++}), are particularly effective in stabilizing the helical conformation.   The nucleic acid behaves as if it formed a stoichiometric complex with these cations and the T_m of such complexes is high even at very low ionic strength.   Under all conditions the helix-coil transition takes place in a remarkably narrow temperature interval, with 90% of the change occurring typically within less than 10°C.

Samples of DNA derived from different organisms may differ widely in the ratio of A–T and G–C base pairs, with the composition ranging approximately from 25 to 75% G–C. This composition has been found to be strongly reflected in the stability of the helical form, which increases sharply with increasing G–C content. Marmur and Doty (1962) have measured T_m values for forty samples of DNA and they found that in solutions containing $0.2N$ Na$^+$ their data were closely fitted by $T_m = 69.3 + 41\ x_{GC}$ where x_{GC} is the fraction of G–C base pairs. A number of factors may be considered as contributing causes of this phenomenon. Pullman and Pullman (1959) have shown that mutual interactions between G–C pairs should be stronger than those between A–T pairs, since G–C is both a stronger electron donor and a stronger electron acceptor. They concluded also that hydrogen bonds between guanine and cytosine are more stable than those between adenine and thymine. Pauling and Corey (1956) suggested that guanine may form three hydrogen bonds with cytosine, while only two such bonds link adenine to thymine. The guanine–cytosine pairs should also be characterized, according to DeVoe and Tinoco (1962), by stronger dipole–dipole interactions. Whatever may be the physical basis for the higher stability of double helices rich in G–C pairs, the phenomenon has some important physico-chemical and biological implications. For instance, since the base pairs may be unevenly distributed along the length of a given species of DNA, it is possible that some "G–C rich" regions are particularly resistant to denaturation (Geiduschek, 1962).

While the ease with which DNA solutions may be denatured has been known for a long time, it has been demonstrated only in recent years (Marmur and Lane, 1960; Doty et al., 1960) that the process may be reversed under appropriate conditions. A detailed consideration will show that this is a truly remarkable result. Typical samples of DNA may consist of chains with some 10,000 monomer units and, if the sequence of the base residues is random, then any arbitrary sequence of four or even five residues will be likely to occur many times. We should, therefore, expect a high probability that two chains encountering one another will find short matching sequences in sites other than the unique site which allows pairing of the entire chain molecules. Obviously, this correct matching would have a negligible probability if association of the base pairs were not reversible, so as to allow the "melting out" of complexes which have formed in the wrong locations. It is, therefore, not surprising that "renaturation" of heat denatured DNA, in which the two macromolecular strands have been fully separated from one another, requires very slow cooling through the temperature region of T_m in which the association process is easily reversible, so that the most stable complex—corresponding to the longest sequence of correctly matched base residues—can be arrived at. It is also essential that the DNA in solution should be derived from a single species, or at least from very closely related organisms (Schildkraut et al., 1961, 1962b) so that formation of the double helix involves only a small number of regions in which the base residues facing one another are mismatched.

Geiduschek (1962) showed that reversal of the thermal denaturation process is very rapid if the two chains have not been completely separated from each other.   In this case it is also possible to reform the double helices in systems containing widely different species of DNA.   The possibility of producing rapid and complete renaturation of methanol-denatured DNA (Geiduschek and Herskovits, 1961) appears also to be a consequence of incomplete separation of the two strands of the double helix.   The ease with which the transitions between the double helical and the disordered conformations may be made reversible, if it is insured that the two chains cannot fully separate from each other but have to remain "in register" in a small number of loci, was illustrated beautifully by Geiduschek (1961). He showed that chemical treatment could produce a small number of cross-links between the two strands of native DNA, and that all changes in the solution properties accompanying the usual denaturation procedures became reversible with this modified material.

3. Ordered Structures in Solutions of RNA and Synthetic Polyribonucleotides

Ribonucleic acid (RNA) consists of chain molecules with segments of type

where three of the base residues (adenine, guanine, cytosine) are identical with the bases contained in DNA, while the fourth base, uracil (U) is very closely related to the base thymine found in DNA:

$$\underset{\text{thymine}}{\begin{array}{c} O \\ \parallel \\ C \\ HN^{\diagup} \diagdown C-CH_3 \\ \mid \quad \parallel \\ O=C \diagdown_{N} \diagup CH \\ \mid \end{array}} \qquad \underset{\text{uracil}}{\begin{array}{c} O \\ \parallel \\ C \\ HN^{\diagup} \diagdown CH \\ \mid \quad \parallel \\ O=C \diagdown_{N} \diagup CH \\ \mid \end{array}}$$

Neither the substitution of ribose for deoxyribose nor that of uracil for thymine would lead one to suspect that the conformations of RNA and DNA in solution would be strikingly different from one another.   Yet the solution behavior of these two materials shows, in fact, important differences, which can be explained by the manner in which the two polymers are produced in a living organism.   In the case of DNA, the two strands of the double helix separate and each acts as a template determining the sequence of the base residues in the newly formed chain which must be such as to satisfy the condition of A–T and G–C juxtaposition (Fig. III.24).

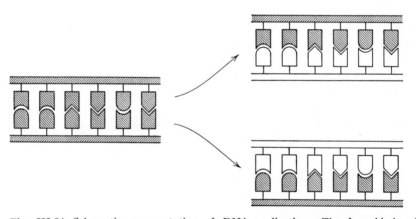

Fig. III.24. Schematic representation of DNA replication. The four kinds of appendages attached to the chain represent the two purine and two pyrimidine bases, with two and two complementary to one another.   The shaded chains separate and each guides the synthesis of a new chain (unshaded) with a complementary sequence of bases.

This process, in which an equal number of complementary chains are produced with a sequence of monomer units identical with that of the original macromolecule, may be demonstrated in a cell-free system as shown by the elegant experiments in Kornberg's laboratory (Kornberg, 1959, 1961). In the biosynthesis of RNA the monomer sequence is also determined by the sequence of monomer units in a DNA template, so that the newly formed

RNA is complementary to the DNA chain present in the cell in which it originated (Doi and Spiegelman, 1962). This process, however, does not appear to lead to two kinds of RNA chains complementary to one another since the adenine content differs, in general, from that of uracil and the guanine content from that of cytosine (Magasanik, 1955). We have then no cause to expect RNA chains to associate to double helical structures and such an association is, in fact, not observed.

Nevertheless, there is considerable evidence for the formation of some ordered conformations along part of the length of the RNA molecular chain. (Doty et al., 1959; Steiner and Beers, 1961). The evidence is based on characterstic spectral shifts, changes in optical activity, anomalies in the titration behavior, and changes in reactivity. The picture which emerges suggests a rather low degree of order and a very gradual transition to the fully disordered form when the temperature is raised, or when other variables are changed in a direction which would be expected to favor denaturation. Since such ordered conformations as do exist in RNA solutions seem to have characteristics similar to those of the DNA double helix and, since an interaction of two chains may be excluded, it is generally believed that the chain bends back on itself in a hairpin-like manner and is twisted into a double helix quite similar to that of DNA (Spencer et al., 1962). Fortunately, it is possible to isolate, as pure chemical species, a series of so-called "transfer ribonucleic acids," substances intimately associated with protein biosynthesis. These species have relatively short chains (with about 80 base residues) and Holley et al. (1965) have recently unraveled the complete sequence of residues in one of them. Their results indicate that the longest two sequences which could form C–G and A–U pairs with one another contain each only five residues and that there are many alternative ways in which the chain could fold so as to bring matching sections into juxtaposition. This confirms evidence, based on studies of RNA solutions, which suggested earlier that only a portion of the chain can assume a helical conformation. Figure III.25 shows a schematic representation of a partially ordered RNA molecule and a model of a typical helical region.

The understanding of the behavior of RNA samples isolated from living organisms may be deepened by comparison with the behavior of synthetic polyribonucleotide analogs. In one of the most fruitful biochemical discoveries of recent years, Grunberg-Manago et al. (1956) discovered that it is possible to carry out an enzymatic synthesis of a polymer, analogous to RNA, in a cell-free system. Moreover, by varying the ratio of the monomers containing the purine or pyrimidine bases, the composition of the

(a)

(b)

Fig. III.25. Hypothetical RNA structure. (a) Schematic representation of the partially helical chain. (b) Model of helical region (courtesy Prof. M. H. F. Wilkins and Dr. W. Fuller).

polyribonucleotide chain can be varied within wide limits. It is possible to obtain homopolymers, such as polyriboadenylic acid (Poly-A) or polyribouridilic acid (Poly-U), as well as copolymers with a random sequence of two or more types of monomer units.

If monomers carrying all the four bases, A, U, C, and G are copolymerized, the resulting product behaves in a manner very similar to that of natural RNA. Since the synthetic material must be presumed to have its monomer units arranged at random, we must conclude that such changes in the properties of RNA solutions as have been ascribed to conformational transitions do not depend on a precisely prescribed sequence of the base residues. On the other hand, when poly-A and poly-U solutions are mixed, a dramatic change takes place in the spectral absorption and hydrodynamic behavior of the solution (Warner, 1957). These and a variety of other observations indicate that the homopolymers associate to two types of complexes which have a stoichiometry of AU and AU_2 (Felsenfeld and Rich, 1957; Steiner and Beers, 1959). The relative stability of these two complexes depends critically on the nature of the solvent medium. Thus a system containing equal concentrations of poly-A and poly-U will form poly(A + U) at low temperatures, but this complex may disproportionate on warming in media of sufficiently high ionic strength to poly (A + 2U) and free poly-A. (Stevens and Felsenfeld, 1964). Crystallographic studies on fibers of the poly(A + U) complex show that it has a double-helical structure very similar to that of DNA (Rich, 1959) and this structure persists apparently in solutions under conditions similar to those governing the stability of DNA in its native form.

4. Theoretical Treatments of Helix-coil Transitions

Transitions between ordered and disordered conformations of chain molecules are important since they concern the conditions which must be met to keep proteins and nucleic acids in the form required for their biological function. At the same time, the phenomenon of helix-coil transition may be regarded as a one-dimensional analogy to a melting and crystallization process and as such it is of particular theoretical interest. Let us at first disregard the formation of multiple helices, characteristic of nucleic acids and their analogs, and focus our attention on transitions in isolated chains, such as are typical of polypeptides. We have stated previously that the partial double bond character of the C–N linkage precludes rotation around this bond so that a monomer residue behaves as a rigid link and only two internal angles of rotation ϕ need to be specified to

describe the relative orientation of a triplet of amino acid residues.   When
the random coil is transformed into the perfectly ordered conformation, the
freedom to choose the ϕ values is lost.   As a result, for a chain consisting
of Z amino acid residues, transformation to a perfect helix will be opposed
by a free energy gain proportional to $Z - 2$.   On the other hand, helix
formation will be favored by nearest-neighbor interactions of various
types.   These may include intramolecular hydrogen bonding, hydrophobic
bonds, and desolvation effects accompanying the transfer of side chains
from the relatively exposed state in the random coil to the compact packing
around the helix.   Such effects will, in general, be more pronounced for
residues in the interior of the helix than for those at its ends and the contribution to the free energy of helix formation due to nearest neighbor
interactions will, therefore, be proportional to $Z - \delta$, where δ is a number
taking account of the lesser stability of the ends of the helix.   If $\delta > 2$
[for the α-helix $\delta = 4$ has been assumed by Schellmann (1955)] then the
free energy for the transition of the disordered coil to the perfect helix will
become more favorable as Z is increased.   However, to specify properly the
conditions governing helix-coil transitions, we have to take also account of
partially ordered states containing various combinations of helically wound
and randomly coiled sequences.   Results obtained by various workers who
have treated this problem are similar and we shall use the representation
given by Zimm and Bragg (1959) to whom the reader may also be referred
for a bibliography of this field.   Let us designate by h a monomer residue
which forms part of a helical section and by c a residue which is not incorporated into the helical structure.   The statistical treatment of the
transition may then be carried out in terms of two characteristic parameters.   The first one, designated by j is the equilibrium constant for the
addition of one monomer residue from a disordered to a helical sequence
as represented schematically by

$$(-\text{h}-)_n(-\text{c}-)_m \rightleftharpoons (-\text{h}-)_{n+1}(-\text{c}-)_{m-1}$$

We see that j will be a measure of the tendency of a helical section to grow
at the expense of the adjoining randomly coiled sequence.   The second
parameter, designated by ζ, is the equilibrium constant for processes of the
type

$$(-\text{h}-)_{n+p}(-\text{c}-)_m \rightleftharpoons (-\text{h}-)_n(-\text{c}-)_m(-\text{h}-)_p$$

The value of ζ will generally be much smaller than unity.   It may be described as a measure of the driving force toward the nucleation of helical
sequences, since it will generally be more difficult to start a helical section

than to add to an existing one.   The model of Zimm and Bragg contains
also the restriction that at least three consecutive hydrogen bonds of an
α-helix have to be broken simultaneously to allow a break to be formed
in a helical sequence.

The results of the statistical calculation indicate that, for a constant
value of ζ, the helix-coil transition will occur over a range of j-values with
$j = 1$ corresponding to 50% helix content.   For sufficiently long chains, the
effects due to helix labilization at the chain ends will become negligible and
the fraction of residues accommodated in helical sequences (f_h) will then be
independent of chain length.   The transition will sharpen up as ζ is decreased, but an infinitely sharp transition analogous to a melting point is
obtained only as the nucleation parameter approaches zero.   The helical
content is given by

$$f_h = d \ln \lambda^* / d \ln j \qquad (3.34a)$$

where λ^* is the larger value in the expression

$$\lambda^* = \left| (1/2) \left[1 + j \pm \sqrt{(1 - j) + 4\zeta j} \right] \right| \qquad (3.34b)$$

In interpreting the variation of helix content with temperature, Zimm and
Bragg assume that ζ is temperature independent.   Since the parameter j
is an equilibrium constant, its temperature coefficient may be related to the
enthalpy change ΔH_h characterizing the transfer of a monomer residue from
a random sequence to a helical region.   The data obtained by Doty and
Yang (1956) for the helix-coil transition of poly(γ-benzyl-L-glutamate) in
an ethylene dichloride–dichloroacetic acid mixture containing 76 volume-%
DCA could be fitted by the relation (3.34) with $\zeta = 2 \times 10^{-4}$ and $\Delta H_h =$
$+990$ cal/mole of amino acid residues.

While for long chains f_h approaches the limiting value given by (3.34),
the extent of helix formation will be very sensitive to Z if the chains are
short.   According to Zimm and Bragg, substantial helix formation requires
that

$$j > 1$$
$$(j - 1)^2 j^{-z+1} \leqslant \zeta \qquad (3.35)$$

A corresponding treatment of the formation of the double helical DNA
conformation is much more complex.   In analyzing helix-coil transitions
in polypeptides, the contribution to the free energy, due to a monomer
residue placed in a randomly coiled section, could be considered independent of the presence of helical sequences in the molecular chain.   With

partially ordered conformations of the DNA type, the two strands of disordered sections placed between two regions where the chains have associated to a double helix must form a closed loop. The probability that a flexible chain forms a closed loop may be evaluated from the probability distribution function of chain end displacements (eq. 3.7). It is inversely proportional to the $^3/_2$ power of its contour length (Kuhn, 1934) so that we have to consider free energy changes for processes of the type

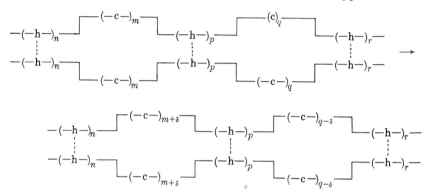

The problem has been treated by Rice and Wada (1958), Gibbs and Di Marzio (1959), Hill (1959), Zimm (1960), and by Lifson and Zimm (1963). The characteristics of the conformational transition are again independent of chain length for sufficiently long chains and a rather sharp transition with temperature variation is predicted. However, before theoretical results may be compared to experimentally observed helix-coil transitions in DNA solutions, two additional factors have to be taken into account. Since DNA consists of molecules with a very high density of ionic charges, the disorganization of the double helix will lead to a pronounced decrease in electrostatic free energy. This would lead one to expect that increasing electrolyte addition, which decreases the mutual interactions of the ionic charges attached to the macromolecule, would tend to stabilize the helical form. Experimental observations are qualitatively in agreement with this view, and a quantitative theory of the effect was proposed by Schildkraut and Lifson (1965). A second complication arises because A–T base pairing produces a weaker bond than G–C pairing and because the base composition may vary along the length of the chain. This should, in general, lead to a broadening of the melting range. Lifson (1963) has discussed a mathematical approach to a consideration of this factor, but its application is at present limited by our inability to ascertain the sequence of the base residues in a given sample of nucleic acid.

5. The Tertiary Structure of Proteins

In describing a protein molecule, the sequence of the amino acid residues along the polypeptide chain must first be specified. The next problem, concerned with the definition of the molecular conformation, is then customarily separated into two parts. We first specify the nature of the helical conformation characterizing various segments of the polypeptide chain; this is referred to as "the secondary structure" of the protein. The "tertiary structure" then describes the manner in which the sequence of helical and nonhelical chain segments is folded up into the very compact particle characteristic of the molecules of globular proteins.

The availability of synthetic polypeptides has done a great deal to clarify the conditions governing the stability of the secondary structure, but the problem posed by the tertiary structure is much more complex. This has been illuminated by the determination of the conformations of myoglobin (Kendrew et al., 1960) and hemoglobin (Perutz et al., 1960) obtained by x-ray crystallographic analysis. In the case of myoglobin, the protein consists of a single polypeptide chain with eight right-handed α-helix segments. The helices vary in length, containing from 7 to 24 amino acid residues; their combined length represents approximately 78% of the polypeptide chain. Two junctions are sharp corners, while the other helical segments are separated by varying lengths of the chain in an irregular conformation. Kendrew (1963) has discussed some striking features of the structure, which is extremely compact, with no more than a maximum of five isolated water molecules trapped in its interior. With very rare exceptions, all polar groups are found on the outside of the molecule, so that the side chains in contact with one another in the interior of the molecular structure are generally of a hydrophobic character. One thus gains the impression that hydrophobic bonding must be the main principle stabilizing the conformation. Yet, the vexing question remains, what determines the points at which breaks occur in the helical conformation? It is known that a proline residue may not be accommodated in an α-helix; but this restriction cannot account for all the nonhelical sequences in the myoglobin molecule. The composition of the nonhelical sections also bears no relation to the classification of synthetic polypeptides according to their tendency to exist in the helical form (Bloom et al., 1962). It is intriguing that the conformations of myoglobin and the four subunits forming the hemoglobin molecule should be very similar to one another in spite of considerable differences in their amino acid sequences (Watson and Kendrew, 1961; Cullis et al., 1962). The tertiary structure appears, then, to be determined by subtle relationships which have so far escaped detection.

The question may be legitimately asked, to what extent is the molecular conformation of a protein in the crystalline state related to its conformation in solution? The various arguments bearing on this problem have been reviewed by Richards (1963). On the whole, the evidence appears to favor the view that no more than minor alterations in molecular conformation accompany the transfer of protein molecules from solution into the crystal structure. At any rate, theoretical considerations inevitably lead to the conclusion that hydrophobic bonding must make a large contribution to the forces maintaining the molecular structure of dissolved proteins in their "native" conformation (Bresler, 1958; Tanford, 1962; Nemethy and Scheraga, 1962c). Since we are interested in proteins mostly because of their biological function, it is natural to take as the standard of reference the state of the molecule in a medium resembling that of living tissues, i.e., aqueous solutions close to pH 7 and an ionic strength around 0.1. It is known that the dimensions of globular protein molecules may be subject to considerable variation with a change of pH (Yang and Foster, 1954; Tanford et al., 1955a, 1959) or on addition of nonpolar solvents to aqueous protein solutions (Bresler, 1958; Tanford and De, 1961). The conformation revealed by crystallographic analysis may, therefore, approach that of the native protein only if the crystallization was carried out from the appropriate solvent medium.

Protein denaturation was classically defined as "any nonproteolytic modification of the unique structure of a native protein, giving rise to definite changes in chemical, physical, and biological properties" (Neurath et al., 1944). Changes of the state of ionization are excluded from the definition, unless they are accompanied by conformational transitions. Denaturation may be the result of heating, changes in pH, and the addition of nonpolar solvents or certain specific denaturation reagents such as urea or guanidine salts. It may also be produced by the reductive or oxidative scission of disulfide bonds, which stabilize the native conformations of some proteins. Denaturation is typically accompanied by decreasing protein solubility. This may be easily understood since the hydrophobic bonding, which serves to stabilize the native conformation, will tend to produce intermolecular aggregation when the polypeptide chains exist in their expanded conformations. Another characteristic effect produced by denaturation is the "unmasking" of reactive groups which are hidden in the interior of the tertiary structure and become accessible to reagents when this structure is disrupted. The most useful methods for following denaturation processes include spectroscopic measurements, measurements of optical activity, and determinations of the catalytic activity of enzymes or

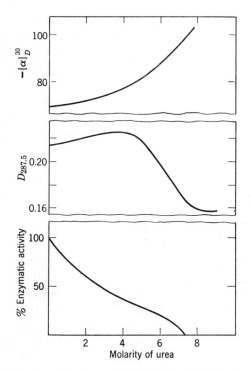

Fig. III.26. Effect of urea on the enzymatic activity, optical density at 287.5 mμ, and the optical activity of ribonuclease.

the biological activity of hormones. The conformational transitions lumped under the concept of denaturation involve a series of processes which may affect to a different extent each of these measurable changes and it is, therefore, meaningless to refer to a "degree of denaturation" unless we specify the criterion by which denaturation is being measured. This point is illustrated in Fig. III.26 showing the variation in optical activity, light absorption and enzymatic activity of ribonuclease with varying urea concentrations (Nelson and Hummel, 1962).

The variation in the stability of the native conformation with changes in the nature of the solvent medium provides a number of clues to the relative importance of the various factors determining the tertiary structure of proteins. The tendency of nonpolar cosolvents to denature aqueous protein solutions is a complex process. The cohesion of nonpolar residues in an aqueous environment will, on the one hand, stabilize the helical conformation, while it may, on the other hand, be the underlying cause of many of the "kinks" by which the helical sections of the polypeptide chain are folded into the compact structure of the globular proteins in the native state. A decrease in the polarity of the medium may, therefore, lead at first to an increase in the content of helical conformations (Bresler, 1958; Weber and Tanford, 1959; Tanford et al. 1960) before they are eventually disrupted. The action of urea, or of guanidine salts, seems to be only partially accountable by the disruption of hydrophobic bonds. It has been shown that aqueous urea is a better solvent medium for non-polar solutes than water itself (Nozaki and Tanford, 1963) but it was also found that aqueous urea or guanidine hydrochloride exerts a specific solvating action on the backbone of a polypeptide chain, an effect which has quite different characteristics than the solubilization of hydrocarbon residues (Robinson and Jencks, 1963). Finally, the decrease in the stability of the native form of globular proteins with increasing temperature proves that the disruption of the tertiary structure is an endothermic process, while the breaking of hydrophobic bonds should be exothermic. This leads to the conclusion (Scheraga et al., 1962) that some other process—possibly the breaking of hydrogen bonds accompanying the unfolding of the polypeptide chain—determines the sign of the enthalpy change.

Minor changes in protein conformation, such as the swelling of the molecules of serum albumin when its solution is acidified to pH 4 (Yang and Foster, 1954; Tanford et al., 1955a), are frequently reversible. The reversibility of conformational transitions is favored, particularly if the polypeptide chain is crosslinked intramolecularly by disulfide bridges, which set a limit to the extent of unfolding. A good example of such reversible denaturation is the study carried out by Hermans and Scheraga (1961) on ribonuclease, whose molecule consists of a single polypeptide chain crosslinked by four disulfide groups. The complete amino acid sequence of this enzyme is known and a schematic representation of the polypeptide chain with the location of the crosslinkages (Smyth et al., 1963) is shown in Fig. III.27(a). The question then arises whether it is possible to break the crosslinkages by reduction, allow the chain to unfold, and recover the native conformation with the correct pairs of thiol groups oxidized to disulfide bridges. The crucial experiment was carried out by White (1960) who showed that most of the enzymatic activity of ribonuclease, which is lost during reduction of the disulfide groups, may be regained by reoxidation. A particularly significant result was obtained by Anfinsen et al. (1961) who found that reformation of disulfide bonds proceeds faster than the recovery of the enzymatic activity of the protein. Since the eight amino acid residues which participate in the four disulfide bridges can

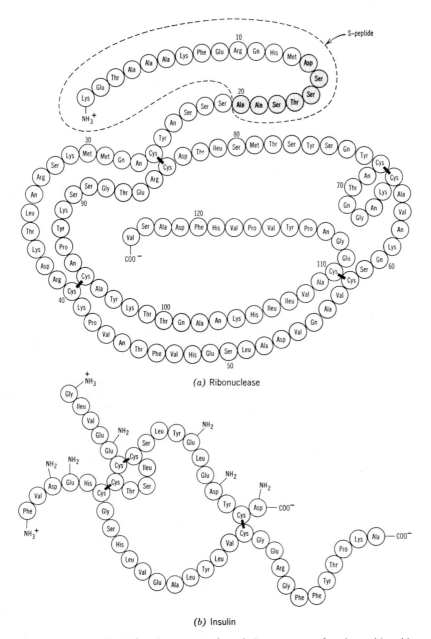

Fig. III.27. Two-dimensional representation of the sequence of amino acid residues and the intramolecular crosslinkages in ribonuclease and in insulin. The shaded portion of the ribonuclease chain is non-essential for enzymatic activity.

be joined to one another in 105 different ways, and intermolecular disulfide bond formation interferes with the intramolecular reaction (Epstein et al., 1962), many of the crosslinkages may form initially in the wrong manner. Such molecules would lack the catalytic activity associated with the unique folding of the polypeptide chain in the native enzyme. It seems, however, that disulfide interchange enables molecular aggregates and incorrectly folded molecules to rearrange until they reach the native conformation, which apparently represents a sharply defined free energy minimum. The renatured enzyme can be crystallized and the crystals give an x-ray diffraction pattern indistinguishable from that of the original protein (Bello et al., 1961). This may be taken as the ultimate proof that the conformation of the native enzyme has been regained in every detail.

The magnitude of the forces which stabilize the tertiary structure of ribonuclease is illustrated also by experiments of a somewhat different kind. It is possible to break selectively the peptide bond linking the alanyl residue in position 20 to the seryl residue in position 21. This splits the enzyme molecule into a short peptide chain ("S-peptide") and a residual structure containing all of the disulfide crosslinkages ("S-protein"). It was found that each component separately is inactive, but almost full enzymatic activity is restored if stoichiometric amounts of the two components are mixed, even in very high dilution (Richards and Vithaya-thil, 1959). The data are consistent with an association constant of S-peptide with S-protein of at least 2×10^8 liters-mole^{-1}. These results show that the advantage inherent in the specific folding of the native enzyme depends so heavily on mutual interactions of the side chains attached to the polypeptide backbone, that the spatial arrangement may be retained when the backbone is broken. It has even been found that most of the enzymatic activity is preserved if the seven amino acid residues 14 to 20 in the S-peptide are eliminated, so that this fairly long gap in the backbone appears to be compatible with the maintenance of the essential features of the tertiary structure characteristic of the native protein (Potts et al., 1963; Hofmann et al., 1963).

The phenomena illustrated above on ribonuclease seem to be typical of the behavior of globular proteins in general. It appears that the extended polypeptide chains are endowed with the ability to assume spontaneously a unique tertiary structure under appropriate conditions. In some cases two or more polypeptide chains participate in the formation of an active protein and even in such cases the denaturation, involving the physical separation of the constituent chains, can be largely reversed. In the case of insulin [Fig. III.27(b)] two different polypeptide chains are joined by two disulfide bonds, which may be reduced to allow separation of the A and B chains. When a solution containing a mixture of these two chains is oxidized, a considerable amount of the active hormone, identical with the original protein is recovered (Wilson et al., 1962).   In the case of the enzyme aldolase, three subunits are associated by secondary valence bonds only.   These subunits may be separated from one another, unfolded to a highly expanded form, and the whole process may be reversed to regain the active enzyme (Deal et al., 1963).   The formation of the tertiary structure in the subunits apparently produces particles with complementary surfaces so that their association to a quaternary structure is highly favored.

Chapter IV

EQUILIBRIUM PROPERTIES OF DILUTE SOLUTIONS

A. THE COLLIGATIVE PROPERTIES

1. Raoult's Law as a Limiting Law

The concept of an ideal solution, in which the activities of the components are equal to their mole fractions, is useful to the physical chemist in two ways. On one hand it is found that the ideal solution law is a reasonable first approximation to the behavior of real systems if they consist of species of similar molecular volume and if the heat of mixing is relatively small. Raoult's law [eq. (2.17)] is then used as a frame of reference with which the properties of real systems are compared. This subject has been discussed in detail in Chap. II. There is, however, another aspect of Raoult's law which is of a far greater fundamental importance, namely, its quite general validity as a limiting law. We may compare the situation with the analogous case of the ideal gas law. Here we find also that the familiar expression $PV = RT$ relating the pressure, volume, and absolute temperature of a gas is meaningful in two ways. Real gases at moderate pressures show relatively small deviations from that simple relation and such deviations as are found in any given case may be interpreted in terms of the excluded volume of the gas molecules and the forces between them. However, *no matter how nonideal a gas may be*, the ideal gas law will always describe accurately its behavior in the limit of vanishingly small pressures.

Let us consider a solution which is so dilute that interactions between solute molecules are negligible. In that case the escaping tendencies of the solute molecules will be additive and the activity of the solute will be proportional to its concentration. Such proportionality is commonly referred to as "Henry's law." If we express concentration in terms of mole fractions, then

$$a_2 = k_H x_2 \qquad (4.1)$$

where the Henry's law constant k_H increases with decreasing solvent power of the medium.   According to the Gibbs–Duhem relation, the changes in the activities of the components of a binary system are related by

$$x_1 d \ln a_1 + x_2 d \ln a_2 = 0 \qquad (4.2)$$

Combining (4.1) with (4.2) and using the condition $dx_2 = -dx_1$ we obtain

$$x_1 d \ln a_1 = dx_1 \qquad (4.3)$$

and since $a_1 = 1$ for $x_1 = 1$,

$$\lim_{x_1 \to 1} (da_1/dx_1) = 1 \qquad (4.4a)$$

$$a_1 = x_1 \qquad (4.4b)$$

We see then that Raoult's law will be valid *for the solvent* as long as Henry's law is applicable to the solute.   The concentration range within which this will be the case will, of course, depend on the nature of the system.   In solutions of nonelectrolytes, energetic interactions of solute molecules may be considered as restricted to nearest neighbors.   Then, if we have solutes of low molecular weight and if there is no pronounced clustering of the solute molecules, a system in which 1% of the volume is occupied by the solute should not deviate greatly from Henry's and Raoult's laws for the dilute and the concentrated component, respectively.   For ionic solutions, in which the Coulombic forces of the charged species are exerted over much longer distances, correspondingly higher dilutions are required for approach to ideal solution behavior.   Such high dilution will also be necessary to eliminate mutual interactions if the solute consists of flexible chain molecules, since the volume occupied by the molecular coil may exceed by a very large factor the volume of the "dry" molecule.

2. Relation of Solvent Activity to Measurable Quantities

In the concentration range in which Raoult's law is valid, the molecular weight M_2 of the solute in a binary system may be calculated from solvent activity by

$$a_1 = x_1 = (w_1/M_1)/[(w_1/M_1) + (w_2/M_2)] \qquad (4.5)$$

where w_1 and w_2 are the weights of solvent and solute.   If the solution is dilute, $(w_1/M_1) \gg (w_2/M_2)$ and the difference of the activity of the solvent in its standard state and in solution will be

$$1 - a_1 \approx w_2 M_1 / w_1 M_2 \qquad (4.6)$$

The molecular weight of the solute may, therefore, be evaluated if a convenient method is available for measuring changes of solvent activity in the concentration range in which Raoult's law is applicable. The methods which may be used for this purpose include measurements of vapor pressure, freezing point depression (cryoscopy), boiling point elevation (ebulliometry), and osmotic pressure. All of them yield, in the limit of highly dilute solutions, results which depend only on the number of solute particles per unit volume and they are commonly referred to as the colligative properties of solutions. If the solutions contain solutes of different molecular weight, then the determination of the number of solute molecules at a known weight concentration leads to the number average molecular weight $\bar{M}_n$ of the solute species.

a. Vapor Pressure

The activity of a component of a solution is defined as the ratio of its fugacities in solution and in the standard state, respectively. We have seen in Chap. II that for a typical solvent the partial vapor pressure p_1 is a close approximation to the fugacity f_1 and since the partial vapor pressure of a solvent over a dilute solution will be very close to the vapor pressure p_1^0 of the pure solvent, we are well justified in assuming $p_1/p_1^0 = f_1/f_1^0$, so that

$$a_1 = p_1/p_1^0 \tag{4.7}$$

b. Cryoscopy and Ebulliometry

The relation between the freezing point T_m of a solution and the freezing point T_m^0 of the pure solvent may be derived simply by considering a cycle consisting of the following operations:

(1) A solution is cooled from T_m^0 to $T_m^0 - dT_m$ and δn_1 moles of the solvent are frozen out at that temperature. The solvent crystals are separated from the residual solution.

(2) The solution and the separated solvent crystals are reheated to T_m^0 and the latent heat of fusion ΔH_1^m is added per mole of solvent crystals to melt them.

(3) The molten solvent is returned to the solution in a reversible operation, yielding $-(\bar{G}_1 - \bar{G}_1^0)\delta n_1 = -\delta n_1 RT \ln a_1$ of work.

We may now relate the fraction of the heat added which was converted into work to the temperature interval of the cycle by the second law of thermodynamics

$$-RT \, d \ln a_1/\Delta H_1^m = -dT_m/T_m^0 \tag{4.8}$$

which leads, for dilute solutions, to the approximate result

$$-\ln a_1 = [\Delta H_1^m / R(T_m^0)^2] (T_m^0 - T_m) \qquad (4.9)$$

It should be emphasized that these relations are valid only if pure solvent crystals separate in the freezing of the solution, i.e., when no solid solutions are formed by the two components of the system. This is not a serious restriction since the formation of solid solutions is a rather rare phenomenon, particularly among organic compounds.

Reasoning similar to that outlined above leads to the relation of the boiling point T_b of a solution to the boiling point T_b^0 of the pure solvent in terms of ΔH_1^v, the latent heat of vaporization of the solvent

$$-\ln a_1 = [\Delta H_1^v / R(T_b^0)^2](T_b - T_b^0) \qquad (4.10)$$

provided the volatility of the solute is negligibly small.

c. Osmotic Pressure

The osmotic pressure Π is defined as the pressure which has to be applied to a solution so as to raise the partial molar free energy of the solvent to the standard state value. Thus,

$$\bar{G}_1^0 = \bar{G}_1 + \int_0^\Pi (\partial \bar{G}_1 / \partial P)_{T, x_1} \, dP \qquad (4.11)$$

The variation of $(\partial \bar{G}_1 / \partial P)_{T, x_1} = \bar{V}_1$ with pressure may be neglected, so that

$$\bar{G}_1 - \bar{G}_1^0 = RT \ln a_1 = -\Pi \bar{V}_1 \qquad (4.12)$$

Since the colligative properties are all essentially methods for measuring solvent activity, their mutual relationship is independent of the deviations from solution ideality. The choice between them is governed merely by experimental convenience. In the range in which Raoult's law applies, we may substitute for $\ln a_1$ in (4.9), (4.10), and (4.12)

$$\ln a_1 = \ln(1 - x_2) \approx -x_2 \qquad (4.13)$$

3. The Scope of the Methods

It is instructive to compare the relative magnitudes of effects produced by the colligative properties on a typical example, i.e., a benzene solution containing 1% by weight of a solute with a molecular weight of 10,000. (We shall assume that the solution behaves ideally.) The mole fraction of the solute is only 7.8×10^{-5} and since the vapor pressure of benzene is 100 mm

Hg at 26.1°C, the vapor pressure of the solution will be 99.9922 mm Hg. Using the proper values for the latent heat of fusion of benzene at 5.5°C and the latent heat of vaporization at 80.2°C, we obtain a freezing point depression of 0.0051°C and a boiling point elevation of 0.0025°C. The osmotic pressure at 26°C will be 25,000 dynes-cm^{-2}. Let us then consider the relative convenience for determining such quantities experimentally.

At first sight it would appear that the extremely slight change in the vapor pressure precludes any possibility of its experimental determination. Nevertheless, an ingenious technique has been developed which allows the estimation of molecular weights up to several thousand by a method utilizing the difference in the vapor pressure of the solution and the pure solvent. In this procedure, referred to usually as the Hill–Baldes thermoelectric osmometer method, drops of solution and solvent are held in a space filled with saturated solvent vapor. As the solvent condenses on the drop of solution, this drop is being warmed by liberation of the latent heat until a steady state is reached in which this heating is balanced by heat losses through conduction. With the use of thermistors for the measurement of the difference of temperature of the solvent and solution drops, and with careful experimental design, temperature differences of the order 10^{-4}°C may be measured with good reproducibility (Muller and Stolten, 1953). The ratio of this temperature differential to the molarity of the solute tends to increase with the volatility of the solvent (Iyengar, 1954). If conduction losses are made negligible, the solution drop will be heated until the partial pressure of the solvent is equal to that of the pure solvent drop at a lower temperature—the temperature difference is then that predicted by the theory of boiling point elevation. Higuchi et al. (1959) have shown that it is possible to approach quite closely to this ideal situation.

The cryoscopic and ebullioscopic methods have been greatly improved in recent years by use of thermistors for the accurate measurement of small differences of temperature. The sensitivities of the two methods are similar and definitely exceed that of the method described above. An outstanding example of high precision cryoscopy is the characterization of polystyrene with $\bar{M}_n$ up to 40,000 (Schulz and Marzolph, 1954), and of polyethylene with $\bar{M}_n$ values up to 60,000 (Ashby et al., 1957). The ebullioscopic technique has been used successfully for the determination of molecular weights up to the 20,000–30,000 range (Ray, 1952; Schön and Schulz, 1954; Dimbat and Stross, 1957). The sensitivity of this method is limited not so much by the smallness of the differences of temperature which have to be measured as by various experimental difficulties, such as the foaming of boiling polymer solutions, introducing uncertainties which

TABLE IV

Characteristics of Cryoscopic and Ebullioscopic Solvents

Solvent	T_m^0, °C	T_b^0, °C	$(T_m^0 - T_m)/m_2^a$	$(T_b - T_b^0)/m_2^a$
Acetic acid	16.55		3.7	
Benzene	5.53	80.2	4.86	2.54
Butanone		79.6		2.56
Camphor	178.4		46.9	
Carbon tetrachloride		76.5		5.02
Chlorobenzene		132.0		4.06
Cyclohexane	7.09	80.9	14.8	2.79
p-Dichlorobenzene	53.2		6.98	
1,2-Dichloroethane		83.5		1.90
Dioxane	11.78		4.63	
Diphenylamine	53.2		7.68	
Ethanol		78.3		1.19
Ethyl acetate		77.1		2.68
Ethyl ether		34.6		2.10
n-Heptane		98.4		3.43
Naphthalene	80.27		7.0	
Nitrobenzene	5.65		6.8	
Phenol	40.8		7.27	
Tetrahydrofuran		63.2		2.50
Toluene		110.7		3.33
Water	0.0	100.0	1.88	0.51

a The symbol m_2 denotes the molality of the solute.

do not lend themselves to a theoretical analysis. Table IV.1 lists the characteristics of some cryoscopic and ebullioscopic solvents. (Bonner et al., 1958)

The determination of osmotic pressure is by far the most sensitive of the techniques by which solvent activity deviating only slightly from unity may be measured. In the usual technique a sample of the solution is separated from the pure solvent by a semipermeable membrane which will allow solvent molecules to diffuse freely but will not allow passage of the solute. Solvent will then pass into the solution until its rising level provides a hydrostatic pressure equal to Π, so that the partial molar free energy of the solvent in the solution becomes equal to that of the pure solvent. If the difference in the levels of the solvent and solution menisci h is expressed in centimeters, ρ is the density of the solution, and g the gravitational acceleration of the earth in cm-sec^{-2}, then the osmotic pressure in dynes-cm^{-2} is given by $\Pi = h\rho g$, so that the osmotic pressure in the example given at the outset of this section corresponds to a hydrostatic head of 28 cm. We see then that a determination of solvent activity in a case which was beyond the precision attainable by measurements of vapor pressure depression and could be achieved only with great care by the use of cryoscopy or ebulliometry, is very far from the limits of sensitivity attainable in osmometry. In fact, osmotic pressure measurements may be carried out comfortably with solutes whose molecular weights range up to 500,000 or even higher. The most difficult problem in the use of this technique is that of the selection of a suitable semipermeable membrane. This problem is less difficult in work with monodisperse natural polymers but becomes serious with synthetic polymers containing continuous distributions of molecular weights. Unless the lowest molecular weight species are removed by careful fractionation, the number-average molecular weight obtained by osmometry may reflect as much the properties of the osmotic membrane as the nature of the specimen. An extensive discussion of osmometric techniques is contained in the monograph on number-average molecular weight determination by Bonner et al. (1958). These authors consider 15,000 as the practical lower limit of molecular weights for which the osmotic pressure method is convenient.

4. Deviations from Raoult's Law in Dilute Solutions

In discussing the nature of the ideal solution law as a limiting law (Sec. A-1) we showed that the validity of Raoult's law for the solvent was assured if the solute particle, subject to nearest-neighbor interactions only, were not in contact with each other. This condition can be satisfied, to any degree of approximation required, by a sufficiently high dilution of the solution. As the solution becomes more concentrated, we should expect at first the appearance of binary interactions between the solute particles and since the number of binary contacts should be proportional to c_2^2, the square of the solute concentration, the measurable intensive properties should also deviate by a term proportional to c_2^2 from the values expected for a solution containing only isolated solute molecules. At still higher concentrations, ternary interactions with a probability c_2^3 or even higher order interactions may contribute to the properties of the system, but the interpretation of such effects is much less certain and theoretical developments are usually restricted to the interpretation of effects arising from binary solute interactions only.

By combining eq. (4.12) and (4.13) we may write for the osmotic pressure of a dilute solution (for which the partial molar volume of the solvent $\bar{V}_1$ is indistinguishable from its molar volume V_1) in the concentration range satisfying Raoult's law

$$\Pi = (RT/\bar{V}_1)x_2 \qquad (4.14)$$

Since $x_2/V_1 = c_2/M_2$ (where the solute concentration c_2 is expressed in grams per ml.) we obtain

$$\Pi = (RT/M_2)c_2 \tag{4.15}$$

At higher concentrations, where binary and higher order interactions of solute particles have to be taken into account,

$$\Pi = RT[(c_2/M_2) + A_2c_2^2 + A_3c_2^3 + \ldots] \tag{4.16}$$

where A_2, A_3 etc. are the second, third, and higher osmotic virial coefficients, which will depend on the shape of the solute molecules and the forces operating between them.   Analogous expressions will be obtained if we use another of the colligative properties as our experimental tool; e.g., in interpreting cryoscopic data [cf. eq. (4.9)],

$$T_m^0 - T_m = [R(T_m^0)^2 V_1/\Delta H_1^m][(c_2/M_2) + A_2c_2^2 + A_3c_2^3 + \ldots] \tag{4.17}$$

where the coefficients A_2, A_3, etc. have the same value as in (4.16).   For the osmotic pressure of a solution in which solute molecules may be represented as rigid spheres much larger than the molecules of the solvent, we obtain from eq. (2.48), after substituting c_2V_2/M_2 for ϕ_2,

$$\Pi = RT[(c_2/M_2) + (4V_2/M_2^2)c_2^2 + \ldots] \tag{4.18}$$

Here the term $4V_2 = U_2$ represents the volume excluded, due to binary interactions, per mole of solute.   It arises from the fact that the centers of two rigid spheres cannot be placed closer to each other than at a distance twice as long as their radius.   Thus, any sphere excludes a volume eight times as large as that which it physically occupies.   Since, however, the excluded volume due to the interaction of any pair of particles is counted twice, the volume excluded by all the particles in the system is only four times as large as this physical volume.

The relation between the second virial coefficient and the volume excluded due to binary interactions

$$A_2 = U_2/M_2^2 \tag{4.19}$$

is perfectly general, but the calculation of U_2 becomes much more difficult for cases other than that of rigid spheres.   For instance, in the case of rigid ellipsoids of revolution, only certain mutual orientations are allowed if the centers of two neighboring particles are separated by a distance lying be-

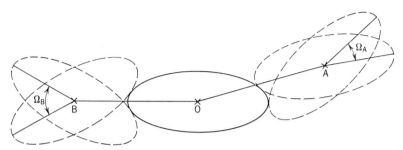

Fig. IV.1. Two-dimensional representation of the excluded volume in a system containing ellipsoidal particles.   Note that for ellipses centered at A and B, at an equal distance from O, the center of a reference ellipse, the excluded angles Ω are different.

tween that of the length of their major and minor axis, as illustrated in Fig. IV.1.   The molar excluded volume is then given by

$$U_2 = (N/2)(1/4\pi) \iiint \Omega(x,y,z)dxdydz \qquad (4.20)$$

where $\Omega(x,y,z)$ is the solid angle excluded by the presence of one ellipsoid for the orientation of the major axis of a second ellipsoid whose center of gravity is placed at x,y,z.   It is intuitively reasonable that the ratio of the excluded volume to the physical volume of the ellipsoid should increase with its eccentricity.   For very elongated rod-like particles, Zimm (1946) obtained

$$U_2/V_2 = p \qquad (p \gg 1) \qquad (4.21)$$

where p is the ratio of the semiaxis of revolution to the equatorial radius. We see then that the second virial coefficient may attain very high values provided the solute particles are sufficiently elongated.

The problem of constructing a theory of the second virial coefficient for solutions containing flexible chain molecules presents difficulties of a different order of magnitude.   The region of space occupied by such macromolecules is not clearly defined and it is possible for the molecular coils to interpenetrate one another.   Such interpenetration will be resisted because of the restriction which it imposes on the number of possible chain conformations, but this factor may be opposed by a mutual attraction of the chain segments in poor solvent media, or it may be magnified by a mutual repulsion of the polymer segments if polymer–solvent interactions are favored.   In general, we may expect the polymer coils to become mutually impenetrable in the limit of very large chain length and this limit should be reached more rapidly as the mutual repulsion of the solute molecules is increased by an increasingly favorable solvent medium.

Since the mathematical treatment of the problem in terms of the molecular chains is extremely complex, it is customary to use a simplified physical model in which the polymer coils are represented either by spherical regions of uniform polymer concentration (Flory, 1945; Emery, 1957) or else by regions in which the continuous polymer segment density, though variable, retains spherical symmetry (Flory and Krigbaum, 1950; Isihara and Koyama, 1956). It has been shown by Carpenter and Krigbaum (1958) that the details of the distribution of the chain segments have little effect on the result obtained and it then seems most convenient to develop the the ory in terms of coils contained within spheres of an effective radius R_e and a molar volume V_e within which the density of polymer segments is uniformly distributed. When the centers of two such spheres approach each other within a distance $2R_e y$, where $y < 1$, they will interpenetrate so as to occupy jointly a volume $(4/3)\pi R_e{}^3 (y^3 - 3y + 2)/2$. If such an interpenetration is associated with an excess free energy $G^E(y)$ the excluded volume will be given by the "binary cluster integral"

$$U_2 = (N/2) \int_{y=0}^{y=1} \{1 - \exp[-G^E(y)/kT]\} 4\pi (2R_e y)^2 d(2R_e y)$$

$$= 4V_e \left[1 - \int_{y=0}^{y=1} \exp[-G^E(y)/kT] \, 3y^2 dy \right] \quad (4.22)$$

To evaluate the integral in (4.22), we have to make an assumption about the form of G^E. Flory and Krigbaum (1950) suggested that it could be approximated by the Flory–Huggins theory as applied to the solution of polymers of infinite chain length, neglecting all terms beyond that which represents binary interactions of chain segments. This leads to an excess free energy of $2kT(^1/_2 - \chi)\phi_{21}^2/V_1$ per unit volume jointly occupied by the two interpenetrating spheres where $\phi_{21} = V_2/V_e$ is the local volume fraction of polymer within the equivalent sphere. Using this value in the estimate of $G^E(y)$, eq. (4.22) becomes

$$U_2 = 4V_e [1 - g(X)]$$

$$X = (^1/_2 - \chi) V_2^2/V_e V_1$$

$$g(X) = \int_{y=0}^{y=1} \exp[-X(y^3 - 3y + 2)] \, 3y^2 dy \quad (4.23)$$

The function $g(X)$ is plotted in Fig. IV.2 and it may be seen that it decays gradually with increasing values of X tending to 0 as $X \to \infty$. We may note that the excluded volume to be expected in the limit of very large values of the dimensionless parameter X represents the behavior of the

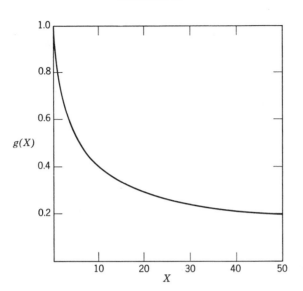

Fig. IV.2. The function $g(X)$ describing the mutual interpenetration of two polymer coils.

macromolecules when the interpenetration of the coils has become negligible and it is, therefore, independent of the form assumed for G^E. When $(\frac{1}{2} - \chi) = 0$, i.e., in a Θ-solvent in which the mutual attraction of chain segments is just sufficient to cancel the effects of the reduction in the number of chain conformations resulting from the interpenetration of molecular coils, $X = 0$ and $g(X) = 1$, so that the excluded volume and the second virial coefficient vanish for chains of any length. The balance of factors, which favor and oppose the mutual penetration of different sections of any one coil, has been shown previously (Chap. III, Sec. B-5) to eliminate chain expansion due to the *intramolecular* excluded volume effect; the same conditions, in eliminating the effect of the excluded volume in *intermolecular* interactions, should assure the validity of Raoult's law in the concentration range in which only binary solute interaction need be considered. With $X \ll 1$ but finite (i.e., in a solvent medium approaching closely to Θ-conditions) the exponential term in (4.23) may be replaced by $-X(y^3 - 3y + 2)$, leading to a molar excluded volume

$$\lim_{X \to 0} U_2 = (\frac{1}{2} - \chi)\, V_2^2 / V_1 \qquad (4.24)$$

which is identical with the results obtained in theories which use models with variable coil segment densities. The formulation of the results in these theories tends to emphasize conditions close to the θ-point; the formulation in (4.23) emphasizes, on the contrary, the asymptotic limit of complete mutual impenetrability of the molecular coils, a condition which is met with much more frequently in practice.

It is instructive to combine (4.19) with (4.23) to

$$A_2 M_2 = (4V_e/M_2)[1 - g(X)] \tag{4.25}$$

and to compare the value of V_e/M_2 obtained in this manner with results derived from the hydrodynamic properties of the polymer coils. We shall see in Chap. VI that the intrinsic viscosity $[\eta]$ of long flexible chain molecules may be represented by $[\eta] = 2.5(V_e/M_2)$ and we should, therefore, expect the second virial coefficient to be related to the intrinsic viscosity by

$$A_2 M_2/[\eta] = (8/5)[1 - g(X)] \tag{4.26}$$

This prediction may be compared with a variety of data compiled by Orofino and Flory (1957) and the more recent data of Casassa and Stockmayer (1962) which are plotted on Fig. IV.3. An asymptotic behavior similar to that predicted by (4.26) is obtained in all other recent theories of

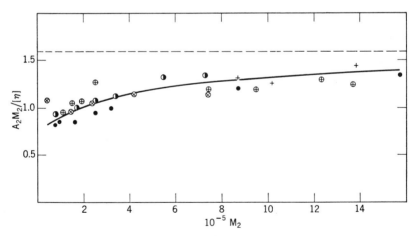

Fig. IV.3. Relation between the second virial coefficient and the intrinsic viscosity for chain molecules in good solvent media. (●) Polystyrene in toluene, (+) poly(vinyl acetate) in butanone, (◐) polyisobutene in cyclohexane, (⊕) poly(methyl methacrylate) in acetone, (⊗) poly(methyl methacrylate) in butanone. The dashed line gives the theoretical value assuming that the thermodynamic excluded volume is equal to the volume of the hydrodynamically equivalent sphere.

the second virial coefficient of flexible chain molecules which differ, however, to some extent in the predicted limiting value of $A_2 M_2/[\eta]$ (Casassa and Stockmayer, 1962). In good solvents and for sufficiently large polymer molecules the ratio $A_2 M_2/[\eta]$ appears, indeed, to approach a limiting value of 1.0–1.5, in fair agreement with the value of 1.6 required by (4.26). These data were derived from osmometry or from the concentration dependence of light scattering which can be interpreted, as we shall see later, in terms of the osmotic virial coefficients. Values of A_2 are rarely available over a range of M_2 extending over two orders of magnitude and within that range they can be represented satisfactorily by the empirical relation

$$A_2 = K M^{-\mu} \tag{4.27}$$

where μ has been found to lie, in good solvent media, within the limits of 0.15 and 0.35 (Isihara and Koyama, 1956). Since the intrinsic viscosity may be represented in a similar manner by $[\eta] = K' M^\gamma$ we may estimate μ for sufficiently long chains (so that the variation of $g(X)$ with M_2 may be neglected) as $1 - \gamma$.

Orofino and Flory (1957) have attempted to improve the agreement of theory with experimental data by taking account of ternary segment interactions in the interpenetrating coils, which are represented, as in the Flory–Krigbaum theory, by a Gaussian distribution of segment densities. Since this procedure requires the use of two adjustable parameters, it is questionable whether it is justified in a theory which should not be expected, in any case, to be more than a rough approximation to physical reality. This is so, particularly since the polydispersity of even the best fractions used in experimental work would be expected to affect A_2 to an extent which is difficult to predict theoretically (Casassa and Stockmayer, 1962). It is, nevertheless, interesting to note that Orofino and Flory are led to the conclusion that the nature of the solvent medium for which A_2 vanishes should vary slightly with the length of the chain molecules. Such an effect was observed by McIntyre et al. (1959).

In all the treatments mentioned above, the theory of the second virial coefficient was based on a model in which a cloud of a spherically symmetrical distribution of chain segments represented the macromolecule. It is incomparably more difficult to formulate a theory in which the joining of these segments into a molecular chain is taken explicitly into account, but the procedures to be followed in such a theory were outlined by Zimm (1946). It is applicable, in practice, only for solutions in media which deviate only slightly from the properties of a 0-solvent (p. 131). With some simplifying approximations, the second virial coefficient may then be expressed in closed form (Yamakawa, 1958; Casassa and Markowitz, 1958; Casassa, 1959) as

$$A_2 = (N\beta_{ex}/2M_0^2)(1 - 2.865z + \ldots) \tag{4.28}$$

where β_{ex} is the mutually excluded volume of two polymer segments, M_0 is the molecular weight of the segment and z is the parameter defined in eq. (3.33).

As for the temperature dependence of the osmotic virial coefficients, we may use the Gibbs–Helmholtz equation (2.12) in conjunction with (4.12) and (4.16) to yield

$$RV_1[(\partial A_2/\partial T)c_2^2 + (\partial A_3/\partial T)c_2^3 + \ldots] = \overline{\Delta H_1}/T^2 \tag{4.29}$$

so that the temperature coefficient of A_2 may be used to estimate the heat of dilution in the low concentration range. Qualitatively, it is evident that in a system in which the mixing of polymer and solvent is endothermic, an increase in temperature will favor solvation and tend to expand the polymer coil; this in turn will increase the excluded volume and lead to a higher value of A_2.

In evaluating experimental data, it is customary to plot the "reduced osmotic pressure" Π/c_2 as a function of solute concentration c_2 and to extrapolate to zero concentration. If Π is given in dynes-cm^{-2} and c_2 in grams per milliliter, the intercept will be RT/M_2, where R is expressed in ergs-deg^{-1}-mole^{-1}. For solutes of moderate molecular weight the extrapolation presents no difficulties, but for very high molecular weight polymers, the concentrations required to obtain measurable osmotic pressures will lie in a region where ternary solute interactions make an important contribution to deviations from solution ideality and the reduced osmotic pressure plot will, therefore, show a considerable curvature. The best method to deal with this situation is to use a relation between A_3 and A_2 derived from theory. It can be shown that the ratio $A_3/A_2^2M_2$, which has the value of 5/8 for hard spheres, falls off with increasing interpenetration of the spheres, tending to zero as the conditions of a Θ solvent are approached (Stockmayer and Casassa, 1952; Koyama, 1957). In practice, the value of this ratio seems to lie frequently in the vicinity of 0.25, so that the concentration dependence of the reduced osmotic pressure may be expressed by

$$\Pi/c_2 = (RT/M_2)[1 + A_2c_2M_2 + (1/4)A_2^2c_2^2M_2^2]$$

$$(\Pi/c_2)^{1/2} = (\Pi/c_2)_{c_2 \to 0}^{1/2}[1 + (1/2)A_2c_2M_2] \tag{4.30}$$

As (4.30) indicates, plots of $(\Pi/c_2)^{1/2}$ against c_2 frequently show much smaller deviations from linearity than the conventional plots of the first power of the reduced osmotic pressure and they lend themselves, therefore, to a safer extrapolation. A typical example of the advantage to be derived from such a plot is illustrated in Fig. IV.4 on data obtained by Krigbaum (1954).

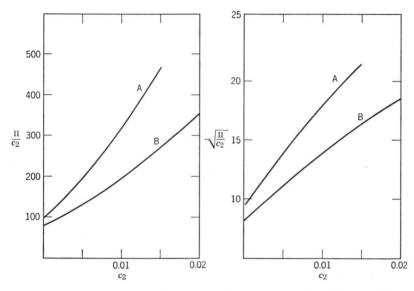

Fig. IV.4. Extrapolation of reduced osmotic pressures Π/c_2. (A) Polyisobutene ($\bar{M}_n = 254{,}000$) in cyclohexane. (B) Polystyrene ($\bar{M}_n = 328{,}000$) in toluene. Π is given in g-cm^{-2}.

5. Osmotic Measurements with Partially Selective Membranes

The experimental determination of osmotic pressures requires the use of a membrane which is permeable to the solvent but will not permit the passage of solute molecules. A typical experimental arrangement is indicated schematically in Fig. IV.5. Here the membrane separates the test solution from a chamber containing pure solvent. The chemical potential gradient causes the solvent to pass into the solution, causing its liquid level to rise in a capillary until the hydrostatic pressure equals the osmotic pressure Π—at this point, as we have seen, the activity of the solvent in the solution will be equal to its activity in the standard state and the driving force towards solvent transfer will disappear. We should then expect the

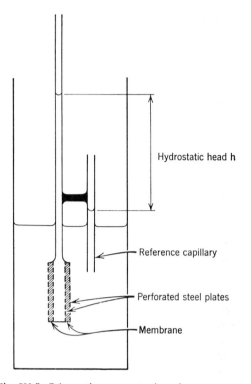

Fig. IV.5. Schematic representation of an osmometer.

hydrostatic head to approach with time exponentially towards its equilibrium value.

In practice, the ideal of perfect semipermeability is often difficult to attain, particularly if the sample has not been subjected to adequate fractionation, so that it contains a significant fraction of low molecular weight material, or if an attempt is made to extend osmotic pressure measurements to samples of relatively low number-average molecular weight. Typical data illustrating this problem (Fox et al., 1962) are shown in Fig. IV.6. We may see that for an unfractionated sample with $\bar{M}_n = 34,000$ the hydrostatic head rises to a maximum and then slowly declines. This decline is clearly due to a diffusion of the solute through the osmotic membrane. Fox et al. found that solute diffusion through the membrane could be eliminated for a material in this molecular weight range by careful fractionation, but even a relatively sharp fraction with $\bar{M}_n = 15,700$ showed evidence of passage through the membrane.

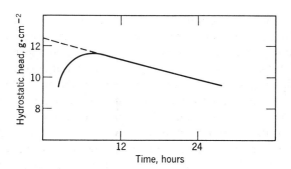

Fig. IV.6. Osmotic pressure measurement with a membrane which is partially permeable to the solute, poly(methyl methacrylate), $\bar{M}_w = 34,000$.

The question then arises how to deal with data obtained under these non-
ideal conditions.   It is a common procedure to allow for the loss of solute
through diffusion by back extrapolation of the declining branch of the plot
of the pressure head to zero time.   However, Staverman (1952) has
criticized this procedure and has pointed out that experimental data obtained with a "leaky" membrane cannot be treated by classical thermodynamics.   The appropriate theoretical analysis of the problem in terms
of the thermodynamics of irreversible processes indicates that the significant
experimental quantity is the apparent osmotic pressure in the steady state,
when the volume flow due to the chemical potential gradient is counterbalanced by flow due to hydrostatic pressure.   This steady-state pressure
Π_{ss} is related to the osmotic pressure representing thermodynamic equilibrium Π_{eq} by

$$\Pi_{ss}/\Pi_{eq} = S[1 - (1 - S)\phi_2 + \ldots] \qquad (4.31)$$

where S is a "selectivity coefficient" characteristic of the membrane.   This
coefficient is defined so that $(1 - S)$ is the ratio of the concentration of the
solution flowing through the membrane under the influence of a hydrostatic
pressure to the concentration of the solution outside the membrane when
the solutions on both sides of the membrane are of identical concentration.
Thus, $S = 1$ corresponds to an ideal semipermeable membrane, while $S = 0$
represents a membrane with no selectivity between solvent and solute so
that no osmotic effects would be observed.   For a homologous series of
polymer molecules in a given solvent medium the selectivity coefficient
would be expected to fall off sharply with decreasing molecular weight

below a certain range determined by the nature of the osmotic membrane and the extent of its swelling.   The average selectivity coefficient observed with solutions of polydisperse polymers will, therefore, for any given number-average molecular weight, tend to decrease with an increasing breadth of the molecular weight distribution (Elias and Männer, 1960).   An outstanding application of the theory of partially selective osmotic membranes was reported by Gardon and Mason (1957) who measured osmotic pressures of solutions of lignin sulfonates in the molecular weight range of 5000. They estimated S by comparing the ratio of the diffusion rates of polymer and a low molecular weight solute through a sintered glass barrier (which would be expected to have $S = 0$) and the membrane used in osmotic measurements.   They demonstrated that proper treatment of the data led to essentially identical molecular weights for membranes with selectivity coefficients ranging from 0.95 to a value as low as 0.75.   Another solution to the problem of how to deal with imperfectly selective membranes was suggested by Elias (1961b) who assumed that the selectivity coefficient should tend towards unity as the viscosity of the solvent tends to infinity.   He proposed a plot of the apparent molecular weight against the reciprocal solvent viscosity which is apparently linear and allows an easy extrapolation. However, the general validity of this procedure appears to be questionable.

6. Surface Pressure

In favorable cases it is possible to deposit a given molecular species in the form of a monomolecular layer on the surface of water, an aqueous solution, or on an oil–water interface.   The establishment of such layers requires the deposited molecules to contain polar groups to be "anchored" in the aqueous phase (hypophase)—yet the solubility of these molecules in the hypophase must be negligible.   If the surface coverage is small, the molecules in the surface layer will behave like a two-dimensional gas, exerting a pressure on any barrier which restricts the area over which they can spread.   It can then easily be shown, by considerations analogous to those of the kinetic gas theory, that in the limit of low surface pressure P_S the equation of state should be

$$\lim_{Ps \to 0} P_S A = nRT \qquad (4.32)$$

where n moles of solute are spread over an area A.   It is necessary to realize that complete surface coverage by a unimolecular layer represents a very small amount of material of the order of 10^{-7} g/cm.[2]   The validity of the ideal law formulated by (4.32) would then require the use of extremely small samples and the measurement of correspondingly small pressures. For instance, with a surface concentration of 10^{-9} g-cm^{-2} of a material with a molecular weight of 10^4, the surface pressure should be about 0.0025 dynes-cm^{-1}.

By analogy with the van der Waals equation of state for nonideal gases, eq. (4.32) may be modified by subtracting from the total area the "excluded area" due to the physical size of the adsorbed molecules.   If we then define the specific area A_S as the surface area per unit weight of adsorbed substance and A_S^0 the corresponding excluded specific area, eq. (4.32) must be modified to

$$P_S(A_S - A_S^0) = RT/M_2 \qquad (4.33)$$

so that the slope of a plot of $P_S A_S$ against P_S gives the excluded specific area, while the intercept defines the molecular weight.

The application of surface pressure measurements to the study of macromolecules has been reviewed by Crisp (1958) and by Beredjick (1963). The technique is a difficult one, particularly since the most meaningful data are obtained at very low sample concentrations, where the problem of excluding adventitious impurities becomes quite serious.   The very small surface pressures require extremely careful experimental design.   In addition, the technique for depositing the surface layer in a manner such that the individual molecules are properly spaced on the hypophase may be critical.   In the case of globular proteins, surface pressures lead to molecular weights which are in very good agreement with results obtained by osmometry (Bull, 1947; Cheesman and Davies, 1954).   With hemoglobin, the apparent molecular weight depends markedly on the nature of the hypophase, indicating dissociation into subunits.   Insulin, on the other hand, appears to be associated in the surface layer above pH 3.   Both these effects are, however, consistent with the behavior of these proteins in solution (cf. Chap. VIII, Sec. B-3) and do not, therefore, represent artifacts.

With synthetic chain polymers a much more complex situation is encountered, as would be expected, since flexible chain molecules deposited on a surface will resist strongly any compression which would force them to interpenetrate and thus restrict the number of available conformations. This effect is analogous to that treated by the Flory–Huggins theory for polymer chains in solution, but is even more pronounced in the two-dimensional case.   A statistical theory of the thermodynamic behavior of flexible chains deposited on a plane lattice with each lattice site occupied by a water molecule or a chain segment was formulated by Singer (1948) who obtained

$$P_s = \frac{RT}{A_s^0 M_0}\left[\ln\left(1 - \frac{A_s^0}{A_s}\right) - \frac{V_2 - V_1}{V_2}\frac{Z}{2}\ln\left(1 - \frac{2A_s^0}{zA_s}\right)\right] \quad (4.34)$$

where M_0 is the molecular weight of the chain segment and z is the coordination number of the lattice. This result shows that for $V_2 \gg V_1$ the surface pressure will be quite insensitive to the molecular weight of the solute, unless $A_s \gg A_s^0$. It is in fact found that fractions of synthetic polymers varying widely in molecular weight give identical surface pressures, since it is not feasible to make measurements at sufficient dilution to avoid extensive chain interpenetration (Hotta, 1954). On the other hand, Singer's parameter z may be used to characterize the stiffness of chain molecules deposited in a surface layer (Schick, 1957). Singer's treatment is limited in its application, since it does not take account of energetic interactions between the macromolecules. The inter-solute forces are particularly large with polyelectrolytes, where they will make an important contribution to the surface pressure. This effect has been demonstrated by Davies and Llopis (1954) who studied the surface behavior of a lysine–glutamic acid–leucine copolypeptide over a range of pH. Recently Motomura and Matuura (1963) proposed a modification of the Singer relation which would take proper account of the energetic interaction between polymer segments.

A very interesting observation was made by Beredjick and Ries (1962) who measured the surface pressures of isotactic and syndiotactic poly-(methyl methacrylate). They found, as shown in Fig. IV.7, that for low

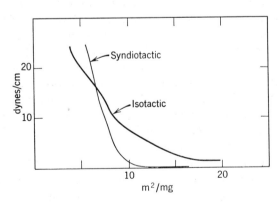

Fig. IV.7. Pressure–area isotherms for isotactic and syndiotactic poly(methyl methacrylate).

surface coverage the isotactic polymer had very much larger surface pressures. This result is particularly intriguing since the properties of poly-(methyl methacrylate) of different stereoregularity are usually very similar in homogeneous solution. More data will have to be gathered before we may decide whether the apparent excluded volume of a chain molecule deposited on a surface is, in general, highly sensitive to the steric configuration of the chain.

B. EQUILIBRIUM CENTRIFUGATION

Although all our experiments are necessarily carried out under the influence of the terrestrial gravitational field g, the effect of this field is generally neglected in considerations of the properties of systems at equilibrium. This neglect is justified in most cases of interest since the change in the gravitational potential of a particle when placed in different locations of the system under consideration will be extremely small compared to kT. The gravitational field will produce an appreciable effect either if the dimension of the system is very large in the direction normal to the surface of the earth, or if the mass of kinetic particles is sufficiently great. The first case is exemplified by the gas distribution in the atmosphere of the earth. The second case was first considered by Einstein (1906b) who pointed out that the distribution of equilibrium concentrations will be experimentally observable for particles of volume v_2 and density ρ_2 suspended in a medium with a density ρ_1 in a system of height h, if $v_2(\rho_2 - \rho_1)gh$ is neither too large nor too small compared to kT. A few years later Perrin (1908) and Westgren (1914) demonstrated that the variation with height of the equilibrium concentration may, in fact, be observed with microscopic particles and may be used to evaluate Avogadro's number.

A consideration of the principles underlying the equilibrium distribution in a gravitational field led Svedberg to the realization that the method should be applicable to the determination of the molecular weight of macromolecules, if gravitational fields of the order of 10^3–10^4 g were available to the experimentalist. With the development of the ultracentrifuge in the Uppsala laboratory, such fields became accessible and by 1926 the instrument had been used for the determination of the molecular weight of hemoglobin (Svedberg, 1926; Svedberg and Fåhraeus, 1926) and of ovalbumin (Svedberg and Nichols, 1926). The popularity of the method declined gradually during the next two decades, largely because of the long times required for sufficiently close approach to equilibrium conditions. However, in recent years the importance of equilibrium centrifugation has again increased due to several factors. A number of advances in instrument design and experimental technique have greatly increased the utility of the method for high precision measurements (Schachman, 1959, 1963). It was realized that the use of Θ-solvents permits the reliable evaluation of entire molecular weight distribution functions of polydisperse polymer samples, as against the limited characterization of such materials by other techniques in terms of molecular weight averages. At the same time cell designs and techniques were developed, which allow observations in liquid columns with heights of 1 mm or less, reducing the time required for a close approach to equilibrium from days to as little as an hour (Van Holde and Baldwin, 1958; Yphantis, 1960). Finally, the development of the technique of density gradient centrifugation provided a badly needed method for the study of distributions of chemical composition, which has found spectacular application in the study of biologically important macromolecules and promises to become equally important in investigations of synthetic polymers.

1. Methods for Determining Solute Distribution in the Ultracentrifuge Cell

It is essential that the distribution of the solute in the test cell should be recorded while it is being spun at high speed in the ultracentrifuge. In Svedberg's original experiments (Svedberg, 1926; Svedberg and Fåhreus, 1926; Svedberg and Nichols 1926), this was accomplished by taking advantage of the absorption of light by the solute. The solution was therefore photographed using light of an appropriate wavelength and the solution concentration in various locations was estimated from the relative blackening of the photographic plate. This method is very advantageous with some important biological samples (e.g., proteins and nucleic acids) which have heavy absorption bands in the ultraviolet, so that convenient optical densities can be obtained at very high dilution (Schumaker and Schachman, 1957). As we shall see, certain complications arise in the interpretation of the data obtained at concentrations such that deviations from Raoult's law are appreciable and it is, therefore, highly desirable to work at as high a dilution as possible.

On the other hand, a number of very sensitive methods have been developed in which the *concentration gradient*, rather than the concentration itself, is the directly observed quantity. Among these methods the so-called "schlieren method" has been utilized by Svensson (1939, 1940) in an optical system which has become very popular. The method depends on the fact that a ray of light passing through a medium with a refractive index gradient perpendicular to the direction of light propagation is bent in the direction of increasing refractive index, n, the deflection being proportional to the magnitude of the gradient. This principle is then used to distort the image of an illuminated slit into a plot of the concentration gradient existing in a test cell through which the light is passed. Since the refractive index of dilute solutions is linear in solute concentration, the schlieren method yields, once the refractive index increment $(\partial n/\partial c_2)_T$ has been determined, the concentration gradient in the centrifuge cell. Refractive index gradients may also be determined by the use of interferometers and this method is considered by Schachman (1959) to hold most promise in the future development of equilibrium ultracentrifugation.

2. Ultracentrifuge Equilibrium in a Two-Component System

In a system subjected to a large gravitational field the gravitational potential makes an appreciable contribution to the chemical potential of the various components. For a solute of a molecular weight M_2 placed in a centrifuge with an angular velocity ω at a distance r from the axis of rotation, the chemical potential $\bar{G}_2$ is then given by

$$\bar{G}_2 = \bar{G}_2^0 + RT \ln \gamma_2 c_2 - M_2 \omega^2 r^2/2 \qquad (4.35)$$

Chemical equilibrium requires $\bar{G}_2$ to be invariant throughout the system, i.e.,

$$d\bar{G}_2/dr = (\partial \bar{G}_2/\partial P)_{c_2} dP/dr + (\partial \bar{G}_2/\partial c_2)_P dc_2/dr - M_2 \omega^2 r = 0 \qquad (4.36)$$

Using the relations

$$(\partial \bar{G}_2/\partial P)_{c_2} = \bar{V}_2 = M_2 \bar{v}_2 \qquad (4.37a)$$

$$dP/dr = \rho \omega^2 r \qquad (4.37b)$$

where ρ is the density of the solution, substituting into (4.36) and rearranging, the molecular weight of the solute may be related to its concentration gradient by

$$\frac{M_2(1 - \bar{v}_2\rho)\omega^2 r c_2}{RT} = [1 + c_2(\partial \ln \gamma_2/\partial c_2)_P]dc_2/dr \qquad (4.38)$$

The term $(1 - \bar{v}_2\rho)$ represents the effect of the buoyancy due to the medium in which the macromolecules are suspended. If this term is positive, the molecules will sediment (i.e., travel outwards from the center of rotation) while a negative value of $(1 - \bar{v}_2\rho)$ will lead to an analogous flotation in the opposite direction.

The interpretation of the data is simplest if the experiment is carried out under conditions under which Raoult's law is valid. In that case, $(\partial \ln \gamma_2/\partial c_2) = 0$ and a plot of $\ln c_2$ against r^2 is linear. From the slope of this plot the molecular weight of the solute may be calculated after evaluation of the partial specific volume $\bar{v}_2$. If the macromolecules are not dissolved in a Θ-solvent, the contribution of the second term in the bracket on the right-hand side of eq. (4.38) must be taken into account. Under conditions such that the plot of the reduced osmotic pressure against solute concentration is linear, it can be shown from the Gibbs–Duhem relation that $(\partial \ln \gamma_2/\partial c_2)_P$ will be related to the osmotic virial coefficients by

$$(\partial \ln \gamma_2/\partial c_2)_P = 2A_2M_2 + 3A_3M_2c_2 + \ldots \quad (4.39)$$

so that (4.38) may be rewritten (Mandelkern et al., 1957) as

$$(1 - \bar{v}_2\rho)\omega^2rc_2/(dc_2/dr) =$$
$$(RT/M_2)\,(1 + 2A_2M_2c_2 + 3A_3M_2c_2^2 + \ldots) \quad (4.40)$$

We see then that for nonideal solutions the plot of $\ln c_2$ against r^2 will no longer be linear, but that the slope will tend to decrease with increasing values of r. The complications introduced by such solution nonideality into the interpretation of the data were discussed by Mandelkern et al. (1957) who stressed the great advantages to be derived from working in Θ-solvents or at least in systems in which deviations from ideal solution behavior are small. Data obtained in nonideal solutions may be treated either by an expression of the form (4.40), or else by an extrapolation of the reciprocal apparent molecular weight (evaluated without regard for the deviation from solution ideality) to zero solution concentration. The latter procedure was first suggested by Wales et al. (1951) who plotted $1/M_2^{app}$ against the original solution concentration, but Williams et al. (1958) pointed out that a more reliable extrapolation could be obtained if $1/M_2^{app}$ is plotted against the arithmetic mean of the solution concentration at the top and the bottom of the cell under centrifugation equilibrium conditions.

In principle, the pressure dependence of $\bar{v}_2\rho$ and $(\partial \ln \gamma_2/\partial c_2)_P$ should be taken into account in the evaluation of experimental data. However, in practice the pressure generated with the relatively low gravitational fields used in equilibrium centrifugation leads to variations in these quantities which are small enough to be neglected.

When the solution concentration at various locations in the test cell is determined directly (i.e., by optical absorption) the use of eq. (4.38) and (4.40) is straightforward.   If however the experimental procedure measures concentration gradients, an integration is required to evaluate $c_2(r)$.   The cells employed in ultracentrifugation are generally sector-shaped so that the amount of solute in a layer between r and $r + dr$ is proportional to $c_2 r$ as is

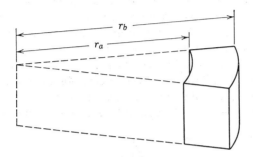

Fig. IV.8. Schematic representation of a sector-shaped ultracentrifuge cell.

apparent from the schematic representation in Fig. IV.8.   From considerations of a material balance the distribution of concentrations must then be related to the initial uniform concentration c_2^0 by

$$\int_{r_a}^{r_b} r c_2 dr = c_2^0 (r_b^2 - r_a^2)/2 \qquad (4.41)$$

where r_a and r_b are the distances of the top and bottom of the cell from the axis of rotation.   Combining (4.41) with (4.38) for the case of an ideal solution for which $(\partial \ln \gamma_2 / \partial c_2)_P = 0$, we obtain for sector-shaped cells

$$[RT/M_2(1 - \bar{v}_2 \rho)\omega^2] \int_{r_a}^{r_b} (dc_2/dr)dr = c_2^0 (r_b^2 - r_a^2)/2 \qquad (4.42)$$

A number of alternative procedures by which similar evaluations may be carried out for data obtained with non-ideal solutions were outlined by Van Holde and Baldwin (1958).

3. Equilibrium Centrifugation of a Polydisperse Polymer Solution

If a solution contains a number of solute species, a relation analogous to (4.38) holds for each of them.   However, if the solution is nonideal, the activity coefficient of each dissolved species will depend on the concentration of all the other species, so that the molecular weight M_i of species i must be represented by a modification of (4.38) to

$$\frac{M_i(1 - \bar{v}\rho)\omega^2 r c_i}{RT} = \frac{dc_i}{dr} + c_i \sum_{k=2}^{n} \left(\frac{\partial \ln \gamma_i}{dc_k}\right)_{P,\,c_j \neq c_k} \frac{dc_k}{dr} \quad (4.43)$$

In this expression the partial specific volume $\bar{v}$ is generally considered to be constant for all members of a polymer-homologous series. Since no satisfactory theory exists for the excluded volume in a system containing chain molecules of different lengths, any estimate of the second term on the right of eq. (4.43) must be considered highly uncertain and a reliable interpretation of the data is possible only when the polymer is dissolved in a Θ-solvent.

Characteristic plots illustrating the effects observed with a solute consisting of species with different molecular weights are illustrated in Fig. IV.9. It may be seen that the plot of log c_2 against r^2, which is linear for an

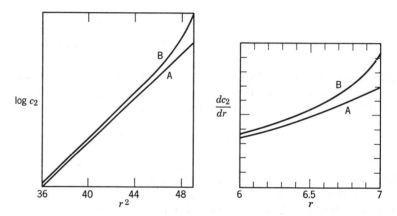

Fig. IV.9. Dependence of the equilibrium solute distribution in the ultracentrifuge on the molecular weight distribution of the solute. (A) Monodisperse solute. (B) Solute with the same weight-average molecular weight, containing 1 g of a fraction with $M = 2\bar{M}_w$ and 5 g of a fraction with $M = 0.8\bar{M}_w$. The symbol c_2 is used here for the total concentration of the polydisperse solute.

ideal solution with a single solute species, exhibits a characteristic upward curvature in the case of a solution containing a small amount of a second solute with a much higher molecular weight. The difference between the two systems is more pronounced in a plot of dc_2/dr against r than in a plot of c_2 against r. It may be noted that the method is particularly sensitive in detecting a small fraction of a high molecular weight component in the solute. When the solute contains a fraction of relatively low molecular weight, this fraction will be distributed almost uniformly under conditions such as represented in Fig. IV.9 and the data would, therefore, not be suitable for determining the shape of the low molecular weight end of the molecular weight distribution function.

The concentration gradient at a distance r from the axis of rotation will be given for a polydisperse sample in a Θ-solvent by

$$dc_r/dr = \sum_i dc_{ir}/dr = [(1 - \bar{v}\rho)\omega^2 r/RT] \sum_i c_{ir}M_i \qquad (4.44)$$

and since the weight average molecular weight at r is defined by $\bar{M}_{wr} = \sum_i c_{ir}M_i/c_r$, we may relate it to the concentration gradient by

$$\bar{M}_{wr} = [RT/(1 - \bar{v}\rho)\omega^2 rc_r](dc_r/dr) \qquad (4.45)$$

The weight average molecular weight of all the solute in the cell may then be obtained by a suitable integration. For a sector-shaped cell, in which the cross-sectional area is proportional to r, a material balance leads to (Williams et al., 1958)

$$\bar{M}_w = \int_{r_a}^{r_b} \bar{M}_{wr}c_r r \, dr \Big/ \int_{r_a}^{r_b} c_r r \, dr = 2RT(c_b - c_a)/(1 - \bar{v}\rho)\omega^2 c^0(r_b^2 - r_a^2) \qquad (4.46)$$

where $c_b - c_a$ may be evaluated by graphical integration of $\int_{r_a}^{r_b} (dc_r/dr)dr$.

Van Holde and Baldwin (1958) have pointed out that for $r = \sqrt{(r_b^2 - r_a^2)/2}$ the local concentration c_r is well approximated by the original concentration c^0 and $\bar{M}_{wr} \approx \bar{M}_w$. Thus, it is possible to obtain a close estimate of the weight average molecular weight from measurements of the concentration gradient at a single level. This procedure will tend to lead to low values of $\bar{M}_w$ if the molecular weight distribution is very broad.

We have noted previously that sedimentation equilibrium data obtained under conditions such that the solute concentration at the top and the bottom of the cell are related by a relatively small factor are not suitable for defining the low molecular weight end of the molecular weight distribution function. Since this portion of the distribution function has a large effect on $\bar{M}_n$, the number average molecular weight cannot be estimated, in general, with any assurance from equilibrium centrifugation data. However, Hermans (1963) has shown that this difficulty can be overcome if the centrifuge is operated at a speed which reduces the solute concentration at the top of the cell to a negligible value. In that case the various molecular weight averages are given by

$$\bar{M}_n = \frac{RT}{\omega^2(1 - \bar{v}\rho)} \cdot \frac{4 \int_{r_a}^{r_b} (r_b^2 - r^2)(dc_r/dr)dr}{\int_{r_a}^{r_b} (r_b^2 - r^2)(dc_r/dr)dr}$$

$$\bar{M}_w = \frac{RT}{\omega^2(1 - \bar{v}\rho)} \cdot \frac{2 \int_{r_a}^{r_b} (dc_r/dr)dr}{\int_{r_a}^{r_b} (r_b^2 - r^2)(dc_r/dr)dr}$$

$$\bar{M}_z = \frac{RT}{\omega^2(1 - \bar{v}\rho)} \cdot \frac{(dc_r/dr)_{r=r_b}}{r_b \int_{r_a}^{r_b} (dc_r/dr)dr}$$

4. Time Required for Approach to Equilibrium

One of the main reasons for the rare use of the ultracentrifuge equilibrium method, in the years immediately following Svedberg's development of the technique, was the extremely long time required for a satisfactory approach to equilibrium conditions. The theory of the approach to equilibrium was developed by Van Holde and Baldwin (1958), who showed that for finite centrifugation times the distribution corresponds to an apparent molecular weight which is too low. The time $t(\epsilon)$ required to approach within a fraction ϵ of the true molecular weight is given by

$$t(\epsilon) = [(r_b - r_a)^2/D\pi^2 U(\alpha)] \ln \left\{ \pi^2 \epsilon U^2(\alpha)/4[1 + \cosh(1/2\alpha)] \right\}$$

$$U(\alpha) = (1 + 4\pi^2\alpha^2)/4\pi^2\alpha^2$$

$$\alpha = 2RT/(1 - \bar{v}\rho)M_2\omega^2(r_b^2 - r_a^2) \tag{4.47}$$

where D is the diffusion coefficient of the sedimenting species. For most practical conditions the logarithmic term changes little with design variables, so that the time requirement of an experiment may be taken as proportional to the square of the height of the liquid column in the centrifuge cell. A shortening of the liquid column in the ultracentrifuge cell from 1 cm to 1 mm led, as expected, to a hundredfold acceleration of the approach to equilibrium (Van Holde and Baldwin, 1958; Yphantis, 1960). The utilization of such short cells represents, therefore, a great advantage, particularly if the experimentalist aims only at an estimate of the weight average molecular weight.   When very large species are studied, the times required to reach sedimentation equilibrium increase because of the decrease in diffusion coefficients.   It is a remarkable fact, nonetheless, that the same instrument operated at different speeds can be used for determining molecular weights of species as small as sucrose or as large as virus particles in the molecular weight range of 10^7–10^8.   The ultimate limit is reached when the speed of the centrifuge is so low that the terrestrial gravitational field is not negligible compared to the gravitational field of the centrifuge.   Stationary "gravity cells" in which the distribution of equilibrium concentration is due to the gravitational field of the earth may then be used for the characterization of virus particles corresponding to molecular weights of the order of 10^9 (Weber et al., 1963).

5. Equilibrium Sedimentation in a Density Gradient

The introduction of the technique of density gradient centrifugation by Meselson et al. (1957) opened the use of the equilibrium centrifuge to a wide range of new problems, many of which cannot be explored by any other presently available technique.   A review of the theoretical development and the application of the method to biochemical problems was published by Vinograd and Hearst (1962) while another review by Hermans and Ende (1963a) emphasizes applications to synthetic polymers.

When a concentrated solution of a low molecular weight solute with a density very different from that of the solvent is subjected to the gravitational field of an ultracentrifuge, the density gradient corresponding to equilibrium conditions may attain relatively large values.   If the solution contains also a macromolecular solute, the macromolecules will tend to sediment or to float depending on whether their effective buoyant density ρ_2^{eff} (a quantity which we shall consider later in more detail) is larger or smaller than the density ρ of the surrounding medium.   The macromolecules will thus tend to concentrate in a band around the distance r_0 from the axis of rotation where the density of the medium equals their buoyant density.   Assuming the density gradient $(d\rho/dr)_0$ to be constant across the width of the macromolecular band and the effects of deviations from solution ideality to be negligible, the potential energy per mole of macromolecular solute due to the gravitational field is

$$E_2 = [(r - r_0)^2/2]M_2(d\rho/dr)_0\omega^2r_0/\rho_2^{\text{eff}} \tag{4.48}$$

and the solute distribution around r_0 is given by the Boltzmann distribution

$$c_2(r) = c_2(r_0) \exp\left[-E_2(r)/RT\right]$$

$$= c_2(r_0) \exp\left[-(r - r_0)^2/2\sigma^2\right] \tag{4.49a}$$

$$\sigma^2 = RT\rho_2^{\text{eff}}/M_2(d\rho/dr)_{r_0}\omega^2 r_0 \tag{4.49b}$$

The density gradient produced by the gravitational field is a consequence of both effects due to a concentration gradient and a compression gradient. It may be represented (Hearst et al., 1961) by

$$(d\rho/dr) = [(1/\beta^0) - (\partial \ln V/\partial P)_T\rho^2]\omega^2 r \equiv \omega^2 r/\beta \tag{4.50a}$$

$$1/\beta^0 = (d\rho/d \ln a_3)M_3(1 - \bar{v}_3\rho)/RT \tag{4.50b}$$

where the subscript 3 refers to the cosolvent. The first term in (4.50a) is usually an order of magnitude larger than the term due to the compressibility of the solution and values of the β parameter for a number of aqueous binary systems useful in concentration gradient centrifugation have been listed by Ifft et al. (1961). Typical values for β are in the range of 10^9 to 10^{10} cm^5 sec^{-2} g^{-1} so that a centrifuge with a mean value of $r = 6.5$ cm and a speed of 40,000 rpm generates density gradients between 0.01 and 0.1 g-cm^{-4}.

In the application of density gradient ultracentrifugation to problems in biochemistry, one aims frequently at an analysis of systems containing macromolecules of identical molecular weight but different effective buoyant density. Our ability to resolve bands representing different solute species will depend on the ratio γ of the distance Δr_0 between the midpoints of the bands and the standard deviation σ of the location of the macromolecules within their band. Since $\Delta r_0 = \Delta\rho_2^{\text{eff}}/(d\rho/dr)$, we obtain by substitution from (4.48) and (4.49).

$$\gamma = \Delta r_0/\sigma = \Delta\rho_2^{\text{eff}}(M_2\beta/RT\rho_2^{\text{eff}})^{1/2} \tag{4.51}$$

The resolution does not depend on the speed at which the centrifuge is being operated, since Δr_0 and σ decrease in the same manner with an increasing gravitational field. The resolution becomes easier with species of very high molecular weight and it will be improved by an appropriate choice of a solvent system with a high β value. A γ value of at least 2 will be needed for a satisfactory separation of solute bands.

For solutes in a binary system the effective buoyant density is related simply to the partial specific volume by $\rho_2^{\text{eff}} = 1/\bar{v}_2$. In ternary systems the situation is considerably more complex, since one of the solvent species will generally be attracted preferentially to the region occupied by the macromolecule. The effective buoyant density will then depend on the density of the solute including this solvation envelope. Hearst and Vinograd (1961) have demonstrated that the buoyant density of DNA in aqueous systems may vary within wide limits depending on the nature and concentration of added salts and a similar effect was observed by Hermans and Ende (1963b) with polystyrene, whose effective buoyant density was found to be almost twice as high in methylcyclohexane–bromoform than in the benzene–bromoform system. This effect is easily understood since the heavy bromoform cosolvent will be concentrated much more effectively in the region occupied by the polymer in a medium rich in methylcyclohexane, which is a much poorer solvent for polystyrene than benzene.

The first experiment reported with the density gradient centrifugation method (Meselson et al., 1957) was a particularly beautiful demonstration of the value of this technique. In this experiment bacteria were grown in a culture medium rich in N^{15}, so that the deoxyribose nucleic acid (DNA) of the organisms, labeled with the heavy nitrogen isotope, had a density slightly higher than normal DNA. At a given time, the bacterial culture medium was swamped with nutrient with the natural nitrogen isotope distribution and the change in the buoyant density of DNA isolated from successive bacterial generations was analyzed in the density gradient centrifuge. On the basis of a suggestion by Watson and Crick (1953), it was assumed that the replication of DNA during cell division involves a separation of the two strands of the double helix (see p. 146) with each strand serving as a template for the synthesis of its complementary chain. If this mechanism is valid, the second generation of cells originating from the N^{15} labeled organisms should contain DNA in which one of the strands of each double helix is labeled with the heavy nitrogen isotope. Succeeding cell generations would have increasing concentrations of DNA containing only the natural distribution of nitrogen isotopes, with some half-labeled DNA. At any time, only DNA molecules with three sharply defined buoyant densities, but no species of intermediate density, should be observed. This expectation was fully confirmed by the density gradient ultracentrifugation data (see Fig. IV.10) so that the DNA replication mechanism, which had previously been of the nature of an inspired theory, could now be accepted as established fact. In the relatively short time following this classical experiment, the density gradient ultracentrifuge method has contributed in a variety of ways to biochemical research. We can cite here a few examples illustrating these developments. By a labeling technique similar to that described above, it was established that some

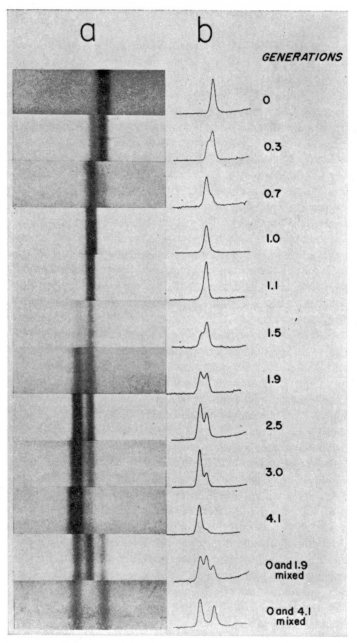

Fig. IV.10. Density gradient untracentrifugation analysis of DNA from the bacterium *E. coli*. The bacteria were grown on a nutrient rich in N^{15} and at time 0 a large amount of N^{14} nutrient was added. (a) Ultraviolet absorption on photographs of density gradient ultracentrifuge cells. (b) Densitometer traces of UV absorption on photographs. (Courtesy Prof. M. Meselson.)

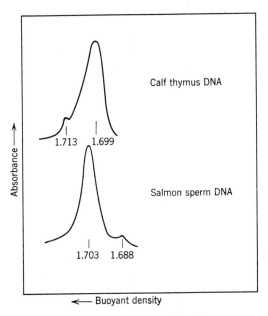

Fig. IV.11. Heterogeneity of DNA from higher organisms as revealed by density gradient centrifugation in an aqueous CsCl solution.

ribose nucleic acid (RNA) is transferred intact through successive cell generations (Davern and Meselson, 1960). The buoyant density of DNA was found to be a linear function of the guanine–cytosine content, which is different in different microorganisms so that the DNA from each species forms in the density gradient a band with a characteristic position (Rolfe and Meselson, 1959; Sueoka et al., 1959). In DNA isolated from tissues of higher organisms the density gradient pattern occasionally reveals satellite bands (Schildkraut et al., 1962a) which may originate from symbiotic organisms or may be due to other, as yet unknown causes. A typical example of this effect is illustrated in Fig. IV.11, which incidentally also exemplifies the sensitivity of the method in detecting a small amount of contaminants differing only slightly from the density of the major component. It has also been established by Schildkraut et al. (1961, 1962b) that the separated strands of DNA originating from different organisms or viruses may recombine to hybrid double helices of intermediate density, if the parent organisms or viruses were closely related. A typical result of these investigations is represented in Fig. IV.12. Another spectacular result was reported by Hall and Spiegelman (1961) who used the density gradient

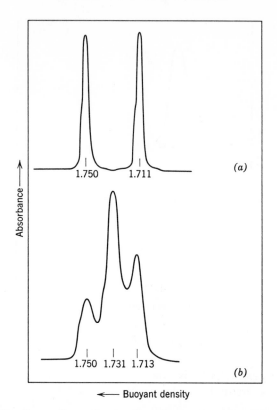

Fig. IV.12. Density gradient ultracentrifugation study of the formation of hybrid DNA. (a) The material with a buoyant density 1.711 came from bacteriophage T-3, that with a buoyant density of 1.750 from N^{15} labeled bacteriophage T-7. (b) After denaturation and renaturation of a mixture of the two DNA species, a new material with an intermediate density is formed.

centrifuge to prove that the RNA synthesized by a bacterium infected by a virus forms a highly specific association complex with the DNA of the infecting virus and by Doi and Spiegelman (1962) who demonstrated a similar specific interaction between the RNA of certain viruses and the DNA of their host cells.

The first application of density gradient ultracentrifugation to the study of synthetic polymers was reported by Bresler et al. (1960) who used the technique for characterizing a system containing a styrene–isoprene block polymer as well as the two homopolymers. This application of the method is potentially of great importance for the characterization of copolymers since fractionation schemes lead generally to separation of materials differing both in chemical composition and molecular weight, so that the separate characterization of the distribution functions of polymer chain length and polymer composition had long been a vexing problem. However, the theoretical difficulties in interpreting data obtained with a solute in which both composition and molecular weight vary continuously (Hermans and Ende, 1963a) are much greater than those encountered in biological studies dealing with well defined chemical species. In particular, we should note that a broad polymer band in the density gradient need not indicate chemical heterogeneity, since it may be due to a low molecular weight of the solute [see eq. (4.49b)]. A separation of two concentration peaks will occur only if the polymer composition has a bimodal distribution and if the molecular weight is sufficiently high. On the other hand, Hermans and Ende (1963a) have pointed out that a chemically homogeneous polymer must yield a concentration distribution in the density gradient which is symmetrical around r_0, regardless of the molecular weight distribution of the solute. An unsymmetrical distribution of the solute concentration is, therefore, necessarily a qualitative indication of a variation in the buoyant density. Buchdahl et al. (1963a) have also shown that density gradient ultracentrifugation is a uniquely sensitive tool for demonstrating the presence of a small amount of microgel in a sample of linear polymer. Such material with an extremely high molecular weight will appear as a very sharp peak on the refractive index gradient plot. The location of this peak at the center of the band in which the lower molecular weight material collects proves that the material represented by the peak has a similar density as the bulk of the solute and renders it unlikely that the large particles might come from an adventitious contamination of the system. In this manner the evidence from density gradient centrifugation is greatly superior, for instance, to that from light scattering, where the presence of large particles may as easily indicate "dust" as a very high molecular weight fraction of the material under investigation.

Data of Buchdahl et al. (1961, 1963b) have indicated that in favorable cases fractions of vinyl polymers with different stereoregularity may be resolved in a density gradient. These investigators found isotactic polystyrene to have a buoyant density in the bromoform–benzene system higher by 0.028 units as compared to the atactic species. This difference is much larger than the difference in the reciprocal of the partial specific volumes of isotactic and atactic polystyrene and it seems, therefore, to indicate that preferential solvent absorption in mixed solvent media is strongly dependent on the stereoregularity of the dissolved polymer.

Chapter V

SPECTROSCOPY, OPTICAL ACTIVITY, AND THE SCATTERING OF LIGHT AND X-RAYS

No group of experimental methods is more versatile in its application to the study of macromolecular solutions than techniques utilizing the interactions of the macromolecules with radiation in various regions of the electromagnetic spectrum. The effects observed may fall into a number of categories. If a quantum of radiation corresponds to an energy transition in the solute molecules which is permitted by quantum-mechanical considerations, the radiation will be absorbed. This principle is utilized in spectroscopy and it will yield information typical of the region of the electromagnetic spectrum to which it is applied. Spectroscopy is used frequently as an analytical tool and as such it is particularly powerful for the study of complex macromolecules which may not lend themselves to classical analytical techniques. However, this use is, in general, not restricted to dissolved macromolecules and we shall consider it as lying within the scope of this book only in cases where the application of the spectroscopic method to macromolecular solutions leads to results which cannot be obtained by an analogous study of polymers in bulk.

Another technique which has been used extensively in recent years for the study of macromolecules is polarimetry. This method is applicable only to optically active substances, but these comprise the most important macromolecules of living organisms. Optical activity is highly sensitive to conformational transitions and has been invaluable in the study of helix-coil transition phenomena. In recent years an increasing number of synthetic optically active polymers have been prepared, so as to take advantage of the peculiar insight afforded by polarimetry to further our understanding of the behavior of dissolved chain molecules in general. The theory of optical activity in general, and optical activity of polymers in particular, has been reviewed by Urnes and Doty (1961), Moscowitz (1962) and by Tinoco (1962).

Radiation which is not absorbed may be scattered by both solvent and solute molecules. This phenomenon which was developed by Debye (1944) into a powerful tool for the investigation of polymer solutions, is studied conveniently in two regions of the electromagnetic spectrum, namely in the x-ray region first employed by Guinier (1939) (for review see Kratky, 1960) and in the region of visible light (Oster, 1948, 1960; Stacey, 1956). Both techniques are applicable to the determination of the weight average molecular weight of the solute and to the evaluation of parameters which describe the thermodynamic interaction of solvent and solute. However, the wave nature of electromagnetic radiation leads also to interference phenomena which may be used to characterize the size and shape of the scattering particles. Here it is most convenient that of the two spectral regions useful in scattering experiments, the x-ray region comprises radiation with a wavelength much smaller than the overall dimensions of macromolecules, while visible light has wavelengths which are usually much larger than the molecules to be investigated. This difference in the relative magnitude of wavelength and particle size suggests that each of these two spectral regions is particularly well adapted to the investigation of a restricted and mutually complementary class of problems.

There is an important qualitative difference between the kind of information obtained on the one hand by spectroscopy and polarimetry and on the other hand by the study of light scattering. The first two methods measure effects produced in relatively small regions and the phenomena observed are generally independent of the size of the solute molecules, except in very short chains where end-group effects may be significant and in the special case of certain oligomers in which the molecular conformation is critically dependent on the molecular chain length. By contrast, light scattering data are eminently suited to the characterization of the macromolecule as a whole. The two methods, therefore, yield complementary information.

The absorption of a quantum of energy by a solute molecule may in certain cases be followed by re-emission in a stepwise process, so that the energy lost in each step is less than the quantum absorbed and the wavelength of the emitted light is correspondingly longer than that of the absorbed radiation. This phenomenon, called fluorescence, has some interesting applications to the study of macromolecules in solution (Steiner and Edelhoch, 1962; Oster and Nishijima, 1964). In this chapter we shall discuss only part of the applications of fluorescence studies to polymer solutions; other applications, associated with the frictional properties of the solute molecules and with the study of molecular association equilibria, will be discussed in Chaps. VI and VIII.

All methods which depend on the interaction of the sample with electromagnetic radiation have the important advantage that the time lag between the occurrence of a change in the system under investigation and the measurement of a quantity reflecting this change is extremely short.   Let us consider, for instance, a process in which two molecules in solution form an association complex.   Such a transformation will, of course, reduce the osmotic pressure, alter the distribution of the solute in the equilibrium ultracentrifuge, and, as we shall see, it may lead to striking changes in the frictional properties of the solution.   However, the measurement of all these changes is generally a slow process and such techniques will not be applicable if our aim is a study of the kinetics of transformations which are accomplished in a very short time.   By contrast, changes in light scattering intensity, optical activity, or absorption spectra of the system manifest themselves instantaneously and the speed of processes which may be followed by changes in these properties is limited only by our ability to record the time dependence of very rapid changes in the intensity of light.

A. ABSORPTION SPECTROSCOPY

The absorption of radiation by solutions containing macromolecules or low molecular weight solutes may be studied in three regions of the electromagnetic spectrum, corresponding to different modes in which the radiant energy is taken up by the system.   In the region of visible and ultraviolet (UV) light the radiation causes electronic excitation.   Organic molecules absorb visible light only if they contain large resonating systems and macromolecules of this type have not been studied in solution.   Strong absorption of visible light is, however, in some important cases due to transition metal ions forming complexes with macromolecules as, for example, in hemoglobin and other proteins containing the iron–porphyrin complex associated with the macromolecule (Lemberg and Legge, 1949). We shall not discuss the highly specialized problems concerning the spectroscopy of such materials and shall restrict ourselves to a consideration of the use of UV spectroscopy, which has wider applications in investigations of macromolecules.   Spectral absorption in the infrared (IR) arises from transitions between vibrational and rotational states.   Both UV and IR spectroscopy are powerful tools for polymer analysis—we may cite, for instance, the use of UV spectra for the analysis of copolymers of styrene or vinyl pyridine with non-aromatic comonomers, or the use of IR spectroscopy for the differentiation of 1,4-*cis*, 1,4-*trans* or 1,2-addition in polybutadiene.   Such analyses depend on the assumption that contributions of monomer residues to observed optical densities are additive and this assumption appears to represent an excellent approximation in a large number of cases.   However, we may note that such spectroscopic studies are generally not dependent on the solubility of the sample and they fall, therefore, outside and the scope of our discussions, which shall deal with studies of UV and IR spectra only insofar as they are specifically characteristic of the *dissolved* molecules.   The situation is quite different with the absorption in the radio frequency region caused by quantized transitions in the orientation of the magnetic moments of certain atomic nuclei in an external magnetic field.   The resolution attainable in nuclear magnetic resonance (NMR) spectroscopy is very much higher in liquid than in solid samples, so that studies of NMR spectra of macromolecular solutions are necessary in order to obtain analytical information about the polymer itself which is not obtainable on solid specimens.

1. Ultraviolet Spectra

The ionization of aromatic acids or bases is generally accompanied by a pronounced change in the near ultraviolet absorption spectrum.   This phenomenon has been used particularly for the study of the ionization of phenolic hydroxyls in tyrosine residues of proteins.   Since proteins contain a variety of ionizable groups, it is, in general, impossible to obtain a reliable interpretation of titration data in terms of the ionization of a given functional group, and the unambiguous significance of the spectral shift characterizing the ionization of the tyrosine residues is, therefore, particularly welcome.   Typical data obtained by use of this method, first introduced by Crammer and Neuberger (1943), are those of Tanford et al. (1955b) and of Tanford and Hauenstein (1956) with the enzyme ribonuclease.   They showed that of the six tyrosyl residues in the enzyme molecule three ionize reversibly between pH 9 and pH 11.5, as would be expected if the negative charge of the protein in this pH range is taken into account.   However, the ionization of the remaining three tyrosyl groups occurs only at higher pH values and is irreversible, suggesting that these groups are stabilized in their acid form by the tertiary structure of the native protein and that their ionization leads to irreversible denaturation.   This view was reinforced when it was demonstrated (Sage and Singer, 1958) that all the tyrosyl residues titrate normally in a solvent medium in which the ribonuclease is denatured.

The technique of spectrophotometric titration may also be employed to advantage in the study of synthetic polymers.   It enabled Katchalsky and Miller (1954) to establish the equilibrium between the dipolar ionic and the uncharged form in copolymers of acrylic acid and 4-vinylpyridine:

$$-CH_2-CH\cdots CH_2-CH- \qquad \rightleftharpoons \qquad -CH_2-CH\cdots CH_2-CH-$$
$$COO^{\ominus} \qquad\qquad\qquad\qquad\qquad COOH$$

Similarly, Ladenheim et al. (1959), who studied the kinetics of nucleophilic displacements by the basic residues of poly(4-vinylpyridine), were able to use UV spectroscopy to obtain a precise estimate of the state of ionization of highly dilute solutions of the polymeric base in various buffer systems.

It has become increasingly apparent in recent years that ultraviolet spectroscopy is also a valuable method for the study of conformational transitions in proteins, nucleic acids, and their synthetic analogs. The UV spectrum of proteins is largely produced by the phenolic groups of the tyrosine and the indole groups of tryptophan residues with a much smaller contribution from phenylalanine. Since the phenolic hydroxyl of tyrosine does not ionize appreciably below pH 8, the spectrum would be expected to remain unchanged with increasing acidification of the medium. It has, however, been found that the UV absorption is pH sensitive even in acid solutions and that it varies also when changing the ionic strength of the solution, on addition of denaturation reagents, such as urea, or on partial hydrolysis of the protein (Williams and Foster, 1959; Laskowski et al., 1960). It should be noted that although the change in optical density caused by these variables is not large, it can be easily observed by measuring directly in the spectrophotometer the difference in the spectra of a protein solution in a given standard state and under some other set of conditions. Figure V.1, showing the wavelength dependence of the enhancement of the optical density of an insulin solution after trypsin-catalyzed hydrolysis, is typical of the effects observed. The various attempts to interpret such data have been critically reviewed by Tinoco et al. (1962) who point out that two effects may contribute to these phenomena:

(a) From general considerations, it is expected that the absorption band of a chromophore will shift to shorter wavelengths (blue-shift) when the polarizability of the medium is reduced. This leads us to expect that a denaturation process, leading to the transfer of a chromophore from the interior of the native protein structure into a more "water-like" medium of lower refractive index should produce a blue shift (Yanari and Bovey, 1960). Such a result might also be expected if an ionic charge is created in the

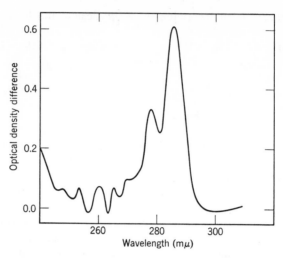

Fig. V.1. Differential spectrum of trypsin digested insulin referred to the native protein.

neighborhood of a chromophore, as was demonstrated on suitably chosen model systems. Wetlaufer et al. (1958) studied O-methyltyrosine in which the ionizable groups are isolated by three saturated bonds from the aromatic chromophore. Nevertheless, conversion of the cationic form to the dipolar ion and to the anionic form

causes the absorption maximum to move to longer wavelengths (red-shift) and an intensification of the absorption band in the 270–290 mμ region, as shown in Fig. V.2. Similar observations have been reported on the behavior of phenylalanine and tryptophan (Donovan et al. 1961). These data suggest that absorption spectra of aromatic residues are subject to perturbation caused by the electrical field of suitably placed charges. Such perturbations must make a contribution to changes in the absorption spectrum of a protein as its state of ionization is being varied.

(b) The interaction of two chromophores, whose transition dipoles have a

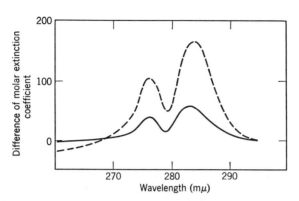

Fig. V.2. Difference spectrum of O-methyltyrosine at pH 5.7 (solid line) and pH 9.6 (dashed line) referred to the spectrum at pH 1.08.

fixed mutual orientation, leads to the intensification of one of the absorption bands at the expense of the other. This principle should lead to characteristic spectral changes during helix-coil transitions. Studies on synthetic polypeptides, used as model systems for the study of conformational transitions in proteins, have led to results in accord with theoretical expectations. The characteristic spectral change, corresponding to formation of the helical conformation, involves a reduction in the intensity of the peak (hypochromic effect) at 190 mμ (Imahori and Tanaka, 1959), and the appearance of a shoulder at 205 mμ (Rosenheck and Doty, 1961). The effect is illustrated in Fig. V.3. Since stability of the helical conformation requires a minimum length of the polypeptide chain and is favored by chain extension, spectral changes similar to those observed by Rosenheck and Doty would be expected when comparing spectra of a homologous series of oligopeptides. This effect was clearly established by Goodman and Listowsky (1962) for oligopeptides of γ-methyl-L-glutamate (Fig. V.4).

Transitions to a helical conformation lead also to a pronounced hypochromic effect in the case of nucleic acids and synthetic polynucleotides. It has been known for some time (Magasanik and Chargaff, 1951) that deoxyribose nucleic acid has an optical density (with a peak at 259 mμ) which is 25–37% lower than that of the mixed nucleotides obtained on base catalyzed hydrolysis of the polymer backbone. However, the cause of this change became apparent only after the double helical structure of the DNA molecule was established. In this structure the base chromophores lie parallel to one another at right angles to the chain axis and Tinoco (1960) has shown that this arrangement would be expected to lead to the observed

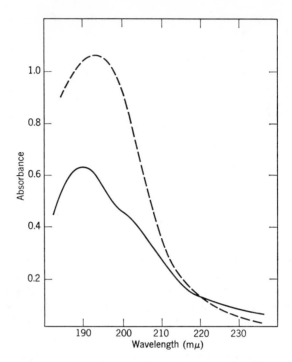

Fig. V.3. Ultraviolet absorption spectra of poly(α-L-glutamic acid) at 30°C; pH 3.2 (solid line); pH 10 (dashed line).

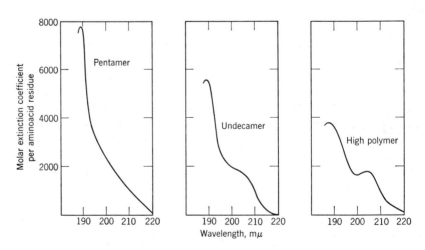

Fig. V.4. Ultraviolet spectra of γ-methyl glutamate oligomers and high polymer.

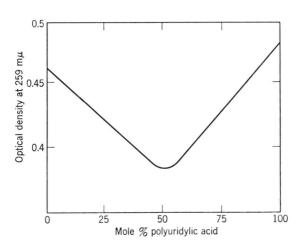

Fig. V.5. Spectrophotometric titration of poly(adenylic acid) with poly(uridylic acid). pH 7.4, temp. = 25°C, 0.1M NaCl, 0.1M glycylglycine.

hypochromic effect. The phenomenon is studied most conveniently on synthetic polynucleotides whose chains consist of units of one type only. Thus, Felsenfeld and Rich (1957) found that the mixing of solutions of poly(adenylic acid) and poly(uridylic acid), which is known to lead to the formation of the double-helical structure, is accompanied by a pronounced reduction of the optical density peak at 259 mμ, so that spectrophotometric titration is a convenient method for establishing the stoichiometry of the reaction (Fig. V.5). Later it was shown (Doty et al., 1959) that changes in optical density may be used to follow the thermal breakdown of the helical conformation in DNA (Fig. V.6). More detailed information may be obtained since dissociation of an adenine–thymine (or adenine–uracil) pair produces an increase in absorption in a different region of the spectrum than the dissociation of a guanine–cytosine pair. Following the changes in optical density at two wavelengths may, therefore, be interpreted in terms of the sequence in which A–T and G–C pairs become separated from one another (Felsenfeld and Sandeen, 1962). This type of analysis may also supply information about the base sequence of nucleic acids. For instance, in a sample of RNA it was found that a large fraction of G–C pairs could be separated from one another without any indication that adenine is being separated from uracil. This implies strongly that the native form of RNA has large regions which contain only G–C base pairs (Felsenfeld and Cantoni, 1964).

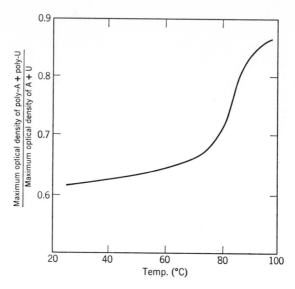

Fig. V.6. Spectroscopic evidence for the dissociation of the double helix of poly(adenylic acid) with poly(uridylic acid) at elevated temperatures.

2. Infrared Spectra

Samples of vinyl polymers differing in stereoregularity have frequently been found to have significantly different IR spectra (for a review of this subject see Bawn and Ledwith, 1962). These differences are most pronounced for bulk samples of the polymers, particularly if the crystalline and amorphous materials are being compared. We have seen, however (Chap. III), that the conformation of dissolved chain molecules is governed to some extent by the nature and degree of their stereoregularity and since the skeletal vibrational frequencies should be conformation-sensitive, some difference in the IR spectra of polymers with different tacticity should persist even in dilute solution. Such an effect has been described by Takeda et al. (1959) who compared CS_2 solutions of isotactic and atactic polystyrene and interpreted their results as indicating that the regular alternation of *trans* and *gauche* conformations, which leads to a helix with a threefold screw axis in crystalline isotactic polystyrene, is partially preserved in the dissolved polymer. However, the quantitative interpretation of the spectra of dissolved vinyl polymers, containing absorption bands characteristic of helical conformations, poses some difficult problems. The intensity of bands characteristic of helical conformations may depend not only on the fraction of the polymer chain segments assuming such a conformation, but also on the length of the helical sequences (Folt et al., 1962). Useful information may be obtainable from the temperature dependence of the infrared spectrum of solutions of vinyl polymers. We have seen (pp. 104–105, 110–111) that in syndiotactic chains all-*trans* sequences and pairs of bonds in the *gauche* conformation are characterized by a relatively small difference of energy. On the other hand, isotactic chains require a very large addition of energy for any transition from the preferred —tgtgtg— conformation. It would then be expected that an increasing dependence of the IR spectrum on temperature would be indicative of an increasing content of syndiotactic sequences in a vinyl polymer chain and this criterion appears to give correct results in the characterization of poly-(vinyl chloride) (Germer et al., 1963).

The dependence of infrared spectra on conformational transitions would be expected to be most pronounced when strong energetic interactions are involved and it is then not surprising that the method is most valuable for the study of the hydrogen-bonded structures characteristic of proteins and synthetic polypeptides which were already discussed (pp. 132–138). Ambrose and Elliott (1951a) have shown in a study of solid films of poly-(γ-methyl-L-glutamate) that the polymer chains may exist in two distinct conformations which exhibit characteristic spectral differences. For instance, the carbonyl stretching vibration was found to give an absorption peak at 1659 cm^{-1} in the contracted α-form, while the extended β-form, in which the chains are laterally connected with each other by hydrogen bonds, has this absorption peak shifted to 1630 cm^{-1}. In a later paper, Ambrose and Elliott (1951b) investigated aqueous solutions of native proteins and found that the evidence from IR spectroscopy indicates that the polypeptide chains exist predominantly in the α-form. This constituted the first identification of the conformation of polypeptide chains in native proteins in terms of the ordered structures observed in solid polypeptides, although the nature of the α-form was not understood before the proposal of the helical structure of Pauling et al. (1951). Later work by Doty et al. (1954) demonstrated that synthetic polypeptides may have spectra characteristic of either the α- or the β-form depending on the solvent medium. They showed also that solutions which have the characteristic IR absorption peaks of the β-form give evidence of molecular association of the polymer chains. The subject has been investigated in great detail by Goodman et al. (1962) on oligomers of γ-methyl-L-glutamate. It was found that none of the oligopeptides containing up to eleven monomer residues shows the absorption band at 1655 cm^{-1} (associated with high polymers in helix-forming solvents). Instead, the carbonyl stretching vibration leads to absorption at 1680 cm^{-1} for oligopeptides containing up to four units, while in the higher homologs this band is shifted to 1635 cm^{-1}. The authors conclude that the 1635 cm^{-1} band is characteristic of end-to-end association of helically wound chains—such chains appear first with the pentapeptide, but the association becomes negligible with very long molecules because of the low concentration of chain ends.

Infrared spectroscopy was used in a particularly elegant manner by Bird and Blout (1959) who studied the behavior of polypeptide solutions subjected to a large rate of shear. As we shall see in more detail in Chap. VII, elongated stiff molecules are partially oriented under these conditions so that their long axes lie preferentially parallel to the flow lines. If such orientation is produced in a solution in which polypeptide chains exist in the form of α-helices and if the solution is now observed with polarized infrared light, the absorption due to the carbonyl stretching vibration (which is parallel to the axis of the helix) should be most intense if the plane of polarization is parallel to the flow lines. This expectation was confirmed by experiment. For a number of other absorption bands the variation in the intensity of the absorption peaks with varying orientation of the plane of polarization was also in agreement with predictions based on the geometry of the α-helix model and the behavior of the α-form of synthetic polypeptides in mechanically oriented films (Ambrose and Elliott, 1951a). This may be considered as one of the most direct demonstrations that this model is really valid for the conformation of polypeptides in suitable solvent media. As would be expected, the infrared dichroism disappears under conditions which are known to lead to the destruction of the helix.

An entirely different problem was attacked, with the use of infrared spectroscopy, by Chang and Morawetz (1956). When a polymer chain carries a small number of widely spaced, strongly interacting groups, association complexes may form involving either groups carried by the same chain or groups carried by different chains. It is then of interest to ascertain what determines the balance between the intramolecular and the intermolecular association processes. This problem may be studied by combining molecular weight measurements, which define the extent of intermolecular association, with spectroscopic data, which measure the total concentration of associated functional groups. Chang and Morawetz studied in this manner copolymers of styrene with 0.8–15.2 mole-% methacrylic acid in nonpolar solvent media. It was found that the overwhelming majority of carboxyl groups which formed hydrogen-bonded dimers did so with carboxyls attached to the same chain. The extent of such intramolecular association was found to be quite independent of the polymer concentration, depending only on the local carboxyl concentration within the swollen polymer coil.

3. NMR Spectra

Nuclear magnetic resonance was discovered only in 1946 and its utility to the investigation of chemical problems became apparent even more recently, when it was found that the frequency at which absorption occurs varies to a small but measurable extent with the chemical environment of the absorbing nucleus (Gutowsky and Hoffman, 1951). For a full treatment of the subject the reader is referred to Pople et al. (1959); very valuable introductory texts directed to the chemist who uses NMR for the solution of problems in organic chemistry were written by Jackman (1959) and by Roberts (1959).

Nuclei of certain isotopes are characterized by a mechanical spin and the rotating charge of these nuclei then produces a magnetic moment. When such nuclei are placed in a magnetic field, the interaction of this field with the nuclear magnetic dipole leads to a dependence of the potential energy on the angle between the axis of rotation of the nucleus and the direction of the applied magnetic field. Quantum mechanical considerations lead to the conclusion that only certain discrete energy levels with corresponding orientations of the spin axis are allowed and that energy absorption leading to the promotion of the nuclei to spin states of higher energy can occur only if $\nu = \gamma H_0/2\pi$, where ν is the frequency of the radiation, H_0 the magnetic field strength in gauss, and γ a characteristic parameter of a given isotope referred to as the gyromagnetic ratio.

Of the main isotopes occurring in organic compounds, C^{12} and O^{16} have no nuclear spin. This leads actually to a great simplification of observed spectra which are largely due to H^1, with a characteristic absorption frequency in a magnetic field of 9400 gauss of about 40 Mc/sec. In a solid sample or media of very high viscosity, interactions of magnetic nuclei in neighboring molecules lead to variations in the effective local magnetic field, so that absorption occurs over a relatively broad frequency range. However, in solutions of low viscosity the rapid molecular tumbling resulting from Brownian motion leads to a cancellation of intermolecular effects on the magnetic field and the absorption band may have a width as narrow as 10^{-8} of the resonant frequency.

The circulation of electrons in the neighborhood of an absorbing nucleus may lead to diamagnetic or paramagnetic shielding, so that the magnetic field actually acting on the nucleus differs slightly from the externally applied field.   The extent of such magnetic shielding is proportional to the external magnetic field and depends on the nature of the chemical bonding in the vicinity of the absorbing nucleus.   The variation of the absorption frequency produced by this effect is referred to as the "chemical shift."   It is customary to use the absorption by the hydrogen atoms of tetramethyl-silane as a point of reference and to express the chemical shift in parts per million (Δ) relative to this absorption frequency.   Some authors use the so-called "τ-scale" (Tiers, 1958) defined by $\tau = 10 - \Delta$.

A typical result is that depicted on Fig. V.7 where the NMR spectrum of ethanol is shown at two levels of resolution.   At relatively low resolution the spectrum consists of three peaks with areas in the ratio $1:2:3$, representing the hydrogens of the hydroxyl, the methylene, and the methyl

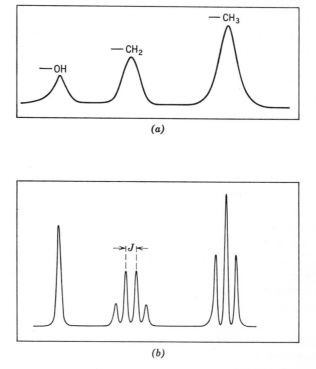

(a)

(b)

Fig. V.7. NMR spectrum of ethanol recorded on a 40 megacycle spectrometer.   (a) Low resolution.   (b) High resolution.

group, respectively. At higher resolution the methyl peak is split into a trip-let and the methylene into a quadruplet. This occurs since each of the protons may be characterized by a spin quantum number of $+\frac{1}{2}$ or $-\frac{1}{2}$. so that the total spin number of the methylene hydrogens may be $+1$, 0, -1 and that of the methyl hydrogens $+\frac{3}{2}$, $+\frac{1}{2}$, $-\frac{1}{2}$, $-\frac{3}{2}$. The spin number of the methylene affects the magnetic field acting on the methyl hydrogens and vice versa, leading to a splitting of the absorption bands.* It may be shown by quantum-mechanical arguments that such splitting occurs only when the interacting nuclei are chemically non-equivalent, e.g., the hydrogens in tetramethylsilane absorb at a single frequency. The separation of the multiplet absorption lines due to spin–spin splitting by non-equivalent nuclei is expressed by a "coupling con-stant" J which is independent of the external magnetic field but depends on the number and the kind of bonds separating the magnetic nuclei and also on the molecular conformation. For instance, for two non-equivalent hydrogens attached to neighboring carbon atoms, J is much larger when the hydrogens are *trans* than when they are *gauche* with respect to each other (Sheppard and Turner, 1959; Gutowsky et al., 1962). In most cases J is negligible for nuclei separated by more than three chemical bonds.

The question whether two nuclei are or are not equivalent may depend on the relative probability that a given molecule will be found in its different conformations. For instance, Nair and Roberts (1957) have shown that 2,3-dibromo-2-methylpropanoate has a spectrum indicating that the methylene hydrogens are non-equivalent. This may be easily understood

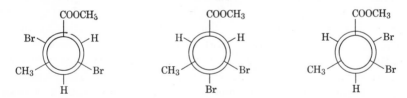

Fig. V.8. Staggered conformations of methyl-2,3-dibromo-2-methyl propanoate.

from a consideration of the conformations of this molecule as represented in Fig. V.8. In every one of the staggered conformations the environment is different for each of the two methylene hydrogens, so that their time-average equivalence would be expected only if all three conformations

---

* The peak corresponding to the hydroxyl hydrogen in ethanol is not split by interac-tion with the methylene hydrogens, since this hydrogen is subject to rapid exchange, so that its absorption corresponds to the time-average state of the neighboring methylene.

were equally populated. Quantum-mechanical analysis leads also to the conclusion that for any given J value, the splitting of an absorption line becomes less and less distinct as J becomes large compared to the difference in the chemical shifts of the interacting nuclei. Since the chemical shift is proportional to the external magnetic field, while J is independent of it, we can reduce the ratio of the coupling constant to the chemical shift by increasing the external magnetic field. Instrumental advances in this direction have led, in recent years, to a pronounced improvement in the resolution of NMR spectra.

Applications of high-resolution NMR spectroscopy to the study of macromolecules have recently been reviewed by Bovey and Tiers (1963). In such studies it is important to ensure that segmental motion of the polymer chain be sufficiently rapid if a highly resolved spectrum is to be obtained.   As a result, the rigid structures which are present in solutions of native proteins yield rather broad spectra and the spectra of synthetic polypeptides in their helical conformation may be broadened to such an extent that they may not even be observable under the conditions used for high resolution NMR spectroscopy. When proteins are denatured or the helical conformations of synthetic polypeptides destroyed by addition of strong hydrogen-bonding reagents, a dramatic sharpening of the spectrum is obtained (Bovey et al., 1959; Kowalsky, 1962). It must be stressed that the macroscopic viscosity is not a measure of the freedom of segmental motions, which determine the degree of resolution of the NMR spectrum.   This may be demonstrated by the fact that resolution is not sacrificed by working typically with solutions containing 20% of polymer, although such solutions may be quite viscous.   A highly resolved spectrum does, however, require conditions which will lead to an effective averaging of the molecular conformations, and measurements must, therefore, frequently be carried out at elevated temperatures.   In the case of poly(vinyl alcohol), it has been demonstrated that resolution of the NMR spectra is greatly improved when the polymer chain-length is reduced by a chemical degradation process (Tincher, 1965).   The significance of this observation is not quite clear.   One might expect that the frequency of conformational transitions depends only on interactions within relatively short segments of the macromolecules, so that it should not be sensitive to the length of high polymer chains.   It is, however, possible that the dependence of the width of the NMR absorption bands on the molecular weight of poly(vinyl alcohol) reflects the high tendency of this polymer to form association aggregates.   This tendency would, of course, be minimized when the chain-length is drastically reduced.

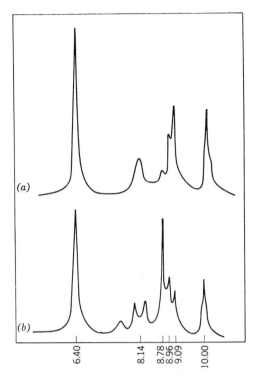

Fig. V.9. NMR spectra of poly(methyl methacrylate) with different stereoregularity.
Sample (a) was prepared with a free radical initiator, sample (b) with an anionic catalyst.
The band at $\tau = 10$ is due to tetramethylsilane added as an internal standard.

At the present time, NMR spectroscopy provides the most powerful
tool for the quantitative characterization of the stereoregularity of some
polymers. The method was first introduced by Bovey and Tiers (1960)
who showed that the NMR spectra of poly(methyl methacrylate) produced under different conditions show characteristic differences (Fig. V.9).
These differences appear in two regions of the spectra. First, the absorption peak due to the hydrogens of the α-methyl group is split into three
bands, with maxima at $\tau = 8.78$, 8.96, and 9.09. Bovey and Tiers showed
that these bands may be assigned to the central α-methyl groups of isotactic, heterotactic, and syndiotactic triads, respectively (see page 97).
Secondly, characteristic differences appear in the region corresponding to
the hydrogens of the methylene groups ($\tau = 8.14$). This absorption is
represented by a singlet in samples rich in syndiotactic triads, while

polymer with a high content of isotactic sequences has this absorption represented by a quadruplet. This difference is easily understood if we consider in detail the stereochemistry of the methylene group placed between two asymmetric centers with the same or the opposite steric configuration:

$$
\begin{array}{cc}
\text{H} \diagdown \text{C} \diagup \text{H} & \text{H} \diagdown \text{C} \diagup \text{H} \\
\text{C} \diagdown \text{CH}_3 \quad \text{C} \diagdown \text{CH}_3 & \text{C} \diagdown \text{CH}_3 \quad \text{C} \diagdown \text{COOCH}_3 \\
\text{COOCH}_3 \quad \text{COOCH}_3 & \text{COOCH}_3 \quad \text{CH}_3 \\
\text{isotactic} & \text{syndiotactic}
\end{array}
$$

We may see that in the isotactic sequence the methylene hydrogens are non-equivalent, one being in the fully extended chain closer to the ester and the other to the α-methyl groups. As a consequence, their chemical shifts are slightly different and each absorption peak is split into a doublet owing to the two possible spin quantum numbers of the other methylene hydrogen. By contrast, the hydrogens of the methylene in a syndiotactic sequence are equivalent and, therefore, give rise to a single absorption peak. It should be emphasized that in this case NMR spectroscopy not only distinguishes between polymers of different tacticity but allows an unambiguous assignment of the nature of stereoregularity.* The same analysis may be applied to poly(α-methylstyrene) (Brownstein et al., 1961) or to polymers which may be converted to poly(methyl methacrylate), such as poly(methacrylic acid) (Morawetz and Rubin, 1962; Bovey, 1963; Lando et al., 1964), polymethacrylonitrile (Sobue et al., 1963), or poly(methacrylic anhydride) (Tiers and Bovey, 1960; Miller et al., 1961). The interpretation of NMR spectra of polymers of vinyl derivatives is much more difficult, since the mutual splitting of the methylene and α-hydrogens leads, in general, to very complex patterns which are not easily analyzed. For instance, in syndiotactic triads of poly(vinyl chloride) the absorption by the equivalent methylene hydrogens is split into a triplet by interaction with the two neighboring α-hydrogens. In an isotactic triad, each absorption peak of the quartet, due to the non-equivalent

---

* While the splitting of the methylene peak of the NMR spectrum into a quadruplet may be regarded as unambiguous proof of an isotactic structure, the absence of such splitting is not conclusive evidence against such a structure. The difference in the chemical shifts of the non-equivalent methylene hydrogens is sometimes too small, relative to J, to lead to an observable splitting of the absorption line. Such behavior has been reported for poly(vinyl chloride) (Johnsen, 1961) and for polystyrene (Bovey et al., 1965).

methylene hydrogens, is further split into a triplet by interaction with the
α-hydrogens, so that the methylene absorption would be expected to be
characterized by a system of 12 absorption bands.   In general it requires a
careful and laborious analysis of the spectrum in terms of the spectra
calculated for perfectly stereoregulated species before an estimate of
tacticity can be obtained (Tincher, 1962).   An unusually favorable case is
that of polypropylene, since it can be prepared in the pure isotactic and
syndiotactic form.   The spectra of these materials, in the region characteristic for absorption by methylene hydrogen, may then be used as a
frame of reference for the calculation of the stereoregularity in less perfectly ordered polypropylene (Woodbrey and Trementozzi, 1964). In other
cases, where polymer samples in the pure isotactic and syndiotactic forms
are not available, the reliability of the analysis is greatly improved by
measurements on model compounds of the type

$$CH_3—\overset{\displaystyle H}{\underset{\displaystyle X}{C}}—CH_2—\overset{\displaystyle H}{\underset{\displaystyle X}{C}}—CH_3 \qquad\qquad CH_3—\overset{\displaystyle H}{\underset{\displaystyle X}{C}}—CH_2—\overset{\displaystyle X}{\underset{\displaystyle H}{C}}—CH_3$$

which may be regarded as analogous to a sequence of two monomer residues in isotactic and syndiotactic chains.   This approach was explored
extensively by McMahon and Tincher (1965) for models of poly(vinyl
chloride), poly(vinyl bromide), polyacrylonitrile, and poly(vinyl alcohol).
The analysis of NMR spectra of fluorine analogs of vinyl polymers, i.e.,
materials of the type $(—CF_2—CFR—)_n$, is generally easier, since fluorine
compounds have much more highly resolved NMR spectra (Tiers and
Bovey, 1963).   A very powerful way to deal with the problem of exces-
sively complex NMR spectra is that provided by the technique of "double
resonance," (sometimes referred to as "spin decoupling").   In this method
the absorption due to one kind of hydrogen is recorded while the sample is
irradiated simultaneously with a high intensity of a radiation with a frequency corresponding to the absorption of non-equivalent neighboring hydrogen atoms.   This irradiation produces rapid transitions between their
spin states, so that they are effectively averaged and the splitting of absorption bands is eliminated.   Bovey et al. (1963) showed that this procedure
leads to a great simplification in the determination of the tacticities of poly-
(vinyl chloride) and poly(vinyl fluoride) from their NMR spectra.

Nuclear magnetic resonance spectroscopy may also be used to study
another feature of the "microstructure" isomerism of addition polymers,
i.e., the relative frequency of "head-to-tail," "head-to-head," and "tail-to-

tail" additions of monomer units. Such an analysis has been carried out for poly(vinylidene fluoride). For a polymerization process involving exclusively head-to-tail monomer addition, the chain would be represented by

$$—CH_2—CF_2—CH_2—CF_2—CH_2—CF_2—$$

and the NMR spectrum of that structure may be easily differentiated (Naylor and Lasoski, 1960; Wilson, 1963) from those corresponding to head-to-head or tail-to-tail additions:

$$—CH_2—CF_2—CF_2—CH_2—$$
head-to-head

$$—CF_2—CH_2—CH_2—CF_2—$$
tail-to-tail

Another case of polymer isomerism which was resolved by high resolution NMR spectroscopy concerns the polymer obtained on cationic polymerization of 3-methyl-1-butene, $CH_2{=}CH–CH(CH_3)_2$ (Kennedy et al., 1964). This polymer was expected to be represented by structure A, which would have an NMR spectrum with a very complex structure, but the spectrum

$$(—CH_2—CH—)_n$$
$$\mid$$
$$CH(CH_3)_2$$
A

$$
(—CH_2—CH_2—\overset{\displaystyle CH_3}{\underset{\displaystyle CH_3}{\overset{\mid}{\underset{\mid}{C}}}}—)_n
$$
B

actually observed had only two sharp peaks. It had to be concluded that the polymerization process involved an isomerization of the propagating carbonium ion, leading to structure B, which contains only two sets of equivalent hydrogens, too far removed from each other to produce spin–spin splitting.

A very interesting phenomenon has been observed in the study of the NMR spectra of styrene polymers and copolymers. Figure V.10 shows a comparison of spectra obtained with polystyrene and with cumene which may be regarded as its low molecular weight analog. It is found (Bovey et al., 1959) that in carbon tetrachloride solution the absorption due to the phenyl hydrogens, which appears as a single sharp peak in cumene, is split into two absorption bands in polystyrene. The areas under these absorption bands are in the ratio of 3:2 and the band appearing at a higher τ value has been shown to represent the *ortho*-hydrogens of the aromatic residues. Bovey et al. interpret the shift in their absorption frequency as due to diamagnetic shielding by the π-electron systems of other aromatic residues of the chain molecule. Such shield-

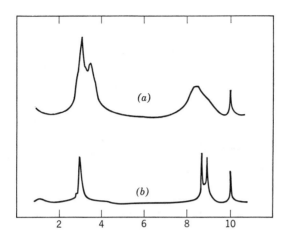

Fig. V.10. Comparison of NMR spectra of polystyrene and its low molecular weight analog in CCl₄ solution. (a) Polystyrene. (b) Cumene. The peak at $\tau = 10$ is due to tetramethylsilane added as an internal standard. Note the broadening of the absorption peaks of the polymer and the splitting of the band between $\tau = 2$ and $\tau = 4$, the absorption region of the hydrogens in the aromatic ring.

$$—CH_2—CH—CH_2—CH—CH_2—CH—$$

polystyrene

$$CH_3—CH—CH_3$$

cumene

ing would be expected to be quite sensitive to the molecular conformation of the polystyrene and it is most significant in this context that the separate absorption band for the *ortho*-hydrogens develops only gradually as the degree of polymerization is being increased up to a value of about 20. This evidence demonstrates in a striking manner that conformational restrictions in chain molecules cannot be predicted by considering interactions between neighboring monomer residues only.

The effect observed in styrene homopolymers may also be utilized in the analysis of styrene copolymers. Thus, NMR spectroscopy has been shown to provide a good method for characterizing the distribution of the monomer residues in copolymers of styrene with butadiene (Bovey et al., 1959) or with methyl methacrylate (Bovey 1962).   We may illustrate the principle of the method by considering the difference in the spectra to be expected in copolymers containing 50 mole-% of styrene, with the styrene residues distributed either at random or in long blocks.   In the first case long sequences of styrene residues will be rare, so that the absorption characteristic of phenyl hydrogens will appear as a single peak, while in the block polymer the splitting of this peak will be similar to that observed in styrene homopolymers.   In addition, the diamagnetic shielding provided by the aromatic rings will affect the location of the bands of the comonomer, so that we may be able to estimate the number of comonomer residues lying next to 0, 1, or 2 styrene residues.   The sequence of monomer units was also studied by NMR spectroscopy in copolymers of vinyl chloride and vinylidene chloride (Chujo et al., 1962).   Here it is most convenient to concentrate the analysis on the region of the spectrum containing the absorption band characteristic of the methylene hydrogens in poly(vinylidene chloride).   This band appears as a singlet in vinylidene chloride homopolymers, but in copolymers in which some vinylidene chloride residues lie next to vinyl chloride units, spin–spin splitting resulting from interactions with the α-hydrogens produces a satellite peak, which may be used to characterize the distribution of the monomer units along the molecular chain.

The results obtained in most of the work carried out so far employed conditions which would lead to the fastest attainable rotation around carbon–carbon bonds, so that the accessible conformations would be effectively averaged and the resolution of the spectrum maximized.   However, in principle it is also possible to utilize the broadening of NMR absorption bands to study the variation of the rotation around carbon–carbon bonds with temperature, thus gaining some insight into the potential energy barriers which have to be overcome in conformational transitions. Liu and Ullman (1965) have found in a study of this type that the widths of the resonance peaks, corresponding to the hydrogens in the phenyl residues of polystyrene, narrow down particularly rapidly in the 40–80°C range for the atactic polymer and in the 50–60°C range for isotactic polystyrene. This phenomenon indicates a rather abrupt structural change and the fact that this transition is sharper in the case of the stereoregular polymer suggests that it may involve a "melting" of helical sequences in the chain conformation.   This interpretation is supported by the observation that the radius of gyration of the polystyrene chain, which generally increases with rising temperature, drops appreciably in the transition range (Reiss and Benoit, 1961). With small molecules, NMR spectroscopy has also been used to estimate the distribution of conformations (Sheppard and Turner, 1959; Gutowsky et al., 1962), and a recent study of solutions of polystyrene and the model compounds

$$
\underset{\overset{|}{\bigcirc}}{CH_3-\overset{\overset{\displaystyle H}{|}}{C}}-CH_2-\underset{\overset{|}{\bigcirc}}{\overset{\overset{\displaystyle H}{|}}{C}}-CH_3 \qquad\qquad \underset{\ }{CH_3-\overset{\overset{\displaystyle\bigcirc}{|}}{\underset{\overset{|}{H}}{C}}}-CH_2-\underset{\overset{|}{\bigcirc}}{\overset{\overset{\displaystyle H}{|}}{C}}-CH_3
$$

has demonstrated that a detailed analysis of NMR spectra may reveal the preferred conformational sequences in long chain molecules (Bovey et al., 1965).

4. Fluorescence Spectra

The possibilities inherent in fluorescence spectroscopy as a tool for the study of dissolved macromolecules were explored first on protein solutions (Weber, 1960; Teale, 1960). Three of the amino acids present in proteins fluoresce; the maxima of the emission spectra lie at 282 mμ for phenylalanine, at 303 mμ for tyrosine, and at 348 mμ for tryptophan (Teale and Weber, 1957). The emission spectra of simple peptides are quite similar to those for the free amino acids, but in proteins they are strikingly modified by radiationless transfer of excitation energy between the amino acid residues. Such processes are known to be highly efficient over distances as long as 40 Å (Förster, 1959). As a consequence of this energy transfer, phenylalanine fluorescence can be observed only if tyrosine and tryptophan are both absent (i.e., in gelatin) and tyrosine fluorescence is detectable only in the absence of tryptophan (i.e., in insulin) while most proteins show an emission spectrum assignable to tryptophan residues. These emission spectra vary considerably in native proteins, but become identical when the proteins are denatured in 8M urea (Teale, 1960); this observation indicates that the nature of the spectrum and the quantum yield of the fluorescence are subject to changes due both to the nature of the medium surrounding a tryptophan residue and to conformational transitions in the polypeptide backbone to which the fluorescent side chain is attached.

Steiner et al. (1964) studied the effect of the solvent medium on the fluorescence of acetyl tryptophanamide, which may be considered a model of a tryptophan residue in a protein. They found that most organic solutes tended to raise the quantum yield of fluorescence, while dipolar ions had a strong quenching effect. However, effects on the fluorescence intensity of proteins produced by cosolvents do not show even a qualitative consistency. Thus, urea, which enhances the fluorescence of acetyl tryptophanamide, may either intensify or quench the fluorescence of proteins. In the case of pepsin, the fluorescence is enhanced by urea with the native, but quenched with the denatured protein (Steiner et al., 1964). Thermal denaturation has been shown in two cases to lead to an increase in fluorescence intensity (Gally and Edelman, 1964), although the transfer of the tryptophan residues from the interior of the native protein molecule (which is presumably rich in nonpolar residues) to a region where it is in direct contact with water would have been expected to have the opposite effect.

It seems then fair to say that the phenomena observed in studies of protein fluorescence are rather imperfectly understood. Since the method uses the tryptophan residues as probes to explore the state of the molecule and these residues are not easily studied by other spectroscopic means, fluorescence studies should complement data obtained by other methods. It is significant, for example, that the fluorescence spectrum changes appreciably when chymotrypsinogen is converted to the native enzyme α-chymotrypsin (Teale, 1960). This is a remarkable result, since the conformational transition accompanying this enzyme activation is otherwise detectable only by the appearance of the catalytic activity. In a similar manner, Steiner and Edelhoch (1963) demonstrated by fluorescence studies a well-defined transition in bovine serum albumin between pH 7.5 and 8.5, although no such transition was suspected from any other property of this thoroughly investigated protein.

Fluorescence spectroscopy has also been demonstrated to be a valuable tool in studying helix-coil transition phenomena (Lehrer and Fasman, 1964). Poly(L-tyrosine), in solvent media which do not support helix formation, has the expected fluorescence spectrum with a maximum at 303 mμ, similar to that of tyrosine. However, in solvent media in which the polymer is known to exist in the helical conformation (pp. 135–136), the emission spectrum contains in addition a new band with a peak at 400 mμ. This must be due to the mutual interaction of the phenolic groups in tyrosine residues which come to lie close to one another when the polypeptide backbone assumes the helical form. In analogy with results obtained in concentrated solutions of simple aromatic compounds (Döller and Förster, 1962) it is believed that the species responsible for radiation at this new frequency is a complex between an excited phenyl group and a phenyl group in the ground state, a so-called "excimer."

A similar observation has been made in a study of the fluorescence from polystyrene solutions (Yanari et al., 1964). It was found that the peak of the emission spectrum, which for atactic polystyrene lies at 292 mμ, is shifted to 324 mμ in the isotactic polymer. Since the emission spectrum of the isotactic polymer contains no trace of the 292-mμ band, it must be concluded that the lifetime of any break in the helical conformation is short compared to the life of the excited species. Fluorescence studies appear, then, to offer a promising approach to the investigation of configurations and conformations of polymer chain molecules.

The emission spectrum of a fluorescent molecule is usually observed at right angles to the direction of the exciting light beam. The emitted light is partially polarized to an extent which depends on a number of factors. If fluorescent macromolecules are dissolved in a viscous solvent medium, so that depolarization of fluorescence due to molecular rotation during the lifetime of the excited species (see pp. 297–298) becomes negligible, then the polarization reflects the relative orientation of the transition moments associated with the absorption and emission of light. If the molecular excitation can be brought about in several ways, each characterized by a different absorption band and a different transition moment, then the polarization of the emitted radiation will depend on the wavelength of the exciting light. This dependence, called the "polarization spectrum," has, in the case of tryptophan, maxima at 270 and at 305 mμ, corresponding to $n \to \pi^*$ and to $\pi \to \pi^*$ excitation processes. In proteins, this spectrum is modified in a manner which varies considerably from one species to another reflecting, presumably, relative orientations of tyrosine and tryptophan residues, between which radiationless energy transfer can take place. The polarization spectra seem to be more sensitive to protein structure than the fluorescence emission spectra and they also change in a more specific manner on protein denaturation (Weber, 1960).

B. OPTICAL ACTIVITY

1. General Considerations

The phenomenon of optical activity has fascinated scientists ever since its discovery in the early nineteenth century. Pasteur, who devoted many years of his life to its study (Dubos, 1950), was particularly impressed with the fact that all substances yielding optically active solutions are derived from products of the life process. He became convinced that the molecular asymmetry, which he perceived to be the fundamental cause of optical activity, must constitute in some manner a principle essential to the existence of living organisms. He searched in vain for that principle—but he would have undoubtedly derived great pleasure from scientific discoveries of our days, which are highly suggestive of the reasons why the evolution of life utilized optically active building blocks for its most important macromolecules.

Optical activity may be observed in crystals of substances inactive in the liquid state if the crystal structure has neither planes of symmetry nor a center of symmetry. However, if a substance is to be optically active in the liquid state, where its molecules are oriented at random with respect to the direction of the light beam, the molecules themselves must lack planes and a center of symmetry. The asymmetry may be of two types as illustrated in Fig. V.11. In a substance such as lactic acid the

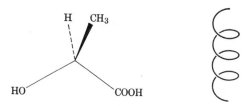

Fig. V.11. Typical examples of asymmetry

asymmetry is due to the attachment of four different substituent groups to a carbon atom. On the other hand, in a helical coil the structure as a whole is asymmetric. It is important to stress that a system containing chain molecules all coiled into helices of the same sense would be optically active even if it contained no asymmetrically substituted atoms.

The theory of optical activity is very complex and can be discussed here only in a cursory manner, but it is the subject of excellent reviews (Kuhn, 1958; Heller and Fitts, 1960) to which the reader is referred for more information. Linearly polarized light may be considered as the resultant of two coherent circularly polarized components of opposite sense of rotation. If the refractive index of the medium depends on the sense of rotation of the circularly polarized rays, the difference in their velocity will bring them out of phase as they emerge from the medium. Addition of the two components will then result in a new plane polarized beam, but one whose plane of polarization has been rotated by an angle α_{obs} with respect to the plane of polarization of the incident beam. If the refractive indices for the two circularly polarized components are n_l and n_d and if light of a wavelength λ (in vacuo) has to pass a thickness l of the liquid, the rotation of the plane of polarization will be

$$\alpha_{obs} = 180(l/\lambda)(n_l - n_d) \tag{5.1}$$

where α_{obs} is expressed in degrees. Since the ratio l/λ is very large in any experimental arrangement, even very small values of $n_l - n_d$ (of the order of 10^{-6}) will be sufficient to produce large optical activities.

Experimental results are expressed conventionally in terms of a specific activity at a wavelength λ denoted by $[\alpha]_\lambda$ which is defined by

$$[\alpha]_\lambda = 10\alpha_{obs}/lc \tag{5.2}$$

where l is in centimeters and c is the concentration of the optically active substance in g-cm^{-3}. A quantity of more fundamental significance is the molar rotation $[M]_\lambda$

$$[M]_\lambda = M[\alpha]_\lambda/100 \tag{5.3}$$

Although rigorous theoretical treatments of optical activity have to utilize quantum-mechanical concepts, the consideration of a classical model suggested by Kuhn (1930), and represented schematically in Fig. V.12,

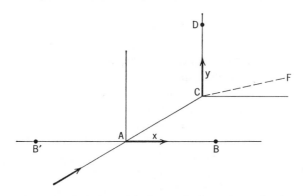

Fig. V.12. Kuhn's model of an optically active molecule.

is helpful for gaining qualitative insight into the phenomenon. Consider two electrical oscillators with equilibrium positions at A and C, which are restrained by interactions with groups B and D so that the first may oscillate only in the x and the second only in the y direction. If a coupling force exists between them, the potential energy may be written as

$$E = \frac{k_1}{2} x_1{}^2 + \frac{k_2}{2} y_2{}^2 + k_{12}x_1y_2 \qquad (5.4)$$

The coupling constant k_{12} may be positive or negative and this will determine the relative energies for a given displacement of the two oscillators for the case when x and y have the same sign or opposite signs. If now a circularly polarized levorotatory beam advances from A to C and if the electrical vector is in the direction A $\rightarrow$ B at point A, it will have rotated to be in the direction C $\rightarrow$ F at point C, so that it will have a positive component in the direction C $\rightarrow$ D. We see then that the displacement of each oscillator induced by the light may be in the same direction or the opposite direction, as the displacement resulting from the coupling with the other oscillator, depending on the sign of the coupling constant and the sense of rotation of the circularly polarized beam. The two circularly polarized beams are then non-equivalent, resulting in a finite value of $n_d - n_l$, whose sign is reversed if B is moved to B'. Even this simple model indicates why the phenomenon of optical activity disappears in the limits of very long wavelengths, since the rotation of the electrical vector between A and C decreases with increasing λ. Also, the coupling of the two oscillators decays rapidly as their mutual distance is increased, so that only groupings relatively close to the center of asymmetry would be expected to contribute to the effect.

A full theoretical consideration of optical activity has to take into account the components of the electrical and magnetic polarizability matrix corresponding to each electronic transition of the molecule. This is, in general, not a feasible approach and various attempts have been made to simplify the model on which calculations are based. Particularly successful has been the "polarization theory" of Kirkwood (1937) in which it is assumed that the molecule may be subdivided into parts whose polarizabilities are cylindrically symmetrical and that only interactions between electric dipoles need be considered, since terms involving magnetic dipoles make a much smaller contribution. We may then characterize each substituent group on an asymmetric carbon by polarizabilities $\alpha_\parallel$ and $\alpha_\perp$ parallel and at right angles to its optical axis, which lead to mean polarizabilities $\alpha_i = (\alpha_\parallel + 2\alpha_\perp)/3$ and an anisotropy ratio $\beta_i = (\alpha_\parallel - \alpha_\perp)/\alpha_i$. If the vector describing the relative position of any two of these groups is $\mathbf{R}_{ij}$, we obtain according to Kirkwood

$$n_l - n_d = (8\pi^2 N^*/\lambda)(n^2 + 2) \sum_i \sum_j \alpha_i\alpha_j\beta_i\beta_j G_{ij}\mathbf{R}_{ij} \cdot (\boldsymbol{b}_i \times \boldsymbol{b}_j)$$

$$G_{ij} = (1/R_{ij}{}^3)[\boldsymbol{b}_i \cdot \boldsymbol{b}_j - 3(\boldsymbol{b}_i \cdot \mathbf{R}_{ij})(\boldsymbol{b}_j \cdot \mathbf{R}_{ij})/R_{ij}{}^2] \qquad (5.5)$$

where N^* is the number of molecules per unit volume, n is the refractive index in unpolarized light, and b_i, b_j are unit vectors in the direction of the symmetry axes of groups i and j.   This expression lends itself readily to estimates of optical activity, since the α_i parameters may be obtained from molar refractivities, while the β_i are obtainable from measurements of depolarization of light scattered by vapors or from the Kerr effect.   A number of values proposed by Kirkwood for typical substituent groups are listed in Table V.1.   Since $R_{ij} \cdot (b_i \times b_j) = 0$ for two groups whose sym-

TABLE V.1
Polarizability and Anisotropy Parameters for Calculations
of Optical Activity

Group	$10^{24}\alpha$ (cm^3)	β
—CH$_3$	2.25	0.35
—C$_2$H$_5$	4.07	0.35
—OH	1.03	0.35
—Cl	2.35	0.35
—CH$_2$Cl	4.17	0.34
—NH$_2$	1.78	0.25
—COOH	2.86	0.55
—C$_6$H$_5$	9.89	—0.58

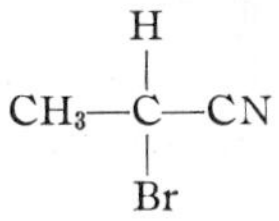

metry axes are coplanar, Kirkwood's theory predicts no contribution to optical activity from the interaction of such groups.   This means, in particular, that a molecule would be optically inactive *even if it possessed an asymmetric center* if the optical axes of all substituents (after averaging their conformations over time) were parallel to the bond joining the substituent groups to the center of asymmetry.   This prediction has not been found to be universally valid.   Kauzmann and Eyring (1949) cite three cases depicted below

$$
\begin{array}{ccc}
\text{H} & \text{H} & \text{H} \\
| & | & | \\
\text{CH}_3\text{—C—CN} & \text{CH}_3\text{—C—CN} & \text{I—C—SO}_3{}^- \\
| & | & | \\
\text{Br} & \text{NH}_3{}^+ & \text{Cl} \\
[M] = 21° & [M] = 13° & [M] = 36°
\end{array}
$$

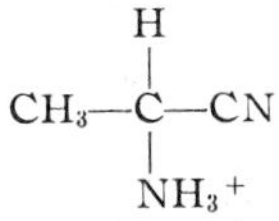

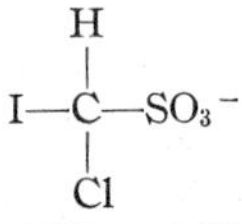

where an appreciable activity was observed.   This could have resulted from ternary group interactions—however, since the data were obtained in polar solvent media, it is possible that the solvated molecules had different symmetry properties than the "bare" molecules depicted above.

The manner in which the distribution of the various conformations of a molecule may determine its optical activity has been studied in detail on 1,2-dichloropropane (Wood et al., 1952). This very instructive case is schematically depicted in Fig. V.13. If the three staggered conformations were all equally populated, the time average optical axis of the —CH$_2$Cl group would coincide with the bond linking that group to the asymmetric carbon. Since the same must necessarily hold for the —CH$_3$, —H, and Cl substituents, the compound would, in Kirkwood's approximation, not exhibit any optical activity. Such activity as is observed is, therefore, largely a consequence of the preference of some of the staggered conformations over others. That such a preference would be expected is obvious from Fig. V.13, since the conformation shown at the extreme right is

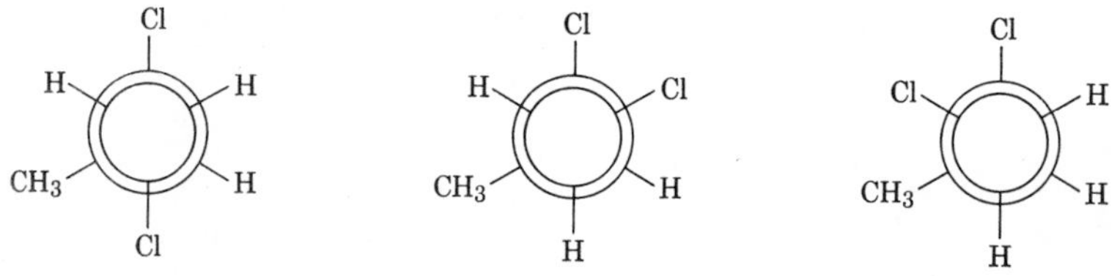

Fig. V.13. Conformations of 1,2-dichloropropane.

clearly much more crowded than the other two. Woods et al. calculated that conformations in which the chlorine atoms are *trans* to each other should lead to $[\alpha] = 40°$ while the conformation in which the chlorine is *trans* to the methyl group would correspond to $[\alpha] = -40°$. The experimental data are close to the former values from which it is concluded that there is a large preference for the conformation in which the chlorine atoms are *trans* to each other. In some cases the distribution of the conformational isomers may be strongly dependent on the nature of the solvent medium. A case of this type, whose significance is particularly easily analyzed, is that of *trans*-2-chloro-5-methyl cyclohexanone (Djerassi et al., 1960) whose two conformations and optical activity data are depicted on Fig. V.14. The conformation with the equatorial substituents is stable in polar solvents, while nonpolar solvents favor the form with the axially oriented substituents. The conformational change is attended here by a change in sign of optical activity. A similar reversal in the sign of optical activity was observed by Tanford (1962) on addition of dioxane to an aqueous solution of N-acetyl-L-glutamic acid. In that case the possible number of conformations is much higher and an interpretation of the data correspondingly more difficult.

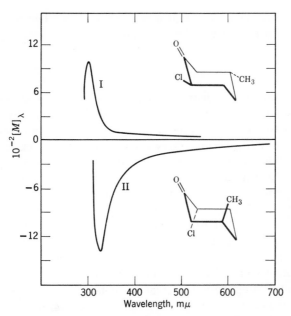

Fig. V.14. Optical activity of *trans*-2-chloro-5-methyl cyclohexanone in methanol solution (I) and in octane solution (II).   Also shown are the conformations believed to be present in the two solvent media.

While most of the data on optical activity are quoted as $[\alpha]_D$, referring to the effect observed with light of the sodium D-line (589 mμ) there has been, in recent years, an increased awareness that more fundamental information is extractable from a knowledge of the wavelength dependence of $[\alpha]_\lambda$, referred to as the "rotatory dispersion" (Djerassi, 1960). The various theories lead generally to a wavelength dependence of $[\alpha]_\lambda$ given by

$$[\alpha]_\lambda = \frac{n^2 + 2}{3} \sum_i \frac{k_i}{\lambda^2 - \lambda_i^2} \tag{5.6}$$

where n is the refractive index of the medium, λ_i are characteristic absorption bands, and k_i are coefficients proportional to the "rotatory strength" of a given electronic transition which depends on electric and magnetic moments associated with it.   It must be emphasized that k_i, which depends on the interaction of pairs of groups, would not be expected to correlate with the absorption intensity observed at λ_i and it is frequently found that weak absorption bands have high values of rotatory strength.   When measurements are carried out in the visible part of the spectrum, far from the important frequencies with high rotatory strength which occur for most compounds of interest in the ultraviolet, relation (5.6) may be approximated by

$$[\alpha]_\lambda = A'/(\lambda^2 - \lambda_c^2) \qquad (5.7)$$

where λ_c depends on the distribution of the terms in the summation of eq. (5.6). This simple relation, generally referred to as the Drude equation, fits the data for many substances provided λ is not too close to λ_c. It may be seen that $[\alpha]_\lambda$ becomes very small if λ is either much larger or much smaller than the critical wavelength λ_c. If $\lambda - \lambda_c$ is very small, the simple one-term Drude equation cannot be considered accurate, but it correctly predicts that the sign of $[\alpha]_\lambda$ is reversed as we vary the wavelength through the region of λ_c. This phenomenon is referred to as the "Cotton effect" and in recent years its study has made very important contributions to the study of steroids and related materials (Djerassi, 1960). The Cotton effect is called positive or negative depending on whether the maximum in $[\alpha]_\lambda$ occurs at a longer or a shorter wavelength than the optical activity minimum. An interesting example is given by Sjöberg (1960) whose data on the isomeric α-(iodophenoxy)-propionic acids are reproduced in Fig. V.15. As may be seen, the optical activity at long wavelengths of light is negative for the *ortho*-derivative, but positive for the *meta*- and *para*-derivatives.

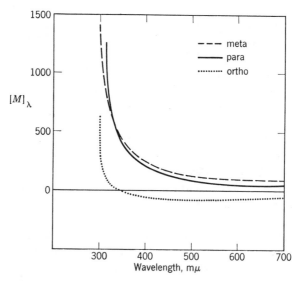

Fig. V.15. Rotatory dispersion of the isomeric α-(iodophenoxy)-propionic acids.

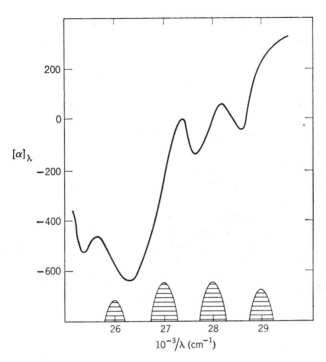

Fig. V.16. Rotatory dispersion of β-octyl nitrite in hexane solution. The cross-hatched areas represent spectral absorption bands.

However, the close similarity in the Cotton band (and the equality of the sign of the Cotton effect) leaves no doubt that the distribution of the substituents around the asymmetric carbon is identical in all three isomers. In favorable cases it may be possible to observe several Cotton effects, as for instance with β-octyl nitrite (Kuhn and Lehmann, 1931) whose $[\alpha]_\lambda$ curve is compared with spectral absorption bands in Fig. V.16. We may, therefore, think of studies of the Cotton effect as a special kind of spectroscopy and one which is peculiarly sensitive to steric relationships within the molecule.

2. Proteins and Synthetic Polypeptides

We have seen in Chap. III that the native forms of proteins and nucleic acids are characterized by a highly specific conformation, which may be disrupted relatively easily by a variety of mild treatments. These treatments cause pronounced changes in the physical and chemical behavior of the macromolecules without any change in their covalent bonding. Such changes, lumped under the generic term of "denaturation" are of great interest to molecular biology, since they illuminate the forces which are responsible for holding the macromolecules in their native conformation, so crucial for their biological function.

Proteins are composed of L-amino acids which are characterized by negative $[\alpha]_D$ values. It has long been observed that this optical activity undergoes a pronounced change when the protein is denatured. In most cases, denaturation leads to an increase in the negative value of $[\alpha]_D$ by an amount which may be as high as 80°. In the case of collagen, the change is in the opposite direction and is frequently very large, e.g. $[\alpha]_D$ of bovine collagen changes from $-350°$ to $-146°$ (Harrington and Von Hippel, 1961). A related phenomenon is the sharp increase in the optical activity of gelatin solutions accompanying the gelation process (Kraemer and Fanselow, 1928; Pchelin et al., 1963) which is known to involve the formation of crystallites, acting as quasi-crosslinkages in the gel network. The optical activity changes during the denaturation of globular proteins were subjected to a detailed kinetic study by Simpson and Kauzmann (1953), Schellman et al. (1953), and Kauzmann and Simpson (1953) who found that the change of $[\alpha]_D$ characterizing the denaturation of ovalbumin is independent of the denaturation reagent used, but that the rates of denaturation under a given set of conditions may vary by many orders of magnitude depending on the protein species.

The physical basis for optical activity would lead to the expectation that changes of conformation result in corresponding changes of $[\alpha]_\lambda$; however, it seemed puzzling that the change should occur in almost all cases in the same direction. Another regularity was pointed out by Linderstrøm–Lang and Schellman (1954) who showed that in a Drude plot the characteristic wavelength λ_c is generally higher in native than in denatured proteins. It was then suggested (Cohen, 1955) that the change in optical activity, characterizing the transition from a native to a denatured protein, may be due to the existence of helical conformations in the native samples. Such helices would, because of their form asymmetry, make a contribution to the optical activity which would be superimposed on that caused by the asymmetric carbons in the chain backbone. Since such helices were believed to be generally wound in the same direction, their destruction by the denaturation reagent would be expected to make always a contribution of the same sign to the observed optical activity.

We have seen in Chap. III that synthetic polypeptides can also undergo helix-coil transitions. It was found that such transitions are typically accompanied by large changes in optical activity and the study of this phenomenon became a powerful tool in the investigation of the principles governing the optical activity changes characteristic of protein denaturation. The original observation made by Doty and Yang (1956) was soon followed by a large number of studies employing a variety of polypeptides and solvent media. The present status of this field has been summarized in a number of excellent reviews (Blout, 1960; Urnes and Doty, 1961; Yang, 1961). It is obvious that the interpretation of data from a syn-

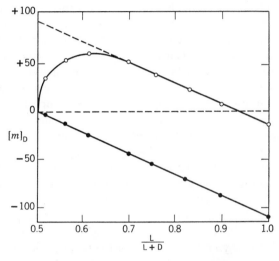

Fig. V.17. Optical activity of copolypeptides of L-leucine and D-leucine in benzene (O) and in trifluoroacetic acid (●). The dashed line extrapolates the data in benzene solution to indicate the optical activity to be expected from a racemic polymer if it could retain the helical conformation.

thetic polypeptide containing one or at most two types of building blocks is incomparably simpler than the analysis of phenomena observed on proteins with their complex (and often unknown) amino acid sequences, disulfide crosslinkages, and a variety of other restraints responsible for their unique tertiary structure. We shall give two typical examples of the striking effects which may be observed with synthetic polypeptides. Figure V.17 represents the results of experiments carried out by Downie et al. (1957) who copolymerized L- and D-leucine and determined the optical activity of the copolymers in benzene, a solvent in which the polypeptides exist in the helical conformation, and in trifluoroacetic acid, in which the polypeptides are present as random coils. The results are expressed in terms of the "mean residue rotation" $[m]_\lambda$ defined by

$$[m]_\lambda = (M_0/100)[\alpha]_\lambda \tag{5.8}$$

where M_0 is the molecular weight of the amino acid residue as a function of x_L the fraction of L residues in the copolymer. It may be seen that for the random coils the optical activity is linear in the composition of the copolymer, indicating that the asymmetric centers make independent contributions to the effect observed. The optical activity behavior is more complex in a solvent medium supporting helix formation. Here the optical activities are more positive than for the random coils, the difference being a constant quantity for copolymers containing more than 70% of the L-isomer, but for copolymers containing 50 to 70% of the L-isomer this difference decreases and it vanishes for the racemic copolymers. The linear portion of the plot of the optical activities in benzene solution may be interpreted as representing the range of copolymer composition in which the helical conformation is stable. Here the form asymmetry of the molecule as a whole makes a constant contribution to the optical activity, which is added to the contributions due to the asymmetric amino acid residues. If this linear portion is extrapolated to $x_L = {}^1/_2$, we obtain $[m]_{589} = 96°$, a value corresponding to the hypothetical racemic copolymer, which retains the helical conformation with the helices wound in the direction characteristic of chains composed of L-amino acid residues. In such copolymers the optical activity would result only from the helical conformation, since the contribution of the asymmetric centers of the L- and D-amino acid residues would be equal in magnitude and opposite in sign. Another example of the manner in which observations on synthetic polypeptides may be used to clarify the conditions required for the stabilization of helical conformations is provided by the work of Goodman and Schmitt (1959) whose results are represented in Fig. V.18. They synthesized a series of oligopeptides containing γ-methyl glutamate residues and measured their optical activity in dichloroacetic acid and in dioxane. It can be seen that the specific rotation is a monotonic function of chain length for solutions in dichloroacetic acid, while the data for the dioxane solutions exhibit a dramatic break at the pentapeptide. These results indicate that the optical activities in the dichloroacetic acid solutions represent the sum of independent contributions from the asymmetric centers of the internal amino acid residues and contributions from the terminal members of the chain. Such simple addition would be expected, as we have seen, for randomly coiled chains. On the other hand, the anomalous behavior of the higher peptides in dioxane is

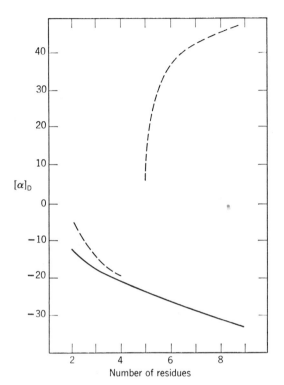

Fig. V.18. Optical activity of γ-methyl-L-glutamate oligomers.   Dioxane solutions
(- -); dichloroacetic acid solutions(——).

suggestive of the formation of helical structures and it is found, in fact, from an inspection of molecular models that the pentapeptide is the first member of the series in which the formation of a hydrogen-bonded helical turn is possible.

It is not surprising that the availability of synthetic polypeptides, whose optical activity behavior can be analyzed with much more assurance than that of proteins, stimulated a number of theoreticians to formulate a mathematical description of the differences to be expected between randomly coiled and helically wound chain molecules.   The first such attempt was made by Moffitt (1956) whose calculations led to the prediction that the contribution made to the optical activity by the asymmetry of a helical conformation should have a qualitatively different wavelength dependence than that predicted by the Drude equation.   In the usual phenomenological formulation of his result (Moffitt and Yang, 1956)

$$[\alpha]_\lambda = (100/M_0)[(n^2 + 2)/3] \left[\frac{a_0\lambda_0^2}{(\lambda^2 - \lambda_0^2)} + \frac{b_0\lambda^4}{(\lambda^2 - \lambda_0^2)^2} \right] \quad (5.9)$$

where λ_0 is a wavelength related to absorption bands with significant rotatory strength. The parameter b_0 which has been found, as predicted by theory, remarkably independent of the solvent medium, describes the deviation of the rotatory dispersion from the "normal" form corresponding to the one-term Drude equation and has been widely employed as an index of the "helicity" of a polypeptide. With a variety of such materials it has been found that "anomalous rotatory dispersion" (e.g., a large deviation from the one-term Drude equation) correlates with a number of physicochemical criteria indicative of helix formation.

More detailed theoretical considerations (Fitts and Kirkwood, 1957; Moffitt et al., 1957; Tinoco et al., 1961) have shown that the validity of Moffitt's original analysis is less certain than was believed at the time it was first proposed and recently his expression has been used more as an empirical rule. The characteristic wavelength λ_0 usually lies in the neighborhood of 210 mμ, but may be shifted to longer wavelengths with polypeptides carrying strong chromophores (e.g., poly(L-tyrosine), poly(L-tryptophan). However, non-zero b_0 values have been found to characterize the rotatory dispersion of, e.g., β-methyl-L-aspartate oligomers too short to form a helix (Goodman et al., 1963a) or poly-(L-tyrosine) solutions in which the polypeptide is known to exist as a random coil (Coombes et al., 1960). In time such "anomalies" will undoubtedly be accounted for and there is no doubt that the rotatory dispersion can, in principle, provide valuable information about optically active chain molecules which can exist in helical conformations. Progress has been hampered, to some extent, by the fact that the Cotton effects which, as we have seen, are particularly valuable regions of the rotatory dispersion spectrum lie, for most proteins and polypeptides, rather far in the ultraviolet. Only recent instrumental advances, which enable the investigator to measure the optical activity at wavelengths in the 185–230 mμ range, have made them accessible (Simmons and Blout, 1960; Simmons et al., 1961; Schmier and Simmons, 1962; Holzwarth et al, 1962; Blout et al., 1963).

Most polypeptides composed of L-amino acid residues have been found to have their rotatory dispersion spectra characterized by negative values of b_0 and negative Cotton effects. Molecular models indicate that such polypeptides should form right-handed helices more easily than left-handed ones, and Moffitt's analysis also associated a right-handed helix with a negative b_0 value. Nevertheless, the correlation of the sense in which the helix is wound with the nature of the rotatory dispersion was definitely settled only by a study of the rotatory dispersion of myoglobin for which the presence of right-handed α-helices (cf. p. 153) had previously been established by x-ray analysis of the protein crystal (Urnes et al., 1961; Beychok and Blout, 1961). Since the possibility of a reversal of the sense of the helix during the dissolution of the protein seems too far-fetched to be seriously considered, the negative Cotton effects in polypeptides composed of the L-isomers of amino acids, such as glutamic acid, alanine, lysine, leucine, and methionine, may be taken as characteristic of right-handed α-helices.

It should be emphasized, however, that a reversal of the sign of the Cotton effect need not necessarily reflect a reversal of the sense of the helix. This can also be brought about by a change in the nature of a chromophore with an asymmetric environment. The two cases may be distinguished by optical activity studies on copolymers, since the helix would be expected to remain intact on varying the composition of copolymers composed of two amino acids which tend to form helices of the same sense. The application of this criterion to poly(β-benzyl-L-aspartate) (Karlson et al., 1960) which has a rotatory dispersion characterized by a positive b_0 value, is illustrated in Figure V.19. It may be seen that on introducing even small proportions of γ-benzyl-L-glutamate into a poly(β-benzyl-L-aspartate) chain the b_0 undergoes an abrupt change of sign, while copolymers of γ-benzyl-L-glutamate and β-benzyl-D-aspartate have very similar b_0 values over the entire composition range. This leads to the conclusion that the positive b_0 in poly(β-benzyl-L-aspartate) is a consequence of a helical sense opposite to that of poly(γ-benzyl-L-glutamate). The application of the same criterion to poly(L-tyrosine), which is also characterized by a positive b_0 value, leads to the opposite result. Here the sense of the helix must be the same as in poly(γ-benzyl-L-glutamate), since for tyrosine–benzyl glutamate copolymers b_0 is linear in composition. We must then conclude that the reversal of sign of the Cotton effect in poly(l-tyrosine) is due to the phenolic chromophore (Fasman, 1962).

A fascinating phenomenon, which would have probably gone undetected without the availability of optical activity as an experimental tool, is the transition of dissolved poly(L-proline) from one helical conformation to another one of the opposite sense. This phenomenon, first discovered by Kurtz et al. (1956), was studied kinetically in great detail by Steinberg et al. (1960). In glacial acetic acid the dextrorotatory form I ($[\alpha]_D = +50°$), obtained when the polymerization is carried out in ether solution, is converted to the strongly levorotatory form II ($[\alpha]_D = -540°$) with a

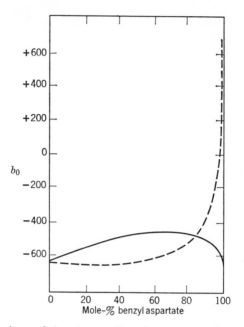

Fig. V.19. Dependence of the rotatory dispersion parameter b_0 on the composition of γ-benzyl-L-glutamate copolymers with β-benzyl-D-aspartate (- -) and with β-benzyl-L-aspartate (———).

half-life of about 4 hours at 25°C.   The reverse process may be studied by diluting a glacial acetic acid solution of form II with large amounts of 1-propanol.   The nature of these transformations has been considered (pp. 138–139); here we should only like to note that poly(L-proline) offers a good example for the importance of obtaining optical activity data in the region of the Cotton effect.   Poly(L-proline)II is characterized by a negative Cotton effect, which is however centered around 203 mμ (Blout et al., 1963) and is distinct from the Cotton effect centered at 225 mμ which dominates the near ultraviolet rotatory dispersion of the helical form of poly(γ-benzyl-L-glutamate) and similar polypeptides (Simmons et al., 1961). These two effects are known to arise from different electronic transitions and they have opposite correlations between the sign of the Cotton effect and the sense of the helix.   As a result, the poly(L-proline) helix has been assigned the left-handed structure (Blout et al., 1963).

While the changes in the rotatory dispersion of synthetic polypeptides undergoing the helix-coil transition constitute in themselves a most fascinating subject for study, their greatest importance lies in the insight which they provide into analogous phenomena occurring in protein molecules. The wavelength dependence of the optical activity of most native proteins may be fitted by the one-term Drude equation, but Yang and Doty (1957) have pointed out that a "normal" rotatory dispersion curve should represent an adequate description of a polypeptide sample containing less than 40% of the material in the α-helical conformation. According to their analysis, an increasing content of α-helices would produce a shift of the characteristic wavelength λ_c toward higher values and λ_c could, accordingly, be taken as an index of the "helical content." An extensive survey of the rotatory dispersion of native and denatured proteins (Jirgensons, 1961) shows, however, that λ_c may remain unchanged during protein denaturation or may even move in a direction opposite to that predicted by Doty and Yang. This lack of regularity is probably caused by the presence, within the protein molecules, of several different types of conformations which contribute to the anomalous rotatory dispersion—as might be expected from the variety of effects observed with synthetic polypeptides (Schellman and Schellman, 1961).

Some proteins have a very high helical content and in their case the anomalous rotatory dispersion is clearly observable. This is particularly so with the muscle protein myosin (Cohen and Szent-Gyorgyi, 1957). Myosin may be split in a very specific manner by treatment with the enzyme trypsin and one of the fractions has a rotatory dispersion characterized by $b_0 = -660°$, i.e., as large as synthetic polypeptides in their fully helical form. Another protein with an unusually high helical content is myoglobin, for which Urnes et al. (1961) estimated, on the basis of the b_0 values, that 73% of the chains are present as α-helices. This estimate is in excellent agreement with the crystallographically determined structure of this protein, but until similar data become available for other proteins of known structure, the reliability of the method will be difficult to assess.

At this time it would seem that the best method of characterizing the nature of helical conformations, and of estimating the helical content of proteins, involves an analysis of the Cotton effect. Simmons et al. (1961) introduced this method for proteins known to contain α-helices and showed that this conformation is characterized by a negative Cotton effect centered at 225 mμ with an optical activity minimum at 233 mμ. Later, when instruments for measurements in the far ultraviolet became available, a second positive Cotton effect centered at 190 mμ and with a very intense maximum at 198 mμ was discovered (Blout et al., 1962). A comparison of $[m]_\lambda$ values of proteins at these maxima or minima with corresponding data for suitably chosen polypeptide standards has been shown to lead to values for helical content which correlate with estimates from b_0 values where these are available (Simmons et al., 1961; Beychok and Blout, 1961). However, the analysis of the Cotton effect is superior in two ways to procedures based on the Moffitt equation. First, it allows us to define two parameters, the location of the Cotton effect (related to the nature of the conformation responsible for it) as well as its intensity. This feature proved valuable in the observation of the rotatory dispersion of collagen (Blout et al., 1963) which was found to exhibit a Cotton effect quite different from that of globular proteins but identical with that of poly(L-proline) II. Secondly, the method is applicable even in cases where the helical content is quite low. For instance, Beychok et al. (1962) used this procedure to estimate the extent of disordering produced in ferrihemoglobin and ferrimyoglobin when these proteins are subjected to various treatments leading to denaturation. Such processes were found to decrease the helical fraction from an initial 75–80% to the range of 10–30%.

3. Vinyl Polymers and Polyethers

The polymerization of optically active monomers would, in general, be expected to lead to optically active products. In the case of homopolymers of vinyl or vinylidene compounds which may be represented by

$$(-\underset{\underset{R_1-\underset{\underset{R_3}{|}}{C}-R_2}{|}}{\overset{\overset{X}{|}}{C}}-CH_2-)_n$$

the optical activity is due to the asymmetric centers in the side chains and it disappears if these side chains are modified so as to remove the centers of asymmetry (Marvel and Overberger, 1946; Overberger and Palmer, 1956). This is easily understood; we have pointed out previously that the tertiary or quaternary carbons in the chain backbone are not truly asymmetric centers (see page 94) and they will, therefore, not contribute to optical activity. In isotactic vinyl or vinylidene polymer chains, only the chain ends contain true asymmetric centers; but for any high molecular weight material the concentration of chain ends is too low to yield measurable optical activities (Frisch et al. 1953). It is true that isotactic chains have a considerable tendency of assuming helical conformations even in solution, but if the chain contains no true centers of asymmetry, these helical sections are equally likely to be right-handed and left-handed, so that their contributions to optical activity will cancel out.

An entirely different situation arises in the polymerization of materials such as propylene oxide. If this monomer is polymerized under conditions leading to an isotactic product (Price and Osgan, 1956)

the polymer chains contain centers of true asymmetry, since the carbons carrying the methyl substituents are preceded by methylene and followed by oxygen in the chain backbone, so that the two directions along the chain are clearly differentiated. This polymer, therefore, exhibits the expected optical activity and fractionation procedures designed to separate the most isotactic fractions will also provide material of the highest optical activity.

Schuerch and his collaborators (Beredjick and Schuerch, 1958; Schmitt and Schuerch, 1960) have pointed out that copolymers of vinyl compounds contain true centers of asymmetry in the chain backbone which may lead to significant optical activities. If we consider, for instance, the repeating unit of an alternating maleic anhydride copolymer

it is clear that the carbon atom marked with an asterisk is a center of asymmetry and that the polymer should be optically active if it can be prepared so that one configuration predominates over the other. This result may be achieved by utilizing the phenomenon of asymmetric induction. For example, if an optically active monomer, such as α-methylbenzyl vinyl ether, is copolymerized with maleic anhydride (Schmitt and Schuerch, 1960), the repeating unit of the alternating copolymer may exist in the two diastereoisometric forms represented below:

It may be assumed that the configuration of the side chain of the optically active vinyl ether will influence the mode of addition of the maleic anhydride to some extent, so that one of the diastereoisomeric forms is kinetically favored.   The existence of such an effect was proven by showing that the copolymer remains optically active after reduction of the ether side chains to hydroxyl groups.

The study of the behavior of homopolymers of optically active monomers has also led to the discovery of interesting effects.   A number of investigators (Bailey and Yates, 1960; Pino and Lorenzi, 1960; Nozakura et al., 1961) have shown that the polymerization of optically active vinyl monomers, under conditions favoring the production of isotactic polymers, leads to products whose optical activities may exceed those of the reagents by a very large factor.   Moreover, Pino and Lorenzi, as well as Bailey and Yates, found that solvent extraction of their polymers, designed to separate the isotactic and atactic fractions, yielded samples of widely different optical activity.   At first sight this result may seem surprising, since we have shown earlier that the pseudo-asymmetric centers in the backbone of vinyl homopolymers cannot be expected to make a significant contribution to optical activity.   The results may, however, be explained in terms of conformational effects.   We have seen in Chap. III that the potential energy of isotactic polymers is minimized when the chains assume a helical conformation.   If the chain carries branches containing centers of asymmetry, helical sections coiled in one direction would be expected to be favored and the form asymmetry of such helices would make a contribution to the observed optical activity.   This is the interpretation of the observed high optical activities advanced by Pino and Lorenzi who stress, in particular, the high temperature coefficient of the optical activities of their isotactic polymers in solution.   These are reminiscent of a similar effect in solutions of polypeptides, where temperature variations are clearly associated with helix-coil transitions.   This interpretation was disputed by Nozakura et al. (1961) who pointed out that the optical activity of poly(l-4-methyl-1-hexene) is relatively insensitive to changes in the solvent medium, which would be expected to affect strongly the equilibrium between a helical and a randomly coiled conformation.   It is also significant that Abe and Goodman (1963), who studied the polymerization of optically active aldehydes, found that the polymeric products invariably had much higher optical activities than the monomeric reagents, even if the polymerization was *not* carried out under conditions leading to stereoregulation.   We may recall that optical activity is highly sensitive to any changes in molecular conformation in the neighborhood of an asymmetric center.   In a small molecule which contains no cyclic structures many conformations are accessible and these will frequently make contributions of opposite sign to the optical activity (Wood et al., 1952) so that the measured effect will be relatively small. On the other hand, if side chains carrying centers of asymmetry are attached at close spacing to a polymer backbone, steric interference will severely restrict the range of accessible conformations. Their probability distribution function will be narrowed down further if the polymer backbone is characterized by a high degree of stereoregularity, so that the side chains find themselves in a similar environment. Such a restriction on accessible conformations ("conformational rigidity") may be entirely sufficient to account for the observed high optical activities and their dependence on stereoregularity, without need to invoke a contribution from the form asymmetry of helices.*

The variety of factors which may influence the optical activity behavior of dissolved chain molecules is illustrated in a study of optically active polyelectrolytes (Kulkarni and Morawetz, 1961; Bruschtein, 1965), such as the polymers of N-acrylyl or N-methacrylyl derivatives of α-amino acids. When such polymeric acids are ionized, the mutual repulsion of the anionic charges will lead to a pronounced expansion of the molecular coil to a highly extended conformation and it is then possible to study the effect of this conformational change of the polymeric chain backbone on the optical activity due to asymmetric centers located in the side chains. Typical data, obtained with poly(N-methacrylyl-L-glutamic acid) and its low molecular weight analog, N-pivalyl-L-glutamic acid

$$
\begin{array}{cc}
\qquad\quad CH_3 & \qquad\quad CH_3 \\
\qquad\quad | & \qquad\quad | \\
(-CH_2-C-)_n & CH_3-C-CH_3 \\
\qquad\quad | & \qquad\quad | \\
\qquad\quad CO & \qquad\quad CO \\
\qquad\quad | & \qquad\quad | \\
\qquad\quad NH & \qquad\quad NH \\
\qquad\quad | & \qquad\quad | \\
\qquad HC-COOH & \qquad HC-COOH \\
\qquad\quad | & \qquad\quad | \\
\qquad\quad CH_2 & \qquad\quad CH_2 \\
\qquad\quad | & \qquad\quad | \\
\qquad\quad CH_2 & \qquad\quad CH_2 \\
\qquad\quad | & \qquad\quad | \\
\qquad\quad COOH & \qquad\quad COOH
\end{array}
$$

Poly(N-methacrylyl-L-
glutamic acid)

N-pivalyl-L-glutamic
acid

* A recent study of poly(L-menthyl methacrylate), prepared under a variety of conditions, showed only a very slight dependence of the optical activity on stereoregularity (Sobue et al., 1964).

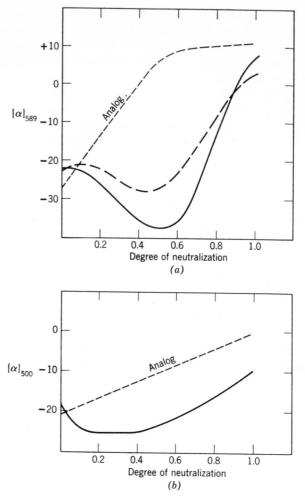

Fig. V.20. Dependence of [α] on the degree of neutralization of optically active polymeric acids. (a) Poly(N-methacrylyl-ʟ-glutamic acid) prepared in neutral aqueous solution (——) and in dioxane solution (- -). (b) Poly(N-acrylyl-ʟ-asparagine).

as well as by poly(N-acrylyl-ʟ-asparagine) and its analog N-*iso*butyryl-ʟ-asparagine are represented in Fig. V.20. There is a striking difference between the behavior of the polymers and their "analogs." In the case of the glutamic acid derivatives, this difference can be partially accounted for by differences in the order in which the α and γ carboxyls are ionized in the polymeric acid and the dibasic acid analog, but no such explanation may be invoked with the asparagine derivatives which have only one type of ionizable groups. The large negative values of $[\alpha]$ observed with the partially ionized polymers seem to be a consequence of changes in the side chain conformations as the polymer backbone assumes a more expanded form. Such changes could be produced either by interactions of side chains with the backbone or by interactions of side chains with each other. It may be noted that the optical activity behavior depends significantly on the conditions under which the polymer was prepared—indicating a sensitivity of the optical activity to small changes in stereoregularity. A copolymer containing 15% of D-monomer units behaves in a manner similar to that observed with the homopolymer of the L-monomer, confirming the assumption that the complex dependence of optical activity on the degree of ionization does not involve effects caused by a helix-coil transition. We are then led to the conclusion that while optical activity studies are a most sensitive tool for revealing qualitatively the existence of conformational transitions, the multiplicity of possible effects renders the detailed interpretation of data correspondingly complex.

C. LIGHT SCATTERING

1. Scattering by Gases

Many of the fundamental concepts in the interpretation of light scattering were formulated by Lord Rayleigh (1871, 1881) who concerned himself with the scattering by gases, in which the scattering molecules are placed at random at large distances from each other and may be considered to make independent contributions to the effects observed. The phenomenon is caused by the fact that the oscillating electrical field of the incident light wave induces an oscillating dipole in molecules lying in its path, which will then radiate light in all directions. It is assumed that only a very small fraction of the incident light beam is scattered, so that the effect of multiple scattering may be neglected. The dependence of the scattered light intensity i_θ on the angle θ, subtended by the directly transmitted and the scattered light ray, is derived most easily if the radiating molecules are electrically isotropic and small compared to the wavelength λ of the light employed. In the schematic representation in Fig. V.21 the scattering from the horizontal incident beam AO is observed in various horizontal directions OC. If the incident light is polarized in the plane AOV, the scattered light will be also polarized in a vertical plane (e.g., COV) and its intensity will be independent of θ. On the other hand, the

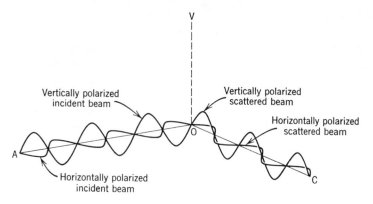

Fig. V.21. Schematic representation of the scattering of light.

intensity of light scattered from a beam polarized in the horizontal plane will be proportional to $\cos^2 \theta$, so that no light will be scattered at an angle of 90°. Since unpolarized light may be treated as the sum of two beams of equal intensity polarized in planes perpendicular to each other, the intensity of the light scattered from an unpolarized beam will be proportional to $(1 + \cos^2 \theta)$ and the scattered light will be fully polarized if observed at a scattering angle of 90°. All the scattered light intensities will be inversely proportional to the square of the distance l from the scattering source O.

The amplitude of the oscillating dipole induced in a molecule by the oscillating field of the incident light is proportional to the polarizability α of the molecule. However, when the scattered ray comes from a large number of molecules spaced at random, the electrical vector due to any one of them may be positive or negative with equal probability at any given time and location. The summation of such vectors is then analogous to the one-dimensional "random walk" problem discussed on p. 113 and it leads to a value in which the amplitude of the vibration characterizing the ray scattered by a single molecule is multiplied by the square root of their number. The intensity of the radiated energy, which is proportional to the square of the amplitude of the ray, is then proportional to the square of the molecular polarizability but the first power of the number of radiating molecules. According to the Rayleigh theory, if I_0 is the intensity of the incident light, the scattered beam intensity i_θ due to a unit volume of the scattering medium containing N^* molecules of polarizability α is given by

$$\mathcal{R}_\theta \equiv i_\theta l^2/I_0 = (8\pi^4 N^* \alpha^2/\lambda^4)(1 + \cos^2\theta) \tag{5.10}$$

where the quantity $\Re_\theta$, commonly referred to as the Rayleigh ratio, is defined so that the scattering may be characterized without reference to the distance l at which the light is observed. Using the Clausius–Mosotti relation between the molecular polarizability α and the dielectric constant $\mathfrak{D}$

$$\alpha = \frac{3}{4\pi N^*} \frac{\mathfrak{D} - 1}{\mathfrak{D} + 2} \tag{5.11}$$

we obtain, after substituting $N^* = \rho N/M$, where ρ is the density and M the molecular weight, for a gas in which $\mathfrak{D} \approx 1$

$$\Re_\theta = \frac{\pi^2}{2} \frac{M(\mathfrak{D} - 1)^2}{\lambda^4 N \rho} (1 + \cos^2 \theta) \tag{5.12}$$

We see then that for a series of substances, such as the homologous series of paraffins, for which the dielectric constant would be expected to remain constant at constant gas densities, the scattering will be proportional to the molecular weight. This is a consequence of the fact that vibrating dipoles in different parts of any one molecule are in phase with one another, in contrast to the random shift in phase between dipole vibrations in different molecules. When the molecular weight of the scattering molecules is known, relation (5.12) may be used to estimate Avogadro's number N.

A more complex situation arises when the scattering molecules are not isotropic. In that case the magnitude and direction of the oscillating dipole of the scattering molecule will depend on its orientation and will not necessarily lie in the plane of polarization of the incident beam. As a consequence, light scattered from a horizontally polarized beam has a vertical component and vice versa. Also, light scattered at a right angle from an unpolarized beam is no longer polarized in a vertical plane but has a horizontally polarized component H_u whose ratio to the vertically polarized component V_u is given by (Rayleigh, 1918)

$$\rho_u \equiv H_u/V_u = \frac{2(\alpha_1{}^2 + \alpha_2{}^2 + \alpha_3{}^2 - \alpha_1\alpha_2 - \alpha_1\alpha_3 - \alpha_2\alpha_3)}{4(\alpha_1{}^2 + \alpha_2{}^2 + \alpha_3{}^2 + \alpha_1\alpha_2 + \alpha_1\alpha_3 + \alpha_2\alpha_3)} \tag{5.13}$$

where α_1, α_2, and α_3 are the three principal polarizabilities of the scattering molecules. From the form of eq. (5.13) we may see that ρ_u attains a maximum value of 0.5 for long rod-shaped particles in which one of the polarizabilities is much larger than the other two. Depolarization measurements on light scattered from gases lead to ρ_u values ranging from 0 to 0.125. It has also been shown that the intensity of light scattered at 90°

from anisotropic molecules is increased over the value predicted by (5.12) by the factor $(6 + 6\rho_u)/(6 - 7\rho_u)$ (customarily referred to as the "Cabannes factor") (cf. Oster, 1948).

2. Scattering from Solutions of Molecules much Smaller than the Wavelength of Light

When the scattering molecules are not distributed at random, destructive interference will tend to reduce the intensity of the scattered radiation. This factor becomes important in liquids with their partially ordered structure. It could be dealt with, in principle, by calculating explicitly the interference corresponding to a known radial distribution of molecules in a given liquid; but the procedure would be extremely laborious and it is more convenient (Debye, 1944) to approach the problem from fluctuation theory, as first suggested by Einstein (1910).

Let us consider any intensive thermodynamic property g of a system. Typical examples of such properties, with which we shall be particularly concerned, are density in a system of one or several components and concentration in multicomponent systems. Although macroscopic measurements indicate that the system is uniform, characterized by a bulk average value g_0 of the property with which we are concerned, we may conceive of fluctuations in the local value of this property on a scale small compared to the wavelength of the light used. The probability distribution of such fluctuations, subject to the restriction of a constant total volume and constant total energy of the system, will be given by

$$\mathcal{W}(g)dg = \exp\left[-F(g)/\mathbf{k}T\right]\bigg/\int_0^\infty \exp\left[-F(g)/\mathbf{k}T\right]dg \qquad (5.14)$$

where $F(g)$ is the Helmholtz free energy associated with g. For systems close to equilibrium, $F(g)$ may be expanded in a Taylor series around g_0

$$F(g) = F(g_0) + (dF/dg)_{g=g_0}(g - g_0) +$$
$$(^1/_2)(d^2F/dg^2)_{g=g_0}(g - g_0)^2 + \ldots \qquad (5.15)$$

where the first derivative must vanish, since it is evaluated at the position of equilibrium. Neglecting terms in higher than the second power of $(g - g_0)$

$$\mathcal{W}(g)dg = \exp\left[-F(g_0)/\mathbf{k}T\right]\exp\left[-a(g - g_0)^2\right]dg\bigg/\int_0^\infty \exp\left[-F(g)/\mathbf{k}T\right]dg$$

$$a = (1/2\mathbf{k}T)(d^2F/dg^2)_{g=g_0} \qquad (5.16)$$

and since

$$\int_{-\infty}^{+\infty} \exp\left[-ax^2\right]dx = \sqrt{\pi/a}$$

we obtain

$$\mathcal{W}(g)dg = \sqrt{\pi/a}\, \exp\left[-a(g - g_0)^2\right]dg \tag{5.17}$$

A local fluctuation in any given property will, in general, lead to a corresponding fluctuation in the dielectric constant $\mathfrak{D}$. Such a fluctuation will, according to the Rayleigh theory, lead to

$$\mathfrak{R}_\theta = (\pi^2/2\lambda^4)\,\langle\Delta\mathfrak{D}^2\rangle\,\delta V(1 + \cos^2\theta) \tag{5.18}$$

where $\langle\Delta\mathfrak{D}^2\rangle$ is the mean square deviation of the local dielectric constant, within a volume element δV, from the bulk average value of $\mathfrak{D}$. Using the distribution function (5.17),

$$\langle\Delta\mathfrak{D}^2\rangle = (\partial\mathfrak{D}/\partial g)^2\langle\Delta g^2\rangle$$

$$= (\partial\mathfrak{D}/\partial g)^2 \int_{-\infty}^{+\infty} (g - g_0)^2\,\sqrt{\pi/a}\, \exp\left[-a(g - g_0)^2\right]dg$$

$$= (\partial\mathfrak{D}/\partial g)^2 kT/(d^2F/dg^2)_{g=g} \tag{5.19}$$

We may now apply this result to two cases of special interest. In a pure liquid, fluctuations in the local value of the dielectric constant may, in principle, be caused by both density and temperature fluctuations, but the effect of temperature fluctuations is generally negligible. It can be shown from thermodynamics that

$$(\partial^2F/\partial\rho^2)_T = (V/\rho^2)[(1/\beta) - 2P] \tag{5.20}$$

where β is the isothermal compressibility. We may neglect the second term on the right and we obtain then, by substitution into (5.18) and (5.19),

$$\mathfrak{R}_\theta = (\pi^2/2\lambda^4)kT\beta[\rho_0(\partial\mathfrak{D}/\partial\rho)_T]^2(1 + \cos^2\theta) \tag{5.21}$$

For light of $\lambda = 4358$ Å, frequently employed in light scattering studies, typical $\mathfrak{R}_{90}$ values (i.e., Rayleigh ratios for scattering at an angle of 90°) for pure liquids range from 5×10^{-6} to 5×10^{-5} (Stacey, 1956).

If, on the other hand, we deal with a solution, the scattering resulting from density fluctuations and that caused by local fluctuations in the concentration of the solute may be considered to be additive. It may be shown that

$$(\partial^2 F/\partial c_2{}^2)_T = -(\delta V/\bar{V}_1 c_2)(\partial \bar{F}_1/\partial c_2)_T \qquad (5.22)$$

and with the osmotic pressure $\Pi = -(\bar{F}_1 - \bar{F}_1{}^0)/\bar{V}_1$, we obtain by substitution into (5.18) and (5.19) for the contribution $\Delta\Re_\theta$ to the Rayleigh ratio resulting from fluctuations in solute concentration

$$\Delta \,\Re_\theta = \frac{\pi^2(\partial\mathfrak{D}/\partial c_2)_T^2}{2\lambda^4(\partial\Pi/\partial c_2)_T} \, kT c_2(1 + \cos^2\theta) \qquad (5.23)$$

The dielectric constant may be equated to the square of the refractive index n and for dilute solutions we may approximate

$$(\partial\mathfrak{D}/\partial c_2)_T^2 = 4\mathrm{n}^2(\partial\mathrm{n}/\partial c_2)_T^2 \approx 4\mathrm{n}_0^2(\partial\mathrm{n}/\partial c_2)_T^2 \qquad (5.24)$$

where n_0 is the refractive index of the solvent. The Rayleigh ratio is then given by

$$\Delta\Re_\theta = K_\theta RT c_2/(\partial\Pi/\partial c_2)_T$$

$$K_\theta = [2\pi^2\mathrm{n}_0{}^2(\partial\mathrm{n}/\partial c_2)_T^2/\lambda^4 N](1 + \cos^2\theta) \qquad (5.25)$$

Finally, expressing the osmotic pressure as in eq. (4.16), we obtain

$$(\partial\Pi/\partial c_2)_T = RT[(1/M_2) + 2A_2 c_2 + 3A_3 c_2{}^2 + \ldots] \qquad (5.26)$$

so that

$$K_\theta c_2/\Delta\Re_\theta = (1/M_2) + 2A_2 c_2 + 3A_3 c_2{}^2 + \ldots \qquad (5.27)$$

and a plot of $K_\theta c_2/\Delta\Re_\theta$ against c_2 will yield the reciprocal molecular weight of the solute as the intercept. Let us now consider the qualitative significance of this result. We may think of the local fluctuations in the concentration of the solute as reflecting an equilibrium in which the buildup of concentration gradients, due to random molecular motion, is being opposed by osmotic pressure gradients, which tend to restore the uniformity of the system. Since the osmotic forces for any given concentration gradient become smaller with an increase in the size (and decrease in number) of the solute molecules, the extent of fluctuations in concentration will increase with an increasing molecular weight of the solute. Because of this intimate relationship between osmotic and fluctuation phenomena, the concentration dependence of light scattering may be used for the evaluation of the osmotic virial coefficients A_2 and A_3, whose significance was discussed in Chap. IV.

The result derived above for a single solute species may be easily extended to a polydisperse polymer sample, in which the refractive index increment $(\partial n/\partial c_i)_T$ may be considered to be identical for all molecular weight fractions. We have then in the limit of very high dilution

$$\lim_{c_i \to 0} (K_\theta c_i/\Delta\mathcal{R}_{\theta i}) = 1/M_i$$

$$\Delta\mathcal{R}_\theta = \sum_i \Delta\mathcal{R}_{\theta i} = K_\theta \sum c_i M_i \qquad (5.28)$$

so that

$$\lim_{c_2 \to 0} K_\theta c_2/\Delta\mathcal{R}_\theta = \sum_i c_i / \sum_i c_i M_i = 1/\bar{M}_w \qquad (5.29)$$

where c_2 stands for the sum of concentrations of all species in a polymer-homologous solute.

The range of molecular weights which are conveniently investigated by the light scattering technique extends from about 20,000 to several millions. The lower limit corresponds to the molecular weight of the solute for which the excess in the light scattering intensity is small compared to the scattering intensity of the pure solvent. The upper limit is brought about by the experimental difficulty of separating satisfactorily very high molecular weight solutes from adventitious extraneous impurities ("dust") which are inevitably introduced into the system. As the size of the dissolved macromolecules is increased beyond a certain limit, any procedure to "clean" the solution becomes either inadequate to remove all the "dust," or else it removes with it also the highest molecular weight fraction of the sample under investigation. This problem is particularly severe because of the angular dependence of the intensity of the light scattered from large particles to be discussed in the following section.

3. Estimation of the Size and Shape of Macromolecules from the Angular Dependence of the Scattered Light Intensity

When the dimensions of the scattering particles exceed about one-twentieth of the wavelength of the light used, the intensity of the scattered light will be reduced to a measurable extent as a consequence of destructive interference. A schematic representation of light scattered by two point scatterers is given in Fig. V.22. The displacement of the scattering elements from one another is characterized by a vector **r** which is pictured for simplicity as lying in the plane defined by the incident and the scattered light beam. If **r** subtends an angle γ with the incident beam and the

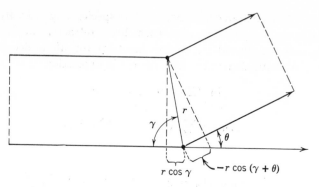

Fig. V.22. Two-dimensional representation of the difference in the path length of rays scattered by a particle with two scattering centers.

scattered light is observed at an angle θ from the directly transmitted beam, the difference in the path length of two parallel rays scattered by the two point scatterers is $r[\cos \gamma - \cos (\gamma + \theta)]$ so that the two scattered rays will be out of phase by an angle $2\pi r[\cos \gamma - \cos (\gamma + \theta)]/\lambda'$, where λ' is the wavelength of the light in the scattering medium. It can be seen that this phase angle will increase with increasing θ, leading to a corresponding increase in the destructive interference and a decrease in the intensity of the scattered light. To carry out a quantitative evaluation of this effect for a particle which may be represented as an assembly of N scatterers, the destructive interference must be averaged over all possible relative orientations of the assembly to the incident beam. Such a calculation leads to

$$\mathcal{P}(\theta) = \frac{1}{N^2} \sum_i \sum_j \frac{\sin kr_{ij}}{kr_{ij}}$$

$$k = 4\pi \sin (\theta/2)/\lambda' \tag{5.30}$$

where $\mathcal{P}(\theta)$ is the factor by which the beam scattered at an angle θ is attenuated because of destructive interference. If the scattering particle is deformable so that the distances r_{ij} between the scattering points are variable, the double summation in (5.30) has to be averaged over time. Although the relation (5.30) has been originally derived for the angular dependence of x-ray scattering from gases (Debye, 1915) it may be equally applied to the light scattering by dissolved macromolecules provided the difference in the refractive index of the solution and the solute is small (Debye, 1947). In practice, this is a condition which does not represent a serious limitation in the study of macromolecular solutions. We may note that for scattering points very close to one another, so that $\sin kr_{ij}/kr_{ij} \approx 1$, the quantity $\mathcal{P}(\theta)$ will approach unity. On the other hand, when the distance between scattering points becomes very large, we shall have $\sin kr_{ij}/kr_{ij} \approx 0$, except for the terms in which $i = j$, and eq. (5.30) reduces then to $\mathcal{P}(\theta) = 1/N$. This result again shows that in dilute systems and at small scattering angles, the intensity of the light scattered by the solute is proportional, for a given solution concentration, to the size of the solute molecules.

From (5.25) and the definition of $\mathcal{P}(\theta)$ we find that a combination of the effects of polarization and of destructive interference gives for the angular dependence of the light scattered from an unpolarized incident beam

$$\Delta\mathcal{R}_\theta = \Delta\mathcal{R}_0 \mathcal{P}(\theta)(1 + \cos^2 \theta)/2 \tag{5.31}$$

If the solution is sufficiently dilute so that the average distances between solute molecules are large compared to the wavelength of light, the form of $\mathcal{P}(\theta)$ may be considered to reflect solely the effects of destructive interference of light scattered from different points of an individual solute molecule. We may expand (5.30) into a power series to yield

$$\mathcal{P}(\theta) = \frac{1}{N^2}\left[N^2 - \frac{1}{3!}\sum_i \sum_j k^2 r^2{}_{ij} + \frac{1}{5!}\sum_i \sum_j k^4 r^4{}_{ij} - \dots \right] \tag{5.32}$$

It can be easily verified that the radius of gyration of any assembly of identical particles is related to the r_{ij} values by

$$\langle s^2 \rangle = (1/2N^2) \sum_i \sum_j r_{ij}{}^2 \tag{5.33}$$

so that $\mathcal{P}(\theta)$ assumes the form

$$\mathcal{P}(\theta) = 1 - \frac{1}{3} k^2 \langle s^2 \rangle + \dots\dots$$

$$= 1 - \frac{1}{3} (4\pi/\lambda')^2 \langle s^2 \rangle \sin^2 (\theta/2) + \dots \tag{5.34}$$

We see then that the dependence of the scattered light intensity on the scattering angle, in the limit of small θ, yields an unambiguous measure of the mean radius of gyration of the scattering particle.* As the kr_{ij} terms

---

* This conclusion is strictly valid only for optically isotropic particles. In the case of scattering by rigid rods, the relation between $\mathcal{P}(\theta)$ and $\langle s^2 \rangle$ has been shown to depend on the optical anisotropy of the scattering particle (Horn et al., 1951; Horn, 1955). For the case of Gaussian chains, the effect of the anisotropy of the chain segment is generally negligible [Horn (1955); Benoit and Weill, 1957].

assume larger values, the shape of $\mathcal{P}(\theta)$ becomes dependent on the higher moments of the distribution of the scattering elements in the solute particle. Calculations of $\mathcal{P}(\theta)$ have been carried out for spheres of uniform density (Rayleigh, 1911), rigid thin rods (Neugebauer, 1942; Zimm et al., 1945), Gaussian chains (Debye, 1947), and for polydisperse Gaussian chains with a normal distribution of chain lengths (Zimm, 1948).

These calculations yield the following expressions in terms of the dimensionless parameter, $u = k^2\langle s^2 \rangle$:

Spheres of radius R:

$$\mathcal{P}(\theta) = [(3/x^2)(\sin x - \cos x)]^2$$

$$x^2 = k^2 R^2 = 5u/3 \tag{5.35}$$

Rods of length L:

$$\mathcal{P}(\theta) = \frac{1}{x}\int_0^{2x} (\sin y/y)dy - (\sin x/x)^2$$

$$x^2 = k^2 L^2/4 = 3u \tag{5.36}$$

Monodisperse Gaussian coils:

$$\mathcal{P}(\theta) = (2/u^2)(e^{-u} + u - 1) \tag{5.37}$$

Polydisperse Gaussian coils:

$$\mathcal{P}(\theta) = 1 - \langle u \rangle_w/(2 + \langle u \rangle_w) \tag{5.38}$$

whereu $\langle u \rangle_w$ corresponds to the weight average chain length.

In principle it should be possible to eliminate the effects of destructive interference by measuring the scattered light intensity at sufficiently small scattering angles θ. In practice, however, it is found that such data are generally subject to large errors. This limitation arises from the presence of dust, which is particularly difficult to eliminate if measurements are to be carried out on aqueous solutions. Since the dust particles are much larger than the dissolved macromolecules, their contribution to the intensity of the scattered light may be very large at small scattering angles. Fortunately, this contribution decreases much more rapidly with increasing θ than the contribution due to the macromolecules so that it may be neglected at θ values above 30°, provided that reasonable precautions are taken in keeping the solution clean. However, at such scattering angles the effect of destructive interference on the intensity of the light scattered by the macromolecules is significant and has to be taken into account to

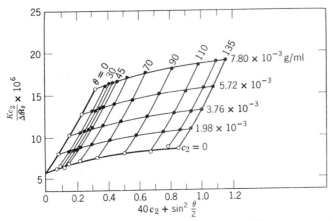

Fig. V.23. Zimm plot of light-scattering data.   Polystyrene, $\bar{M}_w = 170{,}000$, in dioxane solution.

obtain correct molecular weights.   This is done, in principle, by modifying (5.29) for solutions of a single macromolecular species to give

$$\lim_{c_2 \to 0} (K_\theta c_2 / \Delta \mathfrak{R}_\theta) = 1/M_2 \mathcal{P}(\theta) \tag{5.39}$$

A general method for treating experimental light scattering data so as to eliminate the effects of destructive interference and obtain the correct values for the molecular weight of the solute was outlined by Zimm (1948). In this procedure data are obtained for a number of solute concentrations, each at a number of scattering angles θ.   The ratio $K_\theta c_2 / \Delta \mathfrak{R}_\theta$ is then plotted as a function of $\sin^2 (\theta/2) + q c_2$, where q is an arbitrarily selected constant. Experimental points obtained at any given scattering angle may then be extrapolated to $c_2 = 0$.   From (5.39) we know that $K_\theta c_2 / \Delta \mathfrak{R}_\theta$ is proportional to $1/\mathcal{P}(\theta)$ and this must be linear in $\sin^2 (\theta/2)$ for sufficiently small angles (eq. 5.34) so that is should be possible to extrapolate data obtained at different scattering angles to $\theta = 0$.   By a double extrapolation procedure it is, therefore, possible to eliminate both effects due to deviations from solution ideality and effects due to the destructive interference of the scattered light and obtain a value of $\bar{M}_w$ independent of any assumptions.   A typical example of such a "Zimm plot" is shown in Fig. V.23.   It also follows from (5.39) and (5.34) that

$$1/\mathcal{P}(\theta) = \lim_{c_2 = 0} (K_\theta c_2 / \Delta \mathfrak{R}_\theta) / \lim_{c_2 = 0} (K_\theta c_2 / \Delta \mathfrak{R}_\theta)$$

$$= 1 + [16\pi^2/3(\lambda')^2]\langle s^2 \rangle \sin^2 (\theta/2) - \dots \tag{5.40}$$

so that the ratio of the initial slope of the $c_2 = 0$ line to the intercept on the ordinate of the Zimm plot is proportional to the mean square radius of gyration of the dissolved macromolecules.

When the solution contains a polydisperse sample of macromolecules, the $\mathcal{P}(\theta)$ values corresponding to the individual species will be averaged to an experimentally observed $\overline{\mathcal{P}}(\theta)$ given by

$$\sum \Delta\mathcal{R}_i(\theta)/K_\theta \sum c_i = \sum M_i c_i \mathcal{P}_i(\theta) / \sum c_i$$

$$= \overline{M}_w \overline{\mathcal{P}}(\theta) \tag{5.41}$$

which may be expressed in terms of the weight fraction w_i of the individual species as

$$\overline{\mathcal{P}}(\theta) = \sum M_i w_i \mathcal{P}_i(\theta) / \sum M_i w_i$$

$$= \sum N_i M_i^2 \mathcal{P}_i(\theta) / \sum N_i M_i^2 \tag{5.42}$$

so that $\overline{\mathcal{P}}(\theta)$ is a z-average quantity. It follows then that the mean square radius of gyration obtained from a Zimm plot is $\langle s^2 \rangle_z$, involving the z-averaging of the sizes of the individual molecules in the sample.

The experimentally determined shape of $\mathcal{P}(\theta)$ at higher scattering angles may lead to useful conclusions of a qualitative nature. Inspection of eq. (5.32) and (5.33) shows that for any given mean square radius of gyration, $\mathcal{P}(\theta)$ at large scattering angles will be decreased by a sharpening of the distribution of r_{ij} values. The effect has been analyzed quantitatively for a number of special cases. Thus, the magnitude of $1/\mathcal{P}(\theta)$ is increased by a decreasing polydispersity of the molecular weight distribution (Benoit, 1953; Goldstein, 1953), by decreasing polydispersity of size for particles of equal weight (Rice, 1955), by increasing chain branching (Benoit, 1953), and by increased chain flexibility (Peterlin, 1953). Since the excluded volume effect tends to lead to a sharpening of the maximum in the radial distribution function of chain segment densities (pp. 129–130), we should also expect in the case of flexible chains in good solvent media that $1/\mathcal{P}(\theta)$ would rise at large scattering angles above the values predicted by (5.37) for Gaussian coils (Hyde et al., 1958). It is clear from this enumeration that the general case, where all these parameters might be variable, does not lend itself to a reliable interpretation. On the other hand, these general principles may find application in special cases, where one may be reasonably certain that only one of these properties is being varied. When dealing with very large solute particles, the asymptotic behavior of $\mathcal{P}(\theta)$ may be useful as an additional source of information. Two cases are of particular importance.

For polydisperse Gaussian coils Benoit (1953) has derived for the asymptotic behavior of the $c_2 = 0$ line in a Zimm plot (the "Zimm envelope")

$$\lim_{u \to \infty} (K_\theta c_2/\Delta \mathcal{R}_\theta) = 1/2\bar{M}_n + [8\pi^2/(\lambda')^2]\langle s^2 \rangle_w \sin^2(\theta/2)/\bar{M}_w \quad (5.43)$$

so that the intercept of the asymptote yields the number average molecular weight, while its slope defines the weight average radius of gyration. We may note that for chains with a normal distribution, so that $\bar{M}_w = 2\bar{M}_n$, the intercept of the asymptote coincides with that of the initial tangent, i.e., the envelope of the Zimm plot will be linear over the entire course. An upward or downward curvature corresponds, therefore, to a narrower and broader distribution, respectively, than that given by the normal molecular weight distribution function. For the case of a system containing thin rods of constant cross section and variable length L, Casassa (1955) obtained for the asymptotic behavior of the Zimm envelope

$$K_\theta c_2/\Delta \mathcal{R}_\theta = \frac{2}{\pi^2} \frac{\sum M_i w_i/L_i^2}{(\sum M_i w_i/L_i)^2} + \frac{4 \sin (\theta/2)}{\lambda' \sum M_i w_i/L_i} \quad (5.44)$$

so that a plot of $K_\theta c_2/\Delta \mathcal{R}_\theta$ against $\sin (\theta/2)$ yields limiting slopes proportional to the particle length per unit weight (i.e., the cross-sectional area of rods of known density). This result may be used advantageously to distinguish between end-to-end and side-by-side aggregation of rigid elongated macromolecules.

For very large solute particles, the asymptotic behavior of $\mathcal{P}/(\theta)$ may correspond to the smallest scattering angles at which meaningful data may be obtained. In such cases it is important to realize that the Zimm envelope may have a pronounced curvature at scattering angles too small to be experimentally accessible, and that no conclusion about the radius of gyration of the solute molecule can be drawn on the basis of the available information. Failure to realize this limitation, inherent in the analysis of the angular distribution of scattered light intensities, has led in the past to considerable confusion, particularly in connection with the interpretation of data on nucleic acid solutions. It is a fortunate coincidence that the curvature of the Zimm envelope should be slight for Gaussian coils approaching a normal distribution of molecular weights, so that data obtained from such systems may be interpreted with reasonable assurance even if the molecular weight is extremely high.

The collection of the data required for a Zimm plot and their evaluation is fairly time consuming. It is often desired to employ a less rigorous but much more rapid procedure for the estimation of molecular weights and the sizes of dissolved macromolecules. It may be noted that the factor $(1 + \cos^2 \theta)$, which takes into account the variation in the scattered light intensity caused by the polarization of the scattered light, has the same value for any two angles symmetrically distributed around 90°. The ratio of the light intensities observed at two such angles will, therefore, reflect the ratio of the $\mathcal{P}(\theta)$ values. It is customary to make measurements at scattering angles of $\theta = 45°$ and $\theta = 135°$ and to express the results in terms of the dissymmetry $z^* = \mathcal{P}(45°)/\mathcal{P}(135°)$. Substituting $\sin^2(22.5°) = (2 - \sqrt{2})/4$ and $\sin^2(67.5°) = (2 + \sqrt{2})/4$ into eq. (5.34) we obtain

$$z^* = 1 + (8\pi^2 \sqrt{2}/3)\langle s^2 \rangle/(\lambda')^2 + \ldots .$$

$$= 1 + 37.2\langle s^2 \rangle/(\lambda')^2 + \ldots . \qquad (5.45)$$

As long as the radius of gyration is small compared to the wavelength of the light in the scattering medium, z^* will be a reliable measure of $\langle s^2 \rangle^{1/2}/\lambda'$ For larger particles, the terms in the higher moments of the distribution of scattering elements become important and the relation between z^* and $\langle s^2 \rangle^{1/2}/\lambda'$ will depend on particle shape. This is illustrated on values calculated by Doty and Steiner (1950) and plotted in Fig. V.24 which show that for $z^* > 1.7$ a given dissymmetry corresponds to significantly different radii of gyration for spherical, rod-like, and random coil particles.

The dissymmetry z^* may be used also to correct the scattered light intensity observed at 90° for the effects of destructive interference. From eq. (5.34) we have

$$1/\mathcal{P}(90°) = 1 + (8\pi^2/3)\langle s^2 \rangle/(\lambda')^2 - \ldots$$

$$= 1 + 26.3\langle s^2 \rangle/(\lambda')^2 - \ldots \qquad (5.46)$$

and combining this with relation (4.44)

$$1/\mathcal{P}(90°) = 1 + (z^* - 1)/\sqrt{2} + \ldots \qquad (5.47)$$

Again we shall find that the relation between $1/\mathcal{P}(90°)$ and z^* will depend on the particle shape as the dimension of the particles exceeds a certain size. The correlation plotted from values calculated by Doty and Steiner (Fig. V.25) shows that estimates of $1/\mathcal{P}(90°)$ will require information about the shape of the scattering molecules for $z^* > 1.4$.

In studies of synthetic chain molecules, the ratio $\langle s^2 \rangle^{1/2}/\lambda'$ will rarely exceed 0.1, corresponding to a root-mean-square radius of gyration between 300 and 400 Å. In this range the correlation between $\langle s^2 \rangle^{1/2}/\lambda'$, the dissymmetry z^*, and the function $1/\mathcal{P}(90°)$ differs only slightly for monodisperse coils, polydisperse coils, and rods and one might then be tempted to conclude that the analysis based on the dissymmetry measurement is quite adequate both for the molecular weight determination and for the

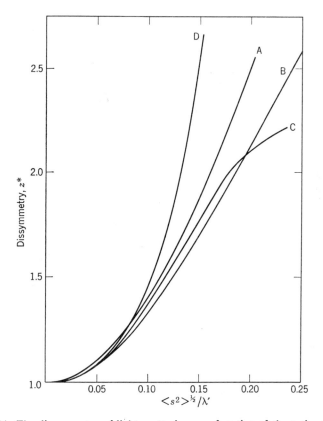

Fig. V.24. The dissymmetry of light scattering as a function of the ratio of the root-mean-square radius of gyration of scattering particles to the wavelength of light. (A) Monodisperse coils. (B) Coils with a normal chain length distribution ($\langle s^2 \rangle = \langle s^2 \rangle_z$). (C) Rods. (D) Spheres.

estimation of the radius of gyration. In practice it is nevertheless desirable, even in such cases, to carry out the double extrapolation procedure, since insufficient care in the removal of dust will lead to a characteristic increase of scattering intensities at small angles, which will be clearly revealed in a Zimm plot.

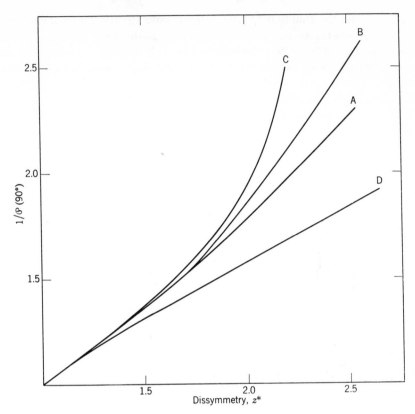

Fig. V.25. Dependence of $1/\mathscr{P}$ (90°) on the dissymmetry z^*. (A) Monodisperse coils. (B) Coils with a normal chain length distribution. (C) Rods. (D) Spheres

4. Light Scattering from Solutions in Mixed Solvent Media

When light scattering measurements are carried out with macromolecular solutions in mixed solvents, it is frequently found that the apparent molecular weight of the solute deduced from relation (5.39) varies from one solvent medium to another. Although such a variation may, in some cases, reflect a molecular association of the solute particles (see Chap. VIII) the variation in the apparent molecular weights is encountered in many cases where such association is extremely unlikely. An analysis of the phenomenon was first carried out by Ewart et al. (1946) who showed that it may be fully accounted for by optical effects caused by the concentration of the thermodynamically better solvent in the domains occupied by the macromolecules. We may illustrate the principle on a typical polymer with a refractive index n_2 dissolved in two solvents with refractive indices n_1 and n_3, where $n_3 > n_2 > n_1$ and n_2 is larger than the refractive index of the mixed solvents. Let us assume, for simplicity, that the mutual interaction of the components does not affect their refractivity, so that the observed n is a linear function of the composition of the system. We shall then obtain the correct molecular weight from light scattering data only if the ratio of the concentrations of the two solvents in the domain occupied by the polymer is the same as in the system as a whole. Only in this case will the macroscopically determined dn/dc_2 value represent correctly the difference of refractive index experienced by a light ray on passing from the mixed solvent medium into the region occupied by the macromolecule. If the macromolecule adsorbs component 3 preferentially, the effective refractive index of the polymer domains will be increased, while that of the intervening regions will decline. This will result in an increased light scattering intensity and a higher apparent molecular weight. Conversely, if the macromolecules bind component 1, the difference in the refractive indices of the polymer domains and the intervening regions will be reduced, resulting in a decrease of the apparent molecular weight. The phenomenon of a variable apparent molecular weight may be used, therefore, to study the relative affinities of polymers for the components of a mixed solvent system. According to the analysis reported by Stockmayer (1950) for a three-component system, the apparent molecular weight M_2^{app} is related to the true value M_2 by

$$M_2^{app}/M_2 \approx [1 - (a_{23}/a_{33})(\Upsilon_3/\Upsilon_2)^2]/[1 - a_{23}^2/a_{33}a_{22}]$$

$$\Upsilon_i = (\partial n/\partial c_i)_{T,P,m_{j\neq i}}$$

$$a_{ij} = (\partial \bar{G}_i/\partial m_j)_{T,P,m_{k\neq j}} \qquad (5.48)$$

where m_j are the quantities of the various components in the systems and the index 2 refers to the polymeric component. An alternative formulation which has a more easily visualized significance (Strazielle and Benoit, 1961) has the form

$$X_3 = [(M_2^{app}/M_2)^{1/2} - 1]\Upsilon_2/\Upsilon_3 \qquad (5.49)$$

where X_3 gives the weight of component 3 bound to a unit weight of the polymer.

The experimentalist is frequently not interested in studying preferential solvation phenomena but is merely concerned with obtaining the correct molecular weight from light scattering data on polymers which must be studied in mixed solvent media. This is particularly the case with polyelectrolytes which, as we shall see later in Chap. VII, are most easily studied in solutions containing added salt. Fortunately, Casassa and Eisenberg (1960) proved that the complications produced by preferential solvation in mixed solvent systems can be eliminated by a simple change in the experimental procedure. This requires the excess light scattering and the refractive index increment to be expressed with reference to the solvent mixture with which the polymer solution is in dialysis equilibrium, rather than the solvent mixture used in the preparation of the polymer solution. With this modified procedure the light scattering data of multicomponent systems may be treated in the same manner as data obtained from polymer solutions in a single solvent, yielding the correct value for the molecular weight.

5. Light Scattering from Solutions of Polymers with a Variable Chemical Composition

So far we have considered only samples consisting of either identical macromolecules or of members of a polymer-homologous series. Thus, the molecules might differ in molecular weight, but not in chemical composition. Under such circumstances it is legitimate to assume that the refractive index increment dn/dc_2 is identical for all molecular weight fractions and this assumption was implied in deriving eq. (5.27). If we have to deal with chemically heterogeneous samples, in which both the refractive index and the molecular weight of the individual molecular species will vary, the situation will obviously be considerably more complex. We may note, in particular, one very characteristic difference in the behavior of chemically homogeneous and chemically heterogeneous samples: For homogeneous samples the excess light scattering intensity vanishes if $dn/dc_2 = 0$, while with a heterogeneous sample it is impossible to match the refractive index of the solvent simultaneously with that of all the dissolved species. Thus, a finite excess light scattering intensity will be observed even if the refractive index increment, averaged over all the solute species, is equal to zero. If we do not allow for the chemical heterogeneity of the sample, we will arrive at molecular weights which will be, in general, too high and will tend toward infinity as the average refractive index of the polymer approaches that of the solvent medium.

The complications arising from this problem were first pointed out by Stockmayer et al. (1955) who considered, in particular, light scattering from a copolymer sample of variable composition containing units A and B.   If the average refractive index increment of the sample is linear in the weight fraction x_B of B units, then the apparent molecular weight $\bar{M}_w{}^{\mathrm{app}}$ is related to the true weight average molecular weight value $\bar{M}_w$ by

$$\bar{M}_w{}^{\mathrm{app}} = \bar{M}_w + 2[(\Upsilon_B - \Upsilon_A)/\Upsilon]\langle M\Delta x\rangle$$
$$+ [(\Upsilon_B - \Upsilon_A)/\Upsilon]^2\langle M(\Delta x)^2\rangle \quad (5.50)$$

where Υ_A and Υ_B are refractive index increments of poly-A and poly-B, Υ is the refractive index increment of the copolymer, Δx and $(\Delta x)^2$ denote the deviations and the square deviations from the mean composition and $\langle\ \rangle$ stand for average quantities.   We may note that the second term on the right vanishes if the mean chemical composition, is the same for all molecular weight fractions.   In principle, relation (5.50) allows us to obtain not only the weight average molecular weight, but also a measure of the chemical heterogeneity by evaluating light scattering data in three solvent media (Bushuk and Benoit, 1958; Krause, 1961; Leng and Benoit, 1962a).   It should be pointed out that the statistical variations in the composition of copolymer chains prepared under identical conditions (see pages 23–24) is, for reasonable degrees of polymerization too small to lead to the complications discussed above.   However, unless copolymerization is stopped at very low conversion, it will, in general, be dangerous to disregard the possibility of chemical heterogeneity.

Even if a copolymer is monodisperse with respect to its chemical composition, some complications will arise in connection with the interpretation of the angular dependence of its light scattering intensity.   The theory for this case has been developed by Benoit and Wippler (1960) who showed that the apparent mean square radius of gyration obtained by applying eq. (5.34) to solutions of such copolymers may be interpreted by

$$\langle s^2\rangle^{\mathrm{app}} = \alpha^2\langle s^2\rangle_A + \beta^2\langle s^2\rangle_B + \alpha\beta[\langle s^2\rangle_A + \langle s^2\rangle_B + \langle r_g^2\rangle]$$
$$\alpha = \Upsilon_A(1 - x_B)/\langle\Upsilon\rangle$$
$$\beta = \Upsilon_B x_B/\langle\Upsilon\rangle \quad (5.51)$$

where x_B is the weight fraction of B units in the copolymer $\langle s^2\rangle_A$ and $\langle s^2\rangle_B$ are the mean square radii of gyration of the A and B units in the copolymer, while $\langle r_g^2\rangle$ is the mean square distance between their centers of gravity.   If Υ_A and Υ_B have opposite signs, $\alpha\beta$ may be negative and it can then happen that $\langle s^2\rangle^{\mathrm{app}}$ assumes negative values, particularly with a block copolymer containing two blocks, so that $\langle r_g^2\rangle$ is relatively large (Leng et al., 1963).

If the refractive index of the solvent matches that of one or the other kind of monomer units of a copolymer (i.e., α or β vanishes in eq. 5.51) then the angular dependence of the scattered light reflects only the spatial distribution of the units with a non-zero refractive index increment. Such a measurement has been used in an interesting manner by Leng and Benoit (1962b) who studied a block copolymer containing a central sequence of styrene residues flanked by two poly(methyl methacrylate) blocks. If this block copolymer is dissolved in a medium which matches the refractive index of poly(methyl methacrylate), then only the central section will contribute to the light scattering. By studying the angular dependence of the light scattered from such a system, it is possible to characterize the expansion of the polystyrene block and to compare it with that of a styrene homopolymer of the same chain length. Such a comparison shows the influence of the excluded volume effect due to the mutual spatial interference of the "invisible" poly(methyl methacrylate) blocks.

D. X-RAY SCATTERING

The theory outlined in the previous chapter for the scattering of electromagnetic radiation is, of course, valid for radiation of any wavelength and the basic principles will apply as well in the x-ray region as in the region of visible light. However, while the wavelength of the visible light usually employed in light scattering experiments ranges in different solvent media between 3000 and 4000 Å, the most commonly employed x-ray frequency (that of Cu Kα radiation) has a wavelength of only 1.54 Å. We employ then, in the case of visible light, a radiation whose wavelength is much longer than the dimensions of the scattering macromolecules, while the wavelength of the x-rays is very much shorter than even the most compact of the macromolecules which we may want to investigate. This quantitative difference allows us to obtain from x-ray scattering information about the distribution of scattering centers over distances which are much shorter than those which may be studied by the angular distribution of the scattering intensity of visible light.

In the limit of zero scattering angle, the amplitude of the x-rays scattered by an atom is proportional to its number of electrons. The quantity which is analogous to the refractive index increment in the scattering of visible light, is then in the case of x-ray scattering the "excess electron density" $\Delta\rho_e$ of the solute defined by

$$\Delta\rho_e = (e_2/M_2) - \bar{v}_2\rho_e^0 \qquad (5.52)$$

where e_2 is the number of electrons carried by a solute molecule, $\bar{v}_2$ is the partial specific volume of the solute and $\rho_e{}^0$ is the number of moles of electrons per unit volume of the solvent medium. The molecular weight of the solute may then be obtained, in principle, from values of the Rayleigh scattering ratio extrapolated to $\theta = 0$ using for $\lambda = 1.54$ Å the relation (Kratky and Kreutz, 1960; Kratky, 1962a, b).

$$\Delta\mathcal{R}_0 = 0.048 \; M_2 c_2 (\Delta\rho_e)^2 \tag{5.53}$$

In practice, such determinations are difficult, since they require an absolute determination of the Rayleigh ratio, i.e., a comparison of the very high intensity of the incident beam with the very weak intensity of the scattered x-rays. Although these difficulties can be overcome [Kratky and Kreutz, 1960; Luzzati et al. (1961c)], the technique is not particularly advantageous for molecular weight determinations.

The main value of x-ray scattering studies lies in the possibilities inherent in the interpretation of the angular dependence of light scattering intensities. Relations (5.30) and (5.34) show that the factor by which the scattered light is attenuated as a result of the destructive interference of rays scattered from two points of a scattering particle separated by a distance r_{ij} is a function of $(r_{ij}/\lambda') \sin (\theta/2)$. Thus, the same relative attenuation which will be observed with $\lambda' = 3000$ Å over an angular range of 0–90°, will be compressed for x-rays with $\lambda = 1.54$ Å to an angular range of about one minute of arc. This means that we should have to make measurements with x-rays at exceedingly small angles to characterize the size of macromolecules whose expansion is studied conveniently by the angular distribution of scattered visible light. On the other hand, the angular distribution of scattered x-ray intensities will vary appreciably over a narrow angular range for scattering particles with dimensions of the order of 10–50 Å, which are much too small to lead to any measurable destructive interference effects in the scattering of visible light. This is the range of dimensions characteristic of many globular proteins, and their radii of gyration may be estimated from the relative intensity of scattered x-ray intensities over a range of scattering angles. For small θ values, relation (5.30) may be approximated by

$$\mathcal{P}(\theta) = \exp \left[-(4\pi^2/3\lambda^2)\langle s^2\rangle\theta^2\right] \tag{5.54}$$

and the square radius of gyration may, therefore, be obtained from the slope of a plot of the logarithm of the x-ray intensity against the square of the scattering angle. (It should be noted that the "radius of gyration" obtained from x-ray scattering is defined in terms of the distribution of excess electron densities, rather than the distribution of mass.) Early measurements of this type were carried out by Kratky (1948) and Kratky et al. (1955). More recently, similar studies using improved methods were reported by Kratky and Kreutz (1960) and by Luzzati et al. (1961d) who were able to observe by the x-ray scattering method the expansion of bovine serum albumin molecules at pH 3.6, which had previously been inferred from the hydrodynamic behavior of its solutions.

For rod-like particles, $\mathcal{P}(\theta)$ depends on the length of the particles only at very small scattering angles. It soon reaches its asymptotic behavior where $\mathcal{P}(\theta)$ depends only on the distribution of scattering electrons around the axis of the rod. This asymptote has the form

$$\ln\left[\theta\mathcal{P}(\theta)\right] = \ln\left[\theta\mathcal{P}(\theta)\right]_0 - (2\pi^2/\lambda^2)\langle s_a{}^2\rangle\theta^2 \qquad (5.55)$$

where $\langle s_a{}^2\rangle$ is the mean square radius of gyration of the excess electron density around the axis of the rod (Kratky and Kreutz, 1960; Kratky, 1962b). The intercept of this asymptote may be used, provided the absolute value of the ratio of incident and scattered light intensity is known, to calculate the mass per unit length of the rod m_L (Luzzati, 1961; Kratky, 1962b) from

$$m_L = 27.3(\theta\Delta\mathcal{R}_\theta)_0/c_2\Delta\rho_e \qquad (5.56)$$

This type of analysis has been used by Luzzati et al. (1961b) to show that the behavior of DNA in solution conforms to the mass-to-length ratio required by the Watson–Crick double-helical model. Very similar results were obtained by Timasheff et al. (1961) for RNA solutions, in agreement with the suggestion that the single stranded chain has a structure resembling that of a twisted hair-pin.

Interpretation of data from flexible chain molecules is much more complex. The problem was analyzed by Kratky and Porod (1949) who pointed out that different types of properties will determine the distribution of scattering intensities in different ranges of scattering angles. We may distinguish five characteristic regions: (1) At very small angles the scattering envelope will depend on the overall dimensions of the macromolecules and $\mathcal{P}(\theta)$ will have the shape of an error curve. (2) At somewhat larger angles the scattering intensity will be that characterized by a Gaussian distribution of scattering particles, with $\mathcal{P}(\theta)$ proportional to $1/\theta^2$. (3) When the scattering angles are of the same order of magnitude as the ratio of the wavelength of the x-rays to the persistence length of the chain (pp. 120–121), then the intensity of the scattered x-rays is largely determined by interference effects between rays originating in short sections of the chain.

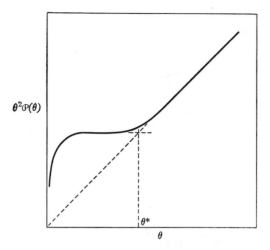

$\theta^2\mathcal{P}(\theta)$

θ^*

θ

Fig. V.26. Schematic representation of the angular dependence of x-ray scattering intensity to be expected in solutions of flexible chain molecules.

Such sections may be considered to be essentially rod-like and to have $\mathcal{P}(\theta)$ proportional to $1/\theta$. (4) At still larger angles the shape of $\mathcal{P}(\theta)$ may be determined by the spacing of nearest neighbor scattering centers, particularly if the chain carries heavily scattering atoms of a high atomic number. (5) Finally, we may reach a region where the scattering intensity reflects the distribution of electrons in the individual atoms contained in the system. One of the difficulties encountered in the interpretation of x-ray scattering data is due to the overlap of these various effects. Nevertheless, in flexible chains much longer than the persistence length, the transition between the regions 1, 2, and 3 should be clearly marked. A plot of $\theta^2\mathcal{P}(\theta)$ against θ, represented schematically in Fig. V.26, will then have two linear branches intersecting at a point corresponding to θ^* which is related to the persistence length **a** (Porod, 1953; Peterlin, 1960a; Heine et al., 1961) by the simple relation

$$\mathbf{a} = \lambda/2\pi\theta^* \tag{5.57}$$

Typical of this type of analysis is the study of Kratky and Sand (1960) on Hevea rubber and by Heine et al. (1961) on poly(methyl methacrylate). The technique is uniquely suited to clarify the vexing question, to what extent a change in solvent medium modifies the intrinsic flexibility of the chain, as distinct from chain expansion phenomena due to the excluded volume effect.

We have mentioned earlier that chain polymers carrying heavily scattering atoms should have the form of $\mathcal{P}(\theta)$ at large scattering angles controlled by the nearest-neighbor spacing of these heavy atoms. The feasibility of determining such distances in model compounds of low molecular weight has been demonstrated by Kratky and Worthmann (1947) on substances such as p,p' diiododiphenyl, p,p' diiododiphenylmethane and by Kratky et al. (1948) on 1,10-diiododecane. Only a few attempts seem to have been made to apply this principle to a polymer. The data obtained by Kratky and Porod (1949) on poly(vinyl bromide) were interpreted as indicating a distance of 2.4–2.6 Å between nearest-neighbor bromine atoms—a result which appears to be much too low since the van der Waals radius of bromine is 1.95 Å. More recently, three other studies using the same technique were reported. Kirste and Wunderlich (1964) found the scattering pattern to be strikingly different in solutions of isotactic and syndiotactic poly(methyl methacrylate), reflecting the dependence of the preferred conformations on the stereoisomerism of the polymer chain. Brady and Salovey (1964) found no difference in the x-ray scattering of isotactic and atactic poly(p-iodostyrene). In this case, the scattering is dominated by the heavy iodine atoms which are quite far from the chain backbone and the conformation of the chain backbone is apparently not sufficiently sharply defined to give an observable preferred distance between nearest neighbor iodine atoms. Finally, Brady et al. (1965) used the analysis of the x-ray diffraction pattern to study the conformation of poly(3,5-dibromotyrosine) in dimethylformamide solution. In this case, the experimental results were in good agreement with calculations based on a helical conformation of the polypeptide backbone, provided the side chains are allowed small oscillations around the positions corresponding to the potential energy minimum. The interpretation of x-ray scattering data of this type is quite difficult since the shape of the scattering envelope at large angles contains large contributions due to the structure of the solvent and the angular dependence of the x-ray scattering intensity of the heavy atoms. Nevertheless, the examples cited above show that this technique may be quite powerful for the study of conformations of dissolved chain molecules and it is to be expected that its use will be expanded in the future.

In all of the preceding discussion, we have concerned ourselves only with the diffuse scattering from isotropic solutions. However, we have seen (pp. 68–69) that, with solutions containing long rod-shaped macromolecular particles, an anisotropic phase may form. In such a case, sharp x-ray diffraction photographs, characteristic of liquid crystals, may be obtained.

Observations of this type were first recorded by Bernal and Fankuchen (1941) who studied solutions of tobacco mosaic virus and found that the diffraction pattern of the anisotropic phase corresponds to a hexagonal packing of the rodlike virus particles. The spacing between nearest neighbors was inversely proportional to the square root of the concentration of the anisotropic phase. More recently, Luzzati et al. (1961a) carried out similar studies on solutions of poly(γ-benzyl-L-glutamate) in solvents favoring the helical conformation of the polypeptide. Again, the macromolecular particles were arranged in a hexagonal array, but the spacing of the molecules remained, in this case, constant over a wide range of concentrations. The liquid crystals tend to align themselves with the long dimension of the solute particles parallel to the wall of thin capillaries (Bernal and Fankuchen, 1941). Even better orientation is attainable when anisotropic solutions are subjected to a shear gradient. With poly(γ-benzyl-L-glutamate) oriented in this manner, the x-ray diffraction pattern resembles that of a typical fiber and the repeat period, parallel to the axis of the helix, is found to be very close to that observed in solid specimens (Parry and Elliott, 1955).

Chapter VI

FRICTIONAL PROPERTIES OF DISSOLVED MACROMOLECULES

When a driving force acts on a particle suspended in a viscous medium, the particle will accelerate until the driving force is balanced by the frictional forces due to its motion. Phenomena based on this general principle may be used in three ways to obtain information about the nature of the suspended particle: (1) We may measure the steady-state velocity of linear translation of a particle subjected to a driving force. (2) We may determine the velocity with which the particle would rotate under the influence of a force couple. (3) We may determine by viscosimetry the increase in the rate at which energy is dissipated in a viscous fluid under shear because of the presence of a suspended particle. [An excellent discussion of the viscosimetric method has been presented by Frisch and Simha (1956).]

Each of these methods will yield a parameter which depends in a characteristic manner on the size and the shape of the body moving through the fluid. If we know that this body is a rigid sphere, a single parameter will suffice to characterize its size and this may then be obtained from a single measurement. If we are dealing with an ellipsoid of revolution, two parameters will be required, specifying its volume and its axial ratio. It is fortunate that the three methods mentioned above differ in their relative sensitivity to these two parameters, so that an ellipsoidal particle may be characterized by a combination of any two of them. However, a particle with a more complicated shape may require many more parameters for its detailed description and such a description is, therefore, not attainable on the basis of frictional measurements. We must then content ourselves with the statement that the unknown particle behaves in a given experiment (or set of experiments) in the same manner as would be expected for a sphere of a given size or an ellipsoid of revolution with certain specified dimensions. These are commonly referred to as "hydrodynamically equivalent spheres" or "hydrodynamically equivalent ellipsoids." It should, of course, be clearly understood that a comparison of an unknown body to these hydrodynamic equivalents does in no way imply that the body is in reality a sphere or an ellipsoid.

A number of important special cases of the motion of rigid bodies through viscous media have been subjected to hydrodynamic analysis. Such treatments invariably assume that the fluid may be represented as a structureless continuum. This is undoubtedly a valid assumption when we deal with macroscopic particles with dimensions which are many orders of magnitude larger than the molecular dimensions of the fluid through which they move. However, it is by no means obvious that the hydrodynamic results derived for such macroscopic systems will retain their validity when the particle, in whose motion we are interested, is more nearly comparable in size to the molecules of the surrounding fluid. Nevertheless, a great deal of experimental evidence indicates that a treatment of the frictional properties of dissolved macromolecules in terms of theories valid for macroscopic models leads to reasonable conclusions. Had this not been the case, the theoretical development of this subject would have been immensely more difficult.

As is the case with colligative properties and light scattering, the frictional properties of solutions at finite concentrations may be interpreted in terms of the intrinsic particle contributions, to which terms taking account of particle interactions must be added. Only the behavior of the isolated macromolecules lends itself to fairly safe theoretical interpretation. Since macromolecular interactions can frequently not be neglected even in the most dilute solutions on which measurements are possible, a suitable extrapolation procedure for data obtained over a range of concentrations is required to estimate the behavior of the macromolecules at infinite dilution.

A. LINEAR TRANSLATION

1. The Frictional Coefficient of Rigid Particles

As pointed out above, all theories dealing with the frictional properties of dissolved macromolecules assume implicitly that laws derived for macroscopic particles moving in a structureless fluid are applicable. It is also assumed that viscous forces are much larger than inertial forces, so that the flow of the liquid is laminar rather than turbulent. In Fig. VI.1 we represent schematically two parallel plates separated by a distance x with the intervening space filled by a viscous fluid. If one of the plates is to be moved relative to the other, a force has to be applied to overcome the resistance caused by fluid friction. We may consider that a layer of molecules of the liquid adheres to each of the surfaces of the moving plates. A

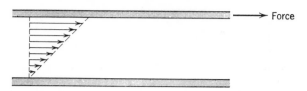

Fig. VI.1. Velocity distribution in viscous fluid between two parallel plates (laminar flow).

layer of the liquid, part of the way between the plates, is subjected to the frictional pull of the two neighboring layers which exert forces in opposite directions. Assuming that the frictional force is proportional to the velocity gradient q (i.e., that the fluid is "Newtonian"), the central layer will experience no net force if $dq/dx = 0$. It follows that the velocity gradient will be uniform in the steady state.

For a spherical particle moving slowly through a Newtonian fluid the viscous force F resisting the motion is proportional to the velocity of the particle

$$F = fu \qquad (6.1)$$

The proportionality constant f, commonly called the "frictional coefficient," denotes the force in dynes required to maintain a particle velocity of 1 cm/sec. For spheres moving through a fluid far from the walls of the container

$$f_{sphere} = 6\pi\eta_0 R_s \qquad (6.2)$$

where η_0 is the viscosity of the fluid and R_s the radius of the sphere. A detailed discussion of this result, first derived by Stokes, is given by Lamb (1945). Experimental studies have shown that Stokes' law is strictly valid for velocities of the spherical particle below $\eta_0/2R_s\rho$, where ρ is the density of the fluid (Schlichting, 1960). Thus, the validity of Stokes' law extends, for particles of colloidal dimensions, far beyond the highest velocities with which we shall be concerned.

If the moving particle is asymmetric (i.e., an ellipsoid of revolution) the solution of the hydrodynamic problem becomes much more difficult, since the motion of the particles may now lead to their orientation. At low rates of shear, where Brownian motion can effectively randomize the particle orientations, the frictional coefficient of ellipsoids of revolution may be expressed as

$$f_{ell} = 6\pi\eta_0 R_s'/x(p) \qquad (6.3)$$

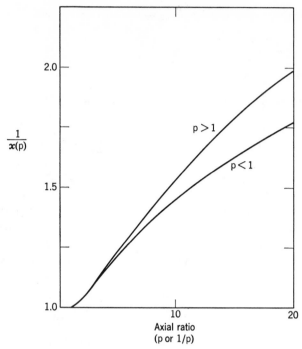

Fig. VI.2. The dependence of translational frictional coefficients on the axial ratio of ellipsoids of revolution.

where R'_s is the radius of a sphere with the same volume as the ellipsoid, p is the ratio of the length of the semiaxis of revolution to the equatorial radius (the "axial ratio") and $x(p)$ is a function calculated by Perrin (1936) as

$$x(p) = (p^{2/3}/\sqrt{1 - p^2}) \ln [(1 + \sqrt{1 - p^2})/p] \qquad p < 1 \quad (6.4a)$$

$$x(p) = (p^{2/3}/\sqrt{p^2 - 1}) \tan^{-1} \sqrt{p^2 - 1} \qquad\qquad p > 1 \quad (6.4b)$$

A plot of $1/x(p)$ against p for prolate ("cigar-shaped") ellipsoids and against $1/p$ for oblate ("disk-shaped") ellipsoids is given in Fig. VI.2. It shows that the frictional ratio is rather insensitive to the dissymmetry of the particle and that the same values may be obtained for f with pairs of prolate and oblate ellipsoids of equal volume.

The behavior of rod-like particles will be similar to that of prolate ellipsoids with large axial ratios.   Under these conditions, $x(p)$ is approximated by

$$x(p) = (\pi/2)/p^{1/3} \qquad p \gg 1 \qquad\qquad (6.5)$$

If the length of the ellipsoid is increased while its cross section is kept constant, R'_s is proportional to $p^{1/3}$. We may then conclude that for long ellipsoids of a given thickness the frictional coefficient will increase as the $2/3$ power of their length. A more exact result was obtained by Riseman and Kirkwood (1950) for thin rods of length L where f_{rod} was found to be proportional to $L/\log L$.

2. Frictional Coefficients of Chain Molecules

In treating the frictional properties of chain molecules, it is customary to represent them by a "pearl-necklace" model in which rigid beads are connected by infinitely thin linkages. Kuhn and Kuhn (1943) and Debye and Bueche (1948) have pointed out that two limiting situations may be envisaged. In the first case, the beads are relatively far from one another, so that the disturbances of the flow caused by the individual beads may be considered not to interact. This model is generally referred to as the "free draining coil." If such a coil is forced to move through a viscous fluid, each unit will be subjected to a frictional resistance independent of the presence of other similar units, and the effective frictional coefficient of the coil as a whole will be proportional to the number of units composing it. In the second limiting case the interactions between the flow disturbances are so large that the solvent is effectively trapped within the coil, which may be treated as a rigid "hydrodynamically equivalent sphere." The radius of this equivalent sphere R_t, controlling the frictional resistance to linear translation, will be proportional to some characteristic dimensions of the coil, such as the root-mean-square radius of gyration $\langle s^2 \rangle^{1/2}$. We have then, in analogy to (6.2),

$$f_{coil} = 6\pi\eta_0 R_t = 6\pi\eta_0 C\langle s^2 \rangle^{1/2} \tag{6.6}$$

where C is a characteristic constant. This result predicts a much lower resistance to translation of the coil than the free draining model. In a θ-solvent, where $\langle s^2 \rangle$ is proportional to chain length (6.6) predicts that the frictional coefficient of chain molecules should increase as the square root of their molecular weight. In better solvent media, where the molecular coil is more expanded, the frictional coefficient assumes correspondingly higher values.

The criteria for the applicability of these limiting cases were discussed by Debye and Bueche for a simplified model in which Z beads, each with a frictional coefficient f_0, are uniformly distributed in a spherical volume v_e. The resistance offered by the beads to the flow of the fluid will cause the fluid velocity to decay exponentially with the distance below the surface of the sphere. The characteristic depth L_f at which the flow velocity has been reduced to e^{-1} of its value at the surface is given by

$$L_f = (\eta_0 v_e / Z f_0)^{1/2} \tag{6.7}$$

The free draining model is then applicable if the radius of the equivalent sphere is much smaller than L_f, while $R_t \gg L_f$ obviously corresponds to a situation when most of the sphere is shielded from any flow outside, so that it may be thought of as a single unit with the entrapped liquid.

The most difficult problem is that of dealing with the intermediate case. The model proposed by Debye and Bueche leads to a result depending on the "shielding factor" R_t/L_f and gives for the frictional coefficient in the limit of very small shielding factors

$$f_{coil} = Z f_0 [1 - (1/5\pi)(R_t/L_f)^2 + \ldots]$$

$$= Z f_0 [1 - (3/20\pi^2) Z f_0 / \eta_0 R_t + \ldots] \qquad R_t/L_f \ll 1 \tag{6.8}$$

while the approach to the impermeable coil is represented by

$$f_{coil} = 6\pi\eta_0 R_t [1 - (L_f/R_t) - \ldots]$$

$$= 6\pi\eta_0 R_t [1 - 2\sqrt{\pi\eta_8 R_t/3Z f_0} - \ldots] \qquad R_t/L_f \gg 1 \tag{6.9}$$

A completely different approach to the problem of the frictional resistance to translation offered by chain molecules was employed by Kirkwood and Riseman (1948). They used the pearl necklace model with perfectly flexible joints for the chain and random flight statistics for the distribution of the chain segments, without consideration of the excluded volume effect. Then taking account of the interactions of the flow disturbances produced by the individual beads, they arrived at a frictional coefficient given by

$$f_{coil} = Z f_0 / [1 + \Xi]$$

$$\Xi = (4/9\pi^{3/2}) Z f_0 \eta_0 \langle s^2 \rangle^{1/2} \tag{6.10}$$

The similarity of this result with that obtained by Debye and Bueche is surprising when we consider the pronounced difference in the models on which the two theories are based. In the limit of $\Xi \gg 1$, eq. (6.10) reduces to the form of (6.6) for an impermeable coil, with

$$R_t / \langle s^2 \rangle^{1/2} = 3\pi^{1/2}/8 \tag{6.11}$$

In practice it appears that even relatively short flexible chain molecules (with molecular weights around 20,000) approach the behavior of impenetrable coils.

3. Diffusion

The diffusion of solute molecules in a concentration gradient may be thought of as a motion of the molecular particles in response to a driving force provided by the gradient of chemical potential. The force acting on a molecule of the ith species is then

$$F = (1/N)(\partial \bar{G}_i/\partial x)$$

$$= kT(\partial \ln c_i/\partial x)[1 + \partial \ln \gamma_i/\partial \ln c_i] \tag{6.12}$$

If the solution is sufficiently dilute, so that Henry's law applies to the solute, $\partial \ln \gamma_i/\partial \ln c_i = 0$ and the velocity of particles with a frictional coefficient f becomes

$$u = F/f = (kT/f)(1/c_i)(\partial c_i/\partial x) \tag{6.13}$$

Experimental data on diffusion are conventionally described in terms of Fick's first law, according to which the rate of transport per unit cross-sectional area is proportional to the concentration gradient, the proportionality constant being the diffusion coefficient D. Since the rate of transport per unit cross-sectional area is also equal to the product of the solute concentration and the flow velocity, we have

$$uc_i = D(\partial c_i/\partial x) \tag{6.14}$$

Comparing (6.13) and (6.14) we see that the diffusion coefficient is related to the frictional coefficient of the diffusing particle by

$$D = kT/f \tag{6.15}$$

This relation was first suggested by Einstein (1905) who believed intuitively that frictional coefficients of even small molecules would be adequately approximated by the values predicted by hydrodynamic theory. This assumption has been shown to be surprisingly close to the real behavior of diffusing molecules. When small, spherical molecules move in a medium of similar particles (i.e., in the self-diffusion of such liquids as argon or mercury) the frictional coefficient calculated from (6.15) is generally smaller than the value predicted by Stokes' law [eq. (6.2)]. However even in such extreme cases, the frictional coefficient deviates from the predicted value by less than a factor of 2 (Corbett and Wang, 1956).

In the diffusion of chain molecules, the impermeable coil model seems to be applicable for most cases of interest.   However, the theory of Kirkwood and Riseman, which neglects excluded volume effects on the spatial distribution of chain segments, is strictly applicable only for chain molecules in Θ-solvents.   In better solvent media the excluded volume effect, which is most pronounced in the central region of the coil (pp. 129–130), tends to distort the distribution of segment densities so as to reduce the ratio $R_t/\langle s^2 \rangle^{1/2}$ below the value given in (6.11).   A quantitative theory of this effect was formulated by Peterlin (1955) and by Ptitsyn and Eizner (1960).   The predictions of these theories were on the whole substantiated by Lütje and Meyerhoff (1963) who measured diffusion coefficients of poly(methyl methacrylate) in media of varying solvent power.   Their results give for $R_t/\langle s^2 \rangle^{1/2}$ a value of about 0.82 in a Θ-solvent; this is only 20% above the value predicted by (6.11).   In better solvents, the decrease in the ratio $R_t/\langle s^2 \rangle^{1/2}$ may be calculated from the exponent γ relating the intrinsic viscosity with the molecular weight of chain molecules [eq. (4.28)].   In any case, $R_t/\langle s^2 \rangle^{1/2}$ varies only by about 20%, so that the diffusion coefficient may be taken as a fairly reliable measure of the mean radius of gyration (see also Tsvetkov and Klenin, 1958).

Fick's law is valid only in the limit of highly dilute systems, in which the diffusing particles are too distant from each other to interact.   As we increase the concentration of the diffusing species, the apparent diffusion coefficient will, in general, not remain constant.   Its variation will be caused both by a thermodynamic and by a hydrodynamic factor.   First, we may recall that the derivation of Fick's law in eq. (6.12)–(6.15) presupposed the validity of Henry's law.   At higher concentrations, where deviations from ideal solution behavior may occur, the driving force due to the chemical potential gradient is no longer adequately represented by $kT\, \partial \ln c_i/\partial x$. In particular, if the solution exhibits a negative deviation from solution ideality, as it will with polymers in any medium better than a Θ-solvent, $\partial \ln \gamma_i/\partial \ln c_i$ will be positive and this factor will tend to increase the diffusion coefficient as the solution concentration is increased.   Secondly, the simple derivation given above assumes that the hydrodynamic resistance to the motion of a particle is independent of the presence of other similar particles.   Again, this assumption is reasonable only if the diffusing particles are distant from one another.   At higher concentrations the hydrodynamic disturbances produced by their motion will interact and this may be expressed as a slow drift in the effective frictional coefficient. Since f will, in general, increase with concentration, this factor will tend to reduce the diffusion coefficient and it should thus act in a direction opposite to the thermodynamic causes for a drift in D.

An excellent study of the concentration dependence of the diffusion coefficient has been reported by Tsvetkov and Klenin (1958, 1959). They found that in polystyrene, poly(methyl methacrylate), and in poly(p-tert-butylphenyl methacrylate) solutions the diffusion coefficient of the polymer is an S-shaped function of concentration in good solvent media. However, when the diffusion coefficient was studied in a Θ-solvent, it was found to remain constant up to a concentration of 1 g/100 ml. It was, therefore, concluded that the variation of the frictional coefficient with concentration is too small to be detected in the concentration range used. This result is difficult to understand, since the molecular weight of the polymer used by these authors was extremely high (4.6×10^6) and considerable interpenetration of the molecular coils would be expected at the higher solution concentrations employed. Results obtained by Cantow (1959) with polystyrene in cyclohexanone also showed D to become independent of solute concentration in dilute solutions at the Θ temperature. Nevertheless, we should be cautious in assuming that such behavior will be encountered in all cases.

The experimental determination of the diffusion coefficient is carried out with highest precision in a cell in which a sharp boundary is initially produced between a solution with a polymer concentration c_2^0 and the solvent. As the solute diffuses, the concentration of the solute at the location of the original boundary remains fixed at $c_2^0/2$ and the concentration gradient at a distance x and a time t is given by

$$dc_2/dx = (c_2^0/2\sqrt{\pi Dt}) \exp(-x^2/4Dt) \qquad (6.16)$$

We see then that an experimental procedure which records directly the concentration gradient as a function of distance (cf. Chap. IV, Sec. B-1) should yield a Gaussian curve, provided that the solution contains a single

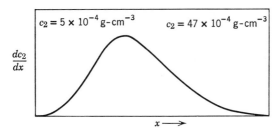

Fig. VI.3. Diffusion of polystyrene ($\bar{M}_w = 10^6$, $c_2 = 4.2 \times 10^{-3}$ g-cm^{-3}) from a more concentrated to a more dilute carbon tetrachloride solution. The skewness of the dc_2/dx plot indicates the concentration dependence of the diffusion coefficient.

solute and the diffusion coefficient is independent of concentration.   If the system contains several solutes with different diffusion coefficients, the variation of the concentration gradient will correspond to the sum of Gaussian curves with different standard deviations, so that the trace will appear broadened at its base.   The magnitude of this effect may be expressed quantitatively as the ratio of the third and the second moments of the dc_2/dx curve.   If the diffusion coefficient changes with concentration, the dc_2/dx curve will lose its symmetry.   This effect is illustrated on Fig. VI.3 for the diffusion of polystyrene in carbon tetrachloride (Tsvetkov and Klenin, 1958).   It can be seen that the curve is much flatter on the side of the original boundary on which the solution is more concentrated, i.e., D is here an increasing function of solution concentration.

4. Sedimentation Velocity

A driving force for the linear translation of a dissolved macromolecule may be provided by a gravitational field.   As we have already seen in the discussion of the equilibrium distribution (Chap. IV B), the gravitational field of the earth is too weak to affect appreciably the distribution of macromolecules, unless we deal with species with a molecular weight higher than about 10^7.   We must, therefore, utilize the large gravitational fields attainable in ultracentrifuges before the motion of macromolecules from the original uniform distribution toward a new equilibrium distribution becomes experimentally observable.

Consider a solute with a molecular mass $m_2 = M_2/N$, a partial specific volume $\bar{v}_2$ in a solution of density ρ placed at a distance r from the axis of rotation of a centrifuge spinning with an angular velocity ω.   The force acting on the particle will then be

$$F = m_2 r \omega^2 (1 - \bar{v}_2 \rho) \tag{6.17}$$

where the second term in the brackets represents the effects of buoyancy. Equating this driving force with the frictional resistance of the medium, we obtain for the steady state velocity in a unit gravitational field (the sedimentation constant)

$$s \equiv (dr/dt)/r\omega^2 = (d \ln r/dt)/\omega^2 \tag{6.18}$$

$$= M_2(1 - \bar{v}_2 \rho)/Nf$$

It may be seen that s does not define the molecular weight of the solute unless the frictional coefficient is known.   If the particle is a hard sphere with a specific volume $\bar{v}_2$, we obtain after use of the Stokes value for the frictional coefficient

$$s = [(1 - \bar{v}_2\rho)/3\eta_0]M_2^{2/3}/(6\pi^2\bar{v}_2)^{1/3}N^{2/3} \qquad \text{(spheres)} \qquad (6.18a)$$

For ellipsoids of revolution, s will be decreased for any given particle weight because of the increase of the frictional coefficient. In the case of rod-like particles of length L, where f is proportional to $L/\log L$ (Riseman and Kirkwood, 1950) while the gravitational driving force is proportional to L, the sedimentation velocity should increase only as $\log L$. For chain molecules in a Θ-solvent with the molecular coil impermeable to solvent flow, the frictional coefficient is proportional to $\langle s^2 \rangle^{1/2}$ and thus also to $M_2^{1/2}$ (cf. page 115); the sedimentation constant will then be proportional to the square root of the molecular weight. In better solvent media f will increase more rapidly with increasing M_2 and s will be correspondingly less sensitive to the molecular weight of the solute.

So far our discussion has been concerned with a single driving force acting on the macromolecules, namely that provided by the gravitational field. If this were, in fact, the only cause for the motion of the solute, all molecules would sediment at identical rates and an infinitely sharp boundary would form between the sedimenting solution and the pure solvent. This is of course not the case, since diffusional flow will be superimposed on sedimentation. As a result, the sedimentation of a single solute species will form a boundary which will broaden with increasing sedimentation time in the manner described by eq. (6.16). This broadening poses no problems in the interpretation of results in which a single sedimenting species is present, since the sedimentation velocity is correctly represented by the rate at which the location of the concentration gradient maximum moves along the test cell. The situation is more complicated when the system contains solutes with a continuous distribution of sedimentation coefficients and in this case the effects of diffusion have to be eliminated before the experimental data may be interpreted. This problem was first considered by Signer and Gross (1934) who recommended the use of solvents with densities differing as much as possible from that of the sedimenting macromolecules. In this manner the time required for a sedimentation run can be shortened and the effects of diffusion correspondingly reduced. A more rigorous method for eliminating the effects of diffusion is based on the fact that the distance covered by a particle subjected to a gravitational force is proportional to time, while the distance through which a particle moves because of random Brownian motion is proportional to the square root of time. As a consequence, the relative importance of diffusive flow decreases with increasing duration of the sedimentation experiment. We may, therefore, eliminate the effect of diffusion by extrapolating the apparent distribution of sedimentation coefficients to infinite time (Williams et al., 1952).

A second complication may arise because of the concentration dependence of the frictional coefficient. Since f is, in general, an increasing function of concentration, it follows from (6.18) that $1/s$ must increase with the solute concentration. The limiting value of s may then be found by extrapolating $1/s$ to $c_2 = 0$. When a polydisperse system is subjected to sedimentation, the more slowly sedimenting compounds find themselves in regions of lower solution concentration and the ratio of the sedimentation

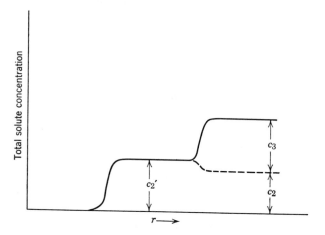

Fig. VI.4. The Johnston-Ogston effect.

velocities of light and heavy molecules is, therefore, reduced. As a result, the apparent distribution of sedimentation constants tends to broaden with a decreasing concentration of the solution. Johnston and Ogston (1946) have treated the case of two components, a heavy component with a sedimentation coefficient s_3 and a light component whose sedimentation velocities are s_2 and s_2' and whose concentrations are c_2 and c_2' in front and behind the sedimentation boundary of component 3, respectively. The concentration of component 2 behind the sedimentation boundary of component 3 will then increase per unit gravitational field at the rate $c_2(s_3 - s_2) - c_2'(s_3 - s_2')$ and for the steady state c_2' and c_2 will be related by

$$c_2'/c_2 = (s_3 - s_2)/(s_3 - s_2') \qquad (6.19)$$

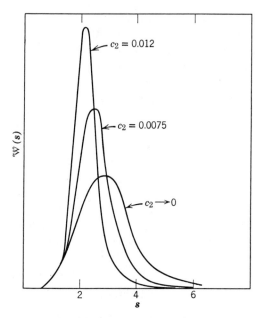

Fig. VI.5. Apparent distribution function of sedimentation constants at two concentrations of dextran and the distribution function obtained by extrapolating experimental data to $c_2 = 0$.

Since $s_2 < s_2'$ we obtain $c_2' > c_2$. The optical methods used in determining the solute distribution in the sedimentation cell do not, in general, distinguish between the various solute species. The uneven distribution of the light component will then lead to an estimate of the heavy component which will be generally too low. The situation is represented schematically in Fig. VI.4. The difficulty described above may, however, be circumvented by the use of a procedure which has been described as "band centrifugation" (Vinograd et al., 1963). In this technique a shallow layer of the solution to be analyzed is layered on a heavier binary solution before centrifugation. Each sedimenting component will then form a band of its own and since the macromolecular species are separated from each other, interaction effects will be eliminated. To use this method successfully, it is necessary to use a system which will yield $d\rho/dr > 0$ at all points so that no complications arise from convection.

If the distribution function of sedimentation constants is to be obtained in a system in which the frictional coefficient is concentration dependent, the apparent distributions obtained at a number of finite solute concentrations have to be extrapolated to $c_2 = 0$. A suitable procedure for accomplishing this result was described by Williams and Saunders (1954). Figure VI.5, taken from the work of these authors, gives a striking illustration of the gradual broadening of the apparent distribution of sedimentation constants as the polymer solution is progressively diluted. Work by Cantow (1959) on polystyrene solutions in cyclohexane suggests that the concentration dependence of the frictional coefficient (as revealed by either D or s) disappears at the Θ-point. If this phenomenon could be generalized (cf. Tsvetkov and Klenin, 1959), the interpretation of sedimentation data would be greatly simplified. However, there is no theoretical reason why the frictional coefficient should be independent of concentration in Θ-media and Scholtan and Marzolph (1962) have found the sedimentation constant of polyacrylonitrile to remain concentration dependent even under Θ conditions. The use of Θ-solvents is in any case desirable, since it appears that the resolution attainable in the sedimentation is maximized in Θ media (McCormick, 1959a).

If the distribution of the molecular weights of a polymer sample is to be determined, we may combine (6.18) with (6.15) to obtain

$$M_2 = [RT/(1 - \bar{v}_2\rho)](s^0/D^0) \tag{6.20}$$

where the superscript $^\circ$ refers to quantities extrapolated to zero concentration. When all the corrections described above are properly carried out, an analysis of sedimentation data becomes the most powerful method for the determination of molecular weight distributions. It is particularly valuable in characterizing samples prepared under conditions which should yield very narrow molecular weight distributions (Cantow, 1959; McCormick, 1959a,b).

The above discussion implies that sedimentation data cannot be interpreted in terms of molecular weights unless we have additional information relating to the frictional coefficient of the macromolecule. However, Archibald (1947) has shown that it is possible to obtain unambiguous molecular weight data from sedimentation velocity data alone. From (6.14) and (6.18) the velocity of the molecules due to both the gravitational field and diffusion is

$$dr/dt = sr\omega^2 - D\,d\ln c/dr \tag{6.21}$$

and since dr/dt must vanish at the bottom and the top of the cell ($r = r_a$ and $r = r_b$), we obtain

$$\omega^2 s/D = (1/r_a c_2)(dc_2/dr)_{r=r_a} = (1/r_b s_2)(dc_2/dr)_{r=r_b} \tag{6.22a}$$

Provided the solution is sufficiently dilute so that s/D may be approximated by s^0/D^0, we obtain by substitution from (6.20)

$$(1/r_a c_2)(dc_2/dr)_{r=r_a} = (1/r_b c_2)(dc_2/dr)_{r=r_b} = M_2 \omega^2 (1 - \bar{v}_2 \rho)/RT \quad (6.22b)$$

Thus, the concentration gradient at the top and the bottom of the cell defines the molecular weight of the sedimenting macromolecules. For optical reasons it is not possible to measure dc_2/dr close to the meniscus or close to the bottom of the cell, but $(1/rc_2)(dc_2/dr)$ may be measured at various values of r and extrapolated to $r = r_a$ and $r = r_b$, where its value should remain invariant with time.

For a detailed treatment of the theoretical foundation of sedimentation analysis the reader is referred to a monograph by Fujita (1962).

5. Mobility of Small Molecules and Ions in Polymer Solutions

Since the translational frictional coefficient is inversely proportional to the viscosity of the medium, both the coefficient of diffusion and the electrophoretic mobility are expected to vary as $1/\eta$. Nevertheless, it is found that the mobility of small particles in a given solvent medium is affected very little by the presence of macromolecules, although the viscosity of the macromolecular solution may be much higher than the viscosity of the pure solvent. A very dramatic demonstration of this effect was carried out more than a century ago (Graham, 1862) when it was shown that the rate of diffusion of salts through a gelatin gel could not be distinguished from the diffusion rate in pure water. Careful quantitative measurements carried out more recently (Taft and Malm, 1939) showed that the presence of gelatin has a small effect on ionic mobilities, but that no change in these mobilities could be detected when the gelatin solution set to a gel.

These results are rather remarkable, since gels which cannot flow in response to a shearing stress must be assigned, by definition, an infinite viscosity. It is, however, clear that the significance of "viscosity" is different, if we consider the macroscopic flow of a system and if we consider the passage of a small molecular particle through the same medium. This leads to the distinction between the "macroscopic viscosity," describing the flow properties of the system as a whole, and the "microscopic viscosity" which characterizes the resistance to the motion of a molecular particle and which will, in general, depend on the dimensions of that particle. We shall see in Sec. C-2 that the viscosity of solutions of chain molecules depends on their length, but it is apparent that the reduction in the diffusion rate of a small particle, resulting from collisions with segments of a polymer chain, will not depend on the length of the chain to which these segments are attached.   Even the formation of a three-dimensional network by these polymer chains will make little difference to the obstacle presented to small diffusing species, although macroscopic flow will now be impossible.

An interesting experiment was carried out by Nishijima and Oster (1956) who studied the diffusion of sucrose in solutions of poly(N-vinylpyrrolidone) of varying molecular weight.   Plots of the microscopic viscosity, obtained from the diffusion coefficients, against the polymer concentration were S-shaped.   The concentration range in which the microscopic viscosity changed most rapidly was apparently related to the concentration at which extensive interpenetration of the molecular coils is to be expected—this critical concentration range decreases, therefore, with increasing molecular weight of the polymer.   At polymer concentrations above 10% the diffusion rate of the sucrose was entirely independent of the chain length of the polymer, as would be expected on the basis of the considerations outlined above.

B. ROTARY DIFFUSION

1. Rotary Diffusion Coefficient of Rigid Particles

We have seen in our discussion of linear diffusion that Brownian motion tends to transport solute molecules from regions of high local concentration to regions of higher dilution.   In the absence of any other driving forces, such diffusion eventually results in a complete equalization of the local composition of the system.   In the presence of another force, such as gravitation, the system approaches an equilibrium in which gravitational and diffusive transport balance one another.

An analogous situation arises if we consider a system containing asymmetric particles and characterize it by the distribution of the particle orientations.   If we consider the behavior of solids of revolution, we may describe their orientation by specifying the distribution function $\mathcal{W}(\varphi)$ such that $\mathcal{W}(\varphi)d\varphi$ is the number of particles whose axes of revolution subtend angles between φ and $\varphi + d\varphi$ with a given direction of the coordinate system.   If the system is completely disordered, $\mathcal{W}(\varphi) = $ const; on the other hand, if $\mathcal{W}(\varphi)$ is variable, there will be a statistical probability for the particle orientations to pass from more occupied to less occupied φ values.   We have then, in analogy with Fick's first law for linear translation (eq. 6.14), a diffusive rotation given by

$$d\varphi/dt = - [D_r/\mathcal{W}(\varphi)]d\mathcal{W}(\varphi)/d\varphi \qquad (6.23)$$

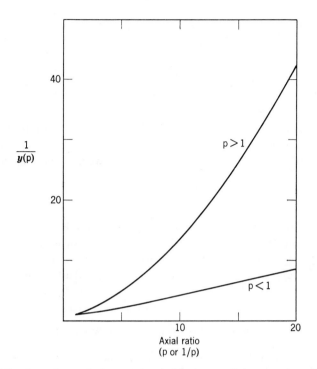

Fig. VI.6. The dependence of the rotational diffusion coefficient on the axial ratio of ellipsoids of revolution.

where D_r is the rotational diffusion coefficient. Again in analogy with linear diffusion, D_r must be inversely proportional to the hydrodynamic resistance to the rotation. This may be expressed as

$$D_r = kT/f_r \tag{6.24}$$

where the rotational frictional coefficient f_r is numerically equal to the force-couple in dyne-centimeters required to impart to the particle a rotational velocity of 1 radian per second around an axis perpendicular to the axis of revolution. For spheres of radius R_s Stokes (1880) obtained

$$f_r = 8\pi\eta_0 R_s^3 \qquad \text{(spheres)} \tag{6.25}$$

while for ellipsoids of revolution with a semiaxis of revolution a_1, an equatorial axis a_2, and an axial ratio $p = a_1/a_2$, the result is (Gans, 1928; Perrin, 1934)

$$f_r = 8\pi\eta_0 a_1 a_2^2/y(p)$$

$$y(p) = \frac{3}{2}\frac{p^2}{p^4-1}\left[1 + \frac{2p^2-1}{2p\sqrt{p^2-1}}\ln\frac{p+\sqrt{p^2-1}}{p-\sqrt{p^2-1}}\right] \qquad p > 1$$

$$y(p) = \frac{3}{2}\frac{p^2}{1-p^4}\left[1 + \frac{1-2p^2}{2p\sqrt{1-p^2}}\tan^{-1}\frac{\sqrt{1-p^2}}{p}\right] \qquad p < 1 \quad (6.26)$$

The function $y(p)$ is plotted in Fig. VI.6 and we may see that the resistance to rotation increases sharply with an increasing elongation of ellipsoids of revolution. For ellipsoids with $p > 5$, we may use in good approximation

$$f_r = 8\pi\eta_0 a_1^3/(3\ln p + 0.57) \tag{6.27}$$

and Gans (1928) obtained a similar expression for long thin rods. It is then apparent that for sufficiently elongated particles the resistance to rotation at right angles to the long axis increases approximately as the cube of the long dimension and is almost independent of the thickness of the particle. For $p < 1$, i.e., for disk-shaped objects, the rotational frictional coefficient is rather insensitive to the axial ratio.

2. Rotary Diffusion of Chain Molecules

In treating the rotary diffusion of flexible polymer chains we may again employ the pearl necklace model for the chain molecule. Let us first consider (Kuhn and Kuhn, 1945a) the behavior of a dumb-bell containing two spheres of radius R_s at a fixed distance $2r$ from each other. If the dumbbell is made to rotate with unit angular velocity, the spheres will move at a velocity r. Assuming $R_s/r \ll 1$, so that the flow disturbances due to the two spheres do not interact appreciably with one another, the viscous force on each sphere will be, according to (6.2) equal to $6\pi\eta_0 R_s r$. The force couple required to maintain the unit rotational velocity will then be $12\pi\eta_0 R_s r^2$ and this will be the rotational frictional coefficient of the dumbbell.

It is easy to see how this picture may be generalized for free draining coils with a random flight distribution of Z spherical chain elements. In that case the frictional coefficient will have a contribution $6\pi\eta_0 R_s r_i^2$ from each unit of the chain placed at a distance r_i from the axis of rotation of the chain. Thus, the total frictional coefficient would be $6\pi\eta_0 R_s \Sigma\langle r_i^2\rangle$. Since r_i^2 must be, on the average, $^2/_3$ of the square distance from the center of gravity, we may estimate $f_{rot} = 4\pi\eta_0 R_s Z\langle s^2\rangle$. We have seen that in random flight chains the mean square radius of gyration is proportional to the chain length [cf. eq. (3.11)] and we are thus led to the conclusion that the rotational frictional coefficient in free-draining coils is proportional to the square of the chain length.

In the previous discussion of the frictional resistance to translation of flexible chain molecules we noted that real chains are far from free draining and that their behavior approaches, in practice, more closely to that of an impermeable spherical body. The general problem for a pearl necklace chain with partial permeability to the fluid in which it moves has been treated by Riseman and Kirkwood (1949). Their result may be expressed in analogy to (6.25) as

$$f_r = 8\pi\eta_0 R_r^3 F(\Xi) \tag{6.28}$$

where R_r is the radius of a sphere which would encounter the same frictional resistance to rotation as a flexible coil in the limit of complete impermeability. The parameter Ξ, defined in eq. (6.10), is equal to the ratio of the frictional coefficients of the sum of the chain elements and the impermeable coil, respectively. As $\Xi \rightarrow \infty$ and the coil becomes impermeable, $F(\Xi) \rightarrow 1$; according to Riseman and Kirkwood a chain molecule with a root-mean-square radius of gyration $\langle s^2 \rangle^{1/2}$ will then behave like a sphere whose radius is $R_r = 0.89\langle s^2 \rangle^{1/2}$. We may note that the sphere which is hydrodynamically equivalent to the coil with respect to rotation is somewhat larger than the sphere which is equivalent to the coil with respect to linear translation [cf. eq. (6.11)].

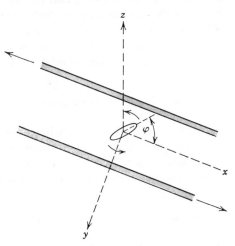

Fig. VI.7. Ellipsoidal particle suspended in a viscous liquid with a velocity gradient.

3. Flow Birefringence

The classical method for evaluation of the rotational diffusion constant employs the anisotropy induced in a solution when a shear gradient leads to a partial orientation of asymmetric particles. This anisotropy is observed most conveniently as an optical birefringence induced by a velocity gradient. An extensive review of the theories of the effect was published by Jerrard (1959); a more recent review by Tsvetkov (1964) also includes experimental results.

The theory of flow birefringence may be divided into two parts. First we have to concern ourselves with the hydrodynamical problem of characterizing the probability distribution of the orientations of particles placed in a velocity gradient of a viscous fluid. Once this problem has been solved, we have to define the optical consequences of this particle orientation.

Any particle placed in a velocity gradient will be subject to a torque which will lead to the rotation of the particle. The situation is represented schematically in Fig. VI.7 where the x direction is the direction of the flow lines and the velocity gradient increases in the y direction, while the particle is being observed in the z direction perpendicular to the x–y plane. If the particle is spherical, its rotational speed will be uniform, but for ellipsoidal particles, the torque due to the viscous drag will depend on particle orientation. In particular, if the axis of symmetry of the ellipsoid lies in the x–y plane, the driving force will be largest with this axis in the y direction and smallest with the long axis parallel to the flow lines, so that the rotational velocity will change periodically during each revolution. The probability $\mathcal{W}(\varphi)$ of finding the particle in any given orientation, where φ is the angle subtended by the symmetry axis of the ellipsoid with the flow lines, will be inversely proportional to the rotational speed so that

$$\mathcal{W}(\varphi)d\varphi/dt = \text{constant} \qquad (6.29)$$

If the particles are small, Brownian motion will counteract the hydrodynamic orientation of the particles. We may then express $d\varphi/dt$ as the sum of ω_h, the angular velocity due to hydrodynamic forces, and the velocity produced by rotational diffusion, related to the rotational diffusion constant by relation (6.23). This leads to*

$$\mathcal{W}(\varphi)\omega_h(\varphi) - D_r d\mathcal{W}(\varphi)/d\varphi = \text{constant} \qquad (6.30)$$

---

* In this treatment it is assumed that inertial forces, which would tend to smooth out the periodic changes in the angular velocity of the rotating particles, are negligible.

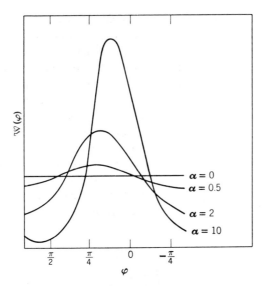

Fig. VI.8. Orientation of ellipsoidal particles as a function of the ratio of the velocity gradient to the rotatory diffusion coefficient.

Equation (6.30) has been solved by Boeder (1932) for ellipsoids whose symmetry axes lie in the x–y plane. Since $\omega_h(\varphi)$ must be proportional to the velocity gradient in the solution, $\mathcal{W}(\varphi)$ becomes a function of the ratio of the velocity gradient q and the rotational diffusion constant D_r

$$\mathcal{W}(\varphi) = f(\alpha)$$
$$\alpha = q/D_r \tag{6.31}$$

Boeder's results are illustrated in Fig. VI.8. We may see that for low values of α the function $\mathcal{W}(\varphi)$ is rather flat but tends to have a maximum at $\varphi = \pi/4$. As α increases, the particles are oriented more nearly parallel to the flow lines as shown by the decreasing value in φ_{max} and the sharpening up of the distribution function $\mathcal{W}(\varphi)$. In reality the long axis of the ellipsoids is of course not restrained to lie in the x–y plane and its orientation will have to be specified by two angles, i.e., the angle φ between the a_1–z plane and the x–z plane and the angle ϑ between a_1 and z. This complicates considerably the problem of deriving the steady state probability distribution function $\mathcal{W}(\varphi,\vartheta)$ of particle orientations, but a solution has been obtained (Peterlin, 1938).

We must now consider the second part of the problem, namely the optical consequences of partial orientation of the solute particles. The experi-

mental arrangement is shown schematically in Fig. VI.9. The test solution is contained in the annulus between two cylindrical surfaces, one stationary and one rotating. A plane-polarized beam of light enters the
solution parallel to the cylindrical axis of the apparatus (the z axis) and is
observed through a crossed analyzer. If the solution is isotropic, no light
will pass through the analyzer, but if it contains an anisotropic particle,
this particle will be visible unless its optical axis is parallel to the plane of
polarization of the polarizer or the analyzer. If we have a solution of
ellipsoided particles and if the φ angle as defined above is the same for all
the particles, then Fig. VI.9 shows that the condition for light extinction
will be met for all particles whose centers lie in a plane rotated around the
z-axis from the plane of polarization of the polarizer or the analyzer by an
angle $\xi = \varphi$. We shall then observe light transmission except for a dark cross

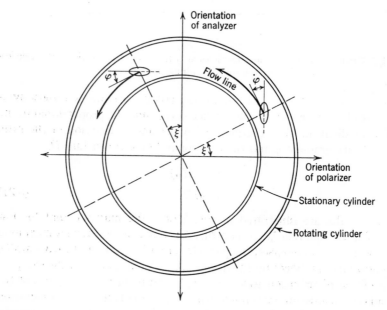

Fig. VI.9. View of doubly refractive medium in the gap between a stationary and a
rotating cylinder.

("the cross of isocline"). For a solution in which the orientation angles φ
are variable, the condition of light extinction will require that the electrical
vectors of light passed by the anisotropic particles have components parallel
to the orientation of the analyzer which add up to zero.

Peterlin and Stuart (1939) showed that for rigid ellipsoids of revolution the extinction angle ξ should be given by

$$\xi = \frac{\pi}{4} - \frac{\alpha}{12}\left[1 - \frac{\alpha^2}{108}\left\{1 - \frac{24}{35}\left(\frac{p^2 - 1}{p^2 + 1}\right)^2\right\} + \cdots\right] \qquad (6.32)$$

We see then that the extinction angle approaches to $45°$ as the velocity gradient approaches zero. The decay of ξ with increasing velocity gradient depends at first only on $\alpha = q/D_r$, so that the rotational diffusion constant may be derived from

$$(d\xi/dq)_{q \to 0} = -1/12D_r \qquad (6.33)$$

At higher values of α, the dependence of the extinction angle on the velocity gradient involves also explicitly the axial ratio p. The course of a plot of ξ against α can, therefore, be used to estimate the length of the two semi-axes of ellipsoidal particles from (6.24), (6.26), and (6.32). The relation given in eq. (6.32) may be considered accurate up to α values of about 1.5; extinction angles for higher α have been computed by Scheraga et al. (1951).

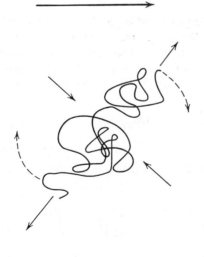

Fig. VI.10. Tensile and compressive stresses on a flexible coil in a viscous fluid with a velocity gradient. The heavy lines indicate the flow lines in the fluid, the light solid lines the stresses on the chain molecule, the dashed lines the direction in which the molecule rotates.

We may inquire at this point how the orientation effect is going to manifest itself in the case of some typical rigid solute particles. Tobacco mosaic virus is known to be rod-shaped with a length of about 3000 Å and a diameter of 150 Å (Williams and Steere, 1951). By using eq. (6.27), this leads to a rotary diffusion constant in water ($\eta_0 = 0.01$) of about 6×10^3 sec.$^{-1}$ This is a very convenient order of magnitude; with a velocity gradient of 10^4 sec^{-1}, the extinction angle would be reduced by 8° from its limiting value of 45°. On the other hand, human serum albumin, which has dimensions approximated by an ellipsoid with $a_1 = 75$ Å, $a_2 = 20$ Å (Edsall, 1953) may be estimated to have in water solution $D_r = 1.5 \times 10^7$ sec.$^{-1}$ This is so high that a flow birefringence experiment is not practicable, since laminar flow could not be maintained at the velocity gradients required for an appreciable orientation effect. The use of very high velocity gradients would also generate heat by fluid friction at a rate which would make it difficult to retain thermodynamic control. We may note that the use of viscous solvents favors orientation studies since they reduce D_r and thus permit the use of proportionately lower velocity gradients. This reduces the rate of heat generation, which is equal to ηq^2 per unit volume of the fluid.

Flow birefringence experiments yield, in addition to the extinction angle, another parameter; the magnitude of the birefringence Δn. This quantity depends both on the extent of orientation of the asymmetric solute particles and on the optical anisotropy $g_1 - g_2$. At a low degree of particle orientation Peterlin and Stuart (1939) give for systems containing a volume fraction ϕ_2 of solute

$$\Delta n/\phi_2 = [(2\pi/15)(g_1 - g_2)/n]f(p,\alpha) \qquad (6.34a)$$

$$g_1 - g_2 = \frac{5}{4\pi} \frac{n_0^2(n_1^2 - n_2^2) + L(p)(n_1^2 - n_0^2)(n_2^2 - n_0^2)}{[(n_1^2 + 2n_0^2) - L(p)(n_1^2 - n_0^2)][(n_2^2 + 2n_0^2) + L(p)(n_2^2 - n_0^2)]}$$

$$(6.34b)$$

$$f(p,\alpha) = \alpha \frac{p^2 - 1}{p^2 + 1}\left[1 - \frac{\alpha^2}{72}\left\{1 + \frac{6}{35}\left(\frac{p^2 - 1}{p^2 + 1}\right)^2\right\} + \dots\right] \qquad (6.34c)$$

where n_0 and n are the refractive indices of the solvent and the solution, n_1 and n_2 are the refractive indices of the ellipsoids parallel and perpendicular to their symmetry axis, while $L(p)$ is a function of the axial ratio which is 0 for $p = 1$, approaches, for $p > 10$, its asymptotic value of $+0.5$ and for $p < 0.1$ its asymptotic value of -1. We may note that only the first term in the numerator disappears when $n_1 = n_2$; thus, the optical anisotropy is made up of two contributions, the first one due to the intrinsic anisotropy of the particle if $n_1 \neq n_2$, while the second one ("the form anisotropy") is produced by the orientation of asymmetric particles in a medium of a different refractive index. If the dimensions of the particles are known from the dependence of the extinction angle on the velocity gradient, $g_1 - g_2$ may be obtained from (6.34a) and we are then given in (6.34b) one relation between n_1 and n_2. The second relation is obtained from measurements of the average refractive index of the solute in bulk which must be $(n_1 + 2n_2)/3$. We may then solve for the principal refractive indices of the solute particle.

The interpretation of flow birefringence data obtained with solutions of flexible chain molecules is much more involved. The frictional forces due to the streaming fluid will not only tend to rotate the coil, but will also lead to a periodic change in its shape as a consequence of the alternating tension and compression indicated in Fig. VI.10. This change of shape will be counteracted by the rubber-like elasticity of the coils, which resist changes to less probable chain conformations (Kuhn and Kuhn, 1943). If we place one chain end at the origin of the coordinate system, while the other lies on one of the axes, we may use the probability distribution function (3.6) to obtain for the elastic retractive force F_{el} (on the assumption that the internal energy of the chain is independent of the chain end separation h)

$$F_{el} = (\partial G/\partial h)_{T,P}$$

$$= -T(\partial S/\partial h)_{T,P} = -kT[\partial \ln W(h)/\partial h]_{T,P}$$

$$= 3(kT/h)(h^2/\langle h_0^2 \rangle) \tag{6.35}$$

where $\langle h_0^2 \rangle$ refers to the mean square end-to-end displacement of the unperturbed chain. However, Kuhn and Kuhn (1946) pointed out also that for any given rate at which the chain is to be stretched or compressed, the potential energy barriers which have to be overcome in conformational transitions require an additional force, which may be characterized by an internal viscosity η_i of the chain. The significance of this parameter is best illustrated if we consider the behavior of coils with very low and with very high η_i. If the internal viscosity can be neglected, the alternating expansion and compression of the rotating coil will be in phase with the alternating tensile and compressive hydrodynamic forces. At the other extreme, coils with very high internal viscosities will not have time to change their shape appreciably during a single rotation and we shall then have an assembly of coils with a statistical distribution of shapes, each coil rotating essentially as if it were a rigid structure.

The complications outlined above are superimposed on the distinction between free draining, partially permeable, and impermeable coils. It is not surprising then that theories of flow birefringence have to utilize idealized models which stress some aspects of the situation while ignoring others. The model of Kuhn and Kuhn (1943, 1946) assumes that the macromolecule may be represented by a free-draining, random flight chain and that its hydrodynamic behavior is adequately approximated by an elastic dumbbell in which each sphere has a translational frictional co-efficient equal to that of one quarter of the chain, while the separation of the spheres is controlled by the elastic forces and the internal viscosity of the chain molecule. The definition of internal viscosity as used by Kuhn and Kuhn (in which η_i is equal to the force required to separate the ends of the chain at a unit rate) was later criticized by Cerf (1957) who used a pearl-necklace model for the chain and defined the internal viscosity in terms of the force f_i required to produce a difference in the radial components of the velocity vectors $\mathbf{u}_r$ of two consecutive beads,

$$f_i = \eta_i(\mathbf{u}_{r,j+1} - \mathbf{u}_{r,j}) \tag{6.36}$$

Zimm (1956) tested the pearl-necklace model taking account of hydro-dynamic interactions, but he neglected the effect of internal viscosity. An intriguing, quite different model has also been suggested (Cerf, 1951; Cerf and Scheraga, 1951). In this model the polymer coil is represented by a deformable isotropic droplet and the viscosity of the droplet produces a similar effect as the internal viscosity of the chain.

From what has been said above, it is clear that the flow orientation of flexible chain molecules is the result of the superposition of two effects. On one hand, the unperturbed coils which are of ellipsoidal shape [cf. eq. (3.13)] tend to be oriented in the streaming fluid. On the other hand, the stresses set up by a shear gradient deform the coil, increasing its asym-metry. Since the orientation is proportional to q and the deformation to q^2 (Peterlin, 1963), the orientational effect is dominant at low velocity gradients and the extinction angle will be governed by $\alpha = q/D_r$, just as with rigid particles. If the coil is completely impermeable, the rotational diffusion coefficient will be given by (6.24) and (6.26) in terms of the dimen-sions of the hydrodynamically equivalent ellipsoid. The initial slope of a plot of ξ against q will then depend on $\langle s^2 \rangle^{3/2} \eta_0 / kT$. We shall see in Part C of this chapter, that the intrinsic viscosity, $[\eta]$, an extremely easily measured quantity, is proportional to $N \langle s^2 \rangle^{3/2} / M_2$. Thus, one may generalize that

$$(\partial \xi / \partial q)_0 = \text{const. } [\eta] \eta_0 M_2 / RT \tag{6.37}$$

Tsvetkov (1964) has confirmed eq. (6.37) in extensive experimental tests.

The dependence of $(\partial \xi / \partial q)_0$ on the viscosity of the solvent medium may be used to characterize the internal viscosity of the chain (Cerf, 1957). At low solvent viscosities, orientational effects are dominant, while coil deformation is the governing factor at very high solvent viscosities. According to Cerf's theory, a plot of $(\partial \xi / \partial q)_0$ against η_0 should have an asymptote with a slope proportional to the chain length of the molecule and an intercept on the ordinate proportional to η_i and independent of M_2, for any polymer-homologous series. Leray (1957) has tested Cerf's theory on a series of polystyrene fractions and found $(\partial \xi / \partial q)_0$ to vary with η_0 as predicted; however, the internal viscosities calculated from his data were proportional to M_2—a result which it is difficult to reconcile with theory.

The magnitude of the flow birefringence of solutions of chain molecules depends, as with rigid particles [cf. eq. (6.34)], on both the intrinsic anisotropy and the form anisotropy of the macromolecule. Random flight chains have an intrinsic anisotropy if the chain segments are anisotropic, since the segments have a statistical preference for pointing in the direction of the chain end displacement. According to Kuhn and Grün (1942) the optical anisotropy of flexible chains is given by

$$g_2 - g_1 = (3/5)(g_2^s - g_1^s)\langle h^2 \rangle / \langle h_0^2 \rangle \tag{6.38}$$

where $g_2^s - g_1^s$ is the optical anisotropy of the statistical chain segment. We see from this relation that $g_2 - g_1$, will be extremely small, unless the chain end displacement is greatly increased over its unperturbed value. The birefringence observed at small α values is proportional to the length of the molecular chain as predicted by Kuhn and Grün, whatever the internal viscosity. However, the relative contributions of the intrinsic and the form anisotropy of the coil change as the velocity gradient is increased; at low α values the intrinsic anisotropy is the important quantity, while at high rates of shear the form anisotropy becomes dominant. The two quantities may have opposite signs and we may then observe a reversal of the sign of Δn in experiments carried out over a range of velocity gradients (Tsvetkov, 1957). (This phenomenon is, of course, quite inconsistent with Cerf's viscous drop model, which interprets flow birefringence on the basis of form anisotropy alone and leads then necessarily to the prediction that Δn is a monotonic function of q). The relative contribution of intrinsic and form anisotropy determine also the dependence of Δn on the chain length of the polymer (Tsvetkov, 1964). If only the intrinsic anisotropy is important, $\Delta n / [\eta]$ (where Δn is measured at a fixed low polymer concentration) is independent of M_2; if form anisotropy makes an appreciable contribution to the birefringence, then $\Delta n/[\eta]$ increases linearly with $M_2/[\eta]$.

In view of the insensitivity of many solution properties to the stereoregularity of chain molecules, it is particularly interesting to note that flow birefringence measurement may be an efficient tool for the characterization of tacticity (Tsvetkov et al., 1961). Thus, the segmental anisotropy $g_2^s - g_1^s$ (in units of 10^{-25} cm^3) is -146 and -224 for atactic and isotactic polystyrene in bromoform, or $+2$ and $+25$ for atactic and isotactic poly(methyl methacrylate) in benzene (Tsvetkov, 1962).

Phenomena similar to flow birefringence may be observed with respect to the anisotropy of other physical properties of polymer solutions subjected to a shear gradient. Hartmann and Jaenicke (1956) described the measurement of the flow induced anisotropy of the dielectric constant. A velocity gradient may also induce an anisotropy of electrolytic conductance, as we shall see in the next chapter in discussing solutions of polyelectrolytes.

4. Disorientation of Oriented Solutions

When polarizable molecules are placed in an electrical field of intensity X, the induced dipole is proportional to X and the potential energy is proportional to X^2, provided effects caused by permanent dipoles are negligible compared to polarization effects. If the molecule may be treated as an ellipsoid of revolution with maximum polarizability in the direction of the symmetry axis, then the distribution function of the angle φ between the symmetry axes of the particles and the electrical field is given by

$$\mathcal{W}(\varphi)d\varphi = (1/2)\sin\varphi \exp[-E(\varphi,X)/kT]d\varphi \qquad (6.39)$$

The partial orientation of the molecules will produce a birefringence given by

$$\Delta n/n = K\phi_2 X^2 \qquad (6.40)$$

where ϕ_2 is the volume fraction of the solute which is being oriented by the field and the Kerr constant K is a function of the polarization anisotropy of the solute particles. If the field is now cut off, Brownian motion will disorient the particles so that the mean value of $\cos\varphi$ will decay according to

$$\langle\cos\varphi\rangle(t) = \langle\cos\varphi\rangle(0)/\exp[-t/\tau_r] \qquad (6.41)$$

leading to a corresponding decay of the birefringence

$$\Delta n(t) = \Delta n(0) \exp\left[-t/\tau_r\right] \tag{6.42}$$

where the relaxation time τ_r is related to the rotational diffusion constant D_r by

$$\tau_r = 1/6D_r \tag{6.43}$$

The relaxation of electrical birefringence was first used by Benoit (1950, 1951) to measure rotational diffusion constants of tobacco mosaic virus particles and DNA molecules. Experimental improvements later allowed Krause and O'Konski (1959, 1963) to apply the method to particles with a much higher rotational diffusion constant, such as aqueous solutions of globular proteins whose longest dimension is of the order of 100 Å.

Polarizable particles will also be oriented in an alternating field. If the frequency ν of the field is low compared to the rotational diffusion constant, the orientation will increase and decrease in phase with the alternating field; at the other extreme, with $\nu \gg D_r$, the orientation will be constant, corresponding to the time average value of X^2. If ν and D_r have comparable magnitudes, the particle orientation will lag behind the variation in the alternating field with the phase angle φ related to the rotational diffusion constant by

$$\tan \varphi = 2\pi\nu/3D_r \tag{6.44}$$

This principle has been employed by Benoit (1952) for the determination of D_r in aqueous solutions of tobacco mosaic virus.

5. Depolarization of Fluorescence

When a fluorescent group is attached rigidly to a globular protein molecule and excited with polarized light, the fluorescence at right angles to the plane of polarization of the incident beam will be partially depolarized to an extent which will depend on how far the molecule has rotated during the lifetime τ_e of the excited state. The use of this principle in the study of rotational diffusion of globular protein molecules was introduced by Weber (1952) and work in this area has been reviewed by Weber (1953) and by Steiner and Edelhoch (1962). If we characterize the extent of polarization by $\mathbf{P} \equiv (I_{\parallel} - I_{\perp})/(I_{\parallel} + I_{\perp})$ where $I_{\parallel}$ and $I_{\perp}$ refer to components of the fluorescence beam, polarized parallel and perpendicular to the direction of polarization of the exciting beam, then it can be shown (Perrin, 1929; Weber, 1952) that

$$(\mathbf{P}^{-1} - \tfrac{1}{3})/(\mathbf{P}_0^{-1} - \tfrac{1}{3}) = 1 + (3\tau_e/\tau_{rh}) \tag{6.45}$$

Here P_0 refers to the polarization of the fluorescent beam when the fluorescent molecule cannot rotate and τ_{rh} is the harmonic mean relaxation time given by $\tau_{rh} = 2\tau_r\tau_r'/(\tau_r + \tau_r')$, where τ_r and τ_r' are relaxation times for rotation around the equatorial axis and the symmetry axis, respectively. The value of P_0 may be obtained by measuring the depolarization of fluorescence in media of increasing viscosity and carrying out a linear extrapolation of P^{-1} against η_0^{-1} to $\eta_0^{-1} = 0$ (Perrin, 1929). For spheres, $\tau_r = \tau_r' = \tau_{rh}$ so that (6.24), (6.25), and (6.43) give τ_{rh} proportional to the volume of the particle. For very elongated ellipsoids of revolution, the hydrodynamic resistance is much less for rotation around the symmetry axis than for rotation around the equatorial axis, so that $\tau_r \gg \tau_r'$ and $\tau_{rh} \approx 2\tau_r'$; for particles of equal volume, τ_{rh} will increase only very slowly with an increasing axial ratio p (Weber, 1953). It may be noted, that this is in sharp contrast to the high sensitivity of flow birefringence or the relaxation of electrical birefringence to increasing particle elongation, since in those techniques only rotations around the equatorial axis are observed.

The range of relaxation times which may be studied by measurement of the depolarization of fluorescence is determined by the lifetimes of the excited species of the fluorescent dyes employed; these range usually from 10^{-9} to 10^{-7} sec. Typical values are $\tau_e = 1.2 \times 10^{-8}$ sec for 1-dimethyl-amino-naphthalene-5-sulfonyl derivatives and 5×10^{-9} sec for fluorescein derivatives (Steiner and Edelhoch, 1962). It is then possible to characterize molecules with diffusion constants of the order of 10^{-8} sec^{-1}, which cannot be studied by flow birefringence. This range of D_r values is important, since it covers the smaller globular protein molecules. It should also be pointed out that depolarization of fluorescence can be measured with equal ease whether the solute molecule is asymmetric or spherical in shape. Thus, we may study rotational diffusion even with particles which cannot be oriented by any means.

Attachment of a fluorescent residue to a flexible chain molecule leads to an entirely different situation. Brechbuhler and Magat (1950) made the first measurements of chain molecules carrying a fluorescent dye at the chain ends and systems of this type were studied in detail by Nishijima (cf. Oster and Nishijima, 1964). As one would expect, rotational motion of the dye residue will not require the macromolecule as a whole to move and the depolarization of fluorescence will, therefore, be independent of the chain length of the polymer, unless the chain is very short. The technique is valuable in defining, in this case, the restraints to the motion of a substituent attached to a more or less flexible chain.

C. SOLUTION VISCOSITY

1. Viscosity of Solutions of Rigid Molecules

When a Newtonian fluid of viscosity η_0 is subjected to a uniform velocity gradient q, the rate at which mechanical energy is transformed into heat by fluid friction per unit volume will be given by

$$J = \eta_0 q^2 \tag{6.46}$$

If we now suspend rigid spheres in the fluid, the flow lines will be perturbed as indicated in Fig. VI.11. The viscous drag will induce the spheres to rotate and it can be shown that the steady state angular velocity ω is half of the velocity gradient. The flow perturbations caused by the spheres will lead to an increase in the rate of energy dissipation, which may be formally related to the viscosity η of the suspension by

$$J + \Delta J = \eta q^2$$
$$\Delta J/J = (\eta - \eta)/\eta_0 \tag{6.47}$$

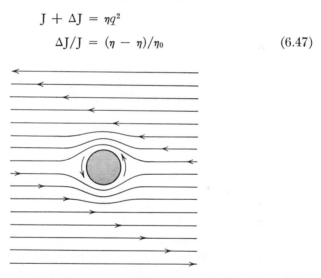

Fig. VI.11. Flow lines around a sphere suspended in a viscous fluid with a velocity gradient.

The calculation of $\Delta J/J$ for a suspension of rigid spheres with interparticle distances very large compared to the particle diameters was carried out by Einstein (1906a, 1911). His result was

$$\eta_{sp} \equiv (\eta - \eta_0)/\eta_0 = (5/2)\,\phi_2 \tag{6.48}$$

where η_{sp} is called the "specific viscosity" and ϕ_2 is the volume fraction occupied by the spheres. The striking aspect of this result is the fact that

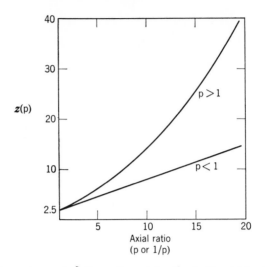

Fig. VI.12. Dependence of η_{sp}^0/ϕ_2 on the axial ratio of ellipsoidal solute particles.

the specific viscosity depends only on the total volume occupied by the spheres but *not on the size of the individual spheres*.

If the thickness of the flow channel d is not very large compared to the radius R_s of the spheres, Guth and Simha (1936) find

$$\eta_{sp} = (5/2)\phi_2[1 + (5/16)\ R_s/d] \qquad (6.49)$$

and if the spheres are not rigid but contain a fluid of viscosity η', Taylor (1932) obtains in the limit of small velocity gradients

$$\eta_{sp} = (5/2)\phi_2\ (\eta' + 0.4\eta_0)/(\eta' + \eta_0) \qquad (6.50)$$

The case of asymmetric particles is more complex. As was already pointed out in our discussion of flow birefringence, the orientation of ellipsoidal particles will be kept random by Brownian motion at low velocity gradients; the extent of orientation will, in general, be a function of $\alpha = q/D_r$. Since the frictional dissipation of energy owing to the presence of the particles must obviously depend on the extent of their orientation with respect to the flow lines, η_{sp} would also be expected to depend on the magnitude of α. In general, the asymmetric particles will tend to orient themselves at high α values so as to offer the least resistance to the streaming fluid and η_{sp} must, therefore, decrease as α increases.

A quantitative treatment of the effect of ellipsoidal solute particles on solution viscosity was carried out by Simha (1940) for the case of $q \ll D_r$, i.e., for systems in which the orienting influence of the velocity gradient is too small to affect the essentially random distribution of particle orientations. The specific viscosity obtained under these conditions will be denoted by η_{sp}^0. The ratio η_{sp}^0/ϕ_2 depends then on the axial ratio of the particles

$$\eta_{sp}^0/\phi_2 \;=\; z(\mathrm{p}) \qquad (6.51)$$

where the function $z(\mathrm{p})$ has the form represented in Fig. VI.12. The ratio η_{sp}^0/ϕ_2 is rather insensitive to p, increasing only from 2.50 to 2.91 and 5.81 as p increases from 1 to 2 and 5. For very large values of p, Simha gives the approximate relation

$$\eta_{sp}^0/\phi_2 = (14/15) + (p^2/5)\,[(3\ln 2p - \tfrac{9}{2})^{-1} + (\ln 2p - \tfrac{1}{2})^{-1}] \quad (6.52)$$

A somewhat different approach was that by Kuhn and Kuhn (1945a), who used as a model for the asymmetric particle a dumbbell in which the radius of the two spheres is small compared to their distance of separation. While this model may appear somewhat more artificial than an ellipsoid of revolution, it has the advantage that the rate of energy dissipation resulting from the presence of the particle may be calculated for any relative orientation of the dumbbell and the streamlines (neglecting only the interactions between the flow perturbations caused by the two spheres of any one dumb-bell). The rate of energy dissipation J_d due to a dumbbell restrained to rotate in the x–y plane (cf. Fig. VI.7) is given by Stokes' law as $2(6\pi\eta_0\,R_s)\,(u_{rh}^2 + u_{rd}^2)$, where u_{rh}^2 and u_{rd}^2 are velocities of the two spheres relative to the fluid, due to hydrodynamic forces and to rotational diffusion, respectively. This rate of energy dissipation depends on the orientation angle φ and the total rate ΔJ at which work is transformed into heat due to N^* dumbbells per unit volume may then be evaluated after determination of the distribution function $\mathcal{W}(\varphi)$ of particle orientation (cf. Sec. B-3) from

$$\Delta J \;=\; N^* \int^\pi J_d\,(\varphi)\mathcal{W}(\varphi)d\varphi \qquad (6.53)$$

The result obtained in the limit of small velocity gradients is similar to Simha's result for ellipsoidal particles. The dependence of η_{sp} on the velocity gradient is generally of the form

$$\eta_{sp}/\eta_{sp}^0 \;=\; 1 \,-\, s_1(\mathrm{p})\alpha^2 + s_2(\mathrm{p})\alpha^4 - \ldots \qquad (6.54)$$

where the coefficients $s_1(\mathrm{p})$, $s_2(\mathrm{p})$, etc., vanish for spherical particles and increase with the axial ratio p. The dumbbell model of Kuhn and Kuhn,

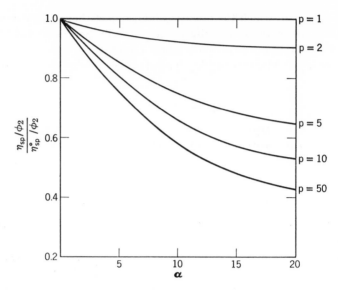

Fig. VI.13. Relative decrease of the specific viscosity of solutions of ellipsoidal particles with an increasing ratio of the velocity gradient to the rotary diffusion coefficient.

which is applicable in the limit of large p values, leads to $s_1 = 1/32$, $s_2 = 0.0017$. Scheraga (1955) has computed η_{sp}/η_{sp}^0 as a function of p up to large values of α and some of his results are shown in Fig. VI.13. The relation (6.54) indicates that the decay of η_{sp} with an increase in the velocity gradient is a function of the rotational diffusion constant of the particles and is, therefore, a measure of the asymmetry of the particles. In practice, this is a more reliable indication of the axial ratio of the particles than η_{sp}^0, since solvation of the macromolecules may increase their effective hydrodynamic volume, so that an interpretation of η_{sp}^0 based on a ϕ_2 value corresponding to the volume of the "dry" solute may involve an appreciable error.

So far, we have considered only systems so dilute that interactions between the disturbances of the flow pattern due to the various solute particles could be neglected. In this limit, η_{sp} is proportional to the number of solute particles. However, as we pass to more concentrated systems where binary solute interactions are no longer negligible, they will add a term proportional to the square of the solution concentration. Simha (1952) has calculated the coefficient of this term for spherical particles and obtained

$$\eta_{sp} = (5/2)\phi_2 + 12.6 \; \phi_2^2 \qquad (6.55)$$

As we noted before, the effective hydrodynamic volume of a mole of solute particles (V_e) may be appreciably different from the molar volume of the solute in bulk. Expressing the solute concentration c_2 in grams per cubic centimeter, we have $\phi_2 = (V_e/M_2)c_2$ and (6.55) may be rewritten as

$$\eta_{sp} = 2.5 \ (V_e/M_2)c_2 + 12.6 \ (V_e/M_2)^2 c_2^2 \qquad (6.56)$$

or, in the usual notation

$$\eta_{sp}/c_2 = [\eta] + k' \ [\eta]^2 c_2 \qquad (6.57)$$

where $[\eta]$ is called the "intrinsic viscosity"* and k', referred to commonly as the Huggins constant (cf. Huggins, 1942), should have, according to (6.63), a value close to 2.0. However, Weissberg et al. (1951) have pointed out that macromolecular particles may form short-lived doublets, with an asymmetry smaller or larger than the isolated solute molecules, and since the concentration of such doublets in dilute systems would be proportional to the square of the concentration, the hydrodynamic consequences of such association may lead to an increase or reduction of k'.

2. Viscosity of Solutions of Flexible Chain Molecules

The intrinsic viscosity is the most frequently used parameter in the characterization of the molecular weight of flexible chain polymers. It is also frequently employed for the estimation of the dimensions of the molecular coil. This is so in spite of the fact that the interpretation of $[\eta]$ in terms of M_2 requires a prior calibration procedure against a primary method (usually osmometry or light scattering) and that the estimation of coil dimensions from $[\eta]$ is based on theoretical treatments which cannot compare in rigor to the relation derived between $\langle s^2 \rangle$ and the angular dependence of the scattered light intensity. The popularity of the viscosimetric method is due to the ease with which experimental data of high precision may be obtained. This factor may frequently outweigh the theoretical uncertainties so that estimates of coil expansion may be arrived at more reliably from intrinsic viscosities than from procedures which are sounder theoretically but experimentally more difficult.

We have already discussed the behavior of a chain molecule, suspended in a viscous fluid and subjected to a velocity gradient, in our previous considerations of flow birefringence. All the factors mentioned in that context

---

* Here we are expressing $[\eta]$ in cm^3-g^{-1} for the sake of consistency of units used throughout the book. It is common to express the solute concentration in grams per 100 ml and in this case $[\eta]$ is given in dl-g^{-1}.

retain their importance in the theory of intrinsic viscosity. We thus have to consider the effect of the extent to which the coil is permeated by the streaming fluid, the extent to which the coil is being periodically deformed during its rotation in the velocity gradient, and the consequences of orientation of coils whose overall shape deviates from spherical symmetry.

Kuhn and Kuhn (1945b) carried out a searching analysis of the intrinsic viscosity to be expected from a free-draining coil. We have already seen in Sec. B-2 that the rotational frictional coefficient for a rigid free-draining coil is proportional to the mean square radius of gyration. Thus, the energy dissipated in fluid friction per unit weight of the solute will also be proportional to $\langle s^2 \rangle$ and if the geometry of the coil may be described by the random flight model (which makes $\langle s^2 \rangle$ proportional to the number of chain links) then $[\eta]$ should be proportional to the length of the chain. Since the coil is not spherically symmetrical but has the overall shape of a slightly elongated ellipsoid, Kuhn and Kuhn concluded that coils with very high internal viscosities should be oriented to some extent towards the flow lines, leading to a decrease of $[\eta]$ with increasing q, as described in the preceding section for rigid ellipsoids of revolution. On the other hand, they reached the important conclusion that coils with zero internal viscosity, which are expanded and compressed in phase with the alternating hydrodynamic stresses during each revolution of the coil, should have an intrinsic viscosity independent of the velocity gradient.

The effect of hydrodynamic interactions between the elements of a Gaussian chain were taken into account by Kirkwood and Riseman (1948) in their theory of intrinsic viscosity. Their result may be written in the form

$$[\eta] = (10/3)\pi R_\eta^3 (N/M_2)F'(\Xi) \qquad (6.58)$$

where $(4/3)\pi R_\eta^3$ is the volume of a rigid sphere which has the same intrinsic viscosity as an impermeable Gaussian coil, Ξ is the parameter defined in eq. (6.10) and $F'(\Xi)$ is a function describing the permeability of the coil. For $\Xi \to \infty$, $F'(\Xi) \to 1$ if $R_\eta = 0.94 \langle s^2 \rangle^{1/2}$. Later it was found that the Kirkwood–Riseman treatment contained errors which led to an overestimate of R_η. According to Auer and Gardner (1955) $R_\eta = 0.87 \langle s^2 \rangle^{1/2}$ and an almost identical result was obtained by Zimm (1956) by a different method. Comparing this result with results quoted previously for the translational and rotational diffusion coefficients, we may note that a rigid sphere which is hydrodynamically equivalent to an impermeable coil will have slightly different radii depending on the property which is used as a basis for comparison.

TABLE VI.1
Intrinsic Viscosities of Polymers in Θ-Media

Polymer	Θ-medium	$[\eta]/M^{1/2}$ (cm³-mole$^{1/2}$-g$^{-3/2}$)
Amylose	0.33M aqueous KCl, 25°C	0.115
Cellulose tricaproate	Dimethylformamide, 41°C	0.245
Cellulose tricaprylate	Dimethylformamide, 140°C	0.113
Poly(*trans* 1,4-butadiene)	*n*-propyl acetate, 60°C	0.232
Poly(*cis* 1,4-butadiene)	*n*-propyl ketone, 14.5°C	0.119
Poly(acrylic acid)	dioxane, 30°C	0.076
Polyacrylonitrile	18% methanol, 82% dimethylform-amide, 20°C[a]	0.325
Poly(*n*-butyl methacrylate)	isopropanol, 23.7°C	0.037
Poly(dimethylsiloxane)	butanone, 20°C	0.081
Poly(ethylene oxide)	0.45M aqueous K₂SO₄, 35°C	0.130
Poly(ethyl methacrylate)	isopropanol, 37°C	0.047
Polyisobutene	benzene, 24°C	0.107
Poly(metaphosphate)	0.415M aqueous NaBr, 25°C	0.049
Poly(methacrylic acid)	0.002M aqueous HCl, 30°C	0.066
Polymethacrylonitrile	dimethylformamide, 20°C	0.220
Poly(methyl methacrylate)	50% butanone 50% isopropanol 25°C[a]	0.059
Poly(α-methylstyrene)	79.4% benzene, 20.6% methanol, 30°C[a]	0.077
Polystyrene	Cyclohexane, 34°C	0.082
Poly(vinyl acetate)	Ethyl-*n*-butyl ketone, 29°C	0.093

[a] Compositions of mixed solvents are given by volume.

In practice the interpretation of intrinsic viscosity data is greatly simplified by the fact that coils formed by flexible chain molecules closely approximate the behavior expected for the limiting case of complete impermeability, even if the chain backbone contains only a few hundred atoms. This generalization proposed by Flory (1949, 1953c) has proved extremely successful in interpreting a wide variety of experimental data. Flory's theory predicts then that the intrinsic viscosity is related to the mean square radius of gyration by

$$[\eta] = \Phi'\langle s^2 \rangle^{3/2}/M_2 \qquad (6.59)$$

where $\Phi' = (10/3)\pi N (R_\eta/\langle s^2 \rangle^{1/2})^3$ should be a universal constant independent of the nature of the macromolecule (provided only that the molecular chain is sufficiently flexible) and independent of the solvent medium.*

* It is customary in the literature to quote the quantity Φ defined by $[\eta] = \Phi \langle h^2 \rangle^{3/2}/M_2$ with $[\eta]$ in deciliters per gram, as originally used by Flory. The formulation given in eq. (6.59) has the advantage that $\langle s^2 \rangle$ is the experimentally measured quantity. If the chains are Gaussian, $\langle h^2 \rangle = 6 \langle s^2 \rangle$ and $\Phi' = 100 \times 6^{3/2} \Phi$.

Using the result of the calculations of Auer and Gardner (1955) or Zimm (1956) for the ratio $R_\eta/\langle s \rangle^{2^{1/2}}$, the constant Φ' should have the value of 4.2 $\times 10^{24}$.

Relation (6.59) leads to a number of interesting consequences. In a Θ-solvent, in which the shape of the chain is described by the random flight model, $\langle s^2 \rangle$ is proportional to M_2, so that the intrinsic viscosity should be proportional to $M_2^{1/2}$. This prediction has been amply verified and Table VI.1 is based on the listing of $[\eta]/M^{1/2}$ values compiled by Kurata and Stockmayer (1963) for a variety of polymers in Θ-media. We have seen above that $[\eta]$ would be proportional to the first power of M_2 if the coil were free draining, the experimental results constitute, therefore, a striking confirmation of Flory's assumption that flexible polymer coils may be considered impermeable. In solvent media better than Θ-solvents, the theory of Flory (1949) predicts that the linear expansion factor α_e increases for any polymer-homologous series with chain length. Thus, the exponent γ in the empirical equation (Mark and Tobolsky, 1950)

$$[\eta] = K'M_2^\gamma. \qquad (6.60)$$

should be larger than 0.5. Specifically, since Flory predicts $\alpha_e^5 - \alpha_e^3$ to be proportional to $M^{1/2}$, we obtain in the limit of $\alpha_e^5 \gg \alpha_e^3$ a proportionality of α_e and $M^{1/10}$. Since $\langle s^2 \rangle^{3/2}$ increases as $(M^{1/2}\alpha_e)^3$, this would lead to the prediction that $[\eta]$ is proportional, in very good solvent media, to $M^{0.8}$. We may note that the theory of Kurata et al. (1960) leads to somewhat different results. Here α_e may become, in powerful solvent media, proportional to $M^{1/6}$. The theory assumes, however, that the molecular coil expands only in the direction parallel to the chain end displacement, so that the chain expansion is not isotropic and the hydrodynamic properties of the coil should be represented by an equivalent ellipsoid of revolution, whose axial ratio increases with the solvent power of the medium. It seems inconsistent (although this has frequently been done) to derive α_e from intrinsic viscosity data using a relationship based on the assumption of an isotropic coil expansion and to compare this expansion factor with the predictions of the theory of Kurata et al.

Careful measurements by Krigbaum and Carpenter (1955), in which the intrinsic viscosity was compared with the radius of gyration derived from light scattering, have shown that relation (6.59) is not strictly valid. The experimentally observed deviation may be expressed in two alternative ways. In the first treatment we change the functional dependence of $[\eta]$ on α_e; Krigbaum and Carpenter found that their data were consistent with $[\eta]$ proportional to $\alpha_e^{2.2}$. Alternatively, $[\eta]$ may be treated as proportional to α_e^3 with the factor Φ' varying with the solvent power of the medium (Ptitsyn and Eizner, 1959). The deviation from Flory's relation (6.59) may be traced to the approximation involved in the assumption that all linear dimensions of a flexible coil change by the same factor when it is transferred from one solvent medium to another. As was pointed out before (cf. pages 129–130, 276), this assumption cannot be rigorously correct, since the excluded volume effect will be most pronounced in the center of the coil, where the chain segment density is largest. As a result, the ratio of the radius of the hydrodynamically equivalent sphere to the radius of gyration of the coil will tend to decrease with an increase in the excluded volume effect. Kurata et al. (1959) carried out a theoretical treatment of this effect and predicted $[\eta]$ to be proportional to $\alpha_e^{2.43}$. Ptitsyn and Eizner (1959), in a different approach to the problem, concluded that a proper consideration of the excluded volume effect requires the factor Φ' in (6.59) to be a function of γ in relation (6.60), so that Φ' should decrease from a value of 4.2×10^{24} for Θ-solvents to 2.5×10^{24} for very strong solvent media in which γ attains its limiting value of 0.8. The formulation of Ptitsyn and Eizner, in which Φ' approaches an asymptotic value, seems physically more reasonable than the result of Kurata et al. and it is also in good agreement with experimental data obtained by Schulz and Kirste (1961). Ptitsyn and Eizner's range of predicted Φ'-values may be compared with $\Phi' = 3.1 \times 10^{24}$ given by Flory (1953c) as an average value found in a variety of systems. We may conclude that although the various refinements seem well justified both theoretically and experimentally, Flory's original formulation, as given by relation (6.59), represents a very close approximation to the solution viscosity behavior of flexible chain polymers.

The interpretation of intrinsic viscosity data obtained with solutions of very short molecular chains is much more uncertain. First we should emphasize that for solutions in which the sizes of the solute and solvent molecules are comparable, theories in which the solute is treated as suspended in a structureless continuum represent a much more questionable approximation when we are concerned with intrinsic viscosity than when we deal with translational or rotational frictional coefficients. This becomes obvious when we consider a solute very similar to the solvent; in this limiting case the frictional coefficients still have a finite value related to their size and shape, but the intrinsic viscosity must necessarily vanish. For solutes somewhat different from the solvent molecules, $[\eta]$ may be positive or negative. A study of solution viscosities of short chains was reported

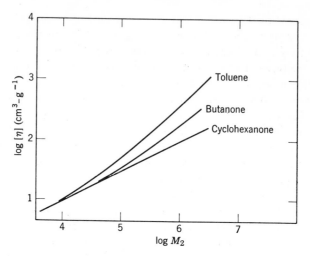

Fig. VI.14. Intrinsic viscosity–molecular weight relation for polystyrene in media of varying solvent power at 34.5°C.

by Sadron and Rempp (1958) who proposed a modification of (6.60) to an empirical relation

$$[\eta] = A + B/M_2 + K'M_2^\gamma \qquad (6.61)$$

The second consideration involves the decrease of the excluded volume effect with decreasing chain length, which is not represented correctly by the Flory treatment if the molecular chains are very short. Stockmayer and Fixman (1963) have proposed that the intrinsic viscosity of impermeable coils should be represented by

$$[\eta] = K^*M_2^{1/2} + K^{**}M_2 \qquad (6.62)$$

where K^{**} is proportional to $(1/2 - \chi)$ in eq. (2.46) so that it vanishes for Θ-solvents and increases with the solvent power of the medium. We may note that the first term on the right of (6.62) becomes dominant for low molecular weights of the solute and the intrinsic viscosity should then become quite insensitive to the nature of the solvent medium. Such an effect has been observed for polystyrene (Rossi et al., 1960; Okada et al., 1963; cf. Fig. VI.14) and for poly(methyl methacrylate) (Fox et al., 1962; Cohn-Ginsberg et al., 1962). (On the other hand, Sadron and Rempp (1958) found that the intrinsic viscosities of very short chain solutes, consisting of a single chemical species, depended very markedly on the solvent medium, as would be expected when solvent and solute molecules are of comparable size.)

Finally, we must consider the effects of permeability of the molecular coils, which must become appreciable as the chains are shortened beyond a certain point. As a consequence, plots of log $[\eta]$ against log M_2 for polymers in Θ-media should exhibit an increasing slope in the low molecular weight range. The absence of any indication of such an effect in published experimental data is difficult to account for.

The viscosity of solutions of flexible chain polymers at finite concentrations may be represented by relation (6.57) where the Huggins constant k'

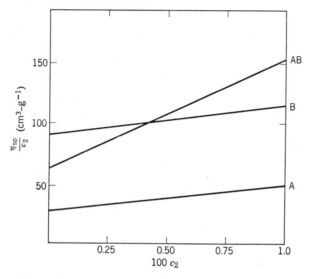

Fig. VI.15. Effect of molecular interactions on the specific viscosity of polymer solutions. Butanone solutions of a methyl methacrylate copolymer with 4.9 mole-% methacrylic acid (A), a methyl methacrylate copolymer with 5.8 mole-% dimethylaminoethyl methacrylate (B) and a mixture of equal weights of the two copolymers (AB).

is independent of the molecular weight but increases from values around 0.35 in strong solvent media to much higher values (as high as 1.4) for solutions in very poor solvents (Alfrey et al., 1950). Bawn (1951) has suggested that k' may be linear with the exponent γ in the empirical intrinsic viscosity equation (6.60). If the solution contains two distinct polymers which interact very strongly with one another, k' for the mixed polymers may be substantially higher than for the components of the mixture. A striking example of such an effect is represented in Fig. VI.15 which shows plots of $\eta_{\rm sp}/c_2$ against c_2 for copolymers of methyl methacrylate with an acidic and a basic comonomer, as well as data for a mixture of the two co-polymers (Morawetz, 1954).

In solutions of very high molecular weight flexible chain polymers, the viscosity depends appreciably on the rate of shear. The form of this dependence has been a subject of considerable controversy. Since the effect observed cannot depend on the sign of the velocity gradient q, only theories which give $[\eta]$ as a function of even powers of q can be physically meaningful and for very low velocity gradients $[\eta]$ should deviate from its limiting value by an amount proportional to q^2. Such a result has been reported by Eisenberg (1957) who studied the viscosity behavior of partially ionized poly(acrylic acid), but Claesson and Lohmander (1961), who studied solutions of a high molecular weight cellulose nitrate at velocity gradients ranging from 0.2 sec^{-1} to 1.5×10^5 sec^{-1}, found η_{sp} to decrease linearly with q at low q values. The interpretation of the deviation from Newtonian behavior exhibited by polymer solutions of finite concentration is a complicated phenomenon which includes effects due to the entanglements of the macromolecular coils. It is of particular theoretical interest that the rate of shear dependence of the contribution of the polymer to the solution viscosity does not vanish in the limit of infinite dilution. The effect of the velocity gradient on $[\eta]$ is measurable for flexible chain polymers only if the molecular weight is above 10^5, but the variation of $[\eta]$ with q becomes pronounced for samples with molecular weights of several millions and the effect tends to be magnified when the polymer is dissolved in thermodynamically better solvents. Two theories have been formulated to account for the phenomena observed. Peterlin and Čopič (1956) stress the fact that the polymer coil is not spherically symmetrical and that it is deformed more easily in the direction of the chain end displacement than in the direction at right angles to it. The rate at which the coil responds to an applied stress requires then the specification of two internal viscosities, $\eta_i^{\parallel}$ and $\eta_i^{\perp}$. According to Peterlin and Čopič, the decrease of $[\eta]$ with increasing q should be proportional to $(\eta_i^{\perp}/\eta_i^{\parallel})(\eta_i^{\parallel} - \eta_i^{\perp}) \langle s^2 \rangle q^2$ and it should, therefore, be finite for $\eta_i^{\parallel} \neq \eta_i^{\parallel}$. An alternative theory by Peterlin (1960b, 1961b) stresses the fact that a decreasing hydrodynamic interaction between chain segments, which move in the rotating coil in the same direction relative to the streaming fluid, increases the energy dissipated by fluid friction, while this energy dissipation is reduced if the distance between segments moving in the opposite direction is increased. The decrease in $[\eta]$ with an increasing velocity gradient is then interpreted as a result of the distortion of the rotating coil which has a larger effect on the mutual distance of distant chain segments, likely to move in opposite directions relative to the flow lines. This theory requires that $[\eta]$ should pass through a minimum and increase again at large shear stresses for very long chain molecules and there seems to be some experimental evidence confirming this prediction (Peterlin and Turner, 1963).

The theory of intrinsic viscosity has played a crucial part in the discovery of the helix-coil transition in synthetic polypeptides (Doty et al., 1956). When the intrinsic viscosity of poly(γ-benzyl-L-glutamate) was measured in dichloroacetic acid solution, log $[\eta]$—log M_2 plots had a slope of 0.87, close to that predicted by the Flory theory for flexible chains in strong solvent media. On the other hand, solutions of these polymers in dimethylformamide gave log $[\eta]$—log M_2 plots with a much steeper slope, (about 1.7) which could not possibly be accounted for by random coils, but was in close agreement with Simha's predictions [eq. (6.52)] for ellipsoids of constant cross section and increasing length. Later it was shown by Yang (1959) that the helical form of the polypeptide in dimethylformamide and the random coil form in dichloroacetic acid could also be clearly differentiated by studies of the rate of shear dependence of the intrinsic viscosity. This dependence is relatively small for random coils of moderate molecular weight, but is very pronounced for the helical form which behaves like a rigid rod and is, therefore, very easily oriented in a velocity gradient. Yang suggests that a comparison of the observed variation of $[\eta]$ with q and the theoretically predicted dependence may even be interpreted in terms of the distribution of lengths of the rod-like particles.

The correlation of intrinsic viscosities with molecular weight also seems to provide a good method for estimating the degree of branching in flexible chain molecules. In our earlier discussion of the statistics of branched chain molecule conformations (Chap. III, Sec. B-4) we referred to the theory of Zimm and Stockmayer by which the ratio g^* of the mean square radii of gyration of branched and unbranched chains containing the same number of chain segments could be calculated. According to (6.59) the intrinsic viscosity is then proportional to $g^{*^{3/2}}$ and since g^* decreases with increasing chain branching, we should expect $[\eta]$ to decrease, for any given molecular weight of the solute, with increasing branching of the molecular chains. Thurmond and Zimm (1952) utilized this principle to estimate the degree of branching in a series of polystyrene samples. The intrinsic viscosity measurements were carried out in a Θ-solvent so as to eliminate the excluded volume effect, which is not considered in the Zimm-Stockmayer theory. Since the method by which the branched samples were obtained would be expected to lead to an increasing degree of branching with an increasing molecular chain length, the reduction in the intrinsic viscosity due to chain branching became more pronounced with an increasing molecular weight of the polymer fraction. It should, however, be stressed again that the Zimm–Stockmayer treatment makes assumptions about the relation between the frequency and length of chain branches which depend on the kinetic characteristics of the processes by which the branched macromolecules are produced. This limitation has to be considered in interpreting intrinsic viscosity data in terms of chain branching.

3. Interpretation of Intrinsic Viscosity in Conjunction with Other Solution Properties

It was pointed out in the introduction to this chapter that a satisfactory characterization of the state of a macromolecule in solution requires the specification of several parameters. Such an evaluation will then frequently call for a combination of information obtained with the use of several experimental methods. Let us first consider the situation with rigid globular particles (Scheraga and Mandelkern, 1953). If we are content with

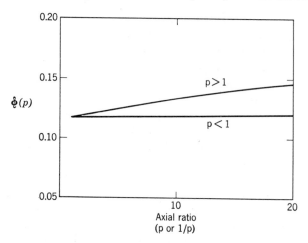

Fig. VI.16. The dependence of the function ξ (p) on the axial ratio of ellipsoids of revolution.

the description of such macromolecules as ellipsoids of revolution (and a more detailed description is beyond the reach of the study of solution properties), we shall require the specification of the molecular weight M_2, the molar volume of the hydrodynamically equivalent ellipsoids V_e and the axial ratio p. Assuming that M_2 is known from osmotic, light scattering, or ultracentrifuge equilibrium measurements, we may obtain V_e and p from the frictional coefficient and the intrinsic viscosity in the limit of low velocity gradients by using (6.3) and (6.59) rewritten in the form

$$f = 6\pi\eta_0 R_s'/x(p) = \sqrt[3]{162\pi^2 V_e/N}\eta_0/x(p)$$

$$[\eta] = (V_e/M_2) z(p) \tag{6.63}$$

Using the sedimentation constant (extrapolated to zero concentration) as a measure of the frictional coefficient, a combination of (6.63) and (6.18) leads to

$$\phi(p) \equiv s°[\eta]^{1/3}\eta_0 N^{2/3}/M_2^{2/3}(1 - \bar{v}_2\rho) = x(p)[z(p)]^{1/3}/\sqrt[3]{162\pi^2} \tag{6.64}$$

The function $\phi(p)$ is given in Fig. VI.16. In a similar manner we may combine (6.24), (6.26), and (6.51) to obtain the axial ratio from a combination of measurements of the rotational diffusion coefficient and the intrinsic viscosity by the use of

$$\xi(p) \equiv 6\eta_0 D_r [\eta] M_2/RT = y(p)z(p) \tag{6.65}$$

The function $\xi(p)$ is plotted in Fig. VI.17 and we may note that it is much more sensitive to the asymmetry of the particle than $\phi(p)$.

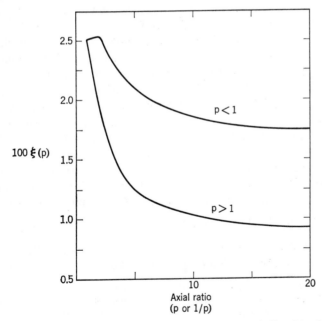

Fig. VI.17. The dependence of the function ξ on the axial ratio of ellipsoids of revolution

The hydrodynamic behavior of flexible chain molecules forming impermeable coils may be treated, as we have seen, in terms of a hydrodynamically equivalent rigid body. If Flory's theory correctly represents the chain expansion, the coil may be considered spherical, so that only two parameters have to be assigned, i.e., the molecular weight and the radius of the hydrodynamically equivalent sphere.* As Mandelkern and Flory (1952) have suggested, the sedimentation coefficient and the intrinsic viscosity for impermeable coils given by

$$s^0 = M_2(1 - \bar{v}_2\rho)/Nf = M_2(1 - \bar{v}_2\rho)/6\pi\eta_0 R_t N \qquad (6.18)$$

$$[\eta] = (10/3)\pi R_\eta^3 N/M_2 \qquad (6.58)$$

may then be combined to

$$\varepsilon = s^0 [\eta]^{1/3}\eta_0 M_2^{-2/3}/(1-\bar{v}_2\rho) = 1.7 \times 10^{-17} R_\eta/R_t \qquad (6.66)$$

where R_η/R_t is the ratio of the radii of spheres which are equivalent to the molecular coil in intrinsic viscosity and in the hydrodynamic resistance to linear translation, respectively. The data of Mandelkern and Flory (1952), Mandelkern et al. (1952) and Mandelkern and Fox (1953) may be represented in our notation by a clustering of the R_η/R_t ratio around a value of 1.15. It may be noted that Ptitsyn and Eizner (1959) predict that $R_\eta/\langle s^2 \rangle^{1/2}$ and $R_t/\langle s^2 \rangle^{1/2}$ vary in a similar manner with the solvent power of the medium, so that R_η/R_t should be almost identical in good and poor solvents. Thus, ε should be almost constant, even if Φ' in the intrinsic viscosity relation (6.59) is subject to some variation. With R_η/R_t known, relation (6.66) may be used to estimate molecular weights of flexible chain polymers from the sedimentation coefficient and the intrinsic viscosity.

More recently, Tsvetkov and Klenin (1958) have reported data on the solution behavior of flexible chain polymers to test the relation between the molecular weight, the intrinsic viscosity, and the frictional coefficient as derived from diffusion measurements in the limit of infinite dilution. These quantities should be related [cf. eqs. (6.6), (6.15), and (6.58)] by

$$\eta_0 D^\circ ([\eta]M_2)^{1/3}/T = k(5N/324\pi^2)^{1/3} R_\eta/R_t = 1.4 \times 10^{-9} R_\eta/R_t \qquad (6.67)$$

The data of Tsvetkov and Klenin lead to R_η/R_t ratios in the range of 1.1 to 1.3, in remarkably good agreement with theoretical predictions.

* If the theory of Kurata et al. (1960) describes correctly the excluded volume effect, the overall shape of the coil would become increasingly elongated with increasing solvation and the coil would have to be described by an ellipsoid with a variable axial ratio. The development which follows would then be invalid.

Chapter VII

POLYELECTROLYTES

The division which exists in classical chemistry between uncharged molecules and electrolytes composed of ions has its counterpart in the field of high polymers. By "polyelectrolytes" we refer to substances containing macromolecules carrying a large number of ionic charges—the polyions—with the small counter ions which render the system electroneutral. A typical example of such a substance, which has been a frequent subject of investigation, is the sodium salt of poly(acrylic acid):

$$
\left[\begin{array}{c} -CH_2-CH- \\ | \\ C=O \\ | \\ O^- \\ Na^+ \end{array} \right]_n .
$$

Polyelectrolytes are usually studied in aqueous solutions. The properties of such solutions are strongly affected by the addition of simple salts, such as sodium chloride. This addition increases the counterion concentration and introduces byions into the system, i.e., small ions carrying charges of the same sign as the charge of the polyion.

Some typical examples of ionizable polymers with flexible molecular chains are represented in Table VII.1 to indicate the wide variety of materials available for study. Much of the early work was carried out on poly(acrylic acid), poly(methacrylic acid), and acidic polysaccharides such as alginic acid and polygalacturonic acid (cf. Fig. III.3). In these materials the ionizable groups are weakly acidic, so that the charge density along the molecular chain can be varied at will by varying the degree of neutralization. Strongly ionizing polymers are available in poly(vinylsulfonic acid) and poly(styrenesulfonic acid). In polyphosphates we have an inorganic polyanion suitable for polyelectrolyte studies. Another interesting class of materials is available in hydrolyzed copolymers of maleic anhydride. It is known that maleic anhydride adds with difficulty to a growing chain terminating with a maleic anhydride unit, so that copolymerization leads to

TABLE VII.1

Typical Examples of Ionizable Chain Molecules

Poly(acrylic acid)	$(-CH_2-CH-)_n$ $\quad\quad\quad\vert$ $\quad\quad COOH$
Poly(methacrylic acid)	$\quad\quad CH_3$ $\quad\quad\quad\vert$ $(-CH_2-C-)_n$ $\quad\quad\quad\vert$ $\quad\quad COOH$
Poly(vinyl sulfonic acid)	$(-CH_2-CH-)_n$ $\quad\quad\quad\vert$ $\quad\quad SO_3H$
Poly(styrene sulfonic acid)	$(-CH_2-CH-)_n$ (benzene ring) SO_3H
Styrene-maleic acid copolymer	$(-CH_2-CH---CH---CH-)_n$ $\quad\quad\quad\vert\quad\quad\quad\vert\quad\quad\quad\vert$ $\quad\quad C_6H_5\quad COOH\quad COOH$
Vinyl methyl ether–maleic acid copolymer	$(-CH_2-CH---CH---CH-)_n$ $\quad\quad\quad\vert\quad\quad\quad\vert\quad\quad\quad\vert$ $\quad\quad OCH_3\quad COOH\quad COOH$
Acrylic acid–maleic acid copolymer	$(CH_2-CH---CH---CH-)_n$ $\quad\quad\quad\vert\quad\quad\quad\vert\quad\quad\quad\vert$ $\quad\quad COOH\quad COOH\quad COOH$
Poly(metaphosphoric acid)	$\quad\quad O$ $\quad\quad\Vert$ $(-O-P-)_n$ $\quad\quad\vert$ $\quad\quad OH$
Poly(vinyl amine)	$(-CH_2-CH-)_n$ $\quad\quad\quad\vert$ $\quad\quad NH_2$
Poly(ethylene imine)	$(-CH_2-CH_2-N-)_n$ $\quad\quad\quad\quad\quad\vert$ $\quad\quad\quad\quad\quad H$
Poly(4-vinylpyridine)	$(-CH_2-CH-)_n$ (pyridine ring) N
Poly(4-vinyl-N-dodecyl pyridinium)	$(-CH_2-CH-)_n$ (pyridinium ring) N^+ $\vert$ $C_{12}H_{25}$

chains in which the maleic anhydride residues are separated from one another by one or more comonomers. Hydrolysis then leads to macromolecules containing closely spaced pairs of carboxyls separated from other such pairs by at least one comonomer unit. Such materials have been called "polydibasic acids." In the case of the acrylic acid–maleic acid copolymer, triplets of backbone carbons carrying carboxyl groups are separated from each other by a methylene residue. Weakly basic polymers are available in polyvinylamine, poly(ethylene imine), and in poly(4-vinyl pyridine) which may be converted into a strong base by quaternization. If the quaternization is carried out with a long chain alkyl halide, the hydrophobic bond between the paraffinic residues will result in a stabilization of compact conformations in analogy to the formation of soap micelles. Such materials have, therefore, been described as "polysoaps." Amphoteric polyelectrolytes may be obtained by copolymerization of suitable acidic and basic monomers, for instance, methacrylic acid and vinyl pyridine. We should also bear in mind that polymers which are weak Lewis bases may acquire polyelectrolyte character in strongly acidic media, although the polymer chains would not be charged in other solvents. Thus, polyamides have been observed to behave like polyelectrolytes in formic acid solutions (Schaefgen and Trivisonno, 1952; Saunders, 1962, 1964).

In addition to polyelectrolytes with flexible chain polyions which may assume a broad range of conformations, we have to concern ourselves with charged macromolecules existing in the specific conformations discussed in the third section of Chap. III. Proteins carry a variety of ionizable groups in the side chains of the amino acids residues, i.e., the carboxyls of glutamic and aspartic acid, the imidazole of histidine, the amino groups of lysine, the phenolic groups of tyrosine, the thiols of cysteine, and the guanidino residues of arginine. They may, therefore, carry a net positive or negative charge depending on their state of ionization. The tertiary structure of globular proteins is usually sufficiently stable to allow the buildup of a considerable net charge density before denaturation sets in. Another polyelectrolyte with a specific conformation is the native form of deoxyribose nucleic acid. We have seen that it exists in solution in the form of a double helix which behaves almost like a rigid rod-like particle. In neutral solution the particle carries one negative charge for each nucleotide residue, owing to the ionization of the acid phosphate function. In acidic or alkaline media the purine and pyrimidine residues participate in ionization equilibria which affect, as we shall see, the stability of the native form of DNA.

There is no question that much of the stimulation for the study of polyelectrolytes has derived from the fact that proteins and nucleic acids, materials which are indispensable to the existence of life as we know it, fall into this category. It was first pointed out by Staudinger (1932) that some characteristic properties of solutions of proteins and nucleic acids may be a consequence of their high ionic charge. Since the complex chemistry of these natural materials would necessarily complicate the interpretation of experimental data, he proposed that appropriate studies be carried out on synthetic polyelectrolytes containing a single type of repeating unit along the molecular chain. With our present knowledge of the specific conformations of globular proteins and DNA, the validity of the analogy between these materials and synthetic polyelectrolytes is much more limited than might have once appeared, but Staudinger's suggestion was nevertheless valuable in directing attention to an interesting field of investigation.

From one point of view, the study of polyelectrolytes may be regarded as an extension of the studies on simple electrolytes. If the polyion has a well-defined shape, as in the case of globular proteins, then the main distinction is due to the high charge of the polyion and the high values which may be assumed by the electrostatic potential. With flexible chain polyions, the fixed charges may be separated from each other, to some extent, as the·chain expands when the system is diluted. Nevertheless, a limit is set to the attainable separation of the fixed charges by their attachment to the chain backbone and the rubber-like elasticity of the molecular chain. Effects produced by the interaction of ionic charges will, therefore, not vanish in the limit of infinite dilution—as they do in solutions of simple electrolytes. On the contrary, a highly dilute solution of flexible chain polyelectrolytes must be viewed as consisting of small regions in which polyions with a high density of "fixed" charges create high local electrostatic potentials, so that counterions are powerfully attracted, while the intervening spaces have very low ion concentrations (cf. Fig. VII.1). The electrochemical behavior of polyelectrolyte solutions also strongly reflects the large difference in the charge of the polyion and the charge of the small ions. As a result of this asymmetry, the concept of ionic strength, which is so useful in characterizing electrostatic interactions in simple salt solutions, may be grossly misleading when applied to systems containing polyelectrolytes. The properties of such systems are generally found to be much more sensitive to the charge of the counterions than the charge of byions.

Whenever an uncharged polymer chain is converted by titration or by chemical modification to a chain carrying a large number of ionized groups, the mutual repulsion of fixed charges may lead to chain expansions which

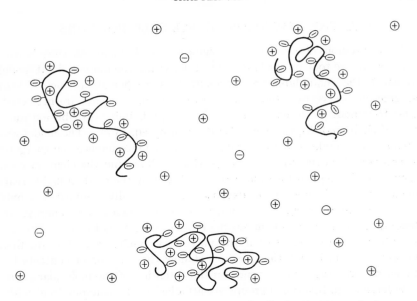

Fig. VII.1. Schematic representation of the ion distribution in dilute solutions containing a salt of a polymeric acid composed of flexible chain molecules and a small concentration of added uni-univalent electrolyte.

are far beyond the range attainable by the transfer of uncharged polymers from poor to good solvent media. But the ionic charges attached to the polymer chain do not affect only the conformation of the macromolecule. They also create a high local charge density which must affect strongly the properties of simple ions present in the solution. Thus, the study of flexible chain polyelectrolytes is concerned with two kinds of phenomena. On the one hand, we wish to know to what extent a polymer chain will be expanded as a result of the mutual repulsion of fixed charges and how this expansion will affect the properties of a polyelectrolyte solution. On the other hand, we are concerned with the electrochemistry of the polyelectrolyte solution, the effect of the polyion on ionic activity coefficients, ion-pair formation, electrophoretic phenomena, etc. It is clear that the two problems cannot be strictly separated. The interaction of the polyion with simple ions will lead to a distribution of the ions which modifies the repulsion of the fixed charges and the polyion expansion. Conversely, not only the charge but also the shape of the polyion will determine its interaction with the small ions. It is this interdependence which is responsible for the complexities and the fascination of this field.

A. THE EXPANSION OF FLEXIBLE POLYIONS

In our previous discussions of the shape of flexible chain molecules (Chap. III, Sec. B) we took as our first point of departure the random flight model in which the chain links are represented as mathematical lines of zero volume and energetic interactions between chain segments are neglected. This treatment led to an expression for the probability distribution function of chain end displacements $\mathcal{W}(h)$ given by eq. (3.7). The model was then refined to take into account both the spatial interference and energetic interactions between chain segments which will expand the chain in good solvent media beyond the dimensions predicted by the random flight treatment. In the theories of this expansion it is generally assumed that only nearest-neighbor interactions contribute to the excess free energy, attending the mixing of chain segments and solvent molecules. This assumption is amply justified if the polymer is uncharged. We are then merely concerned with the question of how the number of contacts between polymer segments depends on the extension of the molecular chain.

When ionized functional groups are attached to the macromolecules, the forces between the charges are very much larger than the dispersion forces or the dipole–dipole interactions between uncharged groups. Moreover, these forces now act over relatively long distances. In formulating a theory of the expansion of such charged chains, it is convenient to think of a polyion with its counterions as if it were being introduced into the system in three consecutive steps:

(a) The polyion and the neutralizing counterions are first added in the discharged state.

(b) Charges are introduced under hypothetical conditions which do not allow them to interact with one another. The free energy of this process depends then on the size of the ions or the fixed ionized groups and the dielectric constant of the medium, but is independent of the expansion of the polyion.

(c) The charges are now allowed to interact with one another while the chain end displacement h of the polyion is held constant. The counterions are allowed to attain their equilibrium distribution in the field of the polyion. The free energy characterizing this step is referred to as the excess electrostatic free energy $G_{elec}^{E}(h)$.

If a polyelectrolyte is added to a solution which contains simple salt, then it is customarily assumed that the change in the excess electrostatic free energy of the salt may be neglected. We shall see later that this assumption appears to be well justified by experimental evidence at very low salt concentration although, with higher concentrations of simple electrolyte, significant deviations from this behavior may be encountered.

We may now obtain the probability distribution of end-to-end displacements of the charged chains by multiplying the *a priori* probability $\mathcal{W}_0(h)$ with the Boltzmann exponential involving the excess electrostatic free energy:

$$\mathcal{W}(h)dh = \mathcal{W}_0(h) \exp[-G_{elec}^E(h)/kT]dh \tag{7.1}$$

The problem to be solved consists then in finding the proper form for $G_{elec}^E(h)$ and its dependence on variables of interest, such as the chain length of the polyion, the density of ionized groups along the chain, the concentration of simple electrolyte, etc. The new distribution of h may be characterized by its most probable value h^* which corresponds to $d\mathcal{W}(h)/dh = 0$

$$[d \ln \mathcal{W}_0(h)/dh]_{h = h*} - (1/kT)[dG_{elec}^E(h)/dh]_{h = h*} = 0 \tag{7.2}$$

Alternatively, the mean-square chain end displacement $\langle h^2 \rangle$ of the charged chain may be evaluated from

$$\langle h^2 \rangle = \int h^2 \mathcal{W}(h)dh \Big/ \int \mathcal{W}(h)dh \tag{7.3}$$

For the random flight chain, for which $\mathcal{W}_0(h)$ is given by eq. (3.7), we have $(h^*)^2 = (2/3)\langle h^2 \rangle$, but as the chain is being extended, the distribution function of h tends to become sharper and $(h^*)^2/\langle h^2 \rangle$ tends toward unity. However, in the theoretical treatments which follow, we shall assume that the chain is sufficiently far from its full extension so that the ratio $(h^*)^2/\langle h^2 \rangle$ maintains the value characteristic of Gaussian chains.

1. Theories in Which the Chain Character of the Polyion Is Taken Fully into Account

The first attempt to treat the problem of the expansion of a charged polymer chain was that by Kuhn et al. (1948). (Cf. also Katchalsky et al., 1950.) They treated the case of a solution so dilute that the counterions could be assumed to have escaped from the field of the polyion and did not influence the mutual repulsion of the fixed charges. In a first simplified model one half of the polyion charge Q is placed at each end of the chain, so that in a medium with a dielectric constant $\mathcal{D}$ the electrostatic free energy becomes $G_{elec}^E(h) = Q^2/4\mathcal{D}h$. Using eq. (3.7) for the *a priori* probability distribution of h in a statistically equivalent random chain, we obtain on substitution into (7.2)

$$-3h^*/Zb_s^2 + 2/h^* + Q^2/4\mathfrak{D}kT(h^*)^2 = 0$$

$$\therefore \alpha_e^2 - 1 = Q^2/8\mathfrak{D}kTh^* \qquad (7.4)$$

where $\alpha_e^2 = 3(h^*)^2/2Z_sb_s^2$ is the square of the linear expansion coefficient. If the charge density along the polymeric chain is held constant, Q^2/h^* will increase with chain length and (7.4) then gives us the qualitative indication that the factor by which the chain is expanded because of the mutual repulsion of the fixed charges will tend to increase with an increasing length of the chain.

In the second approximation, Kuhn et al. use a model in which the charge of the polyion is divided into $Z_s + 1$ equal parts q, which are placed at the chain ends and the junction points of the statistical chain elements. The effective dielectric constant governing the interactions of the fixed charges is assumed to be represented adequately by the macroscopic dielectric constant of water $\mathfrak{D}_w$. The electrostatic free energy is then given by summing contributions from all pairs of charges and averaging the result over all properly weighted chain conformations consistent with a chain end displacement h

$$G_{elec}^E(h) = \left(\sum_i \sum_{j<i} \frac{q_iq_j}{\mathfrak{D}_w r_{ij}}\right)_h \qquad (7.5)$$

where r_{ij} is the distance between the ith and the jth charge. For long chains $Z_s + 1 \approx Z_s$ and $Z_sq = Q$. Since the summation in (7.5) contains $Z_s^2/2$ items and $q_iq_j\mathfrak{D}_w$ is constant,

$$G_{elec}^E(h) = \frac{Q^2}{2\mathfrak{D}_w}\left\langle\frac{1}{r_{ij}}\right\rangle_h \qquad (7.6)$$

where $\langle 1/r_{ij}\rangle_h$ is the mean value of the reciprocal distance of two charges selected at random from all chain conformations with the end-to-end distance h held constant.

As we shall see later, when we consider in more detail the manner in which counterions distribute themselves around polyions in polyelectrolyte solutions, the model underlying the theory of Kuhn et al. is rather unrealistic, since a significant fraction of counterions will always remain in the polyion domain, even under conditions of extreme dilution. The charges of the counterions will shield the ionic charges carried by the macromolecular chain ("the fixed charges") and the expansion of the chain backbone, resulting from the mutual repulsion of the fixed charges, will be correspondingly reduced. To allow for this effect, Katchalsky and Lifson (1956) assumed that each fixed charge will build up in its vicinity an ion atmosphere similar to one which would exist in a simple salt solution with an ionic strength corresponding to the concentrations of the mobile ions in the polyelectrolyte solution. The potential at a distance r from a fixed charge is assumed to be given by the Debye-Hückel limiting law as $q \exp(-\kappa r)/\mathfrak{D}r$ with κ, the reciprocal of the equivalent thickness of the ion atmosphere given by

$$\kappa = \sqrt{4\pi e^2 N \sum m_i \nu_i^2 / 1000 \mathfrak{D}kT} \tag{7.7}$$

where e is the electronic charge and m_i are the molarities of ions with a valency ν_i. Using these screened potentials, (7.6) is modified to

$$G_{\text{elec}}^E(h) = \frac{Q^2}{2\mathfrak{D}_w} \left\langle \frac{\exp(-\kappa r_{ij})}{r_{ij}} \right\rangle_h \tag{7.8}$$

Katchalsky and Lifson evaluated the average value of $\exp(-\kappa r_{ij})/r)_{ij}$ for all pairs of interacting charges and all shapes of the equivalent chain consistent with the chain end separation h and they obtained for the excess free energy of ionization

$$G_{\text{elec}}^E(h) = \frac{Q^2}{\mathfrak{D}_w h} \ln\left[1 + \frac{6h}{\kappa \langle h_0{}^2 \rangle}\right] \tag{7.9}$$

Their theory assumes that the dimensions of the macromolecular chain are large compared to the thickness of the ion atmosphere ($h\kappa \gg 1$). This is in practice an unimportant restriction, requiring a concentration of uni-univalent electrolyte of $0.002M$ and $0.001M$ if the chain end separation of the polyion is 100 and 400 Å, respectively. The expansion of the polyion predicted by this theory is then given by

$$\alpha_e^2 - 1 = \frac{Q^2}{2\mathfrak{D}_w kTh^*}\left[\ln\left(1 + \frac{6h^*}{\kappa\langle h_0^2 \rangle}\right) - \frac{6h^*/\kappa\langle h_0^2 \rangle}{1 + 6h^*/\kappa\langle h_0^2 \rangle}\right] \tag{7.10}$$

If we use, as an example, a polyacrylate with a polymerization degree of 1200, assume that three monomer units form a statistical chain element, and compute the chain extension in a solution containing $0.01M$ uni-univalent salt on the basis of relation (7.10), then we find that h^* increases fivefold with only 5% of the carboxyl groups ionized. We shall see later that the exact magnitude of the polyion expansion is difficult to estimate from experimental data by the techniques applicable to uncharged chain molecules (i.e., light scattering or solution viscosity). Nevertheless, there is no doubt that the Katchalsky–Lifson result greatly exaggerates the effect. The main source of the discrepancy seems to be due to the manner in which Katchalsky and Lifson took account of the different shapes which a chain can assume for any given chain end separation. They used the distribution function applicable to uncharged chains, while in actual fact shapes which are more compact (and correspond, therefore, to a higher electrostatic energy) will occur much less frequently in polyions than in analogous uncharged chains. As a result, the Katchalsky–Lifson treatment tends to overestimate $G_{\text{elec}}^E(h)$ and this error should be largest for the smallest values of h, so that the calculated driving force toward chain expansion is too high.

The elimination of this error from the Katchalsky–Lifson theory would meet with formidable mathematical difficulties and this led Harris and Rice (1954) and Rice and Harris (1954) to the use of a different model for the estimation of polyion expansions. They consider an equivalent chain with the ionic charges carried by the monomer units concentrated at the midpoints of each statistical chain element. The extension of the chain depends then on the probability distribution of the angles γ subtended by two adjoining chain elements. Treating the angle γ in the same manner as a bond angle in Kuhn's theory (cf. Chap. III, Sec. B-3), we obtain for the dependence of h on the angle γ

$$\langle h^2 \rangle / \langle h_0^2 \rangle = \frac{1 - \langle \cos \gamma \rangle}{1 + \langle \cos \gamma \rangle} \tag{7.11}$$

As a first approximation, $\langle \cos \gamma \rangle$ is calculated considering only $G_{j,\,j+1}^E$, the potential energy resulting from the repulsion of two charges q carried by neighboring elements of the statistical chain. For any assumed dependence of $G_{j,\,j+1}^E$ on charge separation, $\langle \cos \gamma \rangle$ may be rigorously obtained from

$$\langle \cos \gamma \rangle = \frac{\displaystyle\int \cos \gamma \, \exp[-G_{j,\,j+1}^E(\gamma)/kT]d\Omega}{\displaystyle\int \exp[-G_{j,\,j+1}^E(\gamma)/kT]d\Omega} \tag{7.12}$$

where $d\Omega = 2\pi \sin \gamma d\gamma$ is the element of solid angle. For a statistical element of length b_s, the separation of two neighboring charges is $b_s \sin (\gamma/2)$ and if the screened Coulomb potential is given by the Debye–Hückel limiting law, then

$$G_{j,\,j+1}^E(\gamma) = q^2 \exp \, [-\kappa b_s \sin(\gamma/2)/\mathfrak{D}_e b_s \sin(\gamma/2)] \tag{7.13}$$

We may note that Rice and Harris do not use here the dielectric constant of water ($\mathfrak{D}_w \approx 80$) but an "effective dielectric constant" $\mathfrak{D}_e$ which takes account of the fact that the charges carried by the polyion are in a region containing a high concentration of nonpolar organic material and that the high local concentration of ionic charges tends to disrupt the water structure (cf. Chap. II, Sec. A-6). Rice and Harris also take into consideration the formation of ion pairs by some of the counterions with the fixed charges of the polyion, so that the charge of the polymeric chain may be substantially reduced at high charge densities. In this way calculated results may be obtained which seem to correspond closely to the physical behavior of polyelectrolytes, such as partially neutralized poly(acrylic acid), but it should be remembered that $\mathfrak{D}_e$ (for which Harris and Rice use a value of 5.5) serves to some extent as an adjustable parameter.

2. Models Using Spherically Symmetrical Continuous Charge Distributions

At the same time that polyelectrolyte theories were being formulated in which the chainlike character of the polyion was taken explicitly into account, the problem of polyion expansion was also investigated by means of models in which the polyion was represented by a spherically symmetrical charge cloud. If the polymer coil is immersed in a large volume of a uni-univalent salt of molarity m_s, then the local concentration of the mobile ions will be related to the local electrostatic potential ψ by the Boltzmann distribution law and the local net charge density ϱ becomes

$$\varrho = (\mathfrak{F}/1000) \, [m_{fl} + m_s e^{-e\psi/kT} - m_s e^{e\psi/kT}] \qquad (7.14)$$

where $\mathfrak{F}$ is the Faraday constant and m_{fl} the molarity corresponding to the local concentration of the fixed charges on the polyion. A second relation between ϱ and ψ is provided by the well known Poisson equation

$$\nabla^2 \psi = -4\pi\varrho/\mathfrak{D} \qquad (7.15)$$

and a combination of (7.14) with (7.15) yields

$$\nabla^2 \psi = -(4\pi\mathfrak{F}/1000\mathfrak{D})[-m_{fl} + 2m_s \sinh(e\psi/kT)] \qquad (7.16)$$

The Poisson–Boltzmann equation was first applied to flexible chain polyelectrolytes by Hermans and Overbeek (1948), who considered the case when $e\psi/kT \ll 1$, so that $\sinh (e\psi/kT) \approx e\psi/kT$. This corresponds to situations in which either the charge density on the polyion is relatively low or the salt concentration relatively high. Calculations were carried out on the basis of a uniform charge distribution within a sphere with radius R_e, which is hydrodynamically equivalent to the polyion coil, but results were found to be rather insensitive to the details of the charge distribution. The result obtained by Hermans and Overbeek has a complicated form, but it can be shown (Morawetz, 1961) to be greatly simplified if it is assumed that the ratio R_e/h is independent of the degree to which the polyion is expanded. For the usual case, where the coil dimensions are very large compared to the thickness of the ion atmosphere, the expression for the linear expansion coefficient α_e assumes the simple form

$$\alpha_e^2 - 1 = (3\nu_p/4)f$$

$$f = m_{fl}/2m_s \tag{7.17}$$

where ν_p is the number of charges carried by the polyion. We may note that for any given chain length of the polyion f is proportional to ν_p/α_e^3, so that (7.17) predicts $\alpha_e^5 - \alpha_e^3$ to be proportional to ν_p^2. In this respect eq. (7.17) bears a striking analogy to Flory's result for uncharged chain molecules, for which eq. (3.30) gives $\alpha_e^5 - \alpha_e^3$ proportional to $V_2^2 \, (1/2 - \chi)$.

The restriction of the Hermans–Overbeek theory to cases in which the electrostatic potential remains relatively small precludes its application to systems which are of greatest interest. It was pointed out by Kimball et al. (1952) that it should be more realistic to assume that the domain occupied by the polyion contains a sufficient excess of counterions over byions to render the net charge of the domain negligible. This assumption is the microscopic analog of the Donnan treatment of the equilibrium distribution of ions across a semipermeable membrane restricting the movement of polyions in macroscopic systems. Extending this concept so as to make it apply to every point within the domain of the polyion, we obtain from (7.14)

$$\sinh (e\psi/kT) = m_{fl}/2m_s = f \tag{7.18}$$

which may be solved to give the distribution of the electrostatic potential and the electrostatic energy of the coil, provided we know the distribution of the fixed charges. If we assume a uniform fixed charge density within an equivalent sphere, then (7.18) leads to a chain expansion (Morawetz, 1961) given by[*]

$$\alpha_e^2 - 1 = (3/2)(\nu_p/f)(\sqrt{(1 + f^2}} - 1) \qquad \text{(for } \varrho = 0) \tag{7.19}$$

[*] Kimball et al. who first used eq. (7.18) to evaluate the expansion of polyions concluded that the increase of linear dimensions due to electrostatic forces does not exceed $\sqrt{2}$. This result is based on an error which was clarified by Flory (1953f) and Lifson (1957a).

It may be verified that (7.19) reduces to (7.17) in the limit of $f \ll 1$. However, in cases of most interest, the local fixed charge concentration will be larger, often much larger, than the concentration of the mobile ions. Under such conditions the theory assuming low values of ϱ will lead to significantly smaller chain expansions than the theory which assumes $e\psi/kT \ll 1$. We shall see later, when we discuss in detail the distribution of the mobile ions, that the Donnan assumption of local electroneutrality is a very good approximation to the conditions existing in polyelectrolyte solutions.

Flory (1953f) has pointed out that, whenever the Donnan assumption is applicable, the swelling of the polyion may be predicted without introducing the concept of electrostatic potential. This is physically obvious if we consider the swelling of a macroscopic gel for which the Donnan condition must apply much more precisely. The driving force of the swelling process may then be assigned with equal justification to osmotic forces (due to an excess of mobile ions in the interior of the gel) or to electrostatic repulsion of ionic charges attached to the gel structure.* Flory's theory of polyion expansion also takes account of the excess free energy resulting from the mixing of solvent and polymer segments. This treatment leads to the expression

$$\alpha_e^2 = (\alpha_e^0)^2 + 1000\nu_p \left\{ \frac{\nu_p}{1.16 N \langle h_0^2 \rangle^{3/2} \sum_i m_i \nu_i^2} + \right.$$

$$\left. (\nu_b - \nu_c) \left(\frac{\nu_p}{0.81 N \langle h_0^2 \rangle^{3/2} \sum_i m_i \nu_i^2} \right)^2 + \ldots \right\} \quad (7.20)$$

where α_e^0 is the expansion factor which would be observed with a solvated but uncharged chain, m_i and ν_i are molarities and valences of all mobile ions, while ν_b and ν_c are the valences of byions and counterions, respectively. The form of (7.20) leads to the conclusion that chains which have already been expanded beyond the unperturbed dimensions by the solvating action of the medium will be less easily expanded further by the mutual repulsion of the fixed ionic charges.

In all theories discussed so far, in which a Donnan equilibrium was assumed to govern the distribution of mobile ions between regions occupied by the polyions and the surrounding space, no account was taken of differences in the ionic activity coefficients in these two portions of the system.

---

* Note that eq. (7.17) and eq. (7.19) give the chain expansion factor in terms of the *number* of the fixed charges carried by the polyion, but do not involve the *magnitude* of the unit ionic charge.

Nagasawa (1961) pointed out that the ionic activity coefficients within the polyion domain must, in fact, be sharply reduced by the large electrostatic forces operative in this region and this will lead to a reduction of the Donnan potential. As a consequence, the driving force toward polyion expansion will be correspondingly reduced.

3. Critique of Theories of Polyion Expansion

It should be realized that all theories of polyion expansion are based on idealized models and necessarily omit many of the features of the real systems which they are designed to represent. With the exception of Flory's treatment, they neglect completely all effects which are not electrostatic in nature. Such effects may contribute to chain expansion (as Flory has pointed out) but they may also render chain expansion more difficult. This will happen, for instance, if the polyion carries hydrophobic residues which effectively attract one another in the aqueous medium. As an example of such an effect, we may cite alternating 1:1 copolymers of maleic acid with styrene and with methyl vinyl ether, respectively (see Table 7.1). The solution behavior of salts of these polymeric acids shows clearly that chain expansion is much more difficult in the case of the polyions carrying the nonpolar phenyl residues (Ferry et al., 1951). An extreme case is represented by the "polysoaps" (Strauss and Gershfeld, 1954; Strauss et al., 1956) in which the polyions carry long aliphatic hydrocarbon sidechains which tend to remain in contact with one another in spite of the repulsive forces between the fixed charges, in analogy to the formation of micelles from long chain paraffinic anions or cations.

For polyions with a high density of fixed charges along the macromolecular chain the use of the Debye–Hückel form for the screened Coulomb potential is questionable, since the thickness of the ion atmosphere will be frequently larger than the distance between neighboring charges attached to the polyion. The use of the Debye–Hückel parameter κ carries the implication that the behavior of the polyion depends on the ionic strength of the medium—yet it is well known that in solutions containing uni–divalent salts, polyions are much more expanded if the byion, rather than the counterion, is the bivalent species (Flory and Osterheld, 1954).

Let us consider eq. (7.17) as typical of those resulting from models in which the polyion charge is smeared out to a spherically symmetrical charge density. We may express the fixed charge density within the swollen polyion as m_{fl}^0 / α_e^3 where m_{fl}^0 refers to the fixed charge density within the unperturbed coil. If we now consider a series of polyions of different length but with the same spacing of fixed charges along the chain, m_{fl}^0 will

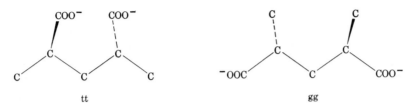

Fig. VII.2. Spacing of nearest-neighbor carboxylates in syndiotactic poly(acrylic acid) with the chain backbone in the *trans-trans* and the *gauche-gauche* conformation.

be inversely proportional to the square root of the chainlength. We find then that (7.17) predicts $\alpha_e^5 - \alpha_e^3$ to be proportional to the square root of the length of the polyion. This is exactly the same functional relationship as that obtained by Flory for the expansion of uncharged chains due to the excluded volume effect [cf. eq. (3.30)]. Yet, the phenomenon of polyion expansion is clearly of a different nature. The charging of a polymer chain leads not only to long-range repulsion analogous to the excluded volume effect, but must necessarily also affect the short-range rigidity of the chain.* This effect is difficult to evaluate and is certainly highly sensitive to the detailed structure of the chain and to its stereoisomerism. Lifson (1958) has pointed out that in syndiotactic poly(acrylic acid) a sequence of two *gauche* conformations in the chain backbone places the carboxylate charges at a longer distance from each other than a sequence of two *trans* conformations. This can be seen from the schematic representation in Fig. VII.2 and it follows then that the repulsion of nearest neighbor charges may actually oppose the attainment of the fully expanded chain conformation. In the case of the isotactic species the situation is more complex but it may be predicted qualitatively that poly(acrylic acid) will expand less on ionization if the chain is syndiotactic rather than isotactic.

One of the most serious limitations of all theories based on models with continuous distributions of charge densities is their failure to account for the formation of ion pairs between fixed charges on the polyion and counterions. Such ion pair formation can only be understood when one considers the close spacing of charges along the macromolecular chain. The difficulty is partially taken care of by the use of calculated activity coefficients for ions within the polyion domain (Nagasawa, 1961) and this procedure

---

* Katchalsky and Lifson (1956) realized the existence of such an effect and took account of it formally by assuming that the length of the statistical chain element is a linear function of the density of charges along the polyion chain. Unfortunately, this procedure introduces an arbitrary adjustable parameter which is not amenable to an independent evaluation.

seems to improve considerably the agreement of theory with experimental data.   However, serious difficulties are not confined to theories treating the polyion as a charge cloud, since the models which explicitly take account of the chain character of the polyion are also unrealistic in some important respects.   For instance, Harris and Rice (1954) use a very low value for the effective dielectric constant $\mathfrak{D}_e$ governing the distribution of the screened Coulomb potential and justify this procedure by the close spacing of the fixed charges.   It is clear, however, that the value of $\mathfrak{D}_e$ should then depend on the density of charged functional groups on the polyion chain and no attempt has been made to take account of such a variation.   We may also note that eq. (7.11) predicts the same expansion factor for chains of different length, as long as the densities of ionized groups along the chain is kept constant.   Thus, the theory of Rice and Harris predicts only the effect of the charges on the chain flexibility, neglecting effects due to long-range interactions.   While it is quite possible that the short-range effects are dominant, it is clear that they cannot be treated adequately without an explicit consideration of the various conformations available to a given molecular chain.

In summary, it seems fair to state that the physical situation in polyelectrolyte solutions is much more complex than the idealized models which must necessarily be used in theoretical treatments, so that any close agreement between experimental and theoretical results should be considered to some extent accidental.

4. Experimental Evidence for Polyion Expansion

The theoretically predicted chain expansion of polyions may be compared, in principle, with estimates calculated from the angular dependence of light scattering or from the frictional properties of polyelectrolyte solutions, particularly their viscosity.   In either case, the interpretation of the experimental data involves considerable uncertainty unless simple salts are added to shield the charges of the polyions.

We have seen (pp. 249–258) that the dissymmetry of light scattered from dilute polymer solutions arises from the interference of the beams scattered by different portions of the molecule.   Therefore, it becomes negligible if the molecular dimensions are small compared to the wavelength of the light used.   However, when solutions of polyelectrolytes which contain no added simple salts are investigated, the very large mutual repulsion of the macroions tends to produce an ordered distribution of these highly charged species even at relatively high dilution.   This effect was observed by Doty and Steiner (1952) on solutions of serum albumin hydrochloride, which exhibited a strong dissymmetry of light scattering, although the dimensions of this globular protein are only of the order of 40 Å.   In this case the phenomenon reflects the interference of light scattered by different macromolecules and conclusions about the extension of the individual particle could be obtained only at dilutions which are too high for significant measurements.   The situation is much more favorable when the polyelectrolyte solution contains simple salts.   Orofino and Flory (1959) have

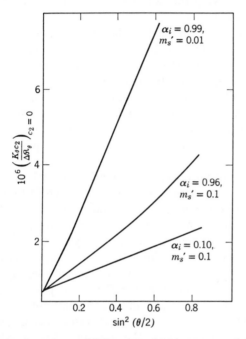

Fig. VII.3. Angular dependence of light scattering in aqueous poly(acrylic acid) solution at varying degrees of neutralization (α_i) and varying concentration of added sodium chloride (m_s').

shown that Zimm's double extrapolation procedure (see pages 253–255) can then be used to estimate the radius of gyration of the polyion.   Their data, plotted in Fig. VII.3, show clearly how the chain expansion of poly-(acrylic acid) increases with an increasing charge of the polyion and a decreasing concentration of the added salt.   It should be stressed, however, that for high m_{fl}/m_s ratios the deviations from ideal solution behavior become very large and that an extrapolation of the light scattering data to zero solution concentration may then become very difficult and uncertain.

We have seen in Chap. VI that the intrinsic viscosity is a most convenient experimental tool for the characterization of the dimensions of flexible polymer chains. However, here again the high charge of the polyion introduces some complicating factors. It can be shown that even in the case of a suspension of rigid spheres the intrinsic viscosity predicted by Einstein's theory should be modified if the spheres carry an electrostatic charge. This is the result of a lag of the counterion atmosphere behind a charged particle moving through a fluid so that electrical work has to be added to the work dissipated by fluid, friction if a steady-state motion of the particle is to be maintained. The magnitude of this "electroviscous effect" has been calculated only for rigid spheres, first by Krasny-Ergen (1936) and later by Booth (1950) who predicted a considerably smaller dependence of the viscosity on the particle charge. It is uncertain to what extent the dependence of the intrinsic viscosity on the ionic charge of globular proteins depends on this relaxation effect, but it may be safely assumed that in the case of flexible chain polyions the relaxation effect is negligible compared to effects produced by the expansion of the macromolecular chain.

If the viscosity of polyelectrolyte solutions containing no added salt is to be investigated, the data cannot be interpreted in terms of polyion expansion, since consequences of the mutual interaction of the polyions cannot be properly taken into account. With uncharged chain molecules, effects of particle interaction are eliminated by an extrapolation of η_{sp}/c_2 to zero solute concentration, but this extrapolation is possible only because the shape of the individual polymer coil depends only slightly on solution concentration. The situation is very different in polyelectrolyte solutions: here an increasing dilution provides increasing volume for the counterions, which will then tend to distribute themselves at larger distances from the polyion. As a consequence, the shielding of the fixed charges will be reduced, their mutual repulsion will increase, and the polyion will tend to expand. It is then not surprising to find that reduced viscosities* of polyelectrolytes will typically increase sharply on dilution. Plots of η_{sp}/c_2 against c_2 are frequently strongly curved, making an extrapolation impossible. A suggestion for the treatment of such data was provided by Fuoss (1948) who suggested a relation of the type

$$\frac{\eta_{sp}}{c_2} = \frac{A}{1 + B\sqrt{c_2}} \tag{7.21}$$

which predicts $(\eta_{sp}/c_2)^{-1}$ to be linear in $\sqrt{c_2}$. While this relation seems to be satisfactory in many cases, it has been shown to be inadequate if the

* The term "reduced viscosity" refers to η_{sp}/c_2.

polyion is very long (Alexander and Hitch, 1951). A complication arises also from the extremely large dependence of the viscosity of polyelectrolyte solutions on the rate of shear (Eisenberg, 1957) as would be expected in a system containing the highly asymmetric polyions. A very careful study carried out by Eisenberg and Pouyet (1954) at very low rates of shear led to results shown on Fig. VII.4. We see that in salt-free solution a plot of

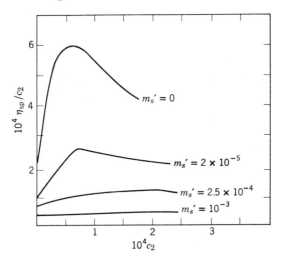

Fig. VII.4. Reduced viscosity plots of poly(N-butyl-4-vinylpyridinium) bromide with various concentrations of added sodium chloride (m_s').

the reduced viscosity against the concentration of the polyelectrolyte passes through a maximum. This effect may be readily understood, since the expansion of the polyion eventually reaches an upper limit and the effects observed on further dilution merely reflect the decreasing interference between the expanded polyions. As salt is added to the system, the value of the intercept decreases, indicating the contraction of the polyions. At the same time, there is a marked decrease in the initial positive slope of the reduced viscosity plot, reflecting a decreasing interaction between the charged macromolecules.

In principle, it should be possible to dilute a salt-free polyelectrolyte solution with a salt solution of a concentration such as to keep the ionic atmosphere surrounding the polyions unchanged during the dilution process. Akkerman et al. (1952) suggested that this result should be achieved if the diluent contains uni-univalent electrolyte with a normality half as great as that of the salt-free polyelectrolyte, so that the concentration of the sum of mobile ions remains unchanged. This procedure has been called "isoionic dilution" and it yields linear plots of reduced viscosity against polyelectrolyte concentration quite similar to plots obtained with uncharged polymers. Using this technique, Flory and Osterheld (1954) obtained intrinsic viscosities of poly(sodium acrylate) at various degrees of ionization α_i and various concentrations of NaCl as shown in Table VII.2. Interpreting the data by assuming that the polyions may

TABLE VII.2

Intrinsic Viscosities (cm³-g⁻¹)of Poly(acrylic acid) at Varying Degrees of Ionization (α_i) and Concentration of Added NaCl (m_s)

(Mol. wt. of poly(acrylic acid) 768,000; temp. 30°C; $[\eta]_\theta = 71$)

| m_s | $[\eta]$ | | |
	$\alpha_i = 0.10$	$\alpha_i = 0.33$	$\alpha_i = 1.00$
0.005	1270		
0.010	920	2130	
0.020	560	1480	2150
0.040			1540
0.060			1170
0.100		630	880
0.200		430	
0.250			550

be treated as impermeable coils in the same manner as uncharged chain molecules, they obtained expansion factors α_e which conformed to the expected linear relation between $\alpha_e^2 - 1$ and $\nu_2 f$ [cf. eq. (7.17) and (7.20)] but the change in the expansion of the polyion with changing salt concentration was much less than predicted, particularly at high degrees of ionization. It is possible that this discrepancy is due both to errors in the estimate of polyion expansion and errors in the interpretation of the viscosity data. For highly charged polyions at low salt concentrations the macromolecular coil is much more asymmetric than the coil formed by an uncharged chain; moreover, it can no longer be considered to be hydrodynamically impermeable. Under such conditions the application of the Flory–Fox theory to the interpretation of intrinsic viscosities in terms of chain expansion (cf. eq. (6.59)] is no longer justified.

B. THE DISTRIBUTION OF COUNTERIONS

1. Long-Range Electrostatic Interactions

We have seen in the previous section that the complexities associated with the behavior of flexible chain polyelectrolytes are largely caused by the interdependence of polyion expansion and the distribution of the mobile ions in the vicinity of the charged chain.   The treatment of a model which incorporates all the characteristics of such a system is extremely difficult and a number of investigators, therefore, have attempted a *partial* solution where they tried to define the distribution of mobile ions consistent with some assumed distribution of fixed charges.   While this approach has obvious inherent limitations, it provides valuable qualitative insight into some important features of polyelectrolyte solutions.

The first study of this type was made simultaneously by Alfrey et al. (1951) and by Fuoss et al. (1951) on a model in which the polyion was treated as a rigid rod of infinite length and with a uniform surface charge in a system containing only polyions and their univalent counterions but no simple salt.   The counterions were contained in a cylindrical space surrounding the reference polyion; at the boundary of this space the electrostatic forces of the surrounding polyelectrolyte were assumed to balance forces due to particles in the space reserved for the reference polyion and its counterions.   The distribution of the electrostatic potential ψ is then given by the Poisson–Boltzmann equation which has for the cylindrically symmetrical case the form

$$\frac{1}{r}\frac{d}{dr}\left(r\frac{d\psi}{dr}\right) = \frac{4\pi N m_f e}{1000\ \mathfrak{D}}\exp\,(e\psi/kT) \tag{7.22}$$

where m_f is the molarity of the fixed charges averaged over the entire volume of the system.   While the Poisson–Boltzmann equation can be solved, for the spherically symmetrical case, only with the Debye–Hückel assumption that $e\psi/kT \ll 1$, for the cylindrically symmetrical charge distribution represented by eq. (7.22) an analytical solution may be obtained for the general case.   Defining the potential so that $\psi = 0$ in regions where the local counterion concentration equals its volume average value, the solution is

$$\psi(r) = \frac{kT}{e}\ln\left\{\frac{1000\delta^2\mathfrak{D}kT}{2\pi N m_f e^2}r^2\cos^2[\delta(\ln r + \beta)]\right\} \tag{7.23}$$

where the integration constants δ and β depend on the thickness of the polyion and its charge density as well as on the concentration of the system. It should be noted that the Poisson–Boltzmann equation for cylindrical symmetry cannot be solved if the system contains added salts, i.e., if the mobile ions contain both counterions and byions.

The distributions of electrostatic potential and of the counterions, obtained from this result, are illustrated in Figs. VII.5 and VII.6 for rod-like

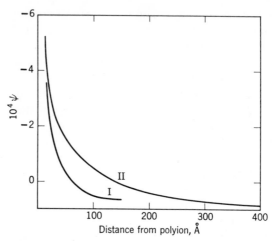

Fig. VII.5. Distribution of electrostatic potential around rod-like polyion with a radius of 6 Å and a uniform surface charge of 0.2 electronic charges per Å. (I) $m_f = 0.01$. (II) $m_f = 0.00125$.

polyions with a radius of 6 Å and a charge density corresponding to half-ionized poly(acrylic acid). The most important conclusions are the following: (1) With polyions of high charge density the electrostatic potentials attain very high values over considerable regions of the system, so that the Debye–Hückel assumption that $e\psi/kT \ll 1$ is clearly inapplicable. (2) Dilution of the polyelectrolyte solution has a surprisingly small effect on the concentration of counterions in the neighborhood of the polyion. In fact, even if the solution were diluted with an infinite volume of water, the reservoir of hydrogen and hydroxyl ions due to the self-ionization of the solvent medium would lead to appreciable counterion concentrations in regions close to the polyion.

The charged rod model represents, of course, an extreme situation which greatly exaggerates the expansion of flexible chains, even if they carry a high charge density. However, the model is most useful since it corresponds to the highest possible dispersal of the fixed charges; for any less extended polyion the electrostatic interaction with counterions will be necessarily even more pronounced. We have seen in the previous section that solutions of polyelectrolytes containing added salts have been frequently treated by assuming a "microscopic Donnan equilibrium," i.e., electroneutrality over the region occupied by a single polyion coil. It is then of particular interest to verify to what extent this assumption is justified. The problem was first attacked by Oosawa et al. (1954) whose

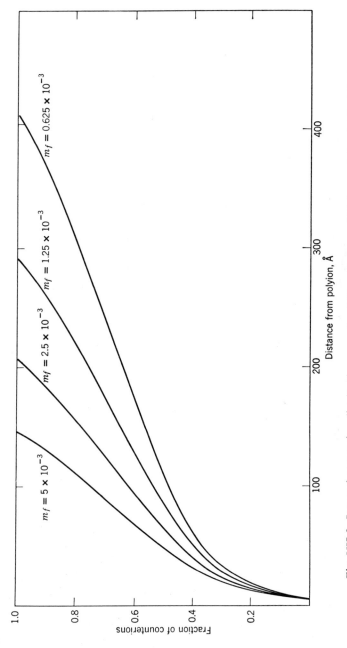

Fig. VII.6. Integral counterion distribution around rod-like polyions. Polyion model as in Fig. VII.5.

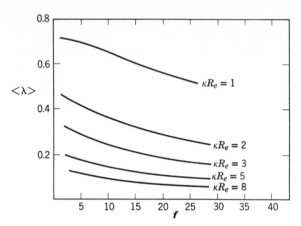

Fig. VII.7. Dependence of the ratio of the net charge to the fixed charge of a spherically symmetrical polyion on its size and charge and on the concentration of added uni-univalent electrolyte.

model contained spherical polyions with a radius R_e, containing a uniform fixed charge density, immersed in a solution of uni-univalent electrolyte. The local charge density at a distance r from the center of the polyion was expressed as $m_{fl}\lambda(r)$ where $\lambda(r)$ was assumed to be small compared to unity. Solving the Poisson–Boltzmann equation with the appropriate boundary conditions, they obtained a distribution of electrostatic potential which gave for the average value of λ over the polyion sphere

$$\langle\lambda\rangle = (\mathfrak{D}kTR_e/\nu_p e^2)\ln\,(f + \sqrt{1 + f^2}) \qquad (7.24)$$

This result indicates that even for polyions of moderate dimensions, deviations from electroneutrality are not very large. In a typical case, with $R_e = 10^{-6}$ cm, $m_{fl} = 0.1M$, $m_s = 0.01M$, eq. (7.24) predicts $\langle\lambda\rangle = 0.08$. As the polyion increases in length, R_e/ν_p will tend to diminish and the Donnan assumption will become a still closer representation of physical reality.

A model similar to that of Oosawa et al. was investigated later by Wall and Berkowitz (1957) with the aid of an electronic computer. Their results show that whenever the dimensions of the polyion are large compared to the thickness of the ion atmosphere in the surrounding salt solution, the net charge density within the polyion sphere is negligible except for regions lying approximately within a distance of $1/\kappa$ of the surface of the sphere. The dependence of $\langle\lambda\rangle$ on κR_e and f, according to these calculations, is represented in Fig. VII.7. A very similar result was reported by

Lifson (1957b) who used the Donnan potential as a first approximation and added to it a correction potential, which can be assumed to be sufficiently small to be treated by the Debye–Hückel approximation.

2. Site-Binding of Counterions

In the preceding treatment of the distribution of mobile ions around a polyion, models were employed which represented the polyion by a continuous distribution of fixed charge density. Any such treatment will necessarily obliterate effects due to the localization of ionic charges carried by the polyion. Moreover, if the fixed charges are considered to be distributed uniformly over the region occupied by a randomly coiled polyion, the mean separation of the fixed charges from their nearest neighbors will appear much larger than what it is since, in fact, these charges are attached to the macromolecular chain. A specific example will illustrate the problem: Schneider and Doty (1954) found that the end-to-end distance of the sodium salt of carboxymethylcellulose of polymerization degree 3300 in $0.05M$ sodium chloride was 2400 Å as against a contour length of 17,000 Å for the fully extended chain molecule. If we take the radius of the equivalent sphere to be equal to the rms radius of gyration of the coil and if we distribute the fixed charges uniformly within this sphere, the distance between neighboring charges will be 110 Å. This is much larger than the characteristic shielding length $1/\kappa = 14$ Å corresponding to the concentration of the sodium chloride. However, in actual fact, the charges are attached to the chain at a spacing of the order of 5 Å, much smaller than the shielding length of the ionic atmosphere. We see then, that the uniform distribution of the charges within the region occupied by the polyion chain leads to the false conclusion that the charges are effectively shielded from each other, while the mobile ions will actually have little influence on the repulsion between neighboring charges of the polyion.

The localization and close spacing of the fixed charges may lead to the binding of counterions at specific sites, which is quite distinct from the consequences of long-range electrostatic field effects operating between the polyion and the mobile ions. Such "site-binding" may be of two types, described as the nonspecific formation of ion pairs and the formation of complex ions.

The concept of ion pair formation was first defined by Bjerrum (1926) who pointed out that for ions of opposite charge the number of ions of charge ν_j to be found in successive concentric shells around a reference ion of charge ν_i passes through a minimum at a characteristic distance $r_{\min} = -e^2\nu_i\nu_j/2\mathfrak{D}kT$. Bjerrum proposed that all ions of opposite charge which are at a mutual distance smaller than r_{min} be considered as associated in ion pairs. With singly charged ions such ion pair formation is usually important only in media of low dielectric constant, but the situation changes significantly when one of the interacting species carries a double charge. In the context of our discussion it is particularly pertinent to consider the behavior of the so-called "bolaform ions" in which two ionized functions are connected by a short flexible chain. Examples of electrolytes with such bolaform ions are salts of bis-quarternary ammonium salts of the general type

$$Cl^- \begin{bmatrix} & CH_3 & & CH_3 \\ & | & + & & | & + \\ CH_3-N- & (-CH_2-)_n- & N-CH_3 \\ & | & & | \\ & CH_3 & & CH_3 \end{bmatrix} Cl^-$$

which were studied by Fuoss and Chu (1951). An analysis of conductance data showed that even in aqueous solution one of the chloride ions is fairly strongly associated with the bolaform cation, corresponding to dissociation constants of 0.125, 0.13, and 0.135 for $n = 3$, 4, and 5, respectively.

It is apparent that the same causes which lead to ion pair formation with bolaform ions will be even more effective in the case of polyions. Unmistakable evidence of such effects has been found by several experimental techniques such as dialysis equilibrium, electrophoresis, and conductance measurements and we shall present some characteristic results when discussing these methods. Here we should only point out that the concept of ion pair formation treats the solvated ion as an integral unit, so that the extent of association would be expected to decrease with an increase in the radius of the *solvated* counterion.

Complex ion formation is distinguished from the formation of ion pairs by the high specificity of forces between the interacting species. It frequently involves binding of the counterion to several functional groups of the polyion, so that a chelate complex is formed. We shall return to a discussion of various types of counterion binding in Chap. VIII where they can be dealt with as special cases of association equilibria in polymer solutions.

C. THERMODYNAMIC PROPERTIES

1. Dialysis Equilibrium

Let us consider a system in which a solution of a typical polyelectrolyte, such as poly(sodium vinylsulfonate), is separated by a semipermeable membrane from pure water. Although the polyelectrolyte contains mobile counterions which are small enough to pass through the membrane, no such passage will actually be possible, since it would involve a separation of polyions and counterions and a rapid buildup of very large electrostatic charges of opposite sign in the two portions of the system. However, if a uni-univalent electrolyte, such as sodium chloride, is added on either side of the membrane, its cations and anions may diffuse together and the problem then arises of how the presence of the polyion affects the equilibrium distribution of the diffusible ionic species.

The problem is solved in Donnan's (1932, 1934) method by imposing two conditions. The first requires the solutions on either side of the membrane to be electroneutral. Thus, if m_f is the molarity of the fixed charges in the solution containing the polyelectrolyte and m_s is the molarity of an added uni-univalent salt, the molarity of byions will be $m_b = m_s$ and that of counterions $m_c = m_f + m_s$. In the dialyzate both ions will be at the same molarity $m_b' = m_c' = m_s'$. Since the diffusible electrolyte must, at equilibrium, have the same thermodynamic activity on both sides of the dialysis membrane,

$$m_b m_c \gamma_{\pm}^2 = m_b' m_c' (\gamma_{\pm}')^2$$

$$(m_f + m_s) m_s \gamma_{\pm}^2 = (m_s')^2 (\gamma_{\pm}')^2 \tag{7.25}$$

where $\gamma_{\pm}$ and $\gamma_{\pm}'$ are the mean ionic activity coefficients in the presence and in the absence of polyelectrolyte, respectively. Let us first consider the result which would be obtained if the activity coefficients could be neglected. In that case (7.25) gives for a relation between m_s and m_s'

$$m_s = -m_f/2 + \sqrt{(m_f/2)^2 + (m_s')^2} \tag{7.26}$$

If $m_s'/m_f \ll 1$ we obtain $m_s = m_s'(m_s'/m_f)$, i.e., the added salt is largely excluded from the polyelectrolyte solution. In the other extreme case, when $m_s'/m_f \gg 1$, an expansion of (7.26) yields

$$m = m_s' - m_f/2 + m_f^2/8m_s' - \ldots \tag{7.27}$$

which leads to a difference in the total molarity of mobile ions Δm_i on the two sides of the membrane

$$\Delta m_i \equiv m_c + m_b - m_c' - m_b' = m_f^2/4m_s' - \ldots \tag{7.28}$$

We shall see later that this difference in mobile ion concentration contributes to the osmotic pressure of polyelectrolyte solutions. Relation (7.28) shows that the effect is minimized by increasing the concentration of added salt.

In practice, the large forces between polyions and their counterions will inevitably depress the ionic activity coefficient, so that $\gamma_\pm < \gamma'_\pm$. This will have the effect of increasing the difference in the counterion concentration and decreasing the difference in the byion concentration on the two sides of the membrane. If the ionic concentrations are determined analytically, eq. (7.25) may be used to calculate $\gamma_\pm$, since the activity coefficient $\gamma'_\pm$, corresponding to a simple salt solution, may be determined by conventional methods or obtained from tabulated data. It should be emphasized, however, that experimental equilibrium data alone are by their very nature incapable of differentiating between effects produced by long-range electrostatic interaction and effects due to site binding.*

2. Ionic Activity Coefficients

We have already seen (cf. Fig. VII.6) that in salt-free polyelectrolyte solutions a considerable fraction of the counterions remains closely associated with the polyion even if the system is highly dilute. Such systems differ, therefore, from solutions of simple electrolytes in that the ionic activity coefficient lies far below unity even at the highest dilutions which allow meaningful measurements.

The activity of a solute species is defined in terms of its partial molar free energy. If the solute is an electrolyte, it is impossible to vary the concentration of only one of its ions and a single ion activity (or activity coefficient) cannot be defined unambiguously in terms of an experimentally measurable quantity. The significant quantity is the activity of the electrolyte as a whole, related to the partial molar free energy of the electroneutral species consisting of cations and anions. It is, of course, possible to divide this partial molar free energy among the constituents ions of the electrolyte, but this can be done only by using extrathermodynamic arguments. (For instance, in the case of potassium chloride, where the two ions have the same size and charge, their activities are frequently considered to be identical). In the case of a salt-free polyelectrolyte, an additional conceptual difficulty is introduced since we cannot take as a frame of reference a highly dilute solution in which all interactions of charged species are eliminated, so that ideal solution behavior is attained.

---

* In the case of dialysis equilibrium measurements with globular proteins many authors have interpreted a deviation of $\gamma_\pm$ from $\gamma'_\pm$ in terms of ion binding by the macromolecule. As long as it is clearly understood that "binding" is defined operationally in this manner, there is no objection to this practice. Since the charge density on the proteins is usually not too high, site binding probably accounts for most of the deviation of $\gamma_\pm / \gamma'_\pm$ from unity.

As soon as a trace of simple electrolyte is added to the polyelectrolyte solution, the activity of this electrolyte species becomes a perfectly well-defined quantity. Marcus (1955) has shown that in this case the mean ionic activity coefficient of the added electrolyte (present in a concentration too low to modify appreciably the electrostatic forces in the polyelectrolyte solution) may be related to the distribution of electrostatic potential over the volume V of the system. For instance, for the addition of uni-uni-valent electrolyte, the mean ionic activity coefficient $\gamma_{\pm}$ is given by

$$\gamma_{\pm}^{2} = V^{2}/\int \exp[-e\psi/kT]dV \int \exp[e\psi/kT]dV \qquad (7.29)$$

Since $\gamma_{\pm}$ is experimentally accessible through measurements of the electromotive force in cells without liquid junction, determinations of dialysis equilibrium, cryoscopy (Mock, 1960), or the determination of changes in the solubility of sparingly soluble salts, we can compare experimental data with results predicted on the basis of theoretically derived distributions of the electrostatic potential.

Although a rigorous determination of a single ion activity is impossible, an approximate value may be obtained from potentiometric measurements and this leads to interesting indications of the difference in the forces experienced by counterions and byions in polyelectrolyte solutions. For instance, if we have a solution containing the sodium salt of a polymeric acid $Na_{n}P$ and added sodium chloride, then the cell

$$Hg,Hg_2Cl_2,sat.KCl \mid Na_nP,NaCl \mid Na\ amalgam \mid NaCl \mid sat.KCl,Hg_2Cl_2,Hg$$

gives an electromotive force $\mathcal{E}$ related to the sodium ion activity by

$$\mathcal{E} = (RT/\mathfrak{F})\ \ln \frac{a_{Na^+}\ (\text{polymer solution})}{a_{Na^+}\ (\text{NaCl solution})} \qquad (7.30)$$

provided we assume that the two liquid junction potentials are the same. Similarly, the cell

$$Hg,\ Hg_2Cl_2,\ sat.\ KCl \mid Na_nP,\ NaCl \mid AgCl,Ag,AgCl \mid NaCl \mid sat.\ KCl,\ Hg_2Cl_2,\ Hg$$

may be employed to estimate the chloride ion activity. Experiments of this type were first carried out by Kern (1948), who found that the activity coefficient of the sodium ion in poly(sodium acrylate) seemed to *decrease* from 0.3 to 0.17 when the solution was diluted from $0.2N$ to $0.0125N$. Later studies, carried out in Japan, substantiated these results and indicated also that the presence of polyelectrolyte has a relatively small effect on the activity coefficients of byions (Kagawa and Katsuura, 1952). For

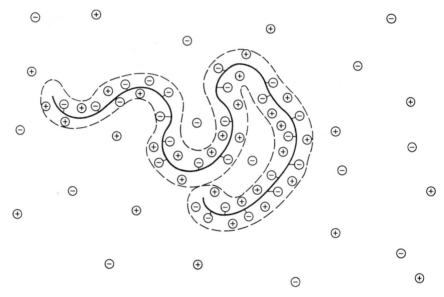

Fig. VII.8. The Strauss-Ander model of a polyelectrolyte solution.

instance, the activity coefficient of the chloride ion in $0.005N$ KCl was estimated as 0.83 in the presence of $0.004N$ polyelectrolyte; when the polyelectrolyte concentration was increased fourfold, the activity coefficient of chloride changed only to 0.76. The extensive Japanese studies of ionic activity coefficients in polyelectrolyte solutions have been summarized by Nagasawa et al. (1959a).

It has generally been found that the electrochemical properties of polyelectrolyte solutions are independent of the chainlength of the polyion. This important fact demonstrates the weakness of all theoretical models in which the fixed charges carried by the polyion chain are smeared out to a spherically symmetrical charge cloud. Since the volume occupied by the polyion coil increases more rapidly than the chainlength, the smeared-out fixed charge density would decline. A much more realistic model has been proposed by Strauss and Ander (1958) who consider as the polyion domain not a spherical volume surrounding the coiled polyion as a whole, but rather a sausage-shaped region encasing the coil as represented in Fig. VII.8. If we think then of the polyion region as separated by a membrane from the rest of the solution, the byions will tend to be excluded from this region owing to the high local concentration of fixed charges. The fraction of the volume from which the salt is excluded in the presence of polyelectrolyte will then reduce its average concentration and thus determine the dialysis equilibrium with a salt solution containing no polyions.

Theoretical considerations of the behavior of dilute systems have led to the conclusion that the addition of simple salts has relatively little effect on the counterion atmosphere in the immediate vicinity of a highly charged polymeric chain. Thus, it seems reasonable that the activities of ions in a system containing both polyelectrolytes and simple salts should be the sums of activities of the ionic species to be expected in a salt-free polyelectrolyte and a polyelectrolyte-free salt solution, respectively. This simple superposition principle was verified experimentally by pH measurements on solutions containing polysulfonic acids and HCl (Mock and Marshall, 1954) and by dialysis equilibrium studies (Nagasawa et al.; 1959a; Alexandrowicz, 1960, 1962). Table VII.3 lists the values given by

TABLE VII.3

Activity Coefficients of Sodium Counterions in Partially Ionized Poly(acrylic acid)

Polymer conc. (g-liter^{-1})	Activity coefficient				
	$\alpha_i = 0.05$	$\alpha_i = 0.1$	$\alpha_i = 0.3$	$\alpha_i = 0.5$	$\alpha_i = 0.8$
36	0.68	0.56	0.41	0.37	0.26
7.2	0.79	0.54	0.41	0.28	0.17
1.44	0.73	0.58	0.35	0.21	0.12

Alexandrowicz (1959) for the apparent activity coefficients of sodium ions in poly(sodium acrylate) as a function of the polymer concentration and its degree of ionization. However, it should be noted that the experimental data obtained by Strauss and Ander (1958) with polyphosphate solutions show an increasing contribution of the polyelectrolyte to the ionic activity at higher salt concentrations. This result is in agreement with predictions based on their model of polyelectrolyte solutions if the radius of the cylindrical space surrounding each polyion backbone, from which byions are supposed to be excluded, is assumed to be linear in the Debye-Hückel shielding length $1/\kappa$.

A complicating feature is introduced by specific interactions of polyions with their counterions, leading to site binding. The existence of such effects is clearly revealed by dialysis equilibrium data on a series of alkali polyphosphates (Strauss and Ross, 1959b), which show that the inactivation of lithium is much more pronounced than that of the other alkali ions. In this case we apparently deal with complex ion formation, which would be expected to increase with a decreasing size of the unsolvated alkali cation. The order of site binding is reversed with polysulfonates where the interaction is purely electrostatic and is, therefore, strongest for the smallest *hydrated* cation (Eisenberg and Mohan, 1959).

3. Osmotic Pressure

We have seen previously that for an uncharged solute species the osmotic pressure is related to the thermodynamic activity of the solvent by

$$\Pi = -\frac{RT}{\bar{V}_1} \ln a_1 \tag{4.12}$$

In the limit of very high dilution, where Raoult's law becomes applicable, (4.12) may be rewritten as

$$\Pi = \frac{RT}{\bar{V}_1} \sum{}' x_i \tag{7.31}$$

where $\sum{}'$ symbolizes a summation over all solute species which cannot pass through the osmotic membrane. In the case of polyelectrolyte solutions containing no added electrolyte, the counterions will also be osmotically active and since their number is, in general, orders of magnitude higher than the number of polyions, the osmotic pressure data will be, for all practical purposes, independent of the molecular weight of the macromolecule.

When we add simple electrolyte to the polyelectrolyte solution, the situation becomes more complex, since the membrane is permeable to the small ions and we shall then have solute on both sides of the osmotic membrane. As we have seen in eq. (7.26), the total concentration of mobile ions will always be greater in the solution containing the polyions, but the differences will tend to decrease with an increasing concentration of simple salt. In the limit of infinite salt concentration the contribution of the Donnan distribution of mobile ions to the observed osmotic pressure will be eliminated.

Let us first neglect the effect of ionic activity coefficients and consider solutions in which the concentration of simple electrolyte is large compared to the concentration of fixed charges. We may then apply eq. (7.28) to the contribution which the unequal distribution of the mobile ions makes to the osmotic pressure and eq. (7.31) becomes

$$\Pi = RT[(c_2/M_2) + (m_j^2/4000\, m_s') + \ldots] \tag{7.32}$$

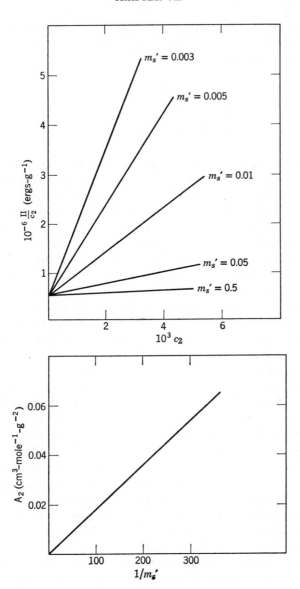

Fig. VII.9. Osmotic behavior of sodium pectinate at various concentrations of added sodium chloride (m_s').

where m_f and m_s are the molar concentrations of fixed charges and of uni-univalent salts, respectively. Since $m_f = 1000c_2\nu_p/M_2$ we obtain for the reduced osmotic pressure

$$\frac{\Pi}{c_2} = RT\left(\frac{1}{M_2} + A_2c_2 + \ldots\right) \qquad (7.33)$$

$$A_2 = 1000(\nu_p/M_2)^2/4m_s'$$

This result would lead one to expect extremely large second virial coefficients in polyelectrolytes containing polyions with a high charge density. For instance, the reduced osmotic pressure of fully ionized poly-(acrylic acid) would rise so rapidly, even in $1M$ salt solution, that for $M_2 = 10^5$ the value of Π/c_2 at a polymer concentration of 0.01 g/ml. would be fifty times as high as the limiting value at infinite dilution! In practice, the second virial coefficients of polyelectrolyte solutions are found to be large, but not nearly as large as predicted by eq. (7.33). Typical data are those by Pals and Hermans (1952) for sodium pectinate, plotted in Fig. VII.9. These data seem to agree with the linear dependence of the second virial coefficient A_2 on $1/m_s'$ predicted by eq. (7.33), but the absolute values are lower by a factor of about thirty. Calculations of A_2 from light scattering data (Trap and Hermans, 1954; Schneider and Doty, 1954; Inagaki and Hirami, 1959; Orofino and Flory, 1959) lead also to relatively low values, particularly at high charge densities of the polyion. This discrepancy is clearly due to the neglect of the ionic activity coefficients. If we interpret the low counterion activity as reducing the effective charge density on the polyion, then the low values of A_2 are easily accounted for, since the contribution to A_2 due to the Donnan distribution of the mobile ions is proportional to the square of the charge density along the polymer chain. A second complication is caused by the excluded volume of the polyions, which must make a separate contribution to A_2. This contribution should decrease with increasing salt concentration owing to the contraction of the charged chains. Attempts to analyze the observed osmotic pressures of polyelectrolytes in terms of contributions made by these various factors were reported by Nagasawa et al. (1959b), Imagaki and Hirami (1959), Alexandrowicz (1962), and Ise (1962, 1963).

4. Ionization Equilibria

Before considering the ionization equilibria of polymeric species with a large number of ionizable groups, let us deal briefly with the titration of materials such as dicarboxylic acids. The ionization equilibria of such substances may be represented schematically by

$$\overline{\text{COOH} \quad\quad \text{COOH}} \overset{K_1}{\rightleftharpoons} \overline{\text{COOH} \quad\quad \text{COO}^-} + \text{H}^+ \quad\quad (7.34a)$$

$$\overline{\text{COOH} \quad\quad \text{COO}^-} \overset{K_2}{\rightleftharpoons} \overline{\text{COO}^- \quad\quad \text{COO}^-} + \text{H}^+ \quad\quad (7.34b)$$

If the ionizable groups are very far from each other, the ease of ionization of each of the carboxyl groups will be independent of the state of ionization of the other. The titration curve will then be indistinguishable from that of a monocarboxylic acid with an ionization constant K° and a concentration equal to the stoichiometric carboxyl concentration of the dicarboxylic acid. For any overall degree of ionization α_i, there will be a fraction $(1 - \alpha_i)^2$ of unionized, $2\alpha_i(1 - \alpha_i)$ of singly ionized, and α_i^2 of doubly ionized molecules. The identical result is obtained if we assign to the first ionization step an equilibrium constant $K_1 = 2K^\circ$ and to the second step an equilibrium constant $K_2 = K^\circ/2$, since two carboxyls may lose a proton in the first step, while a proton may attach itself to two alternative sites in the second equilibrium.

If the carboxyls are sufficiently close to one another, the removal of the second proton will be impeded by the electrostatic attraction of the neighboring carboxylate group. To overcome it, the molar free energy for the second ionization step will have to be increased by an "electrostatic free energy of ionization" ΔG_{el}^i given by

$$\Delta G_{el}^i = N \int_{r=r_e}^{r=\infty} -\frac{e^2}{\mathfrak{D} r^2} dr = Ne^2/\mathfrak{D} r_e \quad\quad (7.35)$$

where r_e is the distance between the two ionizable groups and the ratio of the first and second ionization constant becomes then

$$K_2/K_1 = (1/4)\exp\left(-\Delta G_{el}^i/RT\right) \quad\quad (7.36)$$

If r_e is small, the proper choice of $\mathfrak{D}$ presents some difficulties. Kirkwood and Westheimer (1938) pointed out that it is incorrect to use the value of the dielectric constant of water ($\sim$80) since most of the electrical lines of force will pass through the organic molecule, which is characterized by a much lower dielectric constant ($\sim$2). They showed that experimental data can be accounted for by using a model in which the ionic charges are placed on an ellipsoid with the dielectric constant of an organic substance and this ellipsoid is immersed into the aqueous medium. It should be noted, however, that such agreement between predicted and experimental data presupposes a good knowledge of the conformational distribution of the dicarboxylic acid in its unionized, singly ionized and doubly ionized state. For instance, Eberson (1959) has reported that in the *meso* and the racemic forms of α,β-dialkylsuccinic acids

$$
\begin{array}{cc}
\text{R} \quad \text{R} & \text{R} \quad \text{H} \\
| \quad\ | & | \quad\ | \\
\text{HOOC} - \text{C} - \text{C} - \text{COOH} \qquad\qquad & \text{HOOC} - \text{C} - \text{C} - \text{COOH} \\
| \quad\ | & | \quad\ | \\
\text{H} \quad \text{H} & \text{H} \quad \text{R}
\end{array}
$$

the value of K_2/K_1 may differ by a factor as large as 10^4 if the R groups are sufficiently bulky.

With a polymer carrying a large number of ionizable groups, it is obviously impracticable to specify the successive ionization constants. Instead of this, we define the apparent ionization constant K_{app} of an average ionizable group carried by the polyion in the usual manner by

$$(H^+)\alpha_i/(1 - \alpha_i) = K_{app} \tag{7.37}$$

where K_{app} will, of course, vary with the degree of ionization since the charged polymer will interact with the hydrogen ions. With polymeric acids the polyanion will attract the hydrogen ions and $dK_{app}/d\alpha_i < 0$; with polymeric bases, on the other hand, the hydrogen ions will be repelled by the polycation and the acid strength of the polymer will increase with its charge density. If the required electrostatic free energy for the removal of an equivalent of protons at a given degree of ionization is $\Delta G_{el}^i(\alpha_i)$ then

$$pK_{app} = pK° - 0.43 \Delta G_{el}^i(\alpha_i)/RT \tag{7.38}$$

where $K°$ is characteristic of the ionizing group under conditions where electrostatic interactions with other ionizing groups are absent. The value of $\Delta G_{el}^i(\alpha_i)$ is related to the excess electrostatic free energy, which we have used previously in our discussion of the expansion of flexible polyions, by

$$\Delta G_{el}^i(\alpha_i) = N \partial G_{el}^E/\partial \nu_p \tag{7.39}$$

It is customary to combine (7.37) and (7.38) and write the result in logarithmic form

$$pH = pK° + \log [\alpha_i/(1 - \alpha_i)] + 0.43 \, \Delta G_{el}^i/RT \tag{7.40}$$

For spherical particles with a relatively low density of surface charge, ΔG_{el}^i may be estimated using for a model a sphere with radius R_e and a

uniform surface charge. The application of the Debye-Hückel treatment
to this model (Scatchard, 1949) gives

$$\Delta G_{el}^i = \frac{Ne\nu_p}{\mathfrak{D}}\left(\frac{1}{R_e} - \frac{\kappa}{1 + \kappa R_e}\right) \tag{7.41}$$

This treatment is usually employed for globular proteins. In that case
ν_p represents the net number of unit charges carried by the particle, which
requires not only a knowledge of the number of cationic and anionic groups,
but also information about the numbers of ions of any simple electrolyte
present in the system which may have associated with the protein molecule.
The relation in eq. (7.40) applies then, of course, to every type of ionizable
group, where $K°$ is its intrinsic ionization constant and α_i the fraction of
that type of group which is present in the form of its conjugate base. For
a typical case of a particle with an equivalent radius $R_e = 2 \times 10^{-7}$cm, we
obtain for ΔG_{el}^i at an ionic strength of 0.1 a value of 40 cal/mole per electronic charge carried by the macromolecule. For a negatively charged
particle carrying 50 charges, this corresponds to a reduction of the acid
dissociation constant by a factor of 25. It should be remembered, however, that ΔG_{el}^i values much larger than RT indicate that the Debye-
Hückel approximation, on which the derivation of eq. (7.41) is based, can
no longer be justified.

In applying the principles outlined above to the quantitative interpretation of the titration data obtained with globular proteins, appropriate $K°$
values corresponding to the various titratable groups must first be chosen.
According to Tanford and Hauenstein (1956), data obtained with low
molecular weight analogs would lead one to expect a p$K° = 3.75$ for the
α-COOH group at the polypeptide chain end, p$K° = 4.6$ for side chain
COOH, p$K° = 7.0$ for imidazole, p$K° = 7.8$ for the α-amino group,
p$K° = 9.6$ for the phenolic groups of tyrosine, and p$K° = 10.2$ for side-
chain amino groups. Guanidyl groups of arginine residues would be expected to be titrated well above pH 12, where irreversible denaturation
usually occurs, so that a quantitative interpretation of the data is no
longer possible. In practice, it is often found that the p$K°$ calculated
from protein titration data deviates significantly from these expected
values. There may be several reasons for such a discrepancy. It is
clear that the smearing out of the protein charge over the surface of the
globular molecule obscures the possible effects of spatial proximity of a
given ionizable group to another positively or negatively charged function.
The effective local dielectric constant in the neighborhood of an ionizable
group may differ significantly from the bulk value for water. Finally,

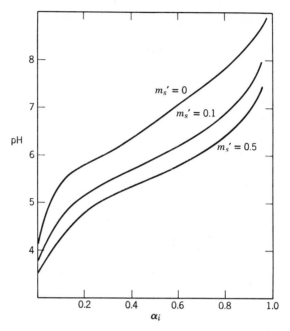

Fig. VII.10. Titration of $0.02N$ poly(methacrylic acid) without added salt and with added KNO$_3$.

conformational transitions (reversible or irreversible) of the protein molecule with a change of its net charge would be expected to influence ionization equilibria. A detailed discussion of the information to be gained from protein titration curves and of the limitations of the methods has been presented by Tanford (1961).

With synthetic polyelectrolytes the situation may at first appear simpler since the polyion usually carries only one type of ionizable groups and we do not have to take account of the consequences of a specific macromolecular conformation. However, these advantages are far outweighed by the complexities introduced by an increasing chain expansion and ion pair formation as the charge density of the polyion is being increased. Both of these effects will tend to reduce the electrostatic potential in the neighborhood of the polyion, so that ΔG_{el}^i would be expected to increase less rapidly than in proportion to the charge of the chain. Typical titration data are those for poly(methacrylic acid) (Kotliar and Morawetz, 1955) plotted in Fig. VII.10, which show the very large effect produced by the addition of simple electrolytes, leading to a drastic reduction in the value of ΔG_{el}^i.

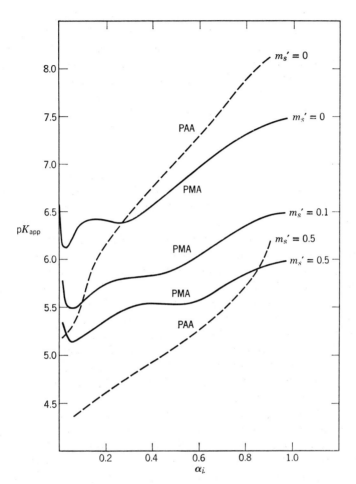

Fig. VII.11. The dependence of the apparent ionization constant of poly(methacrylic acid) and poly(acrylic acid) on the degree of ionization and the concentration of added KNO₃.

The dependence of pK_{app} on the degree of ionization is shown in Fig. VII.11 for poly(acrylic acid) and for poly(methacrylic acid) in the absence and the presence of added salt. We may note the striking difference in the behavior of these two polymeric acids. In the case of the poly(acrylic acid), pK_{app} increases steadily with an increasing charge of the polyion and the data are approximated over much of the titration curve by a linear relation pK_{app} and α_i. The situation is very different with poly(methacrylic acid), where pK_{app} first decreases, then rises to a plateau and eventually increases again at high charge densities of the polyion.   This complicated behavior seems to suggest a conformational transition in the range characterized by a constant pK_{app}; as expected, this occurs at higher charge densities in the presence of simple electrolyte.   Katchalsky and Spitnik (1947) have found in some cases that ΔG_{el}^i is in many cases approximately proportional to log $[\alpha_0/(1 - \alpha_i)]$ over an extended range of the titration of polymeric acids (for $0.1 < \alpha_i < 0.9$) so that (7.40) may be written as

$$\text{pH} = pK^\circ + n' \log \left[\alpha_i/(1 - \alpha_i)\right] \tag{7.42}$$

where the deviation of n' from unity is a measure of the magnitude of the electrostatic effects.   This relation should be considered only an empirical approximation.   If ΔG_{el}^i is relatively small, a plot of pH against log $[\alpha_i/(1 - \alpha_i)]$ will, of course, be approximately linear.   The dependence of ΔG_{el}^i on polyion charge is, therefore, revealed much more reliably by plotting pK_{app} against α_i.   This is seen clearly by comparing Fig. VII.10 with Fig. VII.11.   It is only in the latter that the characteristic behavior of poly(methacrylic acid) becomes obvious.   Titration curves of polyelectrolytes have been found to be independent of the chain length of the polyion.   This indicates that the distance between ionized groups whose interactions contribute significantly to the electrostatic free energy are small compared to the overall dimensions of the polyion.   It would be interesting to see how $\Delta G_{el}^i(\alpha_i)$ approaches its asymptotic value in relatively short polyions of increasing chain length, but such data are not available at the present time.

It should be noted that the electrostatic effect produced by the nearest-neighbor ionized groups cannot be entirely eliminated, even when the added salt concentration is very high.   The theory of titrations of ionizable polymeric chains under conditions where only electrical interactions between neighboring ionized groups need be considered has been formulated by Marcus (1954).   If ΔG_n is the free energy required to move two equivalents of isolated ionized groups to positions on the chain where they form nearest neighbor pairs, then

$$K_{app} = K^\circ \frac{\alpha_i(\sqrt{x + 1} - 2\alpha_i + 1)}{(1 - \alpha_i)(\sqrt{x + 1} + 2\alpha_i - 1)} \tag{7.43}$$

$$x = 4\alpha_i(1 - \alpha_i) \left[\exp\left(\Delta G_n/RT\right) - 1\right]$$

If $\Delta G_n = 0$, the titration behavior of the polymer reduces, of course, to that of the monofunctional analog.   On the other hand, if $\Delta G_n/RT \gg 1$,

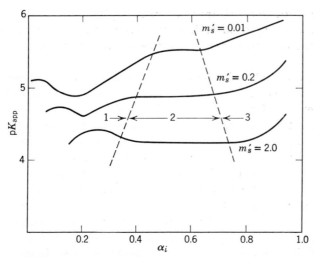

Fig. VII.12. The dependence of the apparent ionization constant of poly(α-L-glutamic acid) on the degree of ionization in solutions containing various concentrations of added NaCl.   In region 1 the polymer is in the helical conformation; in region 3 it has the form of random coils.   Region 2 corresponds to the helix-coil transition.

the ionization of two neighboring groups becomes very difficult and alternate groups on the polymeric chain tend to be ionized first.   Only when $\alpha_i > 1/2$, will it be necessary to ionize the intermediate groups, a process which is being resisted by the electrostatic interactions of two neighboring ionic charges.   The polymer then approximates the behavior of a dibasic acid or base whose two ionization constants differ by a factor of exp $[2 \ \Delta G_n/RT]$.   For reasons which are not understood, such a behavior has never been observed with polymeric acids, although with such polymeric bases as polyvinylamine or poly(ethylene imine) nearest neighbor interactions do dominate the titration behavior even when the concentration of simple electrolytes is relatively low (Katchalsky et al., 1957).

So far, we have tacitly assumed that the ionizable groups are evenly spaced along the backbone of the polymer molecule.   However, as has been stated earlier, it is possible to prepare copolymers of maleic anhydride which after hydrolysis yield chain molecules, in which pairs of closely spaced carboxyl groups are separated from one another by the comonomer unit.   Typical examples of such materials are the maleic acid copolymers with styrene or methyl vinyl ether shown in Table VII.1.   When such polymeric acids are titrated, one carboxyl of each pair ionizes relatively easily.   However, if the neutralization is carried beyond 50%, hydrogen ions have to be removed from a carboxyl lying very close to an anionic group and this is much more difficult; we observe, therefore, a pronounced break in the titration curve at the half-neutralization point (Ferry et al., 1951).

Finally, we should consider the titration behavior of a material such as poly(α-L-glutamic acid). This exists at low degrees of ionization in the form of an α-helix (cf. Chap. III, Sec. C-1) but the repulsive forces of the fixed charges eventually disrupt this specific conformation and at high charge densities the polyion may be described as a random coil (Doty et al., 1957). Since the disruption of the helical conformation leads to a dispersal of the fixed charges, the increase in pK_{app} with an increasing degree of ionization will tend to be interrupted in the range of the helix-coil transition. This effect is illustrated on data reported by Wada (1960) shown in Fig. VII.12. A theoretical analysis of the titration curves, to be expected with poly-electrolytes in which the polyion undergoes a helix-coil transition, was re-ported by Zimm and Rice (1960). It should be noted, however, that the dependence of pK_{app} on α_i, as found by Wada for poly(α-L-glutamic acid), is rather similar to that found for poly(methacrylic acid) (Fig. VII.11), where there can be no question of a helix-coil transition. One should, therefore, exercise great caution in inferring helical structures from anom-alies in the titration curves of chain molecules.

D. TRANSPORT PROPERTIES

1. Electrophoresis

If an ionized macromolecule carrying an electrical charge Q is suspended in a viscous medium with an electrical potential gradient X, the particle will accelerate until the electrical force is equal to the frictional resistance. Since the system as a whole is electroneutral, the charge of the macro-molecule must be counterbalanced by a similar charge of opposite sign carried by the counterions distributed in the surrounding medium. If the macromolecule has the form of a spherical particle with an effective radius R_e and the charge density on its surface is not too high, the theory of Debye and Hückel (1923) may be used to describe the distribution of counterions, which is then best characterized by the "mean thickness of the ion atmosphere" $1/\kappa$ defined by eq. (7.7). For macromolecular solu-tions containing little added salt, the thickness of the counterion atmos-phere may be much larger than the radius of the colloidal particle and in that case the electrical driving force will be given simply by

$$F = (1/300)QX \qquad\qquad \kappa R_e \ll 1 \qquad (7.44)$$

where the numerical factor is required to obtain **F** in dynes when Q is in electrostatic units and X in volts per centimeter. Equating this driving force to the viscous drag as given by Stokes' law [eq. (6.2)], we obtain for the steady state velocity

$$u = (1/300)QX/f = (1/300)QX/6\pi\eta_0 R_t \qquad \kappa R_e \ll 1 \qquad (7.45)$$

where R_t is the effective radius determining viscous resistance to translation.* This result was first obtained by Hückel (1924). On the other hand, Smoluchowski (1921) considered the case of charged colloidal particles in a medium containing a high concentration of small ions, so that the thickness of the double layer is much smaller than the dimensions of the charged sphere. In that case the double layer may be treated as a parallel plate condenser with an area A and a plate separation δ. The viscous resistance to the slippage of the two plates past one another is $\eta_0 A u/\delta$ and equating this to the electrostatic driving force as given in (7.44), we obtain for the steady state velocity

$$u = (1/300)QX\delta/\eta_0 A \qquad \kappa R_e \gg 1 \qquad (7.46)$$

The Hückel and Smoluchowski results may be compared in terms of the surface potential ψ_s, which is given by $\psi_s = \cdot Q/\mathfrak{D}R_e$ for the case of an infinitely thick double layer and by $\psi_s = 4\pi Q\delta/\mathfrak{D}A$ for the parallel plate condenser. We obtain then

$$u = (1/300)X\mathfrak{D}\psi_s/6\pi\eta_0 \qquad \kappa R_e \ll 1 \qquad (7.47a)$$

$$u = (1/300)X\mathfrak{D}\psi_s/4\pi\eta_0 \qquad \kappa R_e \gg 1 \qquad (7.47b)$$

If we want to express the electrophoretic velocity u in terms of the charge of the spherical particle, we may use the results of the Debye–Hückel theory in the form

$$Q = \mathfrak{D}\psi_s R_e \frac{1 + \kappa(R_e + r_i)}{1 + \kappa r_i} \qquad (7.48)$$

where r_i is the radius of the small ions in the solution. The velocity of the spherical macromolecules becomes then, assuming $R_e = R_t$,

$$u = \frac{1}{300} \frac{QX(1 + \kappa r_i) f(\kappa R_e)}{6\pi\eta_0 R_e[1 + \kappa(R_e + r_i)]} \qquad (7.49)$$

where $f(\kappa R_e) \to 1$ as $\kappa R_e \to 0$ and $f(\kappa R_e) \to {}^3/_2$ as $\kappa R_e \to \infty$. For intermediate values of κR_e (i.e., for the case when the thickness of the counterion

* In practice we may disregard the distinction between R_e and R_t.

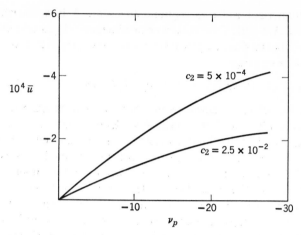

Fig. VII.13. Dependence of the electrophoretic mobility of bovine serum albumin on the net number of charges ν_p.

atmosphere is comparable to the radius of the charged macromolecule) we have $1 < f(\kappa R_e) < {}^3/_2$, where the values of $f(\kappa R_e)$ have been computed by Henry (1931).

In practice there are two complicating features which tend to reduce the velocity u below the value predicted by (7.49). The first effect, referred to as the electrophoretic retardation, is due to the hydration of the counterions, so that they carry a considerable number of water molecules in a direction opposite to that in which the charged macromolecule is moving. The macromolecule may then be considered to be transported against the direction of flow of the streaming solvent and its velocity should be correspondingly reduced. The second effect is caused by the finite time required for re-establishing the counterion atmosphere when the charged particle is changing its location. As a result of this "relaxation effect" the center of the counterion atmosphere tends to lag behind the center of the moving particle, resulting in a backward pull. Experimental data on serum albumin [cf. Möller et al. (1961)] have been interpreted as indicating that most of the reduction in electrophoretic velocity is accounted for by electrophoretic retardation, while the relaxation effect plays a relatively minor role. Figures VII.13 and VII.14, taken from the results of these investigators, show how the electrophoretic mobility, $\bar{u} = u/X$, of salt-free solutions of serum albumin titrated with base, changes with increasing charge at constant protein concentration and with increasing protein concentration at constant charge. As would be expected for the

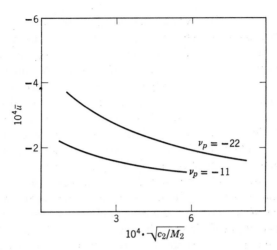

Fig. VII.14. Dependence of the electrophoretic mobility of bovine serum albumin on the concentration of the protein.

various reasons listed above, a plot of the mobility of the protein against its charge has a downward curvature and the mobility decreases also with increasing protein concentration.   In the presence of a fairly high concentration of added salt, the mobility of the protein molecule seems to be proportional to its charge, as found by Longsworth (1941) for ovalbumin in solutions with an ionic strength of 0.1.   The mobilities which he found under these conditions were about 60% of the values predicted according to eq. (7.49).

The treatment of the electrophoresis of flexible chain molecules is considerably more complex.   The problem has been treated by Hermans and Fujita (1955) and by Hermans (1955) who used for the partially draining coil the model introduced by Debye and Bueche (1948) (pp.273–274).   They showed that the electrophoretic velocity depends not only on hydrodynamic factors (i.e., on the ratio of the radius of the hydrodynamically equivalent sphere R_t to the hydrodynamic shielding length L_f) but also on the ratio of the coil dimensions to the thickness of the counter-ion atmosphere. In particular, if the ionic strength is high, so that $R_t\kappa \gg 1$ and the hydrodynamic permeability of the chain is low ($R_t/L_f \gg 1$), Hermans and Fujita predict for a chain of Z units characterized by a frictional coefficient of f_0

$$\bar{u} = \frac{1}{300} \frac{Q}{Zf_0}\left[1 + \frac{1 + 2\kappa L_f}{3\kappa^2 L_f^2(1 + \kappa L_f)}\right] \tag{7.50}$$

From the form of this expression it is apparent that u depends on the ratio of the hydrodynamic shielding length and the thickness of the counterion atmosphere. In the limit of $\kappa L_f \to \infty$, the electrophoretic velocity will be that expected for a free draining coil and will be independent of the chain length as long as the charge density Q/Z is held constant. It is, indeed, found in practice that a sharp electrophoretic boundary is observed in experiments in which unfractionated linear chain polyions are being investigated (Fitzgerald and Fuoss, 1954), and the fractionation of a flexible chain polyelectrolyte yields polyions with identical mobilities, even if their chain length is varied by a very large factor (Noda et al., 1964). It may seem at first sight surprising that a macromolecular coil, which behaves in sedimentation or diffusion as impermeable, should behave in electrophoresis as if it were free draining. However, Hermans and Fujita point out that in the limit of high ionic strength the net charge density vanishes at all points so that the net force acting on any volume element is zero. Under those circumstances there is no reason to expect interaction effects which would render the coil impenetrable. A careful experimental test of the various other features of the Hermans–Fujita result has been reported by Nagasawa et al. (1958). They showed that the polyion mobility measured at finite concentrations of the polymeric species tends to be reduced due to a number of complicating factors so that experimental values of $\bar{u}$ should be extrapolated to zero polymer concentration before being compared to theoretical predictions. At increasing electrolyte concentrations, the mobility asymptotically approaches a limiting value which is almost reached at an ionic strength of 0.01 (corresponding to $1/\kappa = 30$ Å). The mobility of the polymer at high salt concentration is also found to be identical with that of a chain segment carrying a single ionic charge, as predicted by eq. (7.50). In salt-free solution the polyion is highly expanded and the free draining coil model is applicable. The polyion mobility is then the same as that observed at high ionic strength. At intermediate salt concentrations $\bar{u}$ assumes higher values as predicted by Hermans and Fujita.

Electrophoretic measurements have been found to be most useful for the estimation of the extent of counterion binding in polyelectrolyte solutions. For instance, Strauss et al. (1957) found that the electrophoretic mobility of the polyphosphate ion remains almost unchanged when $1M$ tetramethyl ammonium bromide is added to salt-free tetramethylammonium polyphosphate; by contrast, the mobility of the polyphosphate is cut by more than a factor of two when $0.8M$ NaBr is added to sodium polyphosphate. This difference may be ascribed to site-binding of the sodium counterions. Later studies (Strauss and Bluestone, 1959; Strauss and Ross, 1959a) showed that the polyion mobility appears to be proportional to its effective charge, so that quantitative estimates of the extent of ion pair formation may be made if the mobility of the tetramethyl-ammonium polyphosphate is taken as characteristic of conditions when none of the counterions are site-bound to the polyion.

For a detailed discussion of both theoretical and experimental aspects of electrophoresis the reader is referred to an excellent monograph edited by Bier (1959).

2. Conductance

The conductance of solutions containing polyelectrolytes as well as added simple electrolytes may be considered as the sum of contributions made by the small ions and the polyions. It is frequently assumed that the mobility of small ions is the same in a polyelectrolyte solution as in a simple salt solution of the same ionic strength. This assumption has been examined critically by Fujita and Hermans (1955) who found that it applies rigorously in all cases where the electrophoretic behavior of the polyion is that expected for a free draining coil. We have seen in the previous section that this requires the Debye-Hückel shielding length $1/\kappa$ to be small compared to the hydrodynamic shielding length L_f of the polymer coil (for the definition of L_f, see pages 273–274)—a condition which applies even at moderate salt concentrations.

Let us consider a system in which the molar concentration of the charges carried by the polyion is m_f and the concentration of a uni-univalent salt is m_s. If only a fraction α_d of the polyion charges are dissociated from their counterions, then the specific conductivity l_{sp} is given by

$$l_{sp} = [(\mathfrak{F}/1000)\{m_f\alpha_d\bar{u}_p + m_s\bar{u}_b + (m_s + m_f\alpha_d)\bar{u}_c\}] \qquad (7.51)$$

where $\bar{u}_p$, $\bar{u}_b$, and $\bar{u}_c$ are the mobilities of the polyion, byion, and counterion, respectively. Relation (7.51) was first used by Huizenga et al. (1950) to calculate α_d for salt-free poly(acrylic acid) partially neutralized with sodium hydroxide. Their results are plotted in Fig. VII.15, which shows that ion binding is very extensive at high charge densities.

The question then arises how the degree of counterion dissociation α_d depends on the counterion concentration. Mock et al. (1954) found that with polysulfonic acids α_d is independent of the polymeric acid concentration or the concentration of added HCl. This observation parallels the constancy in the mobility of tetramethylammonium polyphosphate, referred to in the previous section, and is obviously characteristic of poly-

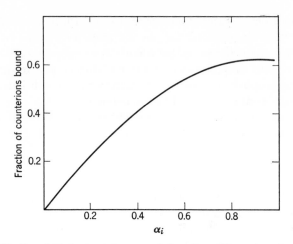

Fig. VII.15. Binding of Na$^+$ counterions to poly(acrylic acid) as a function of the degree of ionization of the polymeric acid.

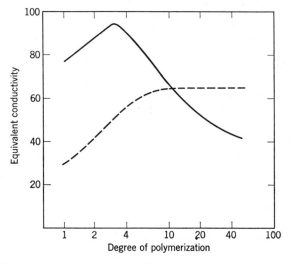

Fig. VII.16. Equivalent conductance of sodium polyphosphate (——) and of the polyphosphate ion (- -) as a function of the degree of polymerization.

ions which would not be expected to form specific complexes with their counterions. With sodium salts of polymeric acids, the equivalent conductance of the polyelectrolyte decreases slowly with increasing sodium ion concentration (Huizenga et al., 1950; Oth and Doty, 1952; Mock et al.,

1954) reflecting apparently an increasing tendency toward specific complex formation.

While the conductance of long chain polyelectrolytes is independent of the chain length of the polyion, a chain length dependence should be observed at relatively low degrees of polymerization. The nature of this dependence was studied by Schindewolf (1954b) on sodium polyphosphate. His results (cf. Fig. VII.16) show that the equivalent conductance of the polyelectrolyte first increases with the degree of polymerization and later decreases to approach an asymptotic value. This behavior may be interpreted as reflecting the superposition of two effects. Firstly, the ratio of the charge of the polyion to its frictional coefficient tends to increase with increasing chain length. Secondly, counterion binding increases as the polyion chain increases in length. If relation (7.51) is used to calculate α_d, the equivalent conductance of the polyphosphate ion may be obtained and this is found to increase monotonically towards a limiting value with an increasing degree of polymerization.

When polyions exist in a highly extended form, their mobility becomes significantly larger in the direction of maximum chain extension than in other directions. Thus, if the polyions are induced to assume a preferred spatial orientation, the electrical conductivity of the solution becomes dependent on the direction in which it is being measured. This fascinating effect has been observed in solutions of polyelectrolytes oriented by high shear gradients (Jacobson, 1953; Schindewolf, 1954a). It is particularly interesting that the same effect may be produced when a flexible chain polyelectrolyte solution is placed in a strong electrical *alternating* field (Eigen and Schwarz, 1957; Schwarz, 1959). In this case the orientation of the chains is due to the fact that the polarizability of the counterion cloud is at a maximum when the chain end displacement lies parallel to the electrical field. The success of this experiment is, therefore, a striking demonstration of the very large anisotropy of the polyion.

3. Diffusion and Sedimentation

The attachment of ionic charges to a macromolecular particle results in a reduction of its sedimentation coefficient. This reduction may be minimized by the addition of simple salts to the polyelectrolyte solution. The effect is observed even with globular molecules which would not be expected to change their shape when their degree of ionization is altered (Tiselius, 1932). The dependence of the sedimentation coefficient on the charge of the particle becomes, of course, more pronounced with flexible chain polyelectrolytes (Rosen et al., 1951; Howard and Jordan, 1954), in which the expansion of the polyion results in an increase of the frictional co-efficient.

When a polyelectrolyte solution is subjected to the gravitational field of the ultracentrifuge, the small ions would tend to sediment much more slowly than the polyion. However, since a macroscopic separation of the polyion from its counterions is not possible, the sedimenting polyion will necessarily have to pull its counterions with it. If the polyion is a hydro-dynamically impermeable coil, all ions which are located within the coil will be carried with it without any additional dissipation of energy by viscous friction. On the other hand, counterions which are outside the coil (or outside a globular protein particle carrying a net electrical charge) will add a relatively large term to the frictional coefficient of the polyelectrolyte and will thus lead to an appreciable decrease of the sedimentation rate. We may note that this effect should decrease with increasing salt concentration, since the polymer coil with the ions located in its interior becomes more nearly a Donnan system with vanishing net charge.

The theory of these phenomena was first formulated by Svedberg and Pedersen (cf. Pedersen, 1958) who considered the sedimentation rate of the polyion as the sum of two virtual motions, the first due to the gravitational field without consideration of electrostatic interactions and the second an electrophoretic flow caused by the electrical field X which is produced by the unequal sedimentation rate of the polyions and the small ions. The aggregate velocity u_i of each species i is then

$$u_i = s_i{}^* \omega^2 r - \bar{u}_i X/300 \qquad (7.52)$$

where $s_i{}^*$ is the sedimentation constant for a hypothetical condition in which the effects of electrical charge interactions are eliminated and $\bar{u}_i$ is the electrophoretic mobility of species i. Since the total current flow $\sum u_i m_i e \nu_i$ must vanish, we have

$$\omega^2 r \sum m_i e \nu_i s_i{}^* - (X/300) \sum m_i e \nu_i \bar{u}_i = 0$$

$$X/300 = \omega^2 r \sum m_i \nu_i s_i{}^* / \sum m_i \nu_i \bar{u}_i$$

$$s_i = s_i^0 - \bar{u}_i \sum m_i \nu_i s_i{}^* / \sum m_i \nu_i \bar{u}_i \qquad (7.53)$$

where s_i^0 is the sedimentation constant of species i as its concentration approaches zero. As a result, we should have for the polyion $s^0 = s^*$ in the limit of zero polyelectrolyte concentration in a solution of uni-univalent salt whose cation and anion have the same frictional coefficient. In practice, Pedersen has noted that s^0 for proteins bearing a net charge is always sig-nificantly smaller than it is at the isoelectric point. He ascribed this discrepancy to a swelling of the globular proteins, but such swelling would have to be improbably large to explain his data.

The discrepancy has been considered by Alexandrowicz and Daniel (1963) who suggested that the virtual electrophoretic mobility $\bar{u}_i$ should be expressed explicitly in terms of the charge and the frictional coefficient of the particle, $\bar{u}_i = e\nu_i/300f_i$ using for the frictional coefficient of the polyion the same value which determines its sedimentation velocity. This may lead, of course, to a mobility quite different from that observed in an electrophoresis experiment, where flexible chain polyions behave under most conditions as if they were free draining (pp. 359–360) even though the frictional coefficient controlling the sedimentation rate corresponds to an impermeable coil. The difference may be understood if it is remembered that in electrophoresis anions and cations move in opposite directions, so that the net force acting on a volume element vanishes if the Donnan approximation is justified. On the other hand, polyions and counterions move in the same direction in a sedimentation experiment, so that the criteria of the hydrodynamic permeability of a chain molecule will not change when the chain carries an ionic charge. Both the Svedberg–Pedersen and the Alexandrowicz–Daniel treatments predict that the charge effect on the sedimentation rate disappears in the limit of infinite dilution of the polyelectrolyte, provided the anions and cations of the supporting electrolyte have the same mobility. This conclusion seems unreasonable, since the friction due to the motion of counterions, pulled behind the polyion, must retard the sedimentation rate no matter how dilute the polyion. The source of the error seems to be in the smearing out of the polymer charge over the entire volume of the solution implied by the manner of calculating X in eq. (7.53).

The conversion of uncharged macromolecules to polyelectrolytes has the effect of increasing the number of osmotically active particles and this increases the driving force for diffusion (Kedem and Katchalsky, 1955). We may note that the forces between the polyions and the counterions produce in sedimentation and in diffusion effects which work in opposite directions. In sedimentation, the driving force on the light counterions is small and they retard the polyion, while in diffusion the driving force is independent of particle size, so that the counterions increase the driving force by a larger factor than the frictional resistance to translation. One interesting effect deserves special attention. Since the expansion of the polyions in salt-free solutions of flexible chain polyelectrolytes increases sharply with the dilution of the system, the frictional coefficient of these polyions is correspondingly increased. This effect and the increasing electrophoretic effect, as discussed above, cooperate in producing a diffusion coefficient which drops sharply as the polyelectrolyte concentration is reduced, instead of increasing slowly as with uncharged polymers. A polyelectrolyte solution diffusing into the pure solvent tends, therefore, to produce a front with an extremely high concentration gradient, frequently giving the appearance of the swelling of a crosslinked gel. A detailed investigation of this phenomenon has been reported by Nagasawa and Fujita (1964).

Chapter VIII

MOLECULAR ASSOCIATION

Dissolved macromolecules frequently form molecular association complexes either with species of low molecular weight or with other macromolecules. We may cite as typical examples of the first class the binding of cations to polymeric acids, the binding of iodine to amylose and the association of enzymes with substrates, inhibitors, coenzymes, and activating ions. Molecular association of macromolecules with one another encompasses an even broader range of phenomena, such as the aggregation of poly(vinyl chloride) molecules in certain solvent media, nonspecific associations of cationic and anionic polymers, the formation of hemoglobin and a number of other biologically important substances from separate protein subunits, the interactions of antigens with antibodies, and the spontaneous formation of the tobacco mosaic virus particle from its nucleic acid and protein. The formation of DNA from the two polydeoxyribonucleotide strands (discussed in Chap. III, Sec. C-2) also falls into this category.

The study of such phenomena may be motivated by a number of different objectives. For example, the binding of cations by polymeric acids raises the question of how a large number of ligand groups attached to the backbone of a flexible chain molecule can cooperate in the formation of chelate complexes. The ion binding equilibria in homogeneous solution have also an obvious relevance to equilibria in heterogeneous systems containing crosslinked polyelectrolytes, i.e., ion exchange resins. It is also clearly necessary to understand molecular aggregation of synthetic or natural macromolecules if the concept of a molecular weight is to have an unambiguous significance. The tendency of randomly coiled macromolecules to aggregate in solution is also frequently related to the ability of a polymer–solvent system to form a thermally reversible gel. However, the most intriguing problems in this field concern the high degree of specificity characteristic of the molecular association behavior of certain biologically important macromolecules. For instance, it is well known that an antibody will associate much more powerfully with one particular macromolecule (its "homologous antigen") than with a number of very similar substances, even if no difference between these substances can be demonstrated by any other method.   It appears that this specificity depends on a complementariness of the "molecular surfaces," particularly closely defined in proteins which retain in solution a highly specific tertiary structure (see pages 153–159).   Although the discovery of the retention of helical conformation in solutions of synthetic polypeptides and polynucleotides demonstrates that it is possible to produce synthetic polymers which are characterized in solution by a high degree of conformational rigidity, it is unknown how a synthetic polymer could be induced to fold in a unique way into a globular particle and such folding may be essential to a high degree of specificity in molecular association, such as is exhibited by antibodies and enzymes.

Many of the methods discussed in previous chapters are applicable to a study of association.   When a small molecular species associates with a macromolecule, the equilibrium may frequently be studied by the distribution of the small species across a semipermeable membrane (dialysis equilibrium).   If the small species has a characteristic spectral absorption, the concentration of the unassociated molecules may be determined from the optical density at the top of the cell after sedimentation of the polymer in an ultracentrifuge.   In some cases, association is accompanied by a spectral shift or a change in fluorescence which may be utilized in estimating the association equilibrium.   If the interacting species bear an electrostatic charge, association may be inferred from electrophoretic measurements.

Similarly, a variety of methods may be employed in studying the association of macromolecules with one another.   Such association will lead to increasing molecular weights and any primary method for molecular weight determination (osmometry, light scattering, equilibrium ultracentrifugation) will lend itself to a study of molecular aggregation phenomena.   The utilization of the frictional properties of macromolecules is often useful, although the interpretation of the experimental data may be somewhat uncertain.   For instance, let us consider the effect of dimerization on the intrinsic viscosity $[\eta]$ of an elongated rigid particle.   We have seen (Chap. VI, Sec. C-1) that $[\eta]$ is a function of the axial ratio of the hydrodynamically equivalent ellipsoid of revolution.   The dimerization process may then lead to an increase or a decrease of intrinsic viscosity, depending on whether the association occurs end-to-end or side-to-side, resulting in an increase or a decrease in the asymmetry of the particle (see Fig. VIII.1).   In fact, it is easy to visualize an association in which the doublet has an asymmetry similar to that of the isolated particle, so that $[\eta]$ remains unaffected by the association process.   In considering the effect of molecular aggregation on the ultracentrifuge sedimentation rate, we may at least make the qualitative

| (a) | (b) | (c) |

Fig. VIII.1. Association of elongated particles.   End-to-end association (a) increases $[\eta]$; side-by-side association (b) reduced $[\eta]$; an intermediate type of association (c) may leave $[\eta]$ unchanged.

prediction that sedimentation will be accelerated.   This follows, since the sedimentation velocity is proportional to the ratio of molecular weight and the translational frictional coefficient, and any hydrodynamic interactions will, in general, reduce the frictional coefficient of the complex below the sum of the frictional coefficients of the associating particles.*   In the case of electrophoresis, molecular association of like particles may or may not lead to a change of mobility.   However, electrophoresis may be employed most usefully for the study of molecular association of dissimilar polymers carrying ionic charges.   An excellent review of these various methods and the treatment of experimental data has been prepared by Nichol et al. (1964).

In interpreting experimental data, it is essential to take into account the relation between the rate of the molecular dissociation or association processes and the time scale of the experimental method.   For instance, if the association of macromolecules and the dissociation of their complex occurs many times during an ultracentrifuge sedimentation run, a single sedimentation boundary will be observed and the velocity with which this boundary moves will reflect a weighted average of the velocities characteristic of the isolated particles and their complex.   It is the unique advantage of optical methods (light scattering, spectroscopy) that they make it possible to study the instantaneous state of the system, so that they enable the investigator to follow the time dependence of a molecular association process up to relatively high velocities.

A. ASSOCIATION OF MACROMOLECULES WITH LOW MOLECULAR WEIGHT SPECIES

1. Ion Binding by Flexible Polyion Chains

In our previous discussion in Chap. VII we listed a variety of evidence for the strong interactions of polyions with their counterions.   However, as

* It is here assumed that the shape of the interacting particles is not altered in the association process.   In the case of the association of randomly coiled single-stranded DNA to the rod-like double-helical structure, the frictional coefficient of the double helix may exceed appreciably the sum of the frictional coefficients of the two single strands.

long as we restrict ourselves to the thermodynamic properties of the system, there is no way of distinguishing between the binding of counterions to specific sites of the polyion and a reduction of the counterion activity due to long-range electrostatic attraction by the highly charged polyion. A clear demonstration that site binding exists, was furnished by Huizenga et al. (1950), who showed that in the electrophoresis of a solution containing poly(sodium acrylate), part of the sodium ions migrate with the polyanion toward the anode. The rate of exchange of bound and free cations was studied later (Wall and Grieger, 1952; Wall et al., 1952) utilizing radioactive sodium. Here a sintered glass plug separated the poly(sodium acrylate) solution into two compartments, one of which contained the radioactive tracer. It is instructive to consider the electrophoretic behavior of the system which would be expected if the exchange of free and bound sodium ions were either infinitely slow or infinitely fast. In the first case the bound cations would migrate toward the anode and the free cations toward the cathode, so that the radioactivity of the solution would have two discontinuities traveling in opposite directions. In the second case, each cation would travel part of the time in one and part of the time in the opposite direction, so that its apparent mobility would be $\bar{u}_b \alpha_d + \bar{u}_f(1 - \alpha_d)$, where $\bar{u}_b$, $\bar{u}_f$ are the mobilities (with the appropriate sign) of the ion in the bound and free state, while α_d is the fraction of cations which are bound to the polyion. The intermediate case, where the rate of exchange is appreciable but not large compared with the experimental time scale, was found to represent the behavior of the poly(sodium acrylate) solution. In this case, the distribution of radioactivity can be interpreted in terms of the rate constant for the exchange of free and bound cations. Alternatively, it is possible to estimate the extent of counterion binding and the rate of exchange of free and bound counterions by measuring the steady-state concentration of a radioactive tracer ion in an apparatus in which a central compartment is separated by porous plugs from electrode compartments in which the tracer concentration is maintained at a constant high and low level (Gill and Ferry, 1962). With this technique it was found that cesium is bound to a polyacrylate chain much less than sodium (Ferry and Gill, 1962; Noll and Gill, 1963) as would be expected since the alkali ion with the smaller crystallographic radius should form more stable complexes.

Counterion binding of alkali cations can also be demonstrated by dilatometric measurements. The water of hydration of a cation is in a highly compressed state, and when such water is replaced by another ligand a characteristic expansion is observed. This effect was demonstrated by Strauss and Leung (1965) on mixing tetramethylammonium salts of polymeric acids with alkali halides.

Much more stable complexes are formed by polyanions with divalent cations. In this case several of the functional groups attached to the polymeric chain may associate simultaneously with a given cation to form a chelate complex. The analysis of such equilibria is simplest if the polymer carries isolated groups of ligands, which form only one type of chelate with the cations under study. For instance, hydrolyzed copolymers of maleic anhydride with a comonomer, which cannot participate in chelation, carry isolated pairs of carboxyl groups which can form only one kind of complex with alkaline earth ions, since these ions are known to associate only with two carboxylate groups. Chelation equilibria in systems of this type

$$....CH_2-CH-CH--C-CH_2-CH... +M^{++} \rightleftharpoons$$
$$\quad\quad\ \ | \quad\ | \quad\ \ | \quad\ |$$
$$\quad\quad\ \ X \quad COO^- \ COO^- \quad X$$

$$....CH_2-CH-CH-CH-CH_2-CH ....$$
$$\quad\quad\quad\quad\quad | \quad\ | \quad | \quad\quad |$$
$$\quad\quad\quad\quad\quad X \quad CO \ CO \quad\quad X$$
$$\quad\quad\quad\quad\quad\quad\quad\ | \quad\ |$$
$$\quad\quad\quad\quad\quad\quad\quad\ O^- \ .O^-$$
$$\quad\quad\quad\quad\quad\quad\quad\quad M^{++}$$

have been studied by Morawetz et al. (1954). Since the associating cation competes with hydrogen ions for the carboxylate groups, the presence of these cations will produce a shift in the titration curve of the polymeric acid. This shift may be interpreted in terms of the extent of ion binding provided it can be assumed that the apparent acidity of carboxyls in polyions carrying bound cations is determined only by the net charge density along the chain. It is desirable to carry out such experiments in the presence of high concentrations of an electrolyte whose ions have as low a tendency as possible to form complexes (e.g., KNO_3). In this manner the contribution of the electrostatic free energy of complexation is minimized, so that the experimental data reflect mostly the specific interaction of polyion and counterion.

A situation which is more difficult to analyze is encountered in solutions of partially ionized poly(acrylic acid) or poly(methacrylic acid) containing Cu^{++} ions. In this case the ligand groups are evenly spaced along the polyion and the cation is capable of forming complexes with up to four carboxylate groups. An unambiguous measure of copper binding may be obtained from measurements of the dialysis equilibrium, preferably at a high concentration of an inert electrolyte, so as to swamp the Donnan effect (Kotliar and Morawetz, 1955). However, such data give no information about the nature of the complex. The titration shift method has been used by Gregor et al. (1955) and, more recently, by Mandel and Leyte

(1964) whose data are plotted in Fig. VIII.2. These data have been interpreted as indicating the presence of chelates with two carboxylate groups bound to a cupric ion. In principle, spectroscopy should offer a more reliable method for identifying a complex ion and the use of this method is illustrated in Fig. VIII.3, which compares the spectrum of Cu^{++} in partially ionized poly(methacrylic acid) solution with Cu^{++} spectra in sodium acetate solutions of various concentrations (Morawetz, 1955). Unfortunately, several types of complex ions are present at any given acetate concentration, so that the spectra of the individual species are unknown. Nevertheless, these spectra suggest that the cupric ion is bound

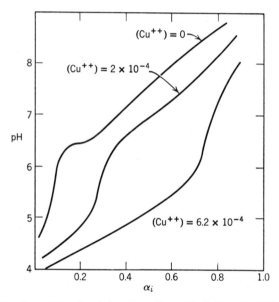

Fig. VIII.2. Titration shift of poly(methacrylic acid) $(1.7 \times 10^{-3}N)$ on addition of cupric nitrate.

to a higher number of carboxylates in the polycarboxylic acid solution than in $3.15M$ sodium acetate, where it is known to be associated with an average of three acetate ions. It is also worth noting that the spectroscopic evidence shows clearly that the nature of the complex is independent of the dilution of the polymeric acid. This is what would be expected, since the number of carboxylates with which a complex-forming cation will associate depends only on conditions within the polyion coil to which this cation is bound.

The spectroscopic method was used advantageously in a study of Cu^{++} binding to poly(ϵ-methacrylyl-L-lysine) (Morawetz and Sammak, 1957). This polymer is represented by

$$
\begin{array}{c}
CH_3 \\
| \\
(-CH_2-C-)_n \\
| \\
CO \\
| \\
NH \\
| \\
(CH_2)_4 \\
| \quad + \\
CH\overset{+}{N}H_3 \\
| \\
COO^-
\end{array}
$$

and the α-amino acid groups at the end of the side chains may form two types of complexes with cupric ions:

$$
\left[
\begin{array}{c}
\quad H \quad H_2 \\
\quad | \quad\; | \\
R-C-N \\
\quad | \qquad\; \searrow \\
\quad C-O \;\nearrow Cu \\
\quad \| \\
\quad O
\end{array}
\right]^{+}
\qquad
\left[
\begin{array}{c}
\;\; H \quad H_2 \qquad H_2 \;\; H \\
\;\; | \quad\; | \qquad\;\; | \quad\; | \\
R-C-N \qquad\quad N-C-R \\
\;\; | \qquad\;\; \searrow \;\; \swarrow \qquad | \\
\;\; C-O \;\nearrow Cu \nwarrow\; O-C \\
\;\; \| \qquad\qquad\qquad\quad \| \\
\;\; O \qquad\qquad\qquad\quad O
\end{array}
\right]
$$

The spectra of these complexes may be determined from solutions containing Cu^{++} and simple amino acids in the appropriate concentrations and these may then be used as standards in the analysis of spectra observed in the polymer solution in terms of the number of cupric ions bound to one or two amino acid residues. The results show that the cupric ion has a very high tendency to bind two amino acid groups carried by the same polymer chain, although such a complex necessitates the formation of very large chelate rings. It is clear that the restriction to form only chelate rings containing five or six atoms, which is characteristic of low molecular weight complexing agents, does not apply to polymers, because of the large number of ligands available for chelate formation. The behavior of an ion in a solution of such a polymer may then be expressed in terms of the "effective concentration" c_{eff} of ligand groups with which a reference ligand group may participate in the formation of a chelate complex. Since the probability of forming a ring of n atoms is proportional to $n^{-3/2}$ (Kuhn, 1934), the aggregate probability of forming any ring with more than n^* atoms fairly rapidly approaches a limiting value as the chain length is being extended, and the chelating properties of high polymers would be

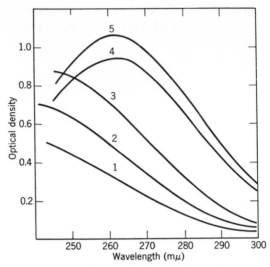

Fig. VIII.3. Absorption spectra of cupric ion complexes in acetate and in partially ionized poly(methacrylic acid) solutions. (1) $0.2M$ NaOAc; (2) $1M$ NaOAc; (3) $3.15M$ NaOAc; (4) $0.1N$ PMA, $\alpha_i = 0.34$; (5) $0.01N$ PMA, $\alpha_i = 0.34$.

expected to be independent of their molecular weight (Morawetz, 1957). This prediction is in accord with experimental data (Strauss and Siegel, 1963).

Interesting results were obtained in studies of cation binding to stereoregular poly(methacrylic acid). In the case of Cu^{++}, the cation was bound more strongly to the isotactic polyion (O'Neill, 1963) while magnesium ions formed a more stable complex with the syndiotactic species (Kandanian, 1964). These findings seemingly suggest that chelate formation involves carboxylate groups which are kept at a well defined spacing from one another by the preferred conformation of the chain backbone. The relative stability of a complex would then depend on the geometry of the chelate characteristic of a given cationic species. The importance of the preferred conformation of the chain backbone is convincingly demonstrated in cases where the polyion may undergo helix-coil transitions. With poly(α-L-glutamic acid) the binding of alkaline earth cations is clearly favored by the helical conformation of the polymeric acid (Jacobson, 1964). Conversely, Mg^{++} is bound more weakly by the native helical form of DNA, although this form binds Na^+ much more strongly than the denatured nucleic acid (Lyons and Kotin, 1964). Another interesting problem arises if the bound species is an organic molecule carrying two cationic groups. In that case it is conceivable that the spacing of the cationic sites in the small molecule matches the spacing of the anionic groups in the polymer and such a fit should produce particularly strong binding. Such an effect has apparently been observed with chondroitin sulfate-A (Ehrenpreis and Fishman, 1960) and hyaluronic acid (Ehrenpreis and Kellock, 1960), which form strong complexes with curare,

$$(CH_3)_2$$

$$-N^+ \quad CH_2 \quad O \quad HO \quad OCH_3$$

$$OCH_3 \quad O \quad HO \quad H_2C \quad N^+$$

$$(CH_3)_2$$

a material consisting of very stiff molecules with a well defined spacing between the two cationic groups. Characteristically, no analogous complexation is observed with bispyridinium cations in which the pyridinium residues are joined by a flexible chain. In a more recent study by Kandanian (1964), in which the binding of bolaform cations of the type

$$N^+-(CH_2)_n-N^+$$

to poly(acrylic acid) and poly(methacrylic acid) was studied, no evidence was found for a specificity based on a steric fit of the interacting species. However, it was found again that binding of the bolaform cations depended (as in the case of Cu^{++} and Mg^{++}) on the stereoregularity of poly(methacrylic acid), with the syndiotactic species forming the more stable complexes. While the complex with poly(acrylic acid) became weaker with an increasing separation of the pyridinium groups, the reverse was true for poly(methacrylic acid), where hydrophobic bonding apparently made an important contribution to the stability of the complex.

The binding of cationic dyes to polymeric acids is frequently accompanied by a characteristic spectral shift. This is usually referred to as the "metachromatic effect" and is similar to the shift which occurs when dye molecules aggregate with one another in the absence of polymer. We may, therefore, think of the polymer as an agent which facilitates the aggregation of the dye molecules. The fraction of the dye molecules occupying neighboring sites on the polymer (and characterized, therefore, by the metachromatic shift) depends not only on the dye:polymer ratio, but also on the nature of the polymer (Bradley and Wolf, 1959). The experimental data may be accounted for quantitatively by assigning to every dye–polymer system a "stacking tendency" which expresses the relative preference of a dye to occupy a site next to another bound dye molecule rather than an isolated site on the polymer chain.   For the dye acridine orange, Bradley and Wolf found stacking tendencies with various anions ranging from 3 for native DNA to 800 for polyphosphate.   As might be expected, native and denatured DNA behave in a different fashion.   The stacking tendency is found to increase markedly on denaturation (Bradley and Felsenfeld, 1959; Stone and Bradley, 1961).   In the case of systems containing a polymer and two dyes, the spectra may not be accountable by the metachromatic shifts of the individual dyes and the "complex metachromasis" reflects then the tendency of dissimilar dye molecules to occupy neighboring positions on the polymer chain (Pal and Schubert, 1963).

Association with a dissolved polymer may result in the quenching of the fluorescence of a dye (e.g., acriflavine in the presence of DNA, cf. Oster, 1957).   Conversely, a number of dyes do not fluoresce unless they are complexed with a polymer.   This is the behavior of certain triphenylmethane dyes in solutions of poly(methacrylic acid) (Oster and Bellin, 1957).   An interesting experiment is described by Oster (1955) who showed that the fluorescence of a dye associated with DNA may be gradually eliminated by displacing it from the complex with a more strongly bound nonfluorescent cationic species.   The depolarization of the fluorescence of a dye bound to a polymeric species may also be used to study the rigidity of the macromolecule.   We have seen in Chap. VI (Sec. B-5) that the depolarization of fluorescence depends on the rotational diffusion coefficient of the fluorescing species.   If this species is attached to a side chain of a flexible polymer molecule, rotational motions of the side chain are possible without significant motion of the backbone.   However, if the polymer forms a rigid structure, rotation of the fluorescing species may involve rotation of the whole macromolecule; under these conditions the motion is greatly slowed down and the depolarization of fluorescence correspondingly reduced.   This principle was used by Ermolenko and Katibnikov (1962) to demonstrate the stiffening of poly(methacrylic acid) chains with an increasing degree of ionization.

When a dye is bound to a chain polymer which exists in solution in a helical conformation, the dye (though consisting of molecules without a center of asymmetry) may exhibit optical activity because of its asymmetrical environment.   Such an effect is observed in the binding of acridine orange to the helical form of poly(α-L-glutamic acid) and the sign of the

Cotton effect in the absorption band of the dye may be correlated with the direction in which the polypeptide helix is wound (Stryer and Blout, 1961). As would be expected, this Cotton band disappears when the pH of the solution is raised to a value which leads to the transition of the helical to the randomly coiled form of the polypeptide chain; the dye thus serves as a probe indicating the asymmetry of a site to which it is adsorbed. A similar phenomenon is observed when acridine orange is added to a solution of native DNA (Neville and Bradley, 1961). However, in this case an added complication is introduced, since the absorption band of the dye shifts when two dye molecules come into close contact with one another. As a result, the location of the Cotton effect changes with the density of dye molecules adsorbed on the nucleic acid and the rotatory dispersion data may be interpreted in terms of the distribution of the dye molecules on the DNA.

While specific cation binding to polymeric acids is a favorite subject of study, the specific binding of anions to cationic polymers has been largely neglected. An interesting example of a process of this type was reported by Strauss et al. (1954), who found by electrophoretic studies that the sign of the charge of quaternized poly(vinyl pyridine) may be reversed in the presence of high concentrations of bromide. This effect may be accounted for by the formation of a charge-transfer complex of the pyridine nucleus with the bromide ion, which may be demonstrated by a shift in the UV absorption spectrum (Slough, 1959).

2. Association of Small Molecules and Ions with Uncharged Chain Molecules

The association equilibria of chain molecules with species of low molecular weight may be of two types. In the first, the functional groups attached to the molecular backbone interact with various reagents in much the same manner as would be expected of low molecular weight analogs of the repeating unit of the macromolecule. A characteristic case of this type is the formation of highly colored charge-transfer complexes of poly(α-vinyl-naphthalene) with strong electron acceptors (Slough, 1962). For instance, a solution of this polymer will develop, on addition of tetracyanoethylene, an absorption spectrum with maxima at 5900 and 4500 Å, quite similar to spectra observed in solutions containing tetracyanoethylene with naphthalene. Of much more interest are, however, macromolecular complexes of the second type, in which cooperative phenomena are essential to the stability of the complex, so that the polymer behaves in a manner which is qualitatively different from that of its low molecular weight analogs.

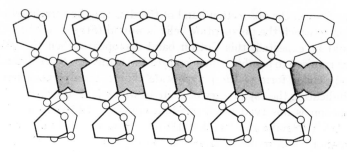

Fig. VIII.4. Model of an amylose helix with iodine molecules stacked up in the helical cavity.

The best known example of this kind of molecular aggregate is the formation of the blue starch–iodine complex. It was described only three years after the discovery of elemental iodine (Colin and Gaultier de Claubry, 1814) and in reading the account of the experiments describing that "la couleur est d'un bleu superbe si ces substances sont en proportions convenable" one may relive the excitement caused by the first observation of this beautiful phenomenon. The first quantitative study seems to be that of Küster (1894) who showed that the iodine content of the complex increases with the concentration of free iodine in solution. In modern times, it was demonstrated that starch consists generally of two fractions, the linear chain amylose and the highly branched amylopectin, and that only amylose forms the blue iodine complex, while the complex of amylopectin is reddish. Bates et al. (1943) introduced the study of the starch–iodine equilibrium by potentiometric titration and they found that the affinity of iodine was much higher for the amylose fraction. This affinity was found to increase with the chainlength of the polymer, so that two titration end points could be detected in a system containing two amylose fractions of widely different molecular weight.

It is now generally believed that the formation of the amylose–iodine complex involves a helical conformation of the amylose chain which leaves in the center of the helix a channel-like cavity with dimensions appropriate for the accommodation of the iodine. (See Fig. VIII.4). This model was first proposed by Hanes (1937) and by Freudenberg et al. (1939) before the discovery of the urea clathrate compounds, whose structure reflects the same general principle. It has been substantiated by the finding that the starch–iodine complex forms hexagonal crystals (Rundle and French, 1943), which would be difficult to account for with any other geometry of the amylose chains, and was strengthened further by the discovery of flow dichroism (Rundle and Baldwin, 1943) proving that the iodine chains lie parallel to the long dimension of the amylose chain.* The formation of the iodine complex has been found to leave the viscosity of amylose solutions unchanged, suggesting that helical conformations are favored even in the absence of iodine (Hollo and Szejtli, 1958). In the case of carboxymethyl-amylose, the iodine complex can form only at low pH, presumably because the helical chain conformation is disrupted by the mutual repulsion of the ionized carboxyls at higher pH values (Rao and Foster, 1965).

Spectroscopic studies of the amylose–iodine complex have shown that the characteristic absorption develops only with amylose chains containing a minimum of six glucose residues (Rundle and Baldwin, 1943; Swanson, 1948). The extinction coefficient increases with the amylose chain length and at the same time the absorption maximum shifts toward longer wavelengths (with λ_{max} moving from 618 to 628 mμ as the degree of polymerization is increased from 250 to 500). It has been suggested that the color observed in the amylopectin–iodine system reflects then the number of glucose units between the branch points of the macromolecule (Baldwin et al., 1944; Swanson, 1948). No color develops if iodide is rigorously excluded from the system; the absorption intensity increases first with increasing iodide concentration, but at high concentrations of iodide the absorption is again reduced with a shift of the absorption maximum to shorter wavelengths. There is also generally a tendency for the absorption to be intensified and the absorption maximum to be shifted to longer wavelengths by an increase in the ionic strength of the solution (Kuge and Ono, 1960). These findings suggest that the complex contains chains with a preferred ratio of I_2 and I^-; this ratio is 3:2 according to the potentiometric studies of Gilbert and Marriott (1948) and 1:1 according to the spectroscopic data obtained by Kontos (1959). At any rate, it has been found that the amylose acquires an increasingly negative charge during complexation with iodine (Beckmann, 1964). Such a process would, of course, be favored by an increase in the ionic strength, which would reduce the electrostatic free energy of the complex formation.

Several attempts have been made to formulate a theory for amylose–iodine complexation. Such a theory would have to account mainly for two features of the phenomenon, i.e., the increasing stability of the complex with an increasing chainlength of the polymer and the observed absorption spectrum. Stein and Rundle (1948) believed that the forces responsible for the formation of the complex originate in the large dipole of the amylose helix; this induces dipoles in the iodine molecules and the effect of dipole interactions increases cooperatively with the number of interacting iodine

* This appears to be the first demonstration showing that chain molecules can exist in solution in a helical conformation.

molecules. The alignment of the iodine within the helix would be expected to lead to electron delocalization, which would tend to shift the absorption maximum to longer wavelengths as the iodine chain is being extended (Ono et al., 1953). The iodine chain may be described as a "one-dimensional metal" and it is significant that the solid amylose–iodine complex gives an electron spin resonance spectrum similar to that observed in metallic lithium or sodium (Bersohn and Isenberg, 1961). In this context it is interesting that the benzamide–triiodide complex $HI_3 \cdot 2C_6H_5CONH_2$, which forms crystals with triiodide chains similar to those which have been postulated for the amylose complex, has also a very similar absorption in the visible spectrum (Reddy et al., 1964; Robin, 1964). On the other hand, there appears to be strong evidence that the integrity of either the I_2 molecule or the I_3^- ion is not preserved in the amylose complex. Cyclohexaamylose, a cyclic analog of amylose, forms iodine inclusion compounds with a spectrum very similar to that of amylose–iodine and single crystals of this compound may be obtained for crystallographic analysis. The x-ray diffraction patterns from such crystals indicate (see Dietrich and Cramer, 1954) that the iodine atoms are stacked up within the cylindrical cavity at a uniform distance of 3.06 Å; this would, of course, make the description of the arrangement as a unidimensional metal even more appropriate.

In analogy with urea inclusion compounds (for a review cf. Cramer, 1954) one would expect the amylose helix to be able to accommodate a variety of linear molecules which might fit into the helical cavity. On the other hand, since polarizability is apparently a prerequisite for the formation of inclusion compounds with amylose, the complexation should not be exhibited by paraffin hydrocarbons, but by their polar derivatives such as alcohols or fatty acids. Experimental results are in agreement with these concepts; in fact, it has been shown by potentiometric titration that fatty acids may displace iodine from its amylose complex (Mikus et al., 1946).

Poly(vinyl alcohol) has been found to produce with iodine (or possibly with triiodide) a highly colored complex similar to that observed with amylose (Staudinger et al., 1927). This is somewhat surprising, since poly(vinyl alcohol) would not be expected to exist in helical conformations which would enclose a cavity of sufficient dimensions to contain the iodine. A more detailed examination has shown that the extinction coefficient of poly(vinyl alcohol)–iodine increases with the chain length of the polymer (suggesting again that a cooperative phenomenon is responsible for complexation) but, in contrast to the behavior of the amylose complex, the location of the absorption maximum is 620 mμ independent of molecular weight (Imai and Matsumoto, 1961). If a specific conformation is required for the formation of the complex, the color should deepen with an increasing stereoregulation of the poly(vinyl alcohol). The findings of Imai and Matsumoto are in accord with this concept, since they show that preparative procedures which should make the poly(vinyl alcohol) more syndiotactic, strongly enhance the color of its iodine complex. A very thorough study of the poly(vinyl alcohol)–iodine system by Zwick (1965) showed that the location of the absorption maximum is shifted to longer wavelengths by reducing the iodine:polymer ratio, and may be displaced up to 700 mμ by the addition of boric acid. However, the spectrum of the complex depends on the sequence in which the reagents are added to each other, indicating that the properties of the system may frequently not reflect equilibrium conditions. The data are interpreted by a model in which helically wound sections of the polymer, enclosing chains of iodine atoms, are separated by randomly coiled portions of the chain, with the helical sections tending to associate with one another. The resulting structures rearrange, apparently, exceedingly slowly when the conditions are changed. At full saturation, the complex contains one iodine atom for twelve monomer residues of the chain molecule. It has also been found that the ability of poly(vinyl alcohol) to bind species of low molecular weight is not limited to iodine. A variety of small molecules, such as polyhydric phenols, naphthylsalicylamide, and the diamide of salicylic acid and benzidine have been found to cause gelation of poly(vinyl alcohol) solutions (McDowell and Kenyon, 1941; Lowe, 1943). It is certain that soluble complexes must be formed before the system sets to a gel but no studies of the association equilibria have been reported. However, detailed studies have been published dealing with the association of poly(vinyl alcohol) with anionic detergents (Saito, 1953, 1954, 1957; Isemura and Imanishi, 1958). This case is remarkable in that the anionic species have to overcome an increasing electrostatic repulsion to associate with the polymer, which acquires in the process a high charge density and behaves in the manner typical of flexible polyion chains.

Another uncharged polymer, poly(N-vinyl pyrrolidone)

$$(-CH_2-CH-)_n$$

$$
\begin{array}{c}
N \\
CH_2 \quad CO \\
CH_2-CH_2
\end{array}
$$

has been observed to bind a wide variety of small molecules and ions (Scholtan, 1954). If the polymer is added to a solution of iodine in potassium iodide, the spectral absorption is strongly intensified but the absorption maximum shifts only slightly from 350 to 360 mμ, i.e., the complex is quite different from the blue species which iodine forms with amylose or poly-(vinyl alcohol). A cooperative phenomenon may not be required in this case to account for the complex formation, since iodine and ethylpyrrolidone also seem to form an association complex as indicated by a shift in the frequency of the carbonyl stretching vibration (Néel and Sébille, 1961). Measurements of the dialysis equilibrium show that both iodide and iodine are bound to the polymer; the I^-/I_2 ratio carried by the polymer tends to increase with increasing concentration of free iodide in the solution (Barkin et al., 1955). In spite of the charge acquired by the poly(N-vinyl pyrrolidone) in this process, the solution viscosity drops sharply, presumably due to poor solvation of the complex.

Poly(N-vinyl pyrrolidone) behaves in a manner similar to that of poly-(vinyl alcohol) in forming association complexes with anionic detergents (Saito, 1957; Barkin, 1957) and dyes (Scholtan, 1953; Saito, 1957; Frank et al., 1957). In some cases, association of a dye with the polymer produces a characteristic change in fluorescence and a shift in the absorption spectrum which then provides a convenient index of the association equilibrium (Bellin and Oster, 1957). A very detailed study of the association of a variety of aromatic molecules to poly(N-vinyl pyrrolidone) has been published by Molyneux and Frank (1961). They found that the association process is typically endothermic, suggesting that hydrophobic bonding (cf. Chap. II, Sec. A-6) is the main driving force. In agreement with other investigators, they found that only neutral and anionic materials are bound, while species such as the anilinium ion do not interact with the polymer. In this respect poly(N-vinyl pyrrolidone) resembles poly(vinyl alcohol) but the cause for the preference of these uncharged macromolecules for anions over cations is completely unknown. The association equilibria approximate the form of a Langmuir adsorption isotherm with a polymer segment of ten monomer units acting as an adsorption site for all of the small molecules investigated, in spite of their rather pronounced difference of size.

Some water-insoluble polymers, such as poly(vinyl acetate) or poly(vinyl formal), dissolve in aqueous solutions of anionic detergents (Saito, 1953, 1954; Isemura and Imanishi, 1958). The solutions are optically clear and have a relatively high specific viscosity, so that they obviously cannot be considered colloidal dispersions of relatively large polymer particles. The behavior of such systems suggests that the individual polymer chains adsorb a large number of the detergent anions, so that they behave like poly-anions with chains highly expanded due to the mutual electrostatic repulsion of the adsorbed species.

3. Binding of Small Molecules and Ions to Globular Proteins

Proteins contain a variety of functional groups which are known to form complexes with multivalent cations.   It is then not surprising to find that these cations form protein association complexes and in many cases the stability of such complexes is in reasonable agreement with predictions made on the basis of complexation data with low molecular weight analogs, taking proper account of the electrostatic free energy characterizing the association with the charged macromolecule.   The nature of the groups participating in the complex formation may be deduced from the pH dependence of the association constant and from spectroscopic data.   Typical examples of cation binding to proteins falling into this category is the binding of cupric ion (Klotz and Fiess, 1951) and of zinc ion (Gurd and Goodman, 1952) to serum albumin.   In the case of enzymes, inhibition by traces of heavy metals is typically encountered if the thiol group of a cysteine residue forms part of the catalytically active site and this inhibition may then be taken as a measure of complex formation by this thiol group.   For instance, with the enzyme urease half of the activity is lost in solutions containing $10^{-10}M$ free silver ion and this result is reasonable in view of the known affinity of low molecular weight mercaptans for Ag^+ (Ambrose et al., 1951).

There are, however, numerous cases of ion binding to globular proteins which do not lend themselves to such a simple interpretation.   It is found, for instance, that certain enzymes which require specific ions for their catalytic activity bind these ions much more tightly than might be expected from the known behavior of the ligand groups carried by the enzyme.   The specificity of ion binding is also frequently quite unlike the behavior of low molecular weight complexation reagents.   For instance, the enzyme enolase is activated by Zn^{++}, which is known to form very stable complexes, as well as by Mg^{++} and Mn^{++}, which are weak complex formers, but by no other ions (Malmström, 1955).   The association constant of enolase with Mg^{++} is 3300 at pH 7.2 (Malmström, 1955) and that of carbonic anhydrase with activating Zn^{++} is 10^{12} at pH 7.5 (Lindskog and Malmström, 1962). These high values clearly imply a cooperative effect of several ligand groups at a spacing highly favorable for the formation of a chelate.   We may think of the ion as fitting neatly into a cavity in the rigid structure of the globular protein, with appropriate ligand groups in favorable juxtaposition.   This

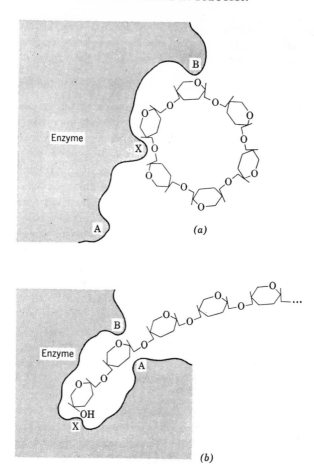

Fig. VIII.5. Schematic representation of the evidence for an "induced fit" of the enzyme β-amylase with its specific substrate amylose. (a) Cyclohexaamylose is bound to the enzyme by energetic interactions of groups B and X, but the catalytic group A is not involved. (b) In interactions with a chain end of amylose, the enzyme undergoes a conformational transition which brings group A into the proximity of the second glucosidic linkage.

suggestion is also supported by the observation that the stability of an enzyme against denaturation is enhanced in the presence of an activating ion (Rosenberg and Lumry, 1964).

Globular proteins are also able to bind small anions and this phenomenon is very poorly understood since no analogous behavior has ever been de-

scribed for low molecular weight organic compounds.   The ability to bind
anions varies widely from one protein to another; it appears to be particularly pronounced for serum albumin.   The association equilibrium of this
protein with chloride and thiocyanate has been studied in considerable detail (Scatchard et al., 1949); as might be expected, the more polarizable
thiocyanate is held more tightly.   Even more mysterious is the specific
activation of the enzyme amylase by chloride ion (Michaelis and Pechstein,
1914; Myrbäck, 1926); the association constant of the enzyme and the
activating ion must be quite large in this case, since $5 \times 10^{-4}N$ chloride is
sufficient to produce half of the full activation.

The specificity of molecular association is exhibited in a particularly
striking manner in the interaction of enzymes with their substrates.   Frequently, it is also found that small molecules which resemble the substrates in some of their stereochemical characteristics act as inhibitors by
competing with the substrates for the specific adsorption site on the surface
of the enzyme molecule.   The nature of enzymatic specificity has been
described in a classical metaphor as being analogous to the fit of a key into a
lock (Fischer, 1894) but recent studies suggest that a modification of this concept, implying the complementariness of two rigid surfaces, is required to explain some important experimental observations.   The nature of the
evidence is represented schematically on a typical example in Fig. VIII.5.
The enzyme β-amylase is known to catalyze the hydrolysis of a glycosidic
bond two glucose units from the end of an amylose chain; the enzyme
catalysis must, therefore, involve some mechanism for recognizing the
distance of the reactive bond of the substrate from the chain end.   Yet,
cyclohexaamylose and cycloheptaamylose, which have no chain ends, were
found to be competitive inhibitors (Thoma and Koshland, 1960) and must,
therefore, be able to be bound at the catalytically active site.   This behavior may be explained by the "induced fit theory" of enzyme action,
which assumes that the active site of the enzyme has some flexibility, so that
it can envelop an amylose chain end, bringing the catalytically active
group into juxtaposition with the sensitive substrate bond.

Although the mechanism of enzymatic catalysis involves in some cases
a more complex sequence, the kinetic pattern may frequently be accounted
for by a reversible association of the enzyme E with the substrate S, followed by an irreversible reaction with regeneration of the enzyme:

$$E + S \underset{k_2}{\overset{k_1}{\rightleftharpoons}} ES$$

$$ES \overset{k_3}{\rightarrow} Products + E \qquad (8.1)$$

Assuming a rapid buildup of the concentration of the complex ES to its steady-state value, the observed reaction rate should be (Briggs and Haldane, 1925)

$$-dS/dt = k_3 E_t S/(S + K_m)$$
$$K_m = (k_2 + k_3)/k_1 \qquad (8.2)$$

where $E_t = E + ES$ is the total enzyme concentration and K_m is customarily referred to as the Michaelis constant. The reaction rate is then first order in substrate when $S \ll K_m$ and approaches an upper limit for $S \gg K_m$; the Michaelis constant is numerically equal to the substrate concentration at which the reaction rate has half of its maximum value. The true dissociation constant k_2/k_1 of the ES complex may be determined spectroscopically in cases where ES has a distinctive absorption spectrum and when the second step of the sequence in eq. (8.1) may be inhibited (Chance, 1943, 1949; Slater and Bonner, 1952). The dissociation constant of the ES complex may also be obtained from kinetic data in the special case when there is independent evidence that $k_3 \ll k_2$, so that $K_m \approx k_2/k_1$. No such ambiguity exists with respect to the dissociation constant K_I of the complex EI formed by an enzyme with a competitive inhibitor I. The value of K_I may be obtained from the reaction rates in the absence and the presence of a competitive inhibitor by the relation

$$(-dS/dt)_0/(-dS/dt)_I = 1 + (K_m/K_I)[I/(K_m + S)] \qquad (8.3)$$

and the relative values of K_I obtained for a series of competitive inhibitors may be used to gain information about the nature and the relative steric disposition of binding sites in the catalytically active site of the enzyme. We may cite, as a typical example, studies of the enzyme acetylcholine esterase, which is known to have two distinct binding sites with an affinity for the quaternary nitrogen ("anionic site") and for the carbonyl of the ester

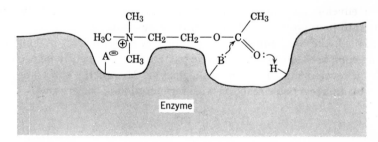

Fig. VIII.6. Model of the interaction of acetylcholine esterase with its substrate.

function ("esteratic site") as indicated schematically in Fig. VIII.6. It would then be expected that a substance which is attracted to one of these sites only, is a much less efficient inhibitor than one which may be bound simultaneously to both sites; such cooperative binding will, however, require a precise matching of the distance of the two interacting groups of the inhibitor with the spacing of the anionic and esteratic sites in the enzyme. Experimental results are in line with this concept, as illustrated by the relative values of K_I characterizing the three substances represented below (Wilson and Quan, 1958).

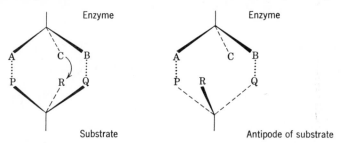

$K_I = 4 \times 10^{-5}$ $K_I = 10^{-8}$ $K_I = 1.5 \times 10^{-7}$

In the case of the enzyme chymotrypsin, the optical antipodes of the asymmetric substrates frequently act as competitive inhibitors. The discrimination between the optical isomers implies a three-point interaction between enzyme and substrate as indicated schematically in Fig. VIII.7.

Fig. VIII.7. Model representing the stereospecificity of enzyme–substrate interactions.

Here the groups P and Q of the substrate are attracted by groups A and B on the surface of the enzyme molecule, while the sensitive bond R is attacked by group C. With the optical antipode of the substrate, the interacting groups P and Q can still bind to A and B, but R is now far removed from the attacking function C. This model would lead one to expect that the dissociation constants of the enzyme–substrate and enzyme–inhibitor complexes are quite similar. Since it is found experimentally that the dissociation constants of many enzyme–inhibitor complexes parallel the K_m values of the substrates, k_3 may be assumed to be, in this case, very much smaller than k_2 and K_m may be taken as a measure of the dissociation constant of ES (Huang and Niemann, 1952; Zerner and Bender, 1964). On the basis of such reasoning, the dissociation constants of chymotrypsin complexes with typical low molecular weight substrates are found to lie in the range of 10^{-3} to 10^{-2} moles per liter.

In a number of enzymatic reactions the catalytic process involves an association complex of three distinct molecular species, i.e., the enzyme, the substrate, and a low molecular weight coenzyme which functions generally as the donor or acceptor of some specific group (e.g., phosphate, acetyl) or as an intermediate in hydrogen transfer processes. Coenzymes are frequently very tightly bound to the protein moiety of the enzyme. Velick (1954) has reviewed the evidence for two typical systems of this kind involving the enzymes glyceraldehyde-3-phosphate dehydrogenase (GDH) and alcohol dehydrogenase (ADH). Both these enzymes employ nicotinamide adenine dinucleotide (NAD) as the coenzyme acting as hydrogen acceptor; the structures of this substance in the oxidized and reduced form are shown below

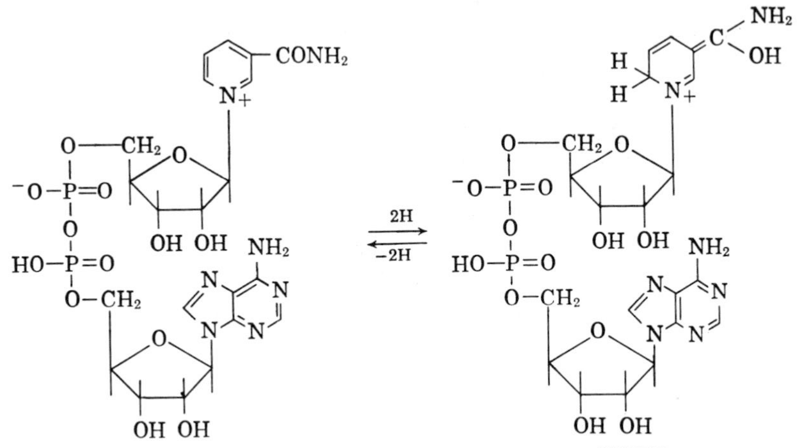

NAD   NADH

The dissociation constant of the GDH complex with NAD has been obtained from ultracentrifuge sedimentation data (since the free coenzyme does not sediment appreciably) and it lies in the neighborhood of 10^{-5} (Velick, 1953). With alcohol dehydrogenase (Theorell and Chance, 1951) there is a remarkable difference in the affinity of the enzyme for the reduced and oxidized form of the coenzyme. The equilibrium may be studied spectroscopically and the data yield a dissociation constant of 10^{-7}

for the ADH–NADH complex, while the dissociation constant for ADH–NAD is found to be a hundred times higher. This large difference in the affinity of the enzyme for two such similar species illustrates rather dramatically the sensitivity of specific association phenomena to minor structural changes of the interacting molecules.

In recent years a great deal of evidence has accumulated which suggests that the activity of many enzymes may be inhibited or enhanced by complexation of an "effector" molecule to a region of the enzyme which is quite distinct from the catalytically active site (Monod et al., 1963). The fact that substrate and effector do not bind to the same sites of the enzyme may be demonstrated in a variety of ways; for instance, it is possible to modify enzymes chemically so that their sensitivity to the effector is lost, although

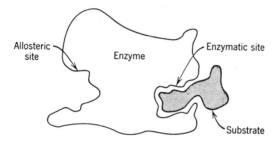

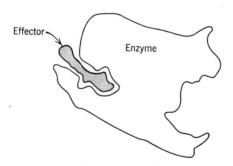

Fig. VIII.8. Inhibition of enzyme by an allosteric effector.

the enzymatic activity observed in the absence of the effector remains unchanged. The effectors are called "allosteric," i.e., they have no particular steric similarity to the substrate of the enzyme whose activity they modify. Monod et al. have suggested a mechanism for allosteric inhibition in which the enzyme carries a catalytic and an allosteric binding site and complexation at the allosteric site modifies the enzyme conformation. A

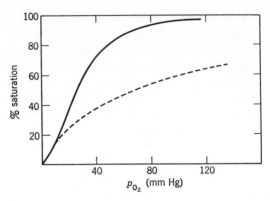

Fig. VIII.9. Association equilibrium of oxygen with human hemoglobin at pH 7.4 and 37°C. The dotted line indicates the equilibrium which would be observed if the heme groups acted independently of each other.

schematic representation of these ideas is shown in Fig. VIII.8. The phenomenon is of fundamental importance in biology, since it makes it possible for metabolic sequences to contain a "feedback" mechanism regulating the production of a metabolite. For instance, in the metabolic sequence

$$\text{Threonine} \xrightarrow{\;1\;} \alpha\text{-ketobutyrate} \xrightarrow{\;2\;} \alpha\text{-acetohydroxybutyrate} \xrightarrow{\;3\;}$$

$$\alpha,\beta\text{-dihydroxy-}\beta\text{-methylvalerate} \xrightarrow{\;4\;} \alpha\text{-keto-}\beta\text{-methylvalerate} \xrightarrow{\;5\;} \text{isoleucine}$$

the final product, isoleucine, is an allosteric inhibitor of the enzyme catalyzing the first step of the sequence, the conversion of threonine to α-ketobutyrate. It is particularly striking that isoleucine has no effect on any of the other reactions and none of the intermediate metabolites affect step 1.

The reversible association of hemoglobin with molecular oxygen may be considered as a special case of enzyme–substrate interaction and it is characterized by an allosteric effect which is particularly well documented. The hemoglobin molecule (cf. Haurowitz, 1963a) is an association complex of four subunits (cf. Sec. B-3 of this chapter) each carrying a heme group, in which ferrous ion is coordinated with four nitrogen atoms of protoporphyrin. A fifth coordination bond is formed between the iron and an imidazole group of a histidine residue in the protein, while a sixth coordination bond may be formed either with water or with O_2. Although crystallographic evidence shows that the heme groups carried by the four subunits are quite distant from one another (Perutz, 1962) their affinity for oxygen exhibits a pronounced cooperative effect, as evidenced from the sigmoid shape of a plot of the degree of hemoglobin oxygenation as a function of oxygen pressure (Fig. VIII.9). A detailed analysis of the oxygen–hemoglobin equilibrium under one set of conditions indicated that oxygenation of three of the heme groups enhances the affinity for oxygen of the fourth heme by a factor of almost 300 (Gibson and Roughton, 1955). This phenomenon may be understood as resulting from a conformational transition of the hemoglobin accompanying the oxygenation of the heme groups. Such a transition is indicated by a number of characteristic differences in the physico-chemical behavior of hemoglobin and oxyhemoglobin (Benesch and Benesch, 1963) and crystallographic analysis has shown that the distance between two of the hemoglobin subunits is larger by 7 Å in the reduced form of the protein (Muirhead and Perutz, 1963). A particularly beautiful experiment was performed by Gibson (1959) who decomposed photochemically the hemoglobin complex with carbon monoxide and showed that the hemoglobin initially liberated from the complex, spectroscopically distinct from "normal" hemoglobin, has a higher affinity for oxygen. The results suggest that the hemoglobin form with the enhanced activity (which reverts to "normal" hemoglobin by a first order process with a rate constant of about 200 sec^{-1}) retains the protein conformation characteristic of hemoglobin complexes with CO or O_2, thus reducing the activation energy required for the binding of these gases. In any case, it is remarkable that a chemical change as small as the coordination of the heme group with carbon monoxide or oxygen should lead to profound changes in the conformation of the entire macromolecule.

Some enzymes require for their catalytic activity the simultaneous presence of both a coenzyme and an activating ion. In that case, a very interesting method may be used for the study of the association complex, provided the activating ion is a paramagnetic species such as Mn^{++}. This ion produces a very large acceleration of the nuclear magnetic relaxation rate of the water protons, but the efficiency of Mn^{++}, in producing this effect, is quite sensitive to its state of complexation. It was found that the effect of Mn^{++} is enhanced much more in ternary complexes with enzyme and coenzyme than in binary complexes with either of them alone (Cohn and Leigh, 1962). Therefore, the technique may be used to decide whether the paramagnetic ion in the ternary complex is coordinated simultaneously with both the enzyme and the coenzyme (Cohn, 1963). It is obvious that methods which can not only demonstrate the existence of an association complex and lead to an estimate of its stability, but can also describe in some detail the manner in which the associating molecules fit together, are of particular value in the development of this field.

B. MOLECULAR AGGREGATION OF MACROMOLECULES

1. Aggregation of Flexible Chain Molecules

It is clear that for each type of molecular association known to exist with small molecules, analogous complexation must exist with polymers carrying the appropriate interacting groups. In fact, as we shall see, the requirements for the association of chain molecules carrying a large number of interacting groups are much less stringent, since the stability of complexes formed by their monofunctional analogs may be too unstable to be experimentally observable.

Typical examples of associating chain molecules are polystyrenes carrying a small number of hydroxyl or carboxyl groups (Trementozzi et al., 1952; Chang and Morawetz, 1956). The apparent molecular weights of such materials are found to depend on the solvent medium and the high values observed in media such as toluene or carbon tetrachloride are obviously due to hydrogen bond formation between the macromolecules. As would be expected, the macromolecular association may be eliminated by the addition of a low molecular weight hydrogen bond acceptor. This effect is illustrated in Fig. VIII.10, where the ratio of the apparent to the true molecular weight of a methyl methacrylate–methacrylic acid copolymer in benzene solution is given as a function of the concentration of various cosolvents (Morawetz and Gobran, 1955). The relative efficiencies of cosolvents in preventing molecular aggregation of the polymer may be taken as a measure of their affinity for the interacting carboxyl groups.

Molecular association is also observed in aqueous solutions of polymers carrying hydrophobic groups. This phenomenon was first described for incompletely hydrolyzed poly(vinyl acetate), which was found to have an apparent light scattering molecular weight increasing with the temperature of the solution (Nord et al., 1951). Similar behavior characterizes aqueous solutions of methylcellulose (Neely, 1963)—decreasing solvation with increasing temperature is in these cases obviously the consequence to be expected from hydrophobic bonding.

A type of macromolecular association which is less well understood is that exhibited by poly(vinyl chloride)(Doty et al., 1947). In this case we may not invoke any association complexes of low molecular weight solutes as models, which would aid us in the understanding of the molecular aggregation of the polymer. However, it is undoubtedly significant that other polymers which behave in a similar fashion, such as cellulose nitrate (Newman et al., 1956) and gelatin (Boedtker and Doty, 1954), are able to form thermally reversible gels under suitable conditions. We have pointed

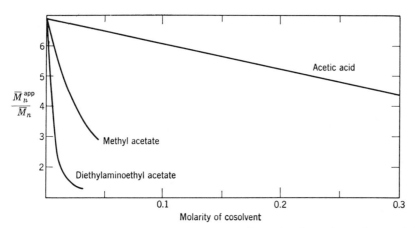

Fig. VIII.10. Effect of cosolvent on the apparent molecular weight of a methyl methacrylate copolymer with 4.9 mole-% methacrylic acid in benzene solution at 30°C ($\bar{M}_n = 34,500$).

out previously (Chap. II, Sec. B-7) that thermally reversible gelation is typical of crystalline polymers and that even dilute gels may yield sharp x-ray diffraction patterns. It appears then that the dissolved molecular aggregates may be thought of as microcrystallites and that their dissociation is analogous to a melting process. Particularly interesting systems in which macromolecular association is of this type are formed by mixtures of isotactic and syndiotactic poly(methyl methacrylate) in good solvent media. We have noted previously (p. 89) that the mixing of solutions of the two stereoregular polymers may lead to gel formation. In more dilute systems the growth of molecular aggregates can be studied by following the increase in the intensity of scattered light and this technique may be used to determine the stoichiometry of the complex. Liquori et al. (1965) obtained the same results by this method and by using as an index of complex formation the intensification of the optical density at 212.5 mμ. They prepared a fiber from the isotactic–syndiotactic complex and clarified its crystal structure. This case is of particular interest since the two interacting polymers are chemically so similar. Molecular association is here a consequence of the steric complementariness of the two interacting species, utilizing a principle similar to that which accounts for such striking specific interactions as those of an enzyme with its substrate or an antigen with its antibody.

While the mixing of solutions containing polymeric acids and polymeric bases leads to mutual precipitation even in extremely dilute systems (Fuoss

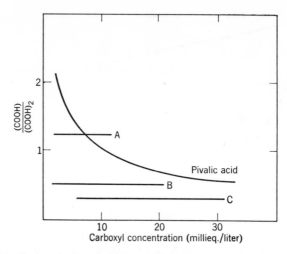

Fig. VIII.11. Carboxyl dimerization in styrene–methacrylic acid copolymers in 1,1′,2,2′-tetrachloroethane. (A) 0.79 mole-% methacrylic acid. (B) 6.5 mole-% methacrylic acid. (C) 11.7 mole-% methacrylic acid.

and Sadek, 1949), the mixing of copolymers carrying relatively low densities of acidic and basic groups leads to soluble complexes (Morawetz and Gobran, 1954). A similar system is one containing poly(ethylene oxide) and poly(acrylic acid) in aqueous solution; in this case the association is due to the interaction of the acidic carboxyls with the ether oxygens, acting as a Lewis base. We have noted previously (Chap. III, Sec. C-5) that the complex of a monofunctional acid with a simple ether would not be observable in an aqueous medium, where water competes both as a hydrogen bond donor and acceptor. The high stability of the polymer aggregate is here the result of the cooperative effect of a large number of interacting groups. At low pH the complex is very insoluble, but as the pH is raised the extent of the molecular association decreases and the complex becomes soluble (Bailey et al., 1964).

Some interesting generalizations may be made about these various systems exhibiting molecular aggregation of flexible polymer chains: (a) If the polymer carries only one kind of interacting groups which tend to dimerize (e.g., carboxyl) then it may happen in dilute solution that very little macromolecular aggregation is observed, even though spectroscopic evidence shows that most of the interacting groups are associated. This means that most of the dimerization involves interacting groups attached to the same polymer chain backbone as would be expected since the local density of the interacting groups is much higher within the domain of the isolated polymer coil than in the system as a whole. Typical results, comparing the extent of carboxyl dimerization in solutions of styrene–methacrylic acid copolymers and solutions of pivalic acid, their mono-carboxylic acid analog (Chang and Morawetz, 1956), are shown in Fig. VIII.11. We may see that carboxyl dimerization is independent of the concentration of the copolymers, merely reflecting conditions within the isolated macromolecule. (b) If we compare the behavior of different molecular weight fractions with a constant density of interacting groups, then it is found that the extent of aggregation increases with the polymer chain length, since a larger number of associating groups are available to stabilize the complex. As a result, molecular association leads to an in-crease in the apparent breadth of the molecular weight distribution. In particular, the ratio of the apparent weight average and number average molecular weights may attain anomalously high values. (c) The dissocia-tion of polymer aggregates is usually a much more rapid process than the association of macromolecules, but both processes may require a long time for an approach to equilibrium conditions (Doty et al., 1947; Strauss et al., 1956; Neely, 1963). A striking demonstration of this effect was pro-vided in studies of poly(vinyl chloride) (Hengstenberg and Schuch, 1964): When the polymer was dissolved in cyclohexanone (a good solvent) and diluted with the poorly solvating butanone, sedimentation diagrams gave no evidence of molecular aggregation. If, however, the same system was prepared by diluting a butanone solution of the polymer with cyclohexa-none, then molecular aggregation was as pronounced as if butanone had been the sole solvent. (d) Osmotic and light scattering data suggest that the size of the molecular aggregates does not change appreciably in the concentration range in which measurements are usually carried out (Mora-wetz and Gobran, 1954). Experimental data obtained in a single solvent and at a single temperature may, therefore, give no warning that the poly-mer molecules are associated. The constancy of the size of the molecular aggregate over a concentration range is reminiscent of the formation of micelles from low molecular weight species. However, the large number of interacting groups makes the polymer aggregates so stable that the con-centration analogous to the "critical micelle concentration" of soaps is too low to be accessible to experimental study.

2. Association of Globular Proteins with other Macromolecules

Living organisms contain solutions of globular proteins in the presence of other highly charged macromolecules such as nucleic acids or acidic polysaccharides. It is, therefore, of interest to find out to what extent these substances interact with one another and how the properties of a highly purified protein species may differ from the properties which will characterize it in a complex mixture.

The behavior of serum albumin has been the subject of particularly extensive studies; it tends to associate with a variety of substances more strongly than most proteins, but the effects observed are qualitatively similar. Below its isoelectric point (about pH 5.1) the protein is positively charged and it tends to precipitate in the presence of polyanions. However, soluble complexes persist within a range of pH above the isoelectric point, as has been demonstrated for systems containing acidic polysaccharides (Chargaff et al., 1941) or DNA (Goldwasser and Putnam, 1950). The extent of association decreases with increasing ionic strength (Noguchi, 1960), as would be expected if Coulombic interactions are the main driving force toward complexation. In a similar fashion, serum albumin above its isoelectric point tends to associate with polycations such as polylysine. An electrophoretic study of this system (Rice et al., 1954) showed that two peaks are observed on the electrophoretic diagram with mobilities depending on the relative concentration of the two interacting species. The results, plotted in Fig. VIII.12, could be interpreted in terms of an albumin-rich and a polylysine-rich complex in equilibrium with each other. The authors of this study preferred to assume that a complex of the two components is in equilibrium with the two free species and that the association and dissociation processes are rapid compared to the time scale of the experiment. It may be noted that complex formation may lead to a reversal of the protein charge; this was also indicated in the interaction of serum albumin with poly(acrylic acid), where the protein–polyacid precipitate tended to redissolve on addition of an excess of the polymeric acid (Morawetz and Hughes, 1952). This study showed also that the composition of the complex is independent of the length of the chain molecule associating with the protein.

In the case of enzymes, complexation with polyions frequently leads to loss of catalytic activity and this phenomenon provides a convenient tool for the study of such association processes. The enzymatic activity is generally fully recovered when the complex is dissociated, suggesting that complexation with polyions does not disturb the tertiary structure of enzymes. In the case of ribonuclease, the enzyme is inhibited by DNA. The data show that DNA and RNA compete for the same site and that the affinity of the enzyme for its substrate is much higher than for the DNA, to which it is attracted only by electrostatic forces (Coleman and

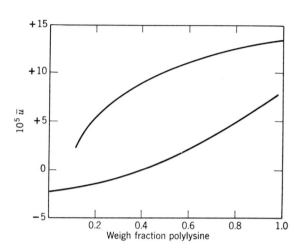

Fig. VIII.12. Electrophoresis of solutions containing bovine serum albumin and poly(L-lysine). (pH 6.3, ionic strength 0.1, temp. 0.9°C.) The two curves represent the mobilities of the two boundaries observed in the electrophoretic diagram of solutions containing the two kinds of macromolecules in various ratios.

Edelhoch, 1956). The importance of other than electrostatic forces in the association of enzymes with charged chain molecules was also demonstrated in studies of the inhibition of lysozyme with synthetic polypeptides (Sela and Steiner, 1963). In this case, a polypeptide containing an equal number

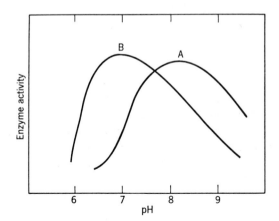

Fig. VIII.13. Effect of poly(acrylic acid) on the rate of hemoglobin hydrolysis catalyzed by trypsin. (A) Enzyme activity in the absence of poly(acrylic acid). (B) Enzyme activity in the presence of 0.5 g. PAA per liter.

of glutamic acid and tyrosine residues was found to be several hundred times more effective than poly(glutamic acid).

If the substrate which is being attacked by the enzyme is also a protein, added polyions may associate with either one of these species. A case of this type was studied in the trypsin–hemoglobin–poly(acrylic acid) system (Morawetz and Sage, 1955). The results are shown in Fig. VIII.13; the enzymatic activity is found to be inhibited by poly(acrylic acid) at high pH but enhanced at lower pH values. This result may be easily understood, since trypsin is a much more basic protein than hemoglobin. Thus, at pH values above 8 only trypsin is positively charged and when it forms a complex with the polymeric acid, its positive charge is reduced, thus reducing the electrostatic attraction for the anionic hemoglobin. Below the isoelectric point of hemoglobin, the situation is entirely different. Now the bulk of the polymeric acid complexes with hemoglobin (which is present in much higher concentration than the enzyme). This reduces the repulsive forces between the cationic enzyme and the cationic substrate and favors their interaction.

3. Dissociation and Association of Protein Molecules

It is extremely common to find that molecules of globular proteins associate in solution. A protein which lends itself particularly well to the study of such an association process is provided by a component of serum albumin, which contains a single thiol group. Since thiols react avidly with mercuric ion, the protein tends to dimerize in the presence of Hg^{++}. Denoting the monomeric albumin by ASH, the process is characterized by the equilibria

$$ASH + Hg^{++} \rightleftharpoons ASHg^+ + H^+$$

$$ASHg^+ + ASH \rightleftharpoons (AS)_2Hg + H^+$$

The second step of the reaction is comparatively slow and may be followed in either direction by changes in the light scattering intensity (Edelhoch et al., 1953). The temperature dependence of the association equilibrium shows that the dimerization is endothermic, so that hydrophobic bonding appears to provide the driving force. This is characteristic of a number of protein association processes, which seem, moreover, to involve typically a precisely defined geometric fit of the protein molecules into the molecular aggregate.

The extensive literature dealing with the association of identical protein molecules has been reviewed by Reithel (1963). We may illustrate the phenomenon on the behavior of insulin, a protein whose chemical structure has been completely clarified, so that its true molecular weight is known to be 5733.   Yet, molecular weight determinations under most experimental conditions yield 12,000 or even much higher values (Oncley et al., 1952; Fredericq, 1956; Marcker, 1960).   The dimeric form of insulin dissociates only in solvent media which usually break up the tertiary structure of proteins, such as aqueous guanidine hydrochloride or mixed organic solvents (Harfenist and Craig, 1952; Kupke and Linderstrøm-Lang, 1954).   Since two insulin molecules related by an axis of rotation form the repeat unit in insulin crystals, it seems reasonable to assume that the dimeric form which is so stable in solution has a similar geometry (Low and Einstein, 1960).

Occasionally, the tendency of proteins to form association complexes is strongly dependent on the presence of various low molecular weight species. The association of insulin is strongly enhanced by small concentrations of zinc ions (Fredericq, 1956) and in alcohol dehydrogenase the association of the protein subunits to form the active enzyme is favored by the presence of the activating cations (Kägi and Vallee, 1960).   Such phenomena could be interpreted by assuming that the cation "bridges" two protein molecules in a manner analogous to the formation of the albumin–mercury dimer discussed above, but it seems more probable that the cation merely serves to stabilize a protein conformation which favors molecular association. With the enzyme glutamic dehydrogenase, four units with a molecular weight of 2.5×10^5 have a strong tendency to form an association complex (Olson and Anfinsen, 1952) but a number of small molecules interfere with the association of these subunits, presumably by effecting a change in the protein conformation (Frieden, 1959, 1963).

A particularly fascinating illustration of the effects which may result from the molecular association of globular proteins is provided in the structure of ferritin, utilized in higher organisms for the storage of iron.   This substance has a molecular weight of 750,000, but more than 20% of this weight is due to ferric oxide and phosphate which seems to be rather loosely associated with the protein.   The iron may be removed without destroying the protein structure and this residual "appoferritin" dissociates in detergent solutions to subunits with a molecular weight of about 20,000.   Crystallographic evidence suggests that these subunits are fitted together into the shape of a hollow sphere, which acts as a receptacle for the inorganic material (Hofmann and Harrison, 1963).

So far, we have concerned ourselves only with associations involving identical protein molecules.   Well-defined complexes may also form, however, from dissimilar units.   An important case of this type is the hemoglobin of man and various mammals. It consists typically of four sub-units, which may be separated from each other at low pH (Reichmann and Colvin, 1956; Hill and Craig, 1959). Two and two of these units are alike and the similar units tend to remain as dimers in less powerful dis-sociating media (Singer and Itano, 1959; Vinograd and Hutchinson, 1959). The asymmetrical splitting of hemoglobin is a fully reversible process and building units of hemoglobins of different species (which differ considerably in their chemical composition) may be recombined to form "hybrid hemo-globins" (Robinson and Itano, 1960). The solution of the crystal struc-ture of hemoglobin has given us a detailed picture of the manner in which the four subunits fit together and we may then speak of a precisely defined "quaternary structure" of the protein. A similar situation seems to exist in the case of the enzyme tryptophan synthetase, which is produced in some living organisms in the form of two dissimilar proteins. The two proteins have entirely different catalytic activities when separated from each other and when allowed to associate to a complex (Crawford and Yanofsky, 1958; Crawford and Ito, 1964). The evidence suggests that each of the subunits of the complex carries part of the enzymatic site, so that the two subunits must fit into each other in a precisely prescribed geometrical relationship. A related phenomenon is the formation of a molecular com-plex from three or four enzymes which catalyze a series of reactions leading to the dehydrogenation of α-keto acids (Koike et al., 1963). This com-plex is remarkably stable and dissociates with considerable difficulty. It is clear that such an association of enzymes, engaged in the catalysis of a sequence of metabolic processes, is very advantageous biologically, since it eliminates the need to form anew the enzyme–substrate complex for every stage of the reaction sequence.

The association complex of proteolytic enzymes with their protein sub-strates is usually not directly observable because of its high reactivity, but in special cases such an association may be studied under favorable conditions. Such a situation is encountered with the enzyme pepsin, which is most active around pH 2, but attacks substrates such as serum albumin only very slowly above pH 5; the pepsin–albumin complex may then be observed as a distinct peak in the electrophoretic diagram (Cann and Klapper, 1961). Living organisms also contain a variety of proteins which function as specific inhibitors for proteolytic enzymes. The most widely studied systems of this type are complexes of trypsin with trypsin inhibitors derived from animal or vegetable sources (Laskowski and Las-kowski, 1954). These associations are stoichiometric, involving one mole-cule of either species, and the geometry of the complex must be very well defined since it may be obtained in crystalline form. The course of the association in solution may be followed conveniently by light scattering or by changes in the depolarization of fluorescence resulting from a decrease in the rotational diffusion constant (Steiner, 1954).

In some cases globular proteins may associate to complexes containing a very large number of molecules, so that the process is frequently referred to as a "polymerization." A particularly interesting case of this type is provided by actin, one of the components of the contractile system of muscle tissues. This protein consists of globular molecules ("G-actin") which have a high tendency to associate in the presence of certain salts in a highly specific manner to form filamentous aggregates ("F-actin"). Each G-actin molecule is associated with one molecule of adenosine triphosphate which is dephosphorylated during the polymerization process (Mommaerts, 1952), but the mechanism which relates F-actin formation with the breakdown of ATP is unknown. A detailed study of actin polymerization by flow birefringence (Oosawa et al., 1959) led to the conclusion that no F-actin forms below a critical actin concentration and that the concentration of G-actin is independent of the concentration of F-actin in the system. A theoretical analysis of thermodynamic and kinetic data has led Oosawa and Kasai (1962) to the conclusion that the globular protein molecules associate to form a helical array in which each unit lies next to four nearest neighbors and that the cooperative nature of this process makes it the intermolecular analog of intramolecular helix-coil transitions. More recently, electron microscopic observations of F-actin (Hanson and Lowy, 1963) have revealed a structure which is somewhat different from that postulated by Oosawa and Kasai, although it satisfied several of the features predicted by them on theoretical grounds. It appears that F-actin consists of two intertwined strings of G-actin molecules as represented schematically on Fig. VIII.14(a). This model is also consistent with the spectacular observation that solutions of F-actin catalyze the dephosphorylation of ATP when they are subjected to sonic vibrations (Asakura, 1961). This behavior may be accounted for by assuming that the vibrations produce breaks in the double-helical aggregate of F-actin, and that the "annealing" of these breaks is attended by the ATP breakdown characterizing actin polymerization. Since the repair of such a break in one strand of a double helix is a first-order process, the rate of ATP decomposition should depend on the first power of F-actin concentration and this is in agreement with experimental data.

Another similar polymerization phenomenon is encountered with fibrinogen, a globular protein responsible for the clotting of blood. The extensive literature dealing with this subject has been reviewed by Scheraga and Laskowski (1957). The native fibrinogen appears under the electron microscope as a linear array of three nodules held together by a relatively thin thread (Hall and Slayter, 1959). In this form the protein has no tendency to form molecular aggregates. However, when it is subjected to attack by the proteolytic enzyme thrombin, a small peptide is split off from fibrinogen and the residual protein ("fibrin monomer") has now a high tendency to associate to large structures which eventually form a cross-linked gel. The crosslinking process may be inhibited by various reagents and under these conditions it is possible to study the association of fibrin monomer to rod-like polymers. Light scattering studies suggest that the cross-section of these rods is twice as great as that of fibrin monomer and

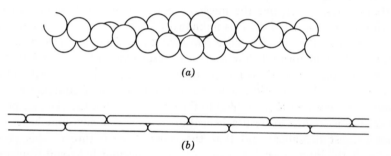

(a)

(b)

Fig. VIII.14. "Polymerization" of globular proteins. (a) The structure of F-actin as suggested by its appearance under the electron microscope. (b) Proposed structure of fibrinogen polymers.

this result led to the proposal (Ferry et al., 1952; Casassa, 1956) that the linear "polymer" of fibrin grows by a staggered overlap of the elongated monomer units as represented schematically on Fig. VIII.14(b). However, the dimensions of the rod-like fibrin polymer observed in the electron microscope seem to rule out such side-by-side association (Hall and Slayter, 1959) and the cause of this discrepancy remains to be clarified.

A very complex situation is encountered with casein, which contains a number of distinct components interacting with one another to form large micellular aggregates (Waugh, 1958, 1961). Partial proteolysis of one fraction ("κ-casein") by the enzyme rennin appears to lead to changes analogous to the conversion of fibrinogen to fibrin monomer and the altered κ-casein may initiate, in the presence of Ca^{++}, the polymerization of the protein leading eventually to the formation of an insoluble clot.

4. The Antigen–Antibody Reaction

When a globular protein from another species is injected into the blood-
stream of mammals or birds, the organism produces a new form of protein
(an "antibody") which interacts in a highly specific manner with the foreign
substance.   Materials which may evoke this response are called antigens
and they include, in addition to proteins, certain polysaccharides as well as
some synthetic polypeptides.   We can touch only briefly on some aspects
of the antigen–antibody reaction and the reader is referred for a fuller
treatment of the subject to the classical monograph of Landsteiner (1946)
and to recent reviews by Haurowitz (1963b) and Nisonoff and Thorbecke
(1964).

When antigen solutions are mixed within certain proportions with solutions of their antibodies, the two substances form an insoluble complex;
when one or the other component is in large excess, the formation of soluble
complexes may be demonstrated by light scattering, ultracentrifuge sedimentation analysis, electrophoresis, and other techniques.   The most
striking aspect of this interaction is its very high degree of specificity.
Antibodies react most powerfully with the antigens which were responsible
for their formation (the "homologous antigens") and the affinity decreases
rapidly even with minor changes in the antigen molecule.   For instance,
although antibodies to chicken egg albumin will interact both with the
homologous antigen and solutions of duck egg albumin, the interaction
with chicken egg albumin leads to much more complete precipitation.
Moreover, when anti-chicken egg albumin is treated with duck egg albumin and the precipitate is removed, the supernatant may still precipitate
the homologous antigen.   This suggests that some of the antibody molecules are specific to portions of the egg albumin molecule which are similar
in the protein originating from chickens and ducks, while other antibody
molecules interact with regions of the antigen which are different in the two
species.   This characteristic heterogeneity of antibody preparations is a
serious obstacle to research in this field.

The antigen–antibody reaction is eliminated if the interacting proteins
are denatured and the interaction must then be considered to depend on a
precise complementariness in the "molecular surfaces" of the two native
proteins.   A powerful method for the study of the specificity of such interactions was developed by Landsteiner, who introduced antigens produced
by coupling proteins with a variety of diazotized aniline derivatives.   He
found that the specificity of antibodies produced by such conjugated antigens is largely determined by the substituent groups (haptens).   Since

the antibody will also bind haptens attached to small molecules, the association equilibrium may be determined in a dialysis experiment (Haurowitz and Breinl, 1933). Typical data of this kind were reported by Karush (1956) who studied the antibody to a conjugated protein carrying the D-isomer of the hapten group

$$-N{=}N-\!\!\bigcirc\!\!-CONH\underset{\underset{COO^-}{|}}{\overset{\overset{H}{|}}{C}}-\bigcirc$$

and determined by dialysis equilibrium the relative affinity of the antibody for the D and L-isomer of

$$O_2N-\!\!\bigcirc\!\!-CONH\underset{\underset{COO^-}{|}}{\overset{\overset{H}{|}}{C}}-\bigcirc$$

It was found that the hapten with the same steric configuration as the antigen was bound 200 times more strongly, illustrating the importance of stereochemical fitting. The dialysis experiments may also be used to define the stoichiometry of the reaction. It is found in this way that antibodies associate with two hapten groups.

Our knowledge of the structure of antibodies has been greatly advanced in recent years by the discovery that they may be split in a highly specific manner in the presence of proteolytic enzymes and reducing agents (Porter, 1959; Fleischman et al., 1963). Two of the fragments, with a molecular weight of 45,000, appear to be identical and behave like univalent antibodies, while the third fragment (with a molecular weight of 155,000) has no affinity for the antigen. The physical basis for the difference in antibodies with different specificities has not been definitely established. According to a theory formulated by Pauling (1940) all antibodies were believed to contain polypeptide chains with the same amino acid sequence, their specificity being entirely due to a variation in the tertiary structure of the protein. This intuitive interpretation was remarkable coming at a time when little was known about macromolecular conformations. Nevertheless, Pauling's theory seems less convincing today because of the accumulating evidence that a unique tertiary structure is imposed on globular proteins by the amino acid sequence in the molecular chain (cf. Chap. III, Sec. C-5). This concept has been demonstrated convincingly on the univalent antibody fragments which may be denatured and recovered, after

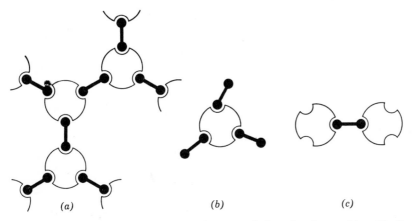

Fig. VIII.15. Schematic representation of the association of antigens with antibodies. (a) A system containing an equivalent concentration of antigen and antibody forms an infinite network. (b) Complex formed with large excess of antibody. (c) Complex formed with large excess of antigen.

removal of the denaturation reagent, with little change in affinity for their homologous antigen (Buckley et al., 1963). We are then forced to assume that the differences in tertiary structure between antibodies of different specificity must reflect differences in chemical composition. Small, but apparently real, variations in the content of some amino acids have, in fact, been reported (Koshland and Englberger, 1963).

The antigen–antibody precipitation may be interpreted as the formation of a gel network through the interaction of bivalent antibody with multivalent antigen. The growth of such a network may be inhibited by an excess of either reagent, as represented schematically in Fig. VIII.15. As would be expected, the monovalent antibody fragments may compete with divalent antibody for the homologous antigen and may thus prevent precipitation. It is also possible to determine the functionality of an antigen by measuring the molecular weight of the complex which is formed when the antigen is saturated with univalent antibody fragments (Cebra et al., 1962).

Quantitative evaluations of the association constant characterizing the interaction of individual antigen and antibody sites may be obtained in a number of ways. A system containing a stoichiometric excess of antigen (AG) over antibody (AB) in terms of interacting sites, will contain mostly the species AG, AG–AB, and AG–AB–AG. If the concentration of any one of these species is determined by electrophoresis or ultracentrifugation

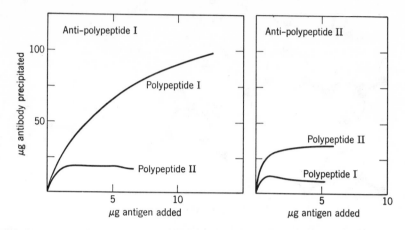

Fig. VIII.16. Specificity of interaction of synthetic polypeptides with their antibodies. Polypeptide I contained 42 mole-% glutamic acid, 28 mole-% lysine, and 30 mole-% alanine. Polypeptide II contained 62 mole-% glutamic acid, 33 mole-% lysine, and 5 mole-% phenylalanine (Gill and Matthews, 1963).

(Singer and Campbell, 1955), the concentration of all the other species may be calculated if it is assumed that the affinity of two interacting sites for one another is independent of the size of the aggregate. A simpler system may be obtained with univalent antigens; these may be synthesized by coupling the single thiol group of serum albumin with a suitable hapten (Pepe and Singer, 1959). It is usually found that the affinity of a hapten group for an antibody site depends little on whether the hapten is attached to a protein molecule or is part of a low molecular weight species, so that data obtained in dialysis equilibration of antibody with haptens are pertinent to the antibody association with conjugated proteins. A particularly elegant technique for evaluating the association equilibrium utilizes the quenching of the tryptophan fluorescence of antibodies when they combine with haptens absorbing in the 300–400 mμ range (Velick et al., 1960). Since fluorescence is detectable at extreme dilution of the fluorescing species, this method may measure with high precision dissociation constants as small as 10^{-8} to 10^{-9}, a range characteristic for the binding of haptens by antibodies.

Additional insight into the nature of the antigen–antibody reaction may be obtainable from experiments with synthetic polypeptides. If we think of antibody synthesis as occurring in response to a precisely defined surface conformation of a globular protein molecule, then it is surprising that synthetic polypeptides should be antigenic, particularly since this property shows no correlation with the stability of a helical conformation. Copolypeptides of L-lysine and L-glutamic acid have been found to be antigens although poly(L-lysine) and poly(α-L-glutamic acid) do not elicit antibody formation (Gill and Doty, 1961). Good antigens are also obtained from copolypeptides of either L-lysine or L-glutamic acid with an amino acid carrying a hydrophobic residue such as alanine or tyrosine (Gill and Matthews, 1963). The antibodies produced in response to these materials cross-react with polypeptides of a range of compositions, but precipitation is clearly maximized with the homologous antigen. Typical data illustrating the extent of the specificity of this interaction are plotted in Fig. VIII.16, which shows the amount of two anti-polypeptide antibodies precipitated as a function of the concentration of various polypeptide antigens.

5. The Tobacco Mosaic Virus Particle

It may come as a surprise to some of the readers of this book to find a discussion of a virus in a chapter dealing with molecular association complexes. However, this is quite proper and the particles of tobacco mosaic virus (TMV) are found to have, in fact, an unexpectedly simple structure (Gierer, 1960; Caspar, 1963) being made up of only two kinds of molecules. The virus particle has the shape of an elongated hollow cylinder with a diameter of 150 Å, a length of 3000 Å, and a central cavity with a diameter of 40 Å. Its weight corresponds to 39×10^6 molecular weight units. It contains 2130 identical protein molecules with a molecular weight of 17,500 and a single chain of RNA with a molecular weight of about 2×10^6. The manner in which the RNA and the protein are fitted together has been deduced from an x-ray crystallographic analysis (Franklin et al., 1958). The picture which emerges is represented schematically in Fig. VIII.17. The protein molecules are arranged in a helical array and the RNA chain, which also forms a spiral, is imbedded between the protein units. It has been shown that it is possible to separate the protein from the RNA and that these two components will reassociate spontaneously under suitable conditions to particles which are biologically and in all other respects identical with the native TMV (Fraenkel-Conrat and Williams, 1955). This phenomenon is the most complex example known to date of the association of molecular units to an aggregate with a precisely defined geometry.

The TMV protein molecules have also a tendency to associate in the absence of RNA to cylindrical particles similar to the complete virus (Lauffer et al., 1958; Ansevin and Lauffer, 1963; Caspar, 1963). The

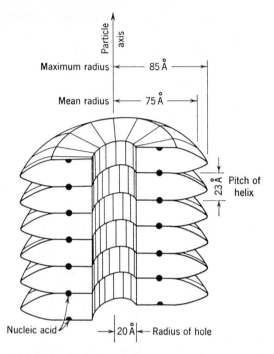

Fig. VIII.17. Model of tobacco mosaic virus, showing schematically the arrangement of the protein subunits and of the nucleic acid strand in six of the 130 turns of
the helix (after Gierer, 1960).

process is endothermic, so that hydrophobic bonding seems to account for
the stability of the aggregates and the aggregation velocity has a sharp
maximum at pH 4.3, about 0.8 pH units above the isoelectric point of the
protein.   The tendency of TMV protein to form helical aggregates is analogous to the formation of F-actin discussed in Sec. B-3 of this chapter.
There are indications that small spherical viruses have a similarly simple
structure, with a spherical shell made up of identical protein molecules
(similarly as in ferritin) enclosing the nucleic acid.   However, in such
cases a reconstitution of the virus from its constituent molecules has not
been accomplished.

Chapter IX

THE REACTIVITY OF MACROMOLECULAR SOLUTIONS

The bulk of the literature dealing with the physical chemistry of macromolecular solutions emphasizes the physical properties of these systems and entirely disregards their chemical reactivity. This seems unfortunate since studies of the reaction kinetics in macromolecular solutions yield information which is pertinent to a number of the problems with which we have dealt in previous chapters of this book. As we shall see, the reactivity of a chain molecule may depend on both its configuration and conformation. In the case of polyelectrolytes, kinetic studies may yield new insight into the magnitude of electrostatic interactions and may, in fact, constitute a valuable method for the characterization of the distribution of the electrostatic potential. In this and other cases, the study of chemical reactivity may provide methods for the exploration of physical properties which are not easily investigated by other means.

In discussing the reactivity of macromolecules we should keep in mind that a functional group attached to a high polymer is characterized in many cases by a chemical reactivity similar to that which would be onserved for such a group in small molecules. This generalization was show by Floryb (1939) to hold for esterification reactions and it accounts for the kinetics observed in polyesterifications. In a similar manner, the rate of hydrolytic cleavage of cellulose has been treated successfully, assuming that the reactivity of the glucosidic linkage is independent of the size of the molecule in which it occurs (Freudenberg et al., 1930; Freudenberg and Blomquist, 1935). However, in this chapter we shall be concerned only with the exceptions to this generalization, where functional groups attached to a high polymer have reactivities deviating to a significant extent from those of monofunctional analogs. We shall also exclude from our discussion polymerization, polymer degradation, and polymer crosslinking processes which are beyond the scope of this book. Finally, we shall have to limit ourselves to a very brief account of the most interesting example of macromolecular reactivity, the catalytic activity of enzymes.

A. REACTIONS OF POLYMERS WITH SMALL MOLECULES AND IONS

1. Effects of Conformation of Globular Proteins on their Reactivity

The unique conformation characterizing proteins in their native state may profoundly modify the reactivity of the various functional groups attached to the polypeptide backbone. Such modifications may be accounted for, in principle, in two ways. Firstly, a reactive group may find itself in the interior of the globular structure and may be inaccessible to a given chemical reagent as long as the conformation of the native state is maintained. Secondly, the reactivity of a given functional group may be either enhanced or reduced by its juxtaposition to another group. Again, the effect is a result of the precisely defined macromolecular conformation and it disappears when the protein is denatured. A large number of examples could be cited to illustrate these effects; we shall limit ourselves to three typical cases, which may be considered characteristic of the phenomena observed.

Most proteins contain thiol groups of cysteine residues. Such groups, when attached to small molecules, are readily oxidized by a variety of oxidizing reagents. Yet, in native globular proteins, such thiol groups are frequently "masked" so that their reactivity is observed only when the protein is denatured. The voluminous literature dealing with this effect has been reviewed by Barron (1951). Typical of such studies is that of Greenstein (1938), who found that ovalbumin will not reduce the dye porphyrindin, a typical thiol reagent, unless the protein is denatured by reagents such as urea or guanidine hydrochloride. The number of thiol groups which become available for reactions increases with the time of exposure to the denaturation reagents and reaches a well-defined limit which depends on the concentration of these reagents. In the case of myosin (Greenstein and Edsall, 1940) some thiol groups are reactive even in the native protein, but the number of reactive thiols increases by 150% on denaturation.

A second example of the effect of macromolecular conformation on reactivity is provided by chymotrypsin, one of the most thoroughly investigated enzymes, which catalyzes the hydrolysis of certain amides and esters. Information on the mechanism by which chymotrypsin performs its function has been summarized by Bender and Kezdy (1964). It is particularly convenient to study this mechanism using nitrophenyl esters as substrates, since the color change due to the appearance of free nitrophenol makes it easy to follow the progress of the reaction spectrophotometrically. Kinetic studies of this system have established that the acyl group is first trans-

ferred from the ester to the enzyme and that the active enzyme is then re-
generated by a very rapid solvolysis of the acyl-enzyme (Hartley and Kilby,
1952, 1954).   It is also known that the hydroxyl group of one specific serine
residue of chymotrypsin functions as the acyl acceptor, so that the process
may be represented by the sequence

$$ChT-OH + ROCO-\langle \bigcirc \rangle-NO_2 \longrightarrow$$

$$ChT-OCOR + HO-\langle \bigcirc \rangle-NO_2 \quad (9.1a)$$

$$ChT-OCOR \xrightarrow{H_2O} ChT-OH + RCOOH \quad (9.1b)$$

It is then necessary to account for the unusually high reactivity exhibited
by the hydroxyl of the specific serine residue and for the unusually high
rate of the ester hydrolysis in step (9.1b).   It was found that the velocity
of both reaction steps is proportional to the fraction of imidazole which is
present, at any given pH, in the form of its conjugate base.   This suggests
that the imidazole group in a histidine residue of chymotrypsin is responsible
for the high rates of both the acylation and the deacylation of the enzyme.
Denaturation of the acyl-enzyme by urea leads to a millionfold reduction in
the speed of deacylation (Bender et al., 1962), suggesting that the active
serine residue and the histidine involved in the catalysis of the deacylation
process are held in juxtaposition only in the native form of the enzyme.
This conclusion, based entirely on kinetic evidence, was recently fully substantiated when the entire sequence of amino acid residues in chymotrypsin
was established (Hartley, 1964).   As a result of this work we now know
that 137 amino acid residues separate the serine and the histidine residue
which together form part of the catalytically active site.   It is, therefore,
clear that only a precisely defined tertiary structure of the enzyme can
hold these residues in the proximity required to produce the catalytic effect.

   For the third example demonstrating the manner in which the conformation of a globular protein can determine its reactivity, we choose the interaction of hemoglobin and myoglobin with oxygen.   As mentioned previously (Chap. VIII, Sec. A-3), hemoglobin carries four heme groups, in
which ferrous iron is coordinated with the four nitrogen atoms of protoporphyrin; a fifth coordinate linkage to the nitrogen of the imidazole group
of a histidine residue provides the attachment to the protein moiety.
Myoglobin has an analogous structure with a single heme group per protein molecule.   The biological function of these oxygen carrying proteins

can be performed only because the coordination of the heme groups with molecular oxygen is an easily reversible process, which does not involve a change in the oxidation state of the iron. Yet, heme groups separated from the protein are rapidly oxidized by atmospheric oxygen to the ferric state and the same holds for "hemochromagens," i.e., heme complexed with imidazole, pyridine, or other nitrogen bases. The protection of the heme from such irreversible oxidation is characteristic only of the native forms of hemoglobin and myoglobin, and denaturation of these proteins is generally followed by rapid atmospheric oxidation of the ferrous iron to the ferric state. The question then arises, why the attachment of the heme group to the protein of hemoglobin or myoglobin leads to such a striking change in its chemical behavior. This problem was considered by Wang et al. (1958) who postulated that the interaction of hemochromagen with molecular oxygen leads first to a coordination complex which is, however, rapidly destroyed by the transfer of an electron from the ferrous iron to the oxygen. Such a transfer involves charge separation in the transition state and it should, therefore, become more difficult as the dielectric constant of the medium is reduced. It was actually demonstrated (Wang et al., 1958; Wang, 1958) that an oil-soluble hemochromagen derivative is not oxidized to the ferric state in organic solvent media but combines with oxygen to form a complex which has spectral properties similar to those of oxyhemoglobin or oxymyoglobin. These experiments suggest that the oxygen carrying proteins owe their remarkable properties to the fact that the heme groups are imbedded in a nonpolar region filled with hydrocarbon side chains of amino acids such as alanine, leucine, isoleucine, and valine.

2. Isotopic Exchange

The secondary and tertiary structure of globular proteins may have a large effect on the ease with which reactive hydrogen atoms may participate in isotopic exchange. The use of such effects for the characterization of protein structure was pioneered at the Carlsberg Laboratory in Copenhagen, particularly by Linderstrøm-Lang, who developed a delicate method for following the exchange process. In this procedure the protein is first treated at elevated temperature with D_2O to replace the hydrogens of the peptide linkages as well as the "active" hydrogens of the side chains (—COOH, —NH$_2$, —OH, —SH, etc.) with deuterium. The deuterated protein is then dissolved in H_2O, aliquots are removed at specified time intervals, frozen at $-60°C$ to stop the exchange reaction, and subjected to high vacuum sublimation. The density of the water in the sublimate is then determined by a density gradient technique (Krause and Linderstrøm-

Lang. 1955). More recently, an alternative experimental method was developed, which utilizes the disappearance of the infrared absorption band at 1550 cm^{-1} when polypeptides or proteins are deuterated (Nielsen, 1960; Blout et al., 1961). This method has the advantage that it may be adapted to relatively fast reaction rates with the use of a stopped flow apparatus. It differs from the density gradient method in that it measures only the isotopic exchange of hydrogens in the peptide groups.

In di- or tripeptides, such as glycylglycine or alanylglycylglycine, isotopic hydrogen exchange is relatively rapid. The process is catalyzed both by acid and base and the rate is at a minimum around pH 2, with half-lives of the order of 1 min at 20°C (Nielsen et al., 1960). With poly(α-L-glutamic acid), the rate of isotopic hydrogen exchange may be compared with data on helix-coil transition obtained by optical activity or solution viscosity. Such a comparison leads to a striking correlation. The hydrogen exchange is practically complete in 10 min at neutral pH, where the polymer molecules are known to be randomly coiled, but the exchange becomes extremely slow (requiring several days) at pH 3.5, where the unionized polymer exists in the form of α-helices (Blout et al., 1961).

Early experiments on globular proteins demonstrated that only some of the hydrogens exchange rapidly. The remainder seemed to fall into several categories, some being apparently unable to participate in isotopic exchange. It seemed at first that the exchange data might be interpretable in terms of the extent to which the protein molecule consists of helical structures (Hvidt and Linderstrøm-Lang, 1955a). This belief was supported by the observation that denaturation eliminates resistance to isotopic exchange in such proteins as insulin and ribonuclease (Hvidt and Linderstrøm-Lang, 1955b; Hvidt, 1955). However, more extensive studies on a number of proteins showed that the interpretation of experimental data must be much more complicated. The fundamental assumption that isotopic hydrogen exchange does not affect appreciably the equilibrium of helix-coil transitions was found to be inexact; both in poly(γ-benzyl-L-glutamate) and in ribonuclease, the stability of helical structures was increased by deuteration (Calvin et al., 1959; Hermans and Scheraga, 1959). It has also been found that a protein such as β-lactoglobulin, which does not seem to contain any helical structures, contains a large number of slowly exchanging hydrogens. Moreover, the hydrogen exchange rate is usually strongly pH dependent, even in a range of pH in which no other technique indicates conformational transitions. These discrepancies have led Hvidt (1964) to reconsider the assumptions on which the interpretation of isotopic exchange data is based. She points out that other techniques used in the study of protein solutions give information about the time-average properties of the system, while measurements of the rate of isotopic exchange may yield, in principle, information about the frequency with which different conformations are interconverted. For instance, if every mole-cule exists 1% of the time in a conformation in which isotopic exchange is extremely rapid and if the interconversion of the molecular conformations occurs, on the average, once every minute, then the labile hydrogen of vir-tually every molecule will have been exposed at the end of 100 min for a total of one minute and isotopic exchange will be practically complete. If, however, the conformational transition occurs so slowly that only half of the molecules will have been in the reactive form at the end of 100 min, then only half of the hydrogen will have been exchanged. It is also clear that a change of pH may affect the rate of isotopic exchange by modify-ing the reactivity of the "exposed" protein conformation, although the equilibrium between the reactive and the unreactive form may not be pH dependent. A low reactivity of a hydrogen need, of course, not imply a helical conformation, but may also be due to side-by-side association of polypeptide chains through hydrogen bonds or to the placement of a por-tion of the chain within an inaccessible nonpolar region in the interior of the globular·molecular structure. Only such "masking" can explain the low exchange rate of a portion of the active hydrogens contained in the side chains of a protein. Such an effect has been demonstrated by compar-ing results obtained with lysosyme using the density gradient and the IR spectrophotometric method for following the isotopic hydrogen exchange. It was found that the total number of active hydrogens which fail to ex-change at pH 3.2 and 0°C is about twice as high as the number of hydrogens in the polypeptide backbone which do not participate in the exchange proc-ess (Hvidt and Kanarek, 1963; Hvidt, 1963).

3. Electrostatic Effects on the Reactivity of Polyions

We saw in our discussion of the titration behavior of chain molecules (Chap. VII, Sec. C-4) that the electrostatic free energy required to remove a hydrogen ion from a highly charged polyion may produce a large shift in the ionization equilibrium. This shift will have a pronounced effect on the rate of a process in which the conjugate base of an ionizable function is the reactive species, if we compare the reaction rates of an ionizable chain molecule and its monofunctional analog at the same pH. The principle may be illustrated by comparing the quaternization rates in aqueous solu-tions of poly(4-vinylpyridine) and 4-picoline, its monofunctional analog (Ladenheim et al., 1959). The 4-picoline is characterized by $pK = 5.2$, so that at pH 3 only one picoline molecule in 150 is in the basic form which participates in the reaction. With poly(4-vinylpyridine), however, the electrostatic repulsion between the polycation and hydrogen ions tends to counteract the buildup of a high density of ionized groups on the chain molecule, so that at pH 3 and an ionic strength of 0.003 there are still 45% of pyridine residues in their basic form. The rate of quaternization with an uncharged alkyl halide will, therefore, drop off with decreasing pH much more slowly for the polymer than for its analog. The reaction of the polymer would also be expected to exhibit a much larger salt effect, since addition of neutral salts will reduce the electrostatic free energy of ionization, reduce the dissociation of the cationic pyridinium residues and lead, as a result, to a decrease in the reaction rate. For instance, an increase of the ionic strength from 0.003 to 0.15 reduces by a factor of three the fraction of pyridine residues in poly(4-vinylpyridine) which remain at pH 3 in their basic form and can function in a chemical reaction as nucleophiles. Similar considerations apply also to the reactions of proteins involving various ionizable groups such as carboxyl, amine, imidazole, thiol, etc. Since the reactivity of these groups depends on their state of ionization, the effect of protein charge on the ionization equilibria has to be considered in the interpretation of kinetic data. For a summary of this field, the reader is referred to a review by Putnam (1953).

However, even when the reaction of a polyion with a second uncharged reagent is compared with the rate of the corresponding reaction of a monofunctional analog *at the same degree of ionization*, some striking differences may be observed. To avoid complications resulting from the change in the nature of the polymeric species with the progress of the reaction, it is best to concentrate on an analysis of initial reaction rates. A study of this type was carried out on the bromine displacement in α-bromoacetamide by partially ionized poly(methacrylic acid):

$$-CH_2-\underset{\underset{COOH}{|}}{\overset{\overset{CH_3}{|}}{C}}-CH_2-\underset{\underset{COO^-}{|}}{\overset{\overset{CH_3}{|}}{C}}-CH_2-\underset{\underset{COO^-}{|}}{\overset{\overset{CH_3}{|}}{C}}-\ +\ BrCH_2CONH_2\ \rightarrow$$

$$-CH_2-\underset{\underset{COOH}{|}}{\overset{\overset{CH_3}{|}}{C}}-CH_2-\underset{\underset{\underset{OCH_2CONH_2}{|}}{CO}}{\overset{\overset{CH_3}{|}}{C}}-CH_2-\underset{\underset{COO^-}{|}}{\overset{\overset{CH_3}{|}}{C}}-\ +\ Br^-\quad (9.2)$$

It was found that the reactivity of the carboxylate groups decreased sharply with an increasing degree of ionization of the polymeric acid (Ladenheim and Morawetz, 1959). On the other hand, when partially ionized poly-(4-vinylpyridine) acted as a nucleophilic catalyst in the hydrolysis of 2,4-dinitrophenyl acetate

$$(9.3)$$

the apparent second-order rate constant, based on the concentration of un-ionized pyridine residues, was found to increase with an increase of the fraction of these residues present in the form of their conjugate base (Letsinger and Savereide, 1962). These two results have the common feature that the basic groups attached to the polymer tend to react with uncharged low-molecular weight reagents at a rate which decreases with an increasing charge density (positive or negative) along the macromolecular chain (cf. Fig. IX.1). This conclusion seems reasonable if we consider the α-bromoacetamide as a relatively nonpolar co-solvent added to the aqueous medium. We would then expect that the region surrounding the macromolecule will have an increasing tendency to exclude this reagent as the polarity of the polymer is being increased with an increasing degree of ionization. A similar effect was found in following to high conversion the quaternization of poly(4-vinylpyridine) with n-butyl bromide in tetramethylene sulfone solution. The apparent second-order rate constant falls off as the uncharged polymer is gradually converted into a more and more highly charged polyion (Coleman and Fuoss, 1955; Fuoss et al., 1960). Recently, Alger (1964) has studied an analogous process, i.e., the reaction of poly(p-chloromethylstyrene) with triethylamine, in various solvent media. He found that the downward drift in the apparent second-order rate constant is reduced and eventually entirely eliminated as the dielectric constant of the solvent medium is diminished. This is what would be expected: As the solvent and the low molecular weight reagent approach

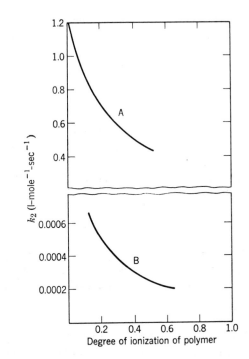

Fig. IX.1. Reactivity of polyions with small molecules. (A) Poly(4-vinylpyridine) with 2,4-dinitrophenyl acetate (50% ethanol, ionic strength 0.04, temp. 36.8°C, rate constant based on concentration of un-ionized pyridine residues). B. Poly(methacrylic acid) with α-bromoacetamide (water solution, ionic strength 0.148, temp. 50°C, rate constant based on concentration of ionized carboxyls).

one another in polarity, the cause for the exclusion of the reagent from the region of the charged polyion is eliminated. Furthermore, in media of low dielectric constant the polyion will be fully associated with its counterions and the polarity of the polymer will, therefore, change much less during the quaternization reaction.

Effects of a different type are encountered when polyions react with charged low molecular weight species. Qualitatively, it would be expected that electrostatic interactions hinder reactions between species which carry charges of the same sign, while they accelerate processes between positively and negatively charged reagents. Additions of electrolyte tend to reduce long-range forces between charged reagents, so that reactions involving species with charges of the same sign are accelerated, while those between oppositely charged species are slowed down. The phenomenon has been studied extensively on reactions of simple ions and is commonly referred to as the "primary salt effect." The magnitude of the kinetic effects may be accounted for quantitatively (Bell, 1941), using the theory of absolute reaction rates and assigning to the reagents and the transition state complex activity coefficients which depend on the ionic strength as predicted by the Debye–Hückel theory.

The modification of reaction rates by electrostatic forces will be particularly large if one of the reagents is a polyion with a high charge density. A typical example of this class of reactions is the hydroxyl ion catalyzed hydrolysis of pectins, the partially esterified derivatives of polygalacturonic acid, which are widely distributed in plants. The polymer may be represented schematically by

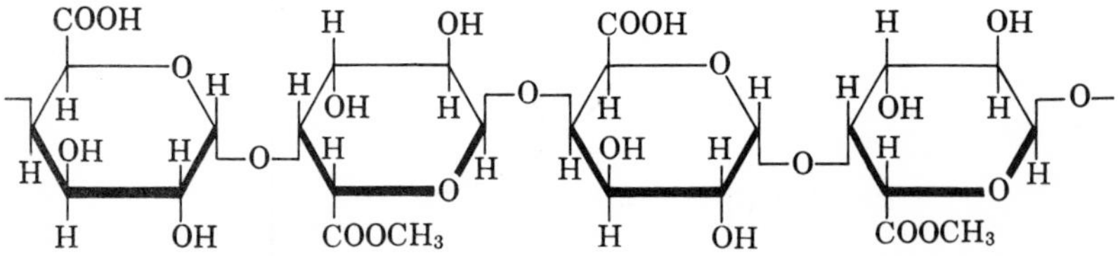

and it was found that the apparent second-order rate constant for its basic hydrolysis falls off rapidly with the progress of the reaction (Deuel et al., 1953). This is what would be expected as a result of the mutual repulsion of the catalyzing hydroxyl ion and the polymer which acquires a higher and higher negative charge as the ester groups are being hydrolyzed. Addition of neutral salts reduces this electrostatic interaction and leads to an acceleration of the process, particularly in its later stages (Lineweaver, 1945; Deuel et al., 1953). A similar inhibition in the reaction of a polyion with a small anionic species was observed in the bromine displacement by the carboxylate group of partially ionized poly(methacrylic acid). We have seen above that this reaction proceeds at an appreciable rate with the uncharged α-bromoacetamide, but if the anionic α-bromoacetate is used as the second reagent, the bromine displacement by the carboxylate groups of the polyanion is too slow to be detected (Ladenheim and Morawetz, 1959). An analogous phenomenon was reported by Lovrien and Waddington (1964) in their study of copolymers of N-azobenzeneacrylamide

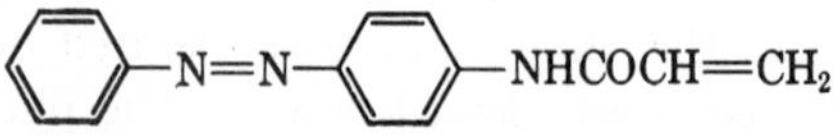

with acrylic or methacrylic acid.   On irradiation with UV light, the azobenzene is isomerized from the *trans* to the *cis* form and the reverse process,
which occurs in the dark, is subject to both hydrogen ion and hydroxyl ion
catalysis.   Attachment of the azobenzene function to a polymeric acid
tends to repress the catalytic effect of the hydroxyl ions which are repelled
from the polyanion and the minimum in the reaction rate, is therefore,
shifted to much higher pH values.

Studies have also been reported in which a polyion reacts with a reagent
of opposite charge.   This is the situation in the reaction of partially ionized poly(4-vinylpyridine) with α-bromoacetate (Ladenheim et al., 1959)

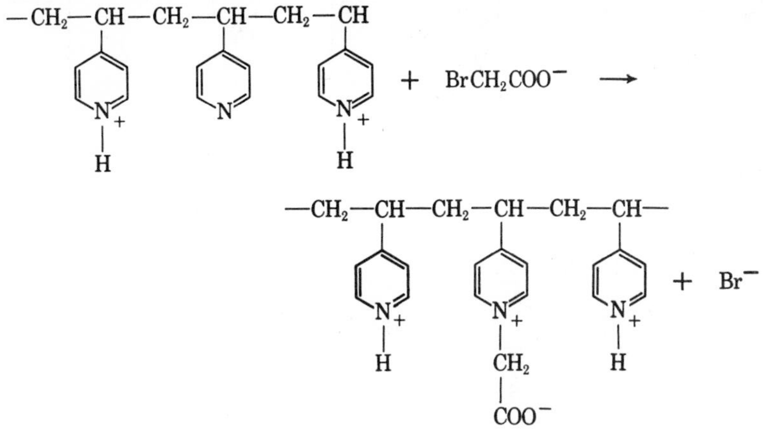

$$-CH_2-CH-CH_2-CH-CH_2-CH$$

$$+ \quad BrCH_2COO^- \quad \longrightarrow$$

$$-CH_2-CH-CH_2-CH-CH_2-CH-$$

$$+ \quad Br^- \quad (9,4)$$

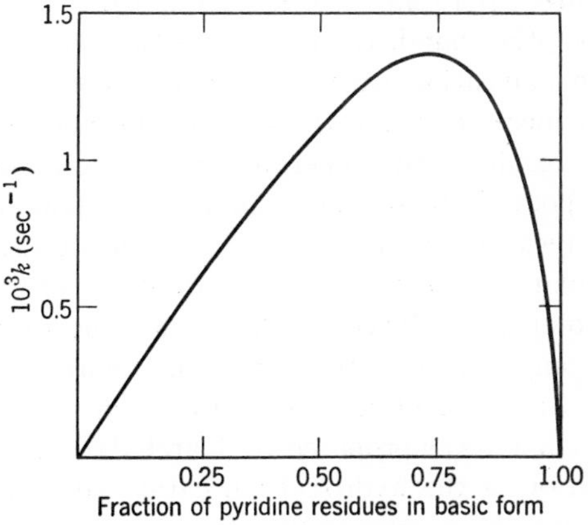

Fig. IX.2. Solvolysis of 3-nitro-4-acetoxybenzenesulfonate catalyzed by 0.01N poly(4-
vinylpyridine) (50% ethanol, ionic strength 0.04, temp. 36.8°C).

where the mutual electrostatic attraction of the two reagents leads to an acceleration of the reaction rate. Therefore, the addition of neutral salt has an inhibiting effect. An analogous effect is revealed by the kinetic pattern observed when the hydrolysis of the anionic ester 3-nitro-4-acetoxy-benzenesulfonate is catalyzed by partially ionized poly(4-vinylpyridine) (Letsinger and Savereide, 1962). This reaction may be presumed to proceed by the sequence

$$(9.5)$$

so that the un-ionized pyridine residue acts as the catalytically active nucleophile. On the other hand, the reaction is favored by the electrostatic interaction of the polycation with the anionic ester and this interaction increases with an increase in the fraction of pyridine residues in the cationic form. The result of the superposition of these two factors is that the reaction rate goes through a maximum when about three quarters of the pyridine residues are in the un-ionized form of the conjugate base (Fig. IX.2). Similar behavior has been reported in a system in which poly-(4(5)-vinylimidazole) is employed as the nuclephilic catalyst for the hydrolysis of an anionic ester (Overberger et al., 1965).

A quantitative theory of electrostatic effects on the reaction rate of a polyion with a small ion was proposed by Katchalsky and Feitelson (1954) for the interpretation of the hydroxyl ion catalyzed hydrolysis of pectin. Their treatment may be expressed by

$$k = k_0 \exp[-\Delta G^{\ddagger}_{el}(\alpha_i)/kT] \qquad (9.6)$$

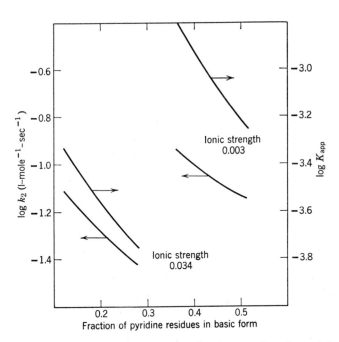

Fig. IX.3. Comparison of the rate constant for the reaction of partially ionized poly(4-vinylpyridine) with α-bromoacetate and the dissociation constant of the pyridinium residues (temp. 50°C, k_2 based on the concentration of un-ionized pyridine residues).

where k is the rate constant observed with the polyion at a degree of ionization α_i while k_0 is the rate constant which would be observed in the hydrolysis of an uncharged ester. The electrical free energy of activation $\Delta G_{el}^{\ddagger}(\alpha_i)$, required to bring the catalyzing hydroxyl ion to the ester group against the repulsion of the polyanion charge, is assumed to be equal to the electrical free energy required to remove a hydrogen ion from a carboxyl group against the field of the polyion, i.e., the electrical free energy of ionization

$$\Delta G_{el}^{\ddagger}(\alpha_i) = \Delta G_{el}^{i}(\alpha_i) \tag{9.7}$$

From a comparison of (9.6) with (7.38) we conclude then that the apparent second-order rate constant for the basic hydrolysis of pectin should change with the progress of the reaction by the same factor as the apparent ionization constant, i.e.

$$k/K_{app} = \text{constant} \tag{9.8}$$

This treatment, which should apply generally to reactions of polyions with small species carrying a single negative charge, is an extension of an analogous suggestion made by Ingold (1930) for the basic hydrolysis of monoesters of dicarboxylic acids. It implies that the electrostatic potential at the point to which the hydroxyl ion has to be brought to attack the ester function is the same as the potential at the location of the acid group whose ionization constant is being compared to the hydrolytic rate constant. For the hydrolysis of esters attached to polyions this is a reasonable assumption since the formation of the transition state complex may be represented as

$$
\begin{array}{cccc}
\vphantom{}\text{C}{=}\text{O} & \text{C}{=}\text{O} & \text{C}{=}\text{O} + \text{OH}^- \longrightarrow & \text{C}{=}\text{O} \quad \text{HO}{-}\text{C}{-}\text{O}^{-\delta} \quad \text{C}{=}\text{O} \\
\text{O}^- & \text{O} & \text{O}^- & \text{O}^- \qquad \text{O}^{-\delta} \qquad \text{O}^- \\
 & \text{R} & & \text{R}
\end{array}
\tag{9.9}
$$

However, in other cases of reactions of polyions with small ionized species, $\Delta G_{el}^{\ddagger}$ need not be equal to ΔG_{el}^{i}. For instance, in the reaction of poly(4-vinylpyridine) with α-bromoacetate, represented by (9.4), the anionic charge of the α-bromoacetate need not be brought nearly as close to the backbone of the polymer to form the transition state as in the association of a hydrogen ion with a pyridine residue. It would then be expected that $\Delta G_{el}^{\ddagger}$ should be appreciably smaller than ΔG_{el}^{i}. This expectation is in accord with experimental data (Ladenheim et al., 1959) which show that the polyion charge has a distinctly greater effect on the ionization equilibrium of poly(4-vinylpyridine) than on its reaction rate with α-bromoacetate (cf. Fig. IX.3).

B. INTRAMOLECULAR INTERACTION EFFECTS ON POLYMER REACTIVITY

1. Neighboring Group Effects on the Reactivity of Chain Molecules

If several kinds of functional groups which may react with one another are attached to the backbone of the same polymer molecule, the probability of collisions between these groups will be increased, leading to correspondingly high reaction rates. This effect is particularly pronounced if the interacting groups are part of neighboring monomer residues. It was first recognized in a study of the hydrolysis of acrylic or methacrylic acid copolymers containing a small proportion of p-nitrophenyl methacrylate (Morawetz and Zimmering, 1954; Zimmering et al., 1957). This hydrolysis was expected to be very slow, in view of the repulsion of hydroxyl ions from the negatively charged polymer chain, but it was found to be much more rapid than the hydrolysis of p-nitrophenyl esters of mono-carboxylic acids. The significance of this observation became clear when the pH dependence of the reaction rate showed that the velocity of the hydrolysis is proportional to the fraction of ionized carboxyls in the macro-molecule. This indicates that the reaction does not involve hydroxyl ions but that the velocity of the process is governed by the attack of an ionized carboxyl on the ester function. It was later demonstrated (Bender and Neveu, 1958) that the first product in this type of reaction is an acid anhydride, so that the reaction may be represented by

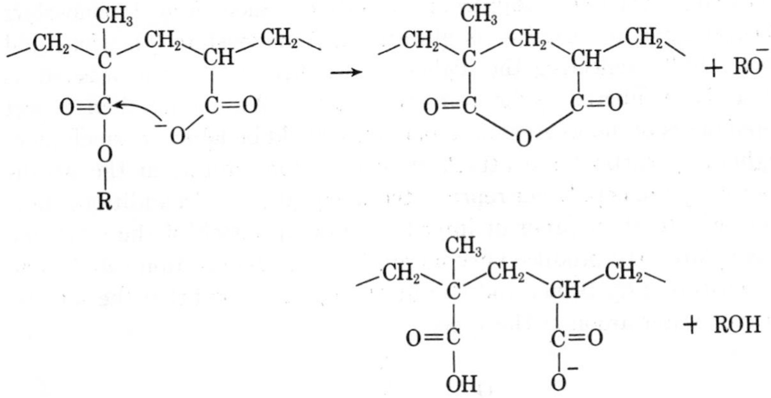

$$+ \text{ROH} \quad (9\cdot10)$$

As would be expected, monoesters of dicarboxylic acids, in which the ester and carboxyl groups have a spacing similar to that in the copolymer, behave in an analogous fashion. Figure IX.4 compares the pH dependence of the hydrolysis rate of the p-nitrophenyl methacrylate–acrylic acid co-polymer with the behavior of the pivalic acid ester (which is analogous to the methacrylate residue in the polymer chain) and the glutaric acid monoester (which is analogous to a chain segment containing a methacrylic ester and an acrylic acid unit). We may note that the hydrolysis rate of

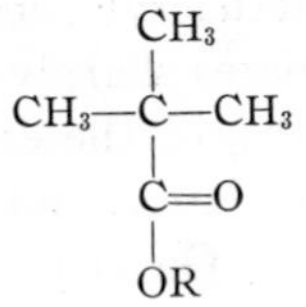

Pivalic acid ester

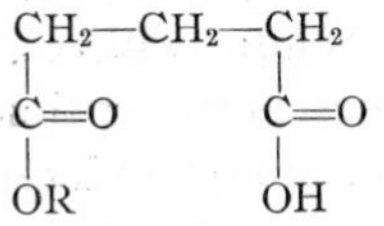

glutaric acid monoester

the pivalate is proportional to (H$^+$) below pH 4 and to (OH$^-$) above pH 6 while the hydrolysis rate of the glutaric monoester rises with increasing pH, levels off to a constant rate between pH 6 and 8, and increases again in more basic solutions. This means that the carboxylate attack on the ester function is rate determining up to pH 8 and the hydroxyl ion attack makes a significant contribution to the observed reaction velocity only in more basic media. In the case of the copolymer, the plateau in the reaction rate extends beyond pH 10, indicating that the direct attack of hydroxyl ion on groups attached to the anionic polymer is effectively inhibited by the Coulombic repulsion discussed in the preceding section.

As would be expected, the effectiveness of the neighboring carboxylate in catalyzing the solvolysis of the phenyl ester group is critically dependent on the spacing of the two groups from each other. Succinic acid monoesters are 120–200 times as reactive as glutaric acid monoesters (Gaetjens and Morawetz, 1960) reflecting the higher probability of a five-membered as against a six-membered cyclic transition state. We should then expect that copolymers of monoesters of maleic acid would be labilized much more by neighboring carboxylate attack than the ester groups in the acrylic acid–methacrylate copolymer represented in eq. (9.10). In addition, steric restraints which either favor or impede a close approach of the ester and the carboxylate may produce very large effects on the reaction rate. This was demonstrated by Bruice and Pandit (1960) who found that the solvolysis of a monoester anion of the type

was 230 times as rapid as that of the anion of the corresponding succinic acid monoester. The same principle may lead to a pronounced dependence of the hydrolysis rate of ester–acid copolymers, depending on the relative steric configurations of the carbon atoms to which the ester and carboxylate groups are attached. The existence of such an effect was revealed by the observation that the hydrolysis of copolymers of methacrylic acid containing about 1% of phenyl methacrylate residues deviates sharply from first-order kinetics and behaves, in fact, as if about 20% of the ester groups were ten times as susceptible to neighboring carboxylate attack as the remaining ester groups (Morawetz and Gaetjens, 1958; Gaetjens and Morawetz, 1961). It seems that the more reactive structure corresponds to the

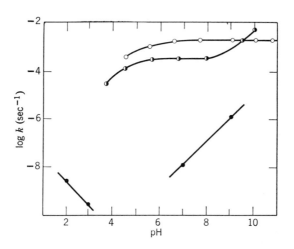

Fig. IX.4. pH dependence of the rate constants for the hydrolysis of *p*-nitrophenyl esters at 0°C. (●) *p*-nitrophenyl pivalate; (◑) mono-*p*-nitrophenyl glutarate; (O) copolymer of acrylic acid with *p*-nitrophenyl methacrylate.

isotactic configuration of the chain backbone. It is interesting that the deviation of the hydrolytic rate from first-order kinetics is observed in the case of methacrylic acid copolymers with both acrylic and methacrylic esters, but *not* in the case of acrylic acid copolymers with either type of monomeric ester. This is a rather remarkable result, since one might have expected that the attack of a neighboring acrylate on a methacrylic ester and the attack of a neighboring methacrylate on an acrylic ester unit

would be subject to similar steric restraints. The fact that these two types of copolymers differ so strikingly in their sensitivity of the reaction rate to stereoisomerism suggests that the cumulative effect of a number of consecutive monomer units in a methacrylic chain leads to steric restraints which cannot be simulated in simple molecular analogs.

In the hydrolysis of acrylic acid copolymers with acrylamide (Smets and Hesbain, 1959) the amide reactivity is also subject to a neighboring group effect, but in this case it is the un-ionized carboxyl which is catalytically active.   A similar situation is encountered in acrylic acid copolymers with the p-nitroanilide of acrylic acid (Westhead and Morawetz, 1958).   The pH profile of the reaction rate is then the mirror image of that shown in Fig. IX.4, i.e., the reaction rate increases with decreasing pH, reaches a plateau in the range in which the carboxyls are virtually un-ionized, and increases again only in strongly acid solutions where hydrogen ion catalysis becomes significant.   It was found that the mono-p-nitroanilide of glutaric acid did not exhibit any neighboring group effect on the reactivity of the nitroanilide group; apparently the steric restraints in the polymeric chain are in this case highly favorable for the neighboring group interaction.

Another well established example of a neighboring group effect in the reaction of dissolved chain molecules concerns the hydrolysis of poly(vinyl acetate) to poly(vinyl alcohol).   In this case the alcoholic hydroxyl groups formed during the reaction have an accelerating effect on the reactivity of neighboring ester functions.   As a result, partially saponified poly(vinyl acetate) can be shown by infrared spectroscopy to have a much higher fraction of ester groups flanked by other unchanged ester residues then would be expected from a statistical distribution of hydrolyzed groups (Nagai and Sagane, 1955).   The accelerating effect of neighboring hydroxyls on ester hydrolysis may also be demonstrated by the acceleration of the reaction rate in the initial stages of the process (Minsk et al., 1941; Fujii et al., 1963).   A similar observation was reported with the hydrolysis of poly(vinyl acetal) in dilute acid solutions (Smets and Petit, 1959). With both poly(vinyl acetate) and poly(vinyl acetal) the syndiotactic polymer seems to be the more reactive species (Fujii et al., 1963).

Neighboring groups may also have an inhibitory effect on the reaction rate.   Such an effect is indicated by the observation that the hydrolysis of polymethacrylamide in strongly basic solutions stops short of completion at the point which would be predicted if it were assumed that an amide flanked by two ionized carboxyls is inert (Arcus, 1949).   This interpretation has been reinforced by the finding that the hydrolysis of various methacrylamide–methacrylic acid copolymers also stops at a conversion predicted by this mechanism (Pinner, 1953).   In the case of acrylic acid polymers carrying a small number of p-nitroanilide groups, the inhibition, by neighboring carboxylate groups, of the hydrolysis in strongly basic media can be demonstrated indirectly by an unusual phenomenon.   It is found that the reaction is strongly catalyzed by Ba^{++}, with the velocity of the process increasing by an amount proportional to the square of the concentration of added barium ions.   This may be interpreted by assuming that carboxylate groups on either side of a nitroanilide function can now form barium chelates, so that their inhibitory effect on the hydrolytic process is eliminated (Westhead and Morawetz, 1958).

2. Statistical Analysis of the Kinetic Pattern

In the previous section we discussed a number of cases in which a chain molecule carries a large number of substituents whose reactivity depends on whether their nearest neighbors have been converted to another group. We have then three rate constants to consider: k_0 characteristic of groups with two unreacted nearest neighbors; k_1 for groups lying next to one reacted and one unreacted residue; and k_2 describing the reactivity of groups lying between two reacted residues of the chain molecule. The mathematical analysis of such a situation is quite difficult, even if additional complications, such as might result from effects due to the stereoisomerism of the chain, are neglected.

We shall first consider some simple results of such a situation. In the first case a given reactive group is strongly activated by the functional group which is formed by the conversion of its nearest neighbor, so that $k_2 \approx k_1 \gg k_0$. We may then regard the slow reaction of a residue in the middle of an unreacted sequence as a "nucleation" process, which is followed by a more rapid "chain reaction" of a series of residues, each activated by the reaction of the preceding unit. Let us denote by (A) the total number of unreacted groups and by (B) the number of sequences consisting of one or more consecutive reacted groups. In the initial stages of the reaction, when (A) deviates only slightly from its original value $(A)_0$ and $(A) \gg (B)$, we may approximate $(B) = k_0(A)_0 t$ and we have then for the observed reaction rate

$$- [d(A)/dt]_{(A) \to (A)_0} \approx k_0(A)_0 + 2k_1 k_0(A)_0 t$$

The conversion will, therefore, be a quadratic function of time in the initial phases of the reaction. The acceleration observed in the hydrolysis of poly(vinyl acetate) and poly(vinyl acetal), as discussed in the previous section, conforms to this kinetic pattern.

A second case of interest arises with chains of finite length and with k_1/k_0 much larger than the degree of polymerization, so that all the groups attached to a given chain molecule may be considered as reacting in a negligible time span, once one of the groups on that chain molecule has reacted. Such a situation might be expected, for instance, in the hydrolysis of poly(p-carboxyphenyl acrylate) at neutral pH

$$(9.12)$$

where the hydroxyl ion catalyzed reaction would be expected to be at least four orders of magnitude slower than the reaction produced by the attack of a neighboring carboxylate on the ester function. Since the hydrolysis of one ester group may be considered the rate-determining step for the destruction of all the ester groups on a given polymer chain, the observed rate constant will be proportional to the length of the chain molecule. For polydisperse samples containing weight fractions w_i of chains with a degree of polymerization P_i the kinetics of the process are represented by

$$(A)/(A)_0 = \sum_i w_i \exp{(-k_0 P_i)} \qquad (9.13)$$

In such a case it should then be possible, in principle, to derive the chain length distribution function from the reaction rate data.

A number of investigators have recently considered the kinetic problem of neighboring group effects for chains of infinite length and have arrived at kinetic expressions for the entire course of the process (Keller, 1962, 1963; Alfrey and Lloyd, 1963; Arends, 1963; Lazare, 1963). The solution of the problem is complicated by the fact that it is necessary to evaluate the rate at which sequences of reacted residues O "run together"

A—A—A—O—O—O—A—O—O—O—O—A—A →
A—A—A—O—O—O—O—O—O—O—O—A—A

thus reducing the number of activated reactive units. Using Keller's results, the fraction of residues N_0 and N_1 which have no reacted nearest neighbors and one reacted nearest neighbor, respectively, may be expressed by

$$N_0(t) = \exp{\left[-(2k_1 - k_0)t - (2/k_0)(k_1 - k_0)e^{-k_0 t} - 1 \right]} \qquad (9.14a)$$

$$N_1(t) = 2[\exp{(k_0 t)} - 1] \exp{\left[-(2k_1 + k_0)t - (2/k_0)(k_1 - k_0)(e^{-k_0 t} - 1) \right]} \qquad (9.14b)$$

The general expression for N_2, the fraction of unreacted residues with two reacted neighbors, is much more complex. It assumes a simpler form for two special cases of interest:

$$N_2(t) = (1/2) + [\exp(-k_0 t) - (3/2)] \exp[2(e^{-k_0 t} - 1)]$$

$$\text{For } k_1 = k_2 = 0 \quad (9.14c)$$

$$N_2(t) = \frac{2k_0 \exp(-2k_0 t)}{k_2 - 2k_0} - \frac{2k_0 \exp(-3k_0 t)}{k_2 - 3k_0} + \frac{2k_0^2 \exp(-k_2 t)}{(k_2 - 2k_0)(k_2 - 3k_0)}$$

$$\text{for } k_0 = k_1 \quad (9.14d)$$

Relation (9.14d) predicts that one-third of the functional groups will remain unreacted at infinite time if the reactivity is unaffected by one neighboring reacted group but is completely eliminated when both nearest neighbors have reacted. This is the model which has been used to interpret the hydrolysis of polymethacrylamide in strong base solutions, as discussed in the preceding section. If even one reacted neighboring residue leads to complete inhibition, then (9.14b) and (9.14c) predict that for $t \to \infty$ a fraction $N_1 + N_2 = (1 + e^{-2})/2$ (i.e., 56.8%) of the potentially reactive groups will remain unreacted.

Comparison of theoretical predictions with experimental data is rendered difficult by several factors: In many cases, the product obtained when a polymeric reaction has gone to completion is insoluble in the solvent media for the original polymeric reagent, so that the reaction may be observed only over a limited range of conversion. This is the case, for instance, in the hydrolysis of poly(vinyl acetate) or poly(methyl acrylate). In other cases, the reaction can be followed over its entire course in a single solvent medium, but neighboring group effects are not sufficiently pronounced (nor experimental data sufficiently precise) to allow the evaluation of three distinct rate constants. For instance, in the quaternization of poly(4-vinylpyridine) with n-butyl bromide, referred to in the previous section, the data may be interpreted by $k_1/k_0 = 1$ and $k_2/k_0 = 0.32$ (Arends, 1963), but no claim is made that other ratios of the three rate constants would not yield an equally acceptable fit of the observed kinetic curve. Finally, we have to bear in mind that ample evidence demonstrates the sensitivity of reaction rates to the stereoisomerism of polymeric reagents (Morawetz and Gaetjens, 1958; Glavis, 1959; Smets and De Loecker, 1959, 1960; Smets and Petit, 1959; Gaetjens and Morawetz, 1961; Fujii et al., 1963). This complicates the situation to such an extent that any interpretation of data collected over a broad range of conversion be-

comes highly uncertain when both neighboring group effects and effects
resulting from stereoisomerism are known to be pronounced.

3. Bifunctional Catalysis

In some cases a reaction rate may be maximized when the reactive function is subjected to a concerted attack by a nucleophilic and electrophilic
reagent.   This type of bifunctional catalysis is of particular interest since
it is believed to account for the effectiveness of a number of enzymatic
catalyses.

Bifunctional catalyses of several types have been observed in solutions
containing polymeric reagents.   In a sense, the processes described earlier
in this chapter may be regarded as involving a bifunctional attack of a
polymer on a low molecular weight reagent.   For instance, in the reaction
given in eq. (9.4) a basic pyridine residue attacks a C—Br bond, while the
carboxylate group of α-bromoacetate interacts electrostatically with
another pyridine residue which is present in its cationic form.   A similar
cooperative effect of a nucleophile and a neighboring positively charged
group is observed in the hydrolysis of anionic esters catalyzed by partially
ionized polyvinylpyridine, as depicted in eq. (9.5).   We should note, however, that in these cases the two functional groups of the polymer do not
both attack the reactive site of the second reagent.   We deal here with a
situation depicted schematically below, in which the group N of the polymer
attacks the reactive group A of a small molecule, while the energetic
interaction of the groups M and B, well removed from the reactive site,
merely serves to stabilize the transition state complex:

While this secondary interaction is between oppositely charged groups in
the re actions of partially ionized poly(4-vinylpyridine) with anionic reagents, it is due to hydrogen bonding in the reaction of partially ionized
poly(methacrylic acid) with α-bromoacetamide [eq. (9.2)].   A bifunctional
catalysis of this type could lead to very fast reaction rates if the spacing of
the groups A and B matched that between the groups M and N, particularly if this spacing were precisely defined in molecules of high conformational rigidity.   This principle is apparently responsible for the high cat-

alytic efficiency of acetylcholine esterase, which has been discussed in the preceding chapter (see p. 386–387).

A phenomenon in which bifunctional catalysis, in the commonly accepted meaning of the term, is apparently involved, has been observed in the hydrolysis of p-nitrophenyl acetate catalyzed by poly-(4(5)-vinyl imidazole) (Overberger et al., 1965). Imidazole is well known to be a powerful catalyst for the hydrolysis of phenyl esters, and the effectiveness of this catalytic activity remains essentially unchanged by attachment of the imidazole residue to the polymer backbone if the reaction rates are studied below 8. However, in a more basic medium, the polymer becomes a much more powerful catalyst. It appears that this phenomenon is due to a small concentration of imidazole residues in their anionic form and that the imidazolate ions cooperate with uncharged imidazole residues attached to the same polymer chain in attacking the ester function.

Bifunctional catalysis may also occur as an intramolecular process. In the ester and amide shown below,

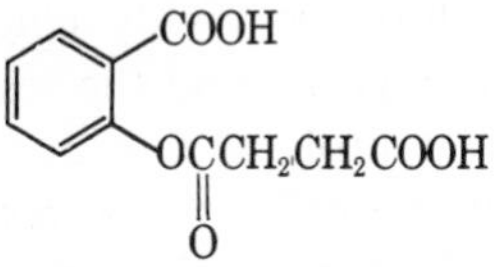

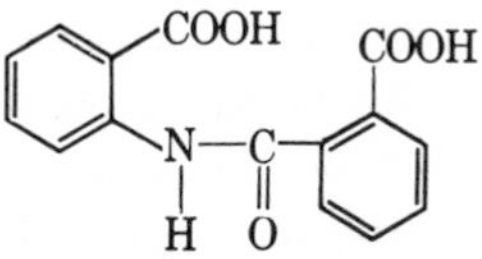

the reactive groups are flanked by two carboxyl groups and the hydrolytic rate of these compounds is found to be at a maximum when one of the carboxyls is ionized and the other un-ionized (Morawetz and Oreskes, 1958; Morawetz and Shafer, 1962). We may interpret this by assuming that the ionized carboxyl acts as a nucleophile in attacking the carbonyl carbon of the ester group, while the un-ionized carboxyl facilitates the process by forming a hydrogen bond with the carbonyl oxygen. Analogous observations have been made on some reactions of chain molecules. Smets and Van Humbeeck (1963) studied the hydrolysis of partially neutralized acrylic acid–ethyl ethacrylate copolymers and found that the rate is highest when half of the carboxyl groups are ionized. Bifunctional intramolecular catalysis was also observed in the case of the condensation product of a methacrylic acid–maleic anhydride copolymer with p-nitroaniline. It was found that the anilide condenses easily with one of its carboxyl neighbors to an imide, the rate of the reaction being a maximum when one of the neighboring carboxyls is ionized and the other un-ionized (Westhead and Morawetz, 1958). The mechanism proposed for this process is

This reaction is interesting in that no analogous observation has been reported with reagents of low molecular weight. This does not mean, of course, that suitable small molecules would not react in the same manner, but such reagents would be much more difficult to prepare than the copolymers.

4. Effects of Non-neighboring Groups

In the neighboring group activations considered in Sec. B-1 we have dealt with situations where a neighboring group attack on a reactive function leads to a five-membered or six-membered cyclic transition state. It is well known that five- and six-membered rings form very easily and such neighboring group effects will, therefore, be highly efficient. The effect of a favorable spacing of the activating group and the reactive function may be illustrated by comparing the hydrolysis rate in monophenyl succinate and monophenyl glutarate with the catalytic power of acetate ion in the hydrolysis of phenyl acetate (Gaetjens and Morawetz, 1960). Such a comparison shows that the neighboring carboxylate group in the succinate and the glutarate is 4000 and 30 times, respectively, as effective as $1 M$ acetate. However, the effectiveness of neighboring groups in accelerating reaction rates would be expected to drop off abruptly if the transition state involves rings of larger size. The relative ease with which rings of various sizes may be formed was studied by Stoll and Rouvé (1935) and by Spanagel and Carothers (1935) who found that rings containing 9–12 atoms form with great difficulty and that the probability of ring formation passes through a second flat maximum (much lower than that characterizing five- and six-membered rings) for rings containing about 18 atoms. These complicated effects are caused by bond angle restrictions and steric hindrance. For longer chains the probability of ring closure may be assumed to be represented satisfactorily by Kuhn's statistical chain model. Thus, if we place one chain end at the origin of the coordinate system, the "effective concentration," c_{eff}, of the other chain end at a distance h may be related to the probability distribution function $\mathcal{W}(h)$ of the chain-end displacement by

$$c_{eff} = (1000/N)\mathcal{W}(h)dh/4\pi h^2 dh \qquad (9.15)$$

where c_{eff} is expressed in moles per liter. If $\mathcal{W}(h)$ has the form given in (3-7), we have for $h \ll \langle h^2 \rangle^{1/2}$

$$c_{\text{eff}} = (1000/N)(3/2\pi\langle h^2 \rangle)^{3/2} \qquad (9.16)$$

In random flight chains, the mean square distance between the ith and jth segment $\langle h_{ij}^2 \rangle$ is proportional to $|j - i|$, so that the probability of ring formation involving the interaction of any two given groups is inversely proportional to the $3/2$ power of their separation along the molecular chain. If a reactive group is attached to the ith unit of a chain of Z units, each carrying an activating group, the aggregate effective concentration of these activating groups will be

$$c_{\text{eff}} = (1000/N) \ (3Z/2\pi\langle h^2 \rangle)^{3/2} \left(\sum_{x=j'}^{x=i} x^{-3/2} + \sum_{x=j'}^{x=Z-i} x^{-3/2} \right) + c'_{\text{eff}} \quad (9.17)$$

where j' represents the smallest group separation for which random flight chain statistics are applicable and c'_{eff} represents the contribution of small rings. We may note that the sums in (9.17) converge fairly rapidly, so that for polymers of moderate molecular weight the effect of the activating groups should be nearly independent of chain length. The term c'_{eff} becomes negligible if attack on the reactive group by a group attached to the neighboring monomer unit is rendered difficult by steric hindrance or if it involves the formation of larger than six-membered rings in the transition state. For such cases we may estimate c_{eff} from (9-17), using known values of $\langle h^2 \rangle/Z$. Replacing the summation by integrals, c_{eff} is given, in the limit of $Z \to \infty$ by $(1500/N) \ (3Z/2\pi \ \langle h^2 \rangle)^{3/2}(j')^{-1/2}$. The data listed by Flory (1953e) give for vinyl polymers in Θ-solvents $(\langle h^2 \rangle/Z)^{1/2}$ values averaging about 7 Å. We obtain then, assuming $j' = 10$, a value of c_{eff} somewhat below $1M$. Data based on chelate formation studies (Chap. VIII, Sec. A-1) and on intramolecular bonding in styrene-methacrylic acid copolymers (Fig. VII.11) are in remarkably good agreement with this estimate. If only a fraction of the monomer residues carry activating groups, the value of c_{eff} will, of course, be correspondingly reduced.

The only experimental study of activation caused by non-neighboring groups seems to have been reported by Loucheux and Banderet (1960, 1964). They studied the reaction of methyl methacrylate–maleic anhydride copolymers with p-toluidine and found that the reaction was appreciably accelerated by the catalytic effect of the carboxyls formed during the reaction. The authors of this study tried to interpret the effect as due to a local carboxyl concentration calculated by averaging it over the volume of a hydrodynamically equivalent sphere. This treatment cannot be correct since it would predict that the catalytic effect should decrease with an increasing polymer chain length.

C. REACTIONS OF TWO LOW MOLECULAR WEIGHT SPECIES IN THE PRESENCE OF POLYIONS

The presence of macromolecules in dilute solution has, in general, little effect on the reactions of small molecules with each other. Although the presence of the polymer may increase appreciably the macroscopic viscosity of the system, the mobility of small molecular species usually remains almost unchanged (cf. Chap. VI, Sec. A-5). Moreover, even if the mobility of the reactive species were reduced, there might be no appreciable effect on the reaction rate. This is so since most chemical processes have an activation energy which requires a very large number of molecular collisions before the reaction will occur. While a lowered mobility of the reactive species will reduce the rate at which they approach one another, it will also diminish the velocity with which they diffuse apart, so that the collision frequency will not be altered (Flory, 1953d).

There exist, however, some interesting cases where an added polymer may exert a pronounced effect on the reaction rate of small molecules. Such an effect may have two different causes. Firstly, if the polymer exerts forces on both the interacting species, it may modify their relative distribution in the system and this will lead to an altered collision frequency. Secondly, the polymer may associate with one of the reagents and this complex may have a reactivity different from that of the unassociated reagent.

The first case is encountered in systems where two small ionic species react in the presence of a polyelectrolyte. Qualitatively, it is obvious that two ionic reagents carrying charges of the same sign will both be attracted to an oppositely charged polyion and the polyion will, in this case, act as a catalyst by concentrating the two reagents in the same region. On the other hand, if one of the reagents is cationic and the other anionic, one will be attracted and the other repelled by the polyion, so that their collision frequency will be reduced and the reaction rate diminished. If both reagents are repelled by the polyion, a catalytic effect should again be observed, but its magnitude would be expected to be much smaller than in the case of a reaction involving two counterions.

In principle, it is possible to utilize the effect of polyions on the reaction of two small ionic species to characterize the distribution of the ions and of the electrostatic potential (Morawetz and Westhead, 1955; Morawetz and Schafer, 1963). If the two reagents carry ν_A and ν_B unit charges, their concentration at a point characterized by an electrostatic potential ψ will be given by

$$c_A = c_A^0 X^{\nu_A}$$
$$c_B = c_B^0 X^{\nu_B} \tag{9.18}$$

where $X = \exp(-e\psi/kt)$, while c_A^0 and c_B^0 are concentrations at a point at which ψ is set at zero. We may consider the reaction rate to be made up additively from contributions in volume elements which are sufficiently small to be at a constant electrostatic potential. Within each such volume element the reaction rate will be governed by the local concentration of the reagents and the effective rate constant will be k_0, the same as would be observed in simple electrolyte solutions at low ionic strength. The observed rate will then be

$$\text{rate} = k_0 \langle c_A c_B \rangle = k_0 c_A^0 c_B^0 \langle X^{\nu_A + \nu_B} \rangle \tag{9.19}$$

where the square brackets indicate averaging over the volume of the system. But the observed rate constant k is conventionally expressed in terms of the volume average concentration of the reagents

$$\text{rate} = k \langle c_A \rangle \langle c_B \rangle = k c_A^0 c_B^0 \langle X^{\nu_A} \rangle \langle X^{\nu_B} \rangle \tag{9.20}$$

Comparing (9.16) and (9.17) we obtain then for the ratio of the intrinsic and the observed rate constant

$$k_0/k = \langle X^{\nu_A} \rangle \langle X^{\nu_B} \rangle / \langle X^{\nu_A + \nu_B} \rangle \tag{9.21}$$

If we have data for only one combination of ν_A and ν_B, eq. (9.21) yields only one parameter for the characterization of the distribution of X. For instance, we may represent the system as containing a region occupied by the polyion with a uniform potential ψ, in Donnan equilibrium with the rest of the solution, and in that case (9.21) may be interpreted in terms of the Donnan potential. From data for reactions with reagents of other charge type, we obtain other ratios of volume average values of various powers of X which will allow us to refine gradually our model to yield a distribution of X consistent with all the data.

Only limited experimental work has been carried out so far from which the magnitude of the effects discussed above could be assessed. Morawetz and Schafer (1963) studied the hydroxyl ion catalyzed hydrolysis of the doubly charged cationic ester, and found that polyanions with higher charge densities may lead to a more than twentyfold reduction in the reaction rate. More recently, Arcus et al. (1964) compared the rate of the benzidine rearrangement in poly(styrenesulfonic acid) and in benzenesulfonic acid of the same normality. It is known that the rate determining step in this reaction involves the attack of a hydrogen ion on the conjugate acid of hydrazobenzene

$$\langle\!\!\!\!\!\bigcirc\!\!\!\!\!\rangle\!-\!\overset{+}{N}H_2\!-\!NH\!-\!\langle\!\!\!\!\!\bigcirc\!\!\!\!\!\rangle$$

i.e., the interaction of two species, each carrying a unit positive charge. The polyanion would, therefore, be expected to act as a powerful catalyst and the polysulfonic acid was found, in fact, to lead to rates more than a hundred times higher than those observed in benzenesulfonic acid solutions of equivalent concentrations. Qualitatively similar results were obtained by Kern et al. (1956) who found that proteins carrying cationic groups are hydrolyzed faster by poly(vinylsulfonic acid) solutions than by solutions of mineral acids at the same pH, and by Painter (1962) who reported that poly(styrenesulfonic acid) attacks with high selectivity polysaccharides carrying basic residues. It must be admitted that all these examples are rather unsuitable for comparison with theoretical predictions, since the interaction of relatively large organic reagent molecules with the polyanion certainly contains contributions from other than electrostatic forces.

We have noted above that a polymer may also affect the reaction of two small molecules by forming a complex with one of the reagents and thus altering its reactivity. A very interesting example, illustrating this principle, is the change in the reactivity of triphenylmethane dyes with reducing agents brought about by the association of the cationic dye with poly(methacrylic acid) (Oster and Bellin, 1957). The reduction of the dyes in the dark by strong reducing reagents is found to be inhibited by association with the polymer. On the other hand, weak reducing reagents, such as ascorbic acid, can photoreduce the dye only when it is bound to a polymer. Several factors seem to play a role in making the dye associated with a polymeric chain more susceptible to photoreduction. The photoreduction involves a long-lived excited state whose formation is favored by a rigid medium; attachment to a polymer backbone acts then to impede internal rotations. It has also been demonstrated in flash spectroscopy experiments that the concentration of the metastable species is unaffected by atmospheric oxygen when the dye is bound to a polymer, while it would be effectively quenched by minute traces of oxygen in solutions containing the free dye molecule (Oster and Oster, 1962).

D. BEHAVIOR OF SOLUTIONS CONTAINING REACTIVE AND CATALYTICALLY ACTIVE MACROMOLECULES

Any survey of studies of polymer solutions by osmometry, light scattering, and by the measurements of various phenomena dependent on the frictional properties of the macromolecules shows clearly that the properties of the isolated macromolecule are understood much better than their interactions. An interesting alternative method for the study of such interactions has recently begun to be explored in the author's laboratory (Song, 1965). It involves measurements of reaction kinetics in solutions containing two similar macromolecules, one carrying a small number of reactive groups, while the other carries a small number of functional groups which are catalytically active. In such a system, the reaction reflects the number of encounters of specific sites on two chain molecules, which remain substantially unaltered by the process which is being observed.

It was found that groups attached to chain molecules have difficulty reacting with one another, unless the functional groups are at some distance from the polymer backbone. A suitable system for study contained a copolymer of acrylamide with the p-nitrophenyl ester of ϵ-acrylamidocaproic acid and an acrylamide copolymer with acrylyl histamine

Ester comonomer   Catalytic comonomer

The questions which the study was designed to clarify may be listed as follows: (a) Are the reactive groups attached to the center of the chain molecules more effectively shielded by the macromolecular coil than groups attached at points close to the chain ends? If so, these groups may exhibit a range of reactivities leading to deviations from first-order kinetics. If such a shielding effect is important, it would be expected to become more pronounced with an increasing chain length of the polymer. (b) What is the effect of variations in the solvent power of the medium on the reaction rate? In poor solvent media the molecular coils are more contracted; on the other hand, the excluded volume calculated from osmotic data becomes very small and actually vanishes under Θ conditions, indicating free interpenetration of the macromolecules. Is this thermodynamic behavior paralled by an increased effectiveness of the catalytic polymer? (c) We have seen (Chap. II, Sec. C-4) that different macromolecules, which mix with an absorption of heat, mix with great difficulty so that a system of two polymers and a good solvent usually separates into two solution phases, each containing one of the polymeric species. As a result, one might expect that a polymer carrying catalytically active species will attack much more easily reactive groups attached to a similar polymer than groups attached to a different type of chain molecule. Such specificity would be of some interest since it is not commonly found in non-enzymatic catalyses of organic reactions.

The results of this investigation showed that in good solvent media the reaction obeyed first-order kinetics and the rate was not dependent on the molecular weight of the polymeric reagents. Since it is not possible to believe that the molecular coils can easily interpenetrate one another under these conditions, we have to conclude that conformational changes in the chain molecule expose all chain segments with approximately equal frequency to the "outside" of the coil, where they may suffer collisions from other polymer chains. The polymer is always a poorer catalyst than its low molecular weight analog, but the relative efficiency of catalytic groups attached to the chain molecules tended to increase in poor solvent media. The kinetics now also deviated significantly from a first-order process. This could be the result of an increase in the differences between energies associated with different chain conformations, since groups which are placed in the "interior" of the molecular coil in conformations which are energetically favored would have a substantially reduced probability of reacting. The specificity effect was not observed: a catalytic copolymer with a polyacrylamide backbone attacked with equal efficiency ester groups attached to a polyacrylamide and a poly(N,N-dimethylacrylamide) chain.

Similar experiments were reported by Letsinger and Klaus (1964) who studied a system in which the ester was attached to a polyanionic backbone and exposed to partially ionized poly(N-vinylimidazole). In this case the attractive forces between the acidic and the basic polymer led to association of the two chain molecules and this resulted in very efficient catalysis of the ester solvolysis.   The reaction rate reached a maximum when complex formation was complete and further increase in the concentration of the catalytic polymer was without effect.   As expected, poly(acrylic acid) competed with the anionic chains carrying ester groups for association with the polycations and functioned, therefore, as a competitive inhibitor.

REFERENCES

Abe, A., and M. Goodman (1963), *J. Polymer Sci.*, **A1**, 2193.

Akkerman, F., D. T. F. Pals, and J. J. Hermans (1952), *Rec. Trav. Chim.*, **71**, 56.

Albertsson, P. A. (1958), *Biochim. Biophys. Acta.*, **27**, 378.

Albertsson, P. A. (1960), *Partition of Cell Particles and Macromolecules*, Wiley, New York.

Alexander, P., and S. F. Hitch (1952), *Biochim. Biophys. Acta*, **9**, 229.

Alexandrowicz, Z. (1959), *J. Polymer Sci.*, **40**, 91.

Alexandrowicz, Z. (1960), *J. Polymer Sci.*, **43**, 337.

Alexandrowicz, Z. (1962), *J. Polymer Sci.*, **56**, 115.

Alexandrowicz, Z., and E. Daniel (1963), *Biopolymers*, **1**, 447.

Alfrey, T., Jr., and G. Goldfinger (1944), *J. Chem. Phys.*, **12**, 205.

Alfrey, T., Jr., and W. G. Lloyd (1963), *J. Chem. Phys.*, **38**, 318.

Alfrey, T., Jr., and H. Morawetz (1952), *J. Am. Chem. Soc.*, **74**, 436.

Alfrey, T., Jr., A. I. Goldberg, and J. A. Price (1950), *J. Colloid Sci.*, **5**, 251.

Alfrey, T., Jr., P. W. Berg, and H. Morawetz (1951), *J. Polymer Sci.*, **7**, 543.

Alfrey, T., Jr., J. J. Bohrer, and H. Mark (1952a), *Copolymerization* (High Polymers, Vol. 8), Interscience, New York, Chap. 8.

Alfrey, T., Jr., R. M. Fuoss, H. Morawetz, and H. Pinner (1952b), *J. Am. Chem. Soc.*, **74**, 438.

Alger, M. S. M. (1964), Ph.D. Thesis, University of London.

Allegra, G., P. Ganis, and P. Corradini (1963), *Makromol. Chem.*, **61**, 225.

Ambrose, E. J., and A. Elliott (1951a), *Proc. Roy. Soc. (London)*, **A205**, 47.

Ambrose, E. J., and A. Elliott (1951b), *Proc. Roy. Soc. (London)*, **A208**, 75.

Ambrose, E. J., C. H. Bamford, A. Elliott, and W. E. Hanby (1951), *Nature*, **167**, 264.

Ambrose, J. F., G. B. Kistiakowski, and A. G. Kridl (1951), *J. Am. Chem. Soc.*, **71**, 1232.

Andon, R. J. L., and J. D. Cox (1952), *J. Chem. Soc.*, 4601.

Andress, K. R. (1928), *Z. Physik. Chem. (Leipzig)*, **A136**, 279.

Andress, K., and L. Reinhardt (1930), *Z. Physik. Chem. (Leipzig)*, **A151**, 425.

Anet, F. A. L. (1962), *J. Am. Chem. Soc.*, **84**, 747.

Anfinsen, C. B., E. Haber, M. Sela, and F. H. White, Jr. (1961), *Proc. Natl. Acad. Sci. U.S.*, **47**, 1309.

Ansevin, A. T., and M. A. Lauffer (1963), *Biophys. J.*, **3**, 239.

Archibald, W. J. (1947), *J. Phys. Chem.*, **51**, 1204.

Arcus, C. L. (1949), *J. Chem. Soc.*, 2732.

Arcus, C. L., T. L. Howard, and D. S. South (1964), *Chem. Ind. (London)*, 1756.

Arends, C. B. (1963), *J. Chem. Phys.*, **38**, 322.

Asakura, S. (1961), *Biochim. Biophys. Acta*, **52**, 65.

Ashby, C. E., J. S. Reitenour, and C. F. Hammer (1957), *J. Am. Chem. Soc.*, **79**, 5086.

Auer, R. L., and C. S. Gardner (1955), *J. Chem. Phys.*, **23**, 1546.

Avery, O. T., C. M. MacLeod, and M. McCarthy (1944), *J. Exptl. Med.*, **79**, 137.

Badger, R. M., and S. H. Bauer (1937), *J. Chem. Phys.*, **5**, 839.

Bailey, F. E., Jr., R. D. Lundberg, and R. W. Callard (1964), *J. Polymer Sci.*, **A2**, 845.

Bailey, W. J., and E. T. Yates (1960), *J. Org. Chem.*, **25**, 1800.

Baker, C. H., W. B. Brown, G. Gee, J. S. Rowlinson, D. Stribley, and R. A. Yeadon (1962), *Polymer*, **3**, 215.

Baldwin, R. R., R. S. Bear, and R. E. Rundle (1944), *J. Am. Chem. Soc.*, **66**, 111.

Bamford, C. H., W. E. Hanby, and F. Happey (1951), *Proc. Roy. Soc. (London)*, **A205**, 30.

Bamford, C. H., L. Brown, E. Elliott, W. E. Hanby, and I. F. Trotter (1954), *Nature*, **173**, 27.

Barker, J. A., and W. Fock (1953), *Discussions Faraday Soc.*, **15**, 188.

Barker, J. A., I. Brown, and F. Smith (1953), *Discussions Faraday Soc.*, **15**, 142.

Barkin, S. M. (1957), Ph.D. Thesis, Polytechnic Institute of Brooklyn.

Barkin, S. M., H. P. Frank, and F. R. Eirich (1955), *Ric. Sci. Suppl.*, **25**, 1, "Symposio internazionale di chimica macromoleculare."

Barron, E. S. G. (1951), *Advances in Enzymology*, Vol. 11, F. F. Nord, ed., Interscience, New York, p. 201.

Bates, F. L., D. French, and R. E. Rundle (1943), *J. Am. Chem. Soc.*, **65**, 142.

Bawn, C. E. H. (1951), *Trans. Faraday Soc.*, **47**, 97.

Bawn, C. E. H., and A. Ledwith (1962), *Quart. Rev. (London)*, **16**, 427–428.

Bawn, C. E. H., and M. A. Wajid (1956), *Trans. Faraday Soc.*, **52**, 1658.

Becker, R. R., and M. A. Stahmann (1952), *J. Am. Chem. Soc.*, **74**, 38.

Beckmann, C. O. (1964), Private communication.

Beijerinck, M. W. (1910), *Kolloid-Z.*, **7**, 16.

Bell, R. P. (1941), *Acid and Base Catalysis*, Clarendon Press, Oxford, pp. 21–35.

Bellemans, A., and C. Colin-Naar (1955), *J. Polymer Sci.*, **15**, 121.

Bellin, J. S., and G. Oster (1957), *J. Am. Chem. Soc.*, **79**, 2461.

Bello, J., and J. R. Vinograd (1958), *Nature*, **181**, 273.

Bello, J., D. Harker, and E. de Jarnette (1961), *J. Biol. Chem.*, **236**, 1358.

Bello, J., H. R. Bello, and J. R. Vinograd (1962), *Biochim. Biophys. Acta.*, **57**, 214, 222.

Bender, M. L., and F. J. Kezdy (1964), *J. Am. Chem. Soc.*, **86**, 3704.

Bender, M. L., and M. C. Neveu (1958), *J. Am. Chem. Soc.*, **80**, 5388.

Bender, M. L., G. R. Schonbaum, and B. Zerner (1962), *J. Am. Chem. Soc.*, **84**, 2540.

Benesch, R., and R. E. Benesch (1963), *J. Mol. Biol.*, **6**, 498.

Benoit, H. (1950), *J. Chim. Phys.*, **47**, 719.

Benoit, H. (1951), *J. Chim. Phys.*, **48**, 612; *Ann. Phys. (Paris,)*, **6**, 591.

Benoit, H. (1952), *J. Chim. Phys.*, **49**, 517.

Benoit, H. (1953), *J. Polymer Sci.*, **11**, 507.

Benoit, H., and G. Weill (1957), *Collection Czech. Chem. Commun.*, **22**, 35 (special issue).

Benoit, H., and C. Wippler (1960), *J. Chim. Phys.*, **57**, 524.

Berdick, M., and H. Morawetz (1954), *J. Biol. Chem.*, **206**, 959.

Beredjick, N. (1963), in *Newer Methods of Polymer Characterization*, B. Ke, ed., Interscience, New York, Chap. 16.

Beredjick, N., and H. E. Ries, Jr. (1962), *J. Polymer Sci.*, **62**, 564.

Beredjick, N., and C. Schuerch (1958), *J. Am. Chem. Soc.*, **80**, 1933.

Bernal, J. D., and I. Fankuchen (1941), *J. Gen. Physiol.*, **25**, 111.

Bernal, J. D., and R. H. Fowler (1933), *J. Chem. Phys.*, **1**, 515.

Berry, K. L., and J. H. Peterson (1951), *J. Am. Chem. Soc.*, **73**, 5195.

Bersohn, R., and I. Isenberg (1961), *J. Chem. Phys.*, **35**, 1640.

Bevington, J. C., H. W. Melville, and R. P. Taylor (1954), *J. Polymer Sci.*, **12**, 449.

Beychok, S., and E. R. Blout (1961), *J. Mol. Biol.*, **3**, 769.

Beychok, S., C. de Lozé, and E. R. Blout (1962), *J. Mol. Biol.*, **4**, 421.

Bianchi, J. P., F. P. Price, and B. H. Zimm (1957), *J. Polymer Sci.*, **25**, 27.

Bianchi, U. (1964), *J. Polymer Sci.*, **A2**, 3083.

Bier, M. (1959), *Electrophoresis, Theory, Method and Applications*, Academic Press, New York.

Binder, H. (1960), German Patent 974,244.

Bird, G. R., and E. R. Blout (1959), *J. Am. Chem. Soc.*, **81**, 2499.

Birshtein, T. M. (1959), *Vysokomolekul, Soedin.*, **1**, 748 (English transl. *Poly. Sci. USSR*, **1**, 276 (1960)).

Birshtein, T. M., and O. B. Ptitsyn (1959), *Zh. Tekhn. Fiz.*, **29**, 1048 (English transl. *Soviet Phys. Tech. Phys.*, **4**, 954 (1960)).

Birshtein, T. M., and O. B. Ptitsyn (1960), *Vysokomolekul. Soedin.*, **2**, 628 (English transl. *Polymer Sci. USSR*, **2**, 396 (1961)).

Birshtein, T. M., Yu. Ya. Gotlib, and O. B. Ptitsyn (1961), *J. Polymer Sci.*, **52**, 77.

Bisschops, J. (1954), *J. Polymer Sci.*, **12**, 583.

Bisschops, J. (1955), *J. Polymer Sci.*, **17**, 89.

Bjerrum, N. (1926), *Proc. Danish Royal Soc., Math.-Phys. Comm.*, **7**, No. 9.

Björnesjö, K. B., and T. Teorell (1945), *Arkiv. Kemi*, **A19**, No. 34.

Blake, C. C. F., D. F. Koenig, G. A. Mair, A. C. T. North, D. C. Phillips, and V. A. Sarma (1965), *Nature*, **206**, 757.

Bloom, S. M., G. D. Fasman, C. de Lozé, and E. R. Blout (1962), *J. Am. Chem. Soc.*, **84**, 458.

Blout, E. R. (1960), in *Rotary Optical Dispersion*, C. Djerassi, ed., McGraw-Hill, New York, p. 238.

Blout, E. R., C. de Lozé, S. M. Bloom, and G. D. Fasman (1960), *J. Am. Chem. Soc.*, **82**, 3787.

Blout, E. R., C. de Lozé, and A. Asadourian (1961), *J. Am. Chem. Soc.*, **83**, 1895.

Blout, E. R., I. Schmier, and N. S. Simmons (1962), *J. Am. Chem. Soc.*, **84**, 3193.

Blout, E. R., J. P. Carver, and J. Gross (1963), *J. Am. Chem. Soc.*, **85**, 644.

Bodo, G., H. M. Dintzis, J. C. Kendrew, and, H. W. Wyckoff (1959), *Proc. Roy Soc. (London)*, **A253**, 70.

Boeder, P. (1932), *Z. Physik*, **75**, 258.

Boedtker, H., and P. Doty (1954), *J. Phys. Chem.*, **58**, 968.

Bohak, Z., and E. Katchalski (1963), *Biochemistry*, **2**, 228.

Bonner, R. U., M. Dimbat, and F. H. Stross (1958), *Number Average Molecular Weights*, Interscience, New York, pp. 191–259.

Booth, C., G. Gee, and G. R. Williamson (1957), *J. Polymer Sci.*, **23**, 3.

Booth, F. (1950), *Proc. Roy. Soc. (London)*, **A203**, 533.

Bothner-By, A. A., and C. Naar-Colin (1962), *J. Am. Chem. Soc.*, **84**, 743.

Bovey, F. A. (1962), *J. Polymer Sci.*, **62**, 197.

Bovey, F. A. (1963), *J. Polymer Sci.*, **A1**, 843.

Bovey, F. A., and G. V. D. Tiers (1960), *J. Polymer Sci.*, **44**, 173.

Bovey, F. A., and G. V. D. Tiers (1963), *Fortschr. Hochpolymer. Forsch.*, **3**, 139.

Bovey, F. A., G. V. D. Tiers, and G.-Filipovich (1959), *J. Polymer Sci.*, **38**, 73.

Bovey, F. A., E. W. Anderson, D. C. Douglass, and J. A. Manson (1963), *J. Chem. Phys.*, **39**, 1199.

Bovey, F. A., F. P. Hood, E. W. Anderson, and L. C. Snyder (1965), *J. Chem. Phys.*, **42**, 3900.

Boyer, R. F., and R. S. Spencer (1948), *J. Polymer Sci.*, **3**, 97.

Bradbury, E. M., A. R. Downie, A. Elliott, and W. E. Hanby (1961), *Proc. Roy. Soc. (London)*, **A259**, 110.

Bradley, D. F., and G. Felsenfeld (1959), *Nature*, **184**, 1920.

Bradley, D. F., and M. K. Wolf (1959), *Proc. Natl. Acad. Sci. U.S.*, **45**, 944.

Brady, G. W., and R. Salovey (1964), *J. Am. Chem. Soc.*, **86**, 3499.

Brady, G. W., R. Salovey, and J. M. Reddy (1965), *Biopolymers*, **3**, in press.

Braun, D. (1959), *Makromol. Chem.*, **30**, 85.

Brechbuhler, T., and M. Magat (1950), *J. Chim. Phys.*, **47**, 679.

Bresler, S. E. (1958), *Discussions Faraday Soc.*, **25**, 158.

Bresler, S. E., L. M. Pyrkov, and S. Ya. Frenkel (1960), *Vysokomolekul. Soedin.*, **2**, 216.

Briggs, G. E., and J. B. S. Haldane (1925), *Biochem. J.*, **19**, 338.

Brown, C. P., A. R. Mathieson, and J. C. J. Thynne (1955), *J. Chem. Soc.*, 4141.

Brown, W., D. Henley, and J. Öhman (1963), *Makromol. Chem.*, **64**, 49.

Brownstein, S., S. Bywater, and D. J. Worsfold (1961), *Makromol. Chem.*, **48**, 127.

Bruice, T. C., and U. K. Pandit (1960), *J. Am. Chem. Soc.*, **82**, 5858.

Bruschtein, F. (1965), Ph.D. Thesis, Polytechnic Inst. of Brooklyn.

Buchdahl, R., H. A. Ende, and L. H. Peebles (1961), *J. Phys. Chem.*, **65**, 1468.

Buchdahl, R., H. A. Ende, and L. H. Peebles (1963a), *J. Polymer Sci.*, **C1**, 143.

Buchdahl, R., H. A. Ende, and L. H. Peebles (1963b), *J. Polymer Sci.*, **C1**, 153.

Buckley, C. E., III, P. L. Whitney, and C. Tanford (1963), *Proc. Natl. Acad. Sci. U.S.*, **50**, 827.

Bull, H. B. (1947), *Advan. Protein Chem.*, **3**, 95.

Bungenberg de Jong, H. G. (1937), *Kolloid-Z.*, **79**, 223; **80**, 221, 350.

Bungenberg de Jong, H. G. (1949), in *Colloid Science*, H. R. Kruyt, ed., Elsevier, Amsterdam, Chap. 10.

Bungenberg de Jong, H. G., and H. R. Kruyt (1930), *Kolloid-Z.*, **50**, 39.

Bunn, C. W. (1939), *Trans. Faraday Soc.*, **35**, 482.

Bunn, C. W., and D. R. Holmes (1958), *Discussions Faraday Soc.*, **25**, 95.

Bunn, C. W., and E. R. Howells (1955), *J. Polymer Sci.*, **18**, 307.

Bushuk, W., and H. Benoit (1958), *Can. J. Chem.*, **36**, 1616.

Butler, J. A. V. (1940), *J. Gen. Physiol.*, **24**, 189.

Cairns, J. (1961), *J. Mol. Biol.*, **3**, 756.

Cairns, J. (1962), *J. Mol. Biol.*, **4**, 407.

Calvin, M., J. Hermans, Jr., and H. A. Scheraga (1959), *J. Am. Chem. Soc.*, **81**, 5048.

Cann, J. R., and J. A. Klapper, Jr. (1961), *J. Biol. Chem.*, **236**, 2446.

Cantow, H. J. (1959), *Makromol. Chem.*, **30**, 169.

Carpenter, D. K., and W. R. Krigbaum (1958), *J. Chem. Phys.*, **28**, 513.

Casassa, E. F. (1955), *J. Chem. Phys.*, **23**, 596.

Casassa, E. F. (1956), *J. Am. Chem. Soc.*, **78**, 3980.

Casassa, E. F. (1959), *J. Chem. Phys.*, **31**, 800.

Casassa, E. F., and H. Eisenberg (1960), *J. Phys. Chem.*, **64**, 753.

Casassa, E. F., and H. Markowitz (1958), *J. Chem. Phys.*, **29**, 493.

Casassa, E. F., and W. H. Stockmayer (1962), *Polymer*, **3**, 53.

Caspar, D. L. D. (1963), *Advan. Protein Chem.*, **18**, 37.

Cebra, J. J., D. Givol, and E. Katchalski (1962), *J. Biol. Chem.*, **237**, 751.

Cerf, R. (1951), *J. Chim. Phys.*, **48**, 59, 85.

Cerf, R. (1957), *J. Polymer Sci.*, **23**, 125.

Cerf, R., and H. Scheraga (1951), *Chem. Rev.*, **51**, 185.

Chance, B. (1943), *J. Biol. Chem.*, **151**, 553.

Chance, B. (1949), *Arch. Biochem.*, **22**, 224.

Chang, S. Y., and H. Morawetz (1956), *J. Phys. Chem.*, **60**, 782.

Chargaff, E. (1950), *Experientia*, **6**, 201.

Chargaff, E. (1955), *The Nucleic Acids*, Vol. 1, E. Chargaff and J. N. Davidson, eds., Academic Press, New York, pp. 348–360.

Chargaff, E., M. Ziff, and D. H. Moore (1941), *J. Biol. Chem.*, **139**, 383.

Cheesman, D. F., and J. T. Davies (1954), *Advan. Protein Chem.*, **9**, 440.

Chujo, R., S. Satoh, T. Ozeki, and E. Nagai (1962), *J. Polymer Sci.*, **61**, S12.

Ciferri, A., C. A. J. Hoeve, and P. J. Flory (1961), *J. Am. Chem. Soc.*, **83**, 1015.

Claesson, S., and U. Lohmander (1961), *Makromol. Chem.*, **44/46**, 461.

Cohen, C. (1955), *Nature*, **175**, 129.

Cohen, C., and A. G. Szent-Gyorgyi (1957), *J. Am. Chem. Soc.*, **79**, 248.

Cohn, E. J., and J. T. Edsall (1943), *Proteins, Amino Acids and Peptides*, Reinhold, New York.

Cohn, E. J., and J. D. Ferry (1943) in *Proteins, Amino Acids and Peptides*, E. J. Cohn and J. T. Edsall, eds., Reinhold, New York, Chap. 24.

Cohn, E. J., F. R. N. Gurd, D. M. Surgenor, B. A. Barnes, R. K. Brown, G. Derouaux, J. M. Gillespie, F. W. Kahnt, W. F. Lever, C. H. Liu, D. Mittelman, R. F. Monton, K. Schmid, and E. Uroma (1950), *J. Am. Chem. Soc.*, **72**, 465.

Cohn, M. (1963), *Biochemistry*, **2**, 623.

Cohn, M., and J. S. Leigh (1962), *Nature*, **193**, 1037. .

Cohn-Ginsberg, E., T. G Fox, and H. F. Mason (1962), *Polymer*, **3**, 97.

Coleman, B. D. (1958), *J. Polymer Sci.*, **31**, 155.

Coleman, B. D., and R. M. Fuoss (1955), *J. Am. Chem. Soc.*, **77**, 5472.

Coleman, J., and H. Edelhoch (1956), *Arch. Biochem. Biophys.*, **63**, 382.

Colin and H. Gaultier de Claubry (1814), *Ann. Chim.*, (*Paris*), **90**, 87.

Coombes, J. D., E. Katchalski, and P. Doty (1960), *Nature*, **185**, 534.

Copp, J. L., and D. H. Everett (1953), *Discussions Faraday Soc.*, **15**, 174.

Corbett, J. W., and J. H. Wang (1956), *J. Chem. Phys.*, **25**, 422.

Corey, R. B., and L. Pauling (1955), *Rend. ist. lombardo sci.*, **89**, 10.

Cox, H. L., and L. H. Cretcher (1926), *J. Am. Chem. Soc.*, **48**, 451.

Cramer, F. (1954), *Einschlussverbindungen*, Springer, Berlin.

Crammer, J. L., and A. Neuberger (1943), *Biochem. J.*, **37**, 302.

Crawford, I. P., and J. Ito (1964), *Proc. Natl. Acad. Sci. U.S.*, **51**, 390.

Crawford, I. P., and C. Yanofsky (1958), *Proc. Natl. Acad. Sci. U.S.*, **44**, 1161.

Crescenzi, V., and P. J. Flory (1964), *J. Am. Chem. Soc.*, **86**, 141.

Creswell, C. J., and A. L. Allred (1962), *J. Phys. Chem.*, **66**, 1469.

Crick, F. H. C. (1963), *Science*, **139**, 461.

Crick, F. H. C., and J. D. Watson (1954), *Proc. Roy. Soc. (London)*, **A223**, 80.

Crisp, D. J. (1958), in *Surface Phenonema in Biology and Chemistry*, J. E. Danielli, K. G. A. Pankhurst, and A. C. Riddiford, eds., Pergamon Press, New York, pp. 23–54.

Cullis, A. F., H. Muirhead, M. F. Perutz, M. G. Rossmann, and A. C. T. North (1962), *Proc. Roy. Soc. (London)*, **A265**, 161.

Davern, C. I., and M. Meselson (1960), *J. Mol. Biol.*, **2**, 153.

Davies, J. T., and J. Llopis (1954), *Proc. Roy. Soc. (London)*, **A227**, 537.

Deal, W. C., W. J. Rutter, and K. E. Van Holde (1963), *Biochemistry*, **2**, 246.

Debye, P. (1915), *Ann. Physik* [4], **46**, 809.
Debye, P. (1944), *J. Appl. Phys.*, **15**, 338.
Debye, P. (1946), *J. Chem. Phys.*, **14**, 636.
Debye, P. (1947), *J. Phys. Colloid Chem.*, **51**, 18.
Debye, P., and F. Bueche (1952), *J. Chem. Phys.*, **20**, 1337.
Debye, P., and A. M. Bueche (1948), *J. Chem. Phys.*, **16**, 573.
Debye, P., and E. Hückel (1923), *Physik. Z.*, **24**, 185.
Delmas, G., D. Patterson, and D. Böhme (1962a), *Trans. Faraday Soc.*, **58**, 2116.
Delmas, G., D. Patterson, and T. Somcynsky (1962b), *J. Polymer Sci.*, **57**, 79.
Derksen, J. C., and J. R. Katz (1932), *Rec. Trav. Chim.*, **51**, 523.
Desmyter, A., and J. H. van der Waals (1958), *Rec. Trav. Chem.*, **77**, 53.
Deuel, H., K. Hutschnecker, and J. Solms (1953), *Z. Elektrochem.*, **57**, 172.
De Voe, H., and I. Tinoco, Jr. (1962), *J. Mol. Biol.*, **4**, 500.
Dietrich, H. V., and F. Cramer (1954), *Chem. Ber.*, **87**, 806.
Dimbat, M., and F. H. Stross (1957), *Anal. Chem.*, **29**, 1517.
Djerassi, C. (1960), *Optical Rotatory Dispersion*, McGraw-Hill, New York.
Djerassi, C., L. E. Geller, and E. J. Eisenbraun (1960), *J. Org. Chem.*, **25**, 1.
Dobry, A. (1945), *J. Chim. Phys.*, **42**, 92.
Dobry, A. (1948), *Bull. Soc. Chim. Belges*, **57**, 280.
Dobry, A., and F. Boyer-Kawenoki (1947), *J. Polymer Sci.*, **2**, 90.
Döller, E., and T. Förster (1962), *Z. Physik. Chem.* (*Frankfurt*), **34**, 134.
Doi, R. H., and S. Spiegelman (1962), *Science*, **138**, 1270.
Donnan, F. G. (1934), *Z. Physik. Chem.* (*Leipzig*), **A168**, 369.
Donnan, F. G., and E. A. Guggenheim (1932), *Z. Physik. Chem.* (*Leipzig*), **162**, 346.
Donovan, J. W., M. Laskowski, Jr., and H. A. Scheraga (1961) *J. Am. Chem. Soc.*, **83**, 2686.
Doolittle, A. K. (1944), *Ind. Eng. Chem.*, **36**, 239.
Doolittle, A. K. (1946), *Ind. Eng. Chem.*, **38**, 535.
Doty, P., and R. F. Steiner (1950), *J. Chem. Phys.*, **18**, 1211.
Doty, P., and R. F. Steiner (1952), *J. Chem. Phys.*, **20**, 85.
Doty, P., and J. T. Yang (1956), *J. Am. Chem. Soc.*, **78**, 498.
Doty, P., H. Wagner, and S. Singer (1947), *J. Phys. Colloid Chem.*, **51**, 32.
Doty, P., A. M. Holtzer, J. H. Bradbury, and E. R. Blout (1954), *J. Am. Chem. Soc.*, **76**, 4493.
Doty, P., J. H. Bradbury, and A. M. Holtzer (1956), *J. Am. Chem. Soc.*, **78**, 947.
Doty, P., S. Wada, J. T. Yang, and E. R. Blout (1957), *J. Polymer Sci.*, **23**, 851.
Doty, P., H. Boedtker, J. R. Fresco, R. Haselkorn, and M. Litt (1959), *Proc. Natl. Acad. Sci. U.S.*, **45**, 488.
Doty, P., J. Marmur, J. Eisner, and C. Schildkraut (1960), *Proc. Natl. Acad. Sci. U.S.*, **46**, 461.
Dove, W. F., and N. Davidson (1962a), *J. Mol. Biol.*, **5**, 467.
Dove, W. F., and N. Davidson (1962b), *J. Mol. Biol.*, **5**, 479.
Downie, A. R., and A. A. Randall (1959), *Trans. Faraday Soc.*, **55**, 2132.
Downie, A. R., A. Elliott, W. E. Hanby, and B. R. Malcolm (1957), *Proc. Roy. Soc.* (*London*), **A242**, 325.

Dubos, R. J. (1950), *Louis Pasteur, Free Lance of Science*, Little, Brown and Co., Boston, Mass., Chap. 6.

Dyke, D. E. L., J. S. Rowlinson, and R. Thacker (1959), *Trans. Faraday Soc.*, **55**, 903.

Eberson, L. (1959), *Acta Chem. Scand.*, **13**, 211.

Edelhoch, H., E. Katchalski, R. H. Maybury, W. L. Hughes, Jr., and J. T. Edsall (1953), *J. Am. Chem. Soc.*, **75**, 5058.

Ehrenpreis, S., and M. M. Fishman (1960), *Biochim. Biophys. Acta*, **44**, 577.

Ehrenpreis, S., and M. G. Kellock (1960), *Biochim. Biophys. Acta*, **45**, 525.

Eigen, M., and G. Schwarz (1957), *J. Colloid Sci.*, **12**, 181.

Einstein, A. (1905), *Ann. Physik.* [4], **17**, 549.

Einstein, A. (1906a), *Ann. Physik.* [4], **19**, 289.

Einstein, A. (1906b), *Ann. Physik.* [4], **19**, 371.

Einstein, A. (1910), *Ann. Physik.* [4], **33**, 1275.

Einstein, A. (1911), *Ann. Physik.* [4], **34**, 591.

Eisenberg, H. (1957), *J. Polymer Sci.*, **23**, 579.

Eisenberg, H., and G. R. Mohan (1959), *J. Phys. Chem.*, **63**, 671.

Eisenberg, H., and J. Pouyet (1954), *J. Polymer Sci.*, **13**, 85.

Edsall, J. T. (1953), in *The Proteins*, Vol. I, H. Neurath and K. Bailey, eds., Academic Press, Part B, p. 684.

Elias, H. G. (1961a), *Makromol. Chem.*, **50**, 1.

Elias, H. G. (1961b), *Z. Physik. Chem. (Frankfurt)*, **28**, 303.

Elias, H. G., and O. Etter (1963), *Makromol. Chem.*, **66**, 56.

Elias, H. G., and E. Männer (1960), *Makromol. Chem.*, **40**, 207.

Emery, A. H., Jr. (1957), *J. Chem. Phys.*, **26**, 1254.

Epstein, C. J., R. F. Goldberger, D. M. Young and C. B. Anfinsen (1962), *Arch. Biochem. Biophys. Suppl.*, **No. 1**, 223.

Ermolenko, J. N., and M. S. Katibnikov (1962), *Vysokomolekul. Soedin.*, **4**, 1249.

Everett, D. H., and F. L. Swinton (1963), *Trans. Faraday Soc.*, **59**, 2476.

Ewart, R. H., C. P. Roe, P. Debye, and J. M. McCartney (1946), *J. Chem. Phys.*, **14**, 687.

Fasman, G. D. (1962a), *Nature*, **193**, 681.

Fasman, G. D. (1962b), *Polyamino Acids, Polypeptides and Proteins*, M. A. Stahmann, ed., Univ. of Wisconsin Press, p. 221.

Fasman, G. D., and E. R. Blout (1963), *Biopolymers*, **1**, 99.

Fasman, G. D., C. Lindblow, and E. Bodemheimer (1962), *J. Am. Chem. Soc.*, **84**, 4977.

Felsenfeld, G., and G. L. Cantoni (1964), *Proc. Natl. Acad. Sci. U.S.*, **51**, 818.

Felsenfeld, G., and A. Rich (1957), *Biochim. Biophys. Acta*, **26**, 457.

Felsenfeld, G., and G. Sandeen (1962), *J. Mol. Biol.*, **5**, 587.

Ferry, G. V., and S. J. Gill (1962), *J. Phys. Chem.*, **66**, 995.

Ferry, J. D. (1948), *Advan. Protein Chem.*, **4**, 1.

Ferry, J. D. (1961), *Viscoelastic Properties of Polymers*, Wiley, New York: (a) pp. 169–173, 175–178, 290; (b) pp. 392–398.

Ferry, J. D., D. C. Udy, F. C. Wu, G. E. Heckler, and D. F. Fordyce (1951), *J. Colloid Sci.*, **6**, 429.

Ferry, J. D., S. Shulman, K. Gutfreund, and S. Katz (1952), *J. Am. Chem. Soc.*, **74**, 5709.

Fischer, E. (1894), *Ber.* **27**, 2985.

Fitts, D. D., and J. G. Kirkwood (1957), *Proc. Natl. Acad. Sci. U.S.*, **43**, 1046.

Fitzgerald, E. B., and R. M. Fuoss (1954), *J. Polymer Sci.*, **14**, 329.

Fixman, M. (1955), *J. Chem. Phys.*, **23**, 1656.

Fixman, M. (1960), *J. Polymer Sci.*, **47**, 91.

Flaschner, O. (1908), *Z. Physik. Chem. (Leipzig)*, **62**, 493.

Fleischman, J. B., R. R. Porter, and E. M. Press (1963), *Biochem. J.*, **88**, 220.

Flory, P. J. (1939), *J. Am. Chem. Soc.*, **61**, 3334.

Flory, P. J. (1940a), *J. Am. Chem. Soc.*, **62**, 1561.

Flory, P. J. (1940b), *J. Am. Chem. Soc.*, **62**, 2261.

Flory, P. J. (1942), *J. Chem. Phys.*, **10**, 51.

Flory, P. J. (1945), *J. Chem. Phys.*, **13**, 453.

Flory, P. J. (1949), *J. Chem. Phys.*, **17**, 303.

Flory, P. J. (1953), *Principles of Polymer Chemistry*, Cornell Univ. Press, Ithaca, New York: (a) p. 56; (b) pp. 596–602; (c) Chap. XIV; (d) p. 76; (e) p. 618.

Flory, P. J. (1953f), *J. Chem. Phys.*, **21**, 162.

Flory, P. J. (1956), *Proc. Roy. Soc. (London)*, **A234**, 73.

Flory, P. J., and W. R. Krigbaum (1950), *J. Chem. Phys.*, **18**, 1086.

Flory, P. J., and J. E. Osterheld (1954), *J. Phys. Chem.*, **58**, 653.

Flory, P. J., and A. Vrij (1963), *J. Am. Chem. Soc.*, **85**, 3548.

Flory, P. J., O. K. Spurr, Jr., and D. K. Carpenter (1958), *J. Polymer Sci.*, **27**, 231.

Flory, P. J., A. Ciferri, and R. Chiang (1961), *J. Am. Chem. Soc.*, **83**, 1023.

Flory, P. J., R. A. Orwill, and A. Vrij (1964), *J. Am. Chem. Soc.*, **86**, 3515.

Förster, T. (1959), *Discussions Faraday Soc.*, **27**, 7.

Folt, V. L., J. J. Shipman, and S. Krimm (1962), *J. Polymer Sci.*, **61**, 517.

Fordham, J. W. L., P. H. Burleigh, and C. L. Sturm (1959), *J. Polymer Sci.*, **41**, 73.

Fowler, R. H., and E. A. Guggenheim (1939), *Statistical Thermodynamics*, Cambridge Univ. Press, New York, pp. 576–581.

Fox, T. G, and P. J. Flory (1951), *J. Am. Chem. Soc.*, **73**, 1909.

Fox, T. G, B. S. Garrett, W. E. Goode, S. Gratch, J. F. Kincaid, A. Spell, and J. D. Stroupe (1958), *J. Am. Chem. Soc.*, **80**, 1768.

Fox, T. G, J. B. Kinsinger, H. F. Mann, and E. M. Schuele (1962), *Polymer*, **3**, 71.

Fraenkel-Conrat, H., and R. C. Williams (1955), *Proc. Natl. Acad. Sci. U.S.*, **41**, 690.

Frank, H. P., S. Barkin, and F. R. Eirich (1957), *J. Phys. Chem.*, **61**, 1375.

Frank, H. S., and M. J. Evans (1945), *J. Chem. Phys.*, **13**, 507.

Frank, H. S., and W. Y. Wen (1957), *Discussions Faraday Soc.*, **24**, 133.

Franklin, R. E., A. Klug, J. T. Finch, and K. C. Holmes (1958), *Discussions Faraday Soc.*, **25**, 197.

Fredericq, E. (1956), *Arch. Biochem. Biophys.*, **65**, 218.

Freeman, P. I., and J. S. Rowlinson (1959), *Polymer*, **1**, 20.

Freudenberg, K., and G. Blomquist (1935), *Ber.*, **B68**, 2070.

Freudenberg, K., W. Kuhn, W. Dürr, and G. Steinbrunn (1930), *Ber.*, **63**, 1510.

Freudenberg, K., E. Schauf, G. Dumpert, and T. Ploetz (1939), *Naturwissenschaften*, **27**, 850.

Frieden, C. (1959), *J. Biol. Chem.*, **234**, 809, 815.

Frieden, C. (1963), *Biochem. Biophys. Res. Commun.*, **10**, 410.

Frisch, H. L., and R. Simha (1956), in *Rheology; Theory and Applications*, Vol. 1, F. R. Eirich, ed., Academic Press, New York, Chap. 14.

Frisch, H. L., C. Schuerch, and M. Szwarc (1953), *J. Polymer Sci.*, **11**, 559.

Fuiji, K., T. Mochizuki, S. Imoto, J. Ukida, and M. Matsumoto (1962), *Makromol. Chem.*, **51**, 225.

Fujii, K., J. Ukida, and M. Matsumoto (1963), *Makromol. Chem.*, **65**, 86.

Fujita, H. (1962), *The Mathematical Theory of Sedimentation Analysis*, Academic Press, New York.

Fujita, H., and J. J. Hermans (1955), *Proc. Roy. Netherland Acad. Sci.*, **B58**, 188.

Fuoss, R. M. (1948), *J. Polymer Sci.*, **3**, 603.

Fuoss, R. M., and V. H. Chu (1951), *J. Am. Chem. Soc.*, **73**, 949.

Fuoss, R. M., and H. Sadek (1949), *Science*, **110**, 552.

Fuoss, R. M., A. Katchalsky, and S. Lifson (1951), *Proc. Natl. Acad. Sci. U.S.*, **37**, 579.

Fuoss, R. M., M. Watanabe, and B. D. Coleman (1960), *J. Polymer Sci.*, **48**, 5.

Gaetjens, E., and H. Morawetz (1960), *J. Am. Chem. Soc.*, **82**, 5328.

Gaetjens, E., and H. Morawetz (1961), *J. Am. Chem. Soc.*, **83**, 1738.

Gally, J. A., and G. M. Edelman (1964), *Biopolymers Symp.* No. 1, 367.

Gans, R. (1928), *Ann. Physik.* [4], **86**, 628.

Gardon, J. L., and S. G. Mason (1957), *J. Polymer Sci.*, **26**, 255.

Garrett, B. S., W. E. Goode, S. Gratch, J. F. Kincaid, C. L. Levesque, A. Spell, J. D. Stroupe, and W. H. Watanabe (1959), *J. Am. Chem. Soc.*, **81**, 1007.

Gaylord, N. G., and H. F. Mark (1959), *Linear Stereoregular Addition Polymers* (Polymer Reviews, Vol. 1), Interscience, New York.

Gee, G. (1942), *Trans. Faraday Soc.*, **38**, 418.

Gee, G. (1944), *Trans. Faraday Soc.*, **40**, 468.

Gee, G., and L. R. G. Treloar (1942), *Trans. Faraday Soc.*, **48**, 147.

Geiduschek, E. P. (1961), *Proc. Natl. Acad. Sci. U.S.*, **47**, 950.

Geiduschek, E. P. (1962), *J. Mol. Biol.*, **4**, 467.

Geiduschek, E. P., and T. T. Herskovits (1961), *Arch. Biochem. Biophys.*, **95**, 114.

Germer, H., K. H. Hellwege, and U. Johnsen (1963), *Makromol. Chem.*, **60**, 106.

Gerngross, O., K. Herrmann, and R. Lindemann (1932), *Kolloid-Z.*, **60**, 276.

Gibbs, J. H., and E. A. DiMarzio (1959), *J. Chem. Phys.*, **30**, 271.

Gibson, Q. H. (1959), *Biochem. J.*, **71**, 293.

Gibson, Q. H., and F. J. W. Roughton (1955), *Discussions Faraday Soc.*, **20**, 195.

Gierer, A. (1960), *Progr. Biophys. Biophys. Chem.*, **10**, 299.

Gilbert, G. A., and J. V. R. Marriott (1948), *Trans. Faraday Soc.*, **44**, 84.

Gill, S. J., and G. V. Ferry (1962), *J. Phys. Chem.*, **66**, 999.

Gill, T. J., III, and P. Doty (1961), *J. Biol. Chem.*, **236**, 2677.

Gill, T. J., III, and Z. S. Matthews (1963), *J. Biol. Chem.*, **238**, 1373.

Glavis, F. J. (1959), *J. Polymer Sci.*, **36**, 547.

Goates, J. R., R. J. Sullivan, and J. B. Ott (1959), *J. Phys. Chem.*, **63**, 589.

Goldstein, M. (1953), *J. Chem. Phys.*, **21**, 1255.

Goldwasser, E., and F. W. Putnam (1950), *J. Phys. Colloid Chem.*, **54**, 79.

Goodman, M., and A. M. Felix (1964), *Biochemistry*, **3**, 1529.

Goodman, M., and I. Listowsky (1962), *J. Am. Chem. Soc.*, **84**, 3770.

Goodman, M., and E. E. Schmitt (1959), *J. Am. Chem. Soc.*, **81**, 5507.

Goodman, M., E. E. Schmitt, and D. A. Yphantis (1962), *J. Am. Chem. Soc.*, **84**, 1288.

Goodman, M., F. Boardman, and I. Listowsky (1963a), *J. Am. Chem. Soc.*, **85**, 2491.

Goodman, M., A. M. Felix, C. M. Deber, A. R. Brause, and G. Schwartz (1963b), *Biopolymers*, **1**, 371.

Gordy, W. (1941), *J. Chem. Phys.*, **9**, 215.

Gordy, W., and S. C. Stanford (1941), *J. Chem. Phys.*, **9**, 204.

Graham, T. (1862), *Ann.*, **121**, 1.

Greenstein, J. P. (1938), *J. Biol. Chem.*, **125**, 501.

Greenstein, J. P., and J. T. Edsall (1940), *J. Biol. Chem.*, **133**, 397.

Gregor, H. P., L. B. Luttinger, and E. M. Loebl (1955), *J. Phys. Chem.*, **59**, 34.

Griffith, J. H., and B. G. Rånby (1959), *J. Polymer Sci.*, **38**, 107.

Grimley, T. B. (1961), *Trans. Faraday Soc.*, **57**, 1974.

Grunberg-Manago, M., P. J. Ortiz, and S. Ochoa (1956), *Biochim. Biophys. Acta*, **20**, 269.

Guggenheim, E. A. (1935), *Proc. Roy. Soc. (London)*, **A148**, 304.

Guinier, A. (1939), *Ann. Phys. (Paris)*, [11], **12**, 161.

Gurd, F. R. N., and D. S. Goodman (1952), *J. Am. Chem. Soc.*, **74**, 670.

Guth, E., and R. Simha (1936), *Kolloid-Z.*, **74**, 266.

Gutowsky, H. S., and C. J. Hoffman (1951), *J. Chem. Phys.*, **19**, 1259.

Gutowsky, H. S., G. G. Belford, and P. E. McMahon (1962), *J. Chem. Phys.*, **36**, 3353.

Haguchi, W. I., M. A. Schwartz, E. G. Rippie, and T. Haguchi (1959), *J. Phys. Chem.* **63**, 996.

Hall, B. D., and S. Spiegelman (1961), *Proc. Natl. Acad. Sci. U.S.*, **47**, 137.

Hall, C. E. (1960), *J. Biophys. Biochem. Cytol.*, **7**, 613.

Hall, C. E., and P. Doty (1958), *J. Am. Chem. Soc.*, **80**, 1269.

Hall, C. E., and H. S. Slayter (1959), *J. Biochem. Biophys. Cytol.*, **5**, 11.

Hanes, C. S. (1937), *New Phytologist*, **36**, 101, 189.

Hanson, J., and J. Lowy (1963), *J. Mol. Biol.*, **6**, 46.

Harfenist, E. J., and L. C. Craig (1952), *J. Am. Chem. Soc.*, **74**, 3087.

Harrington, W. F., and P. H. Von Hippel (1961), *Adv. Protein Chem.*, **16**, 1.

Harris, F. E., and S. A. Rice (1954), *J. Phys. Chem.*, **58**, 725.

Hartley, B. S. (1964), *Nature*, **201**, 1284.

Hartley, B. S., and B. A. Kilby (1952), *Biochem. J.*, **50**, 672.

Hartley, B. S., and B. A. Kilby (1954), *Biochem. J.*, **56**, 288.

Hartmann, H., and R. Jaenicke (1956), *Z. Physik. Chem. (Frankfurt)*, **6**, 220.

Haurowitz, F. (1963), *The Chemistry and Function of Proteins*, 2nd ed., Academic Press, New York: (a) pp. 261–277; (b) pp. 369–384.

Haurowitz, F., and F. Breinl (1933), *Hoppe-Seylers Z. Physiol. Chem.*, **214**, 111.

Hayes, T. L., J. C. Murchio, F. T. Lindgren, and A. V. Nichols (1959), *J. Mol. Biol.*, **1**, 297.

Hearst, J. E., and W. H. Stockmayer (1962), *J. Chem. Phys.*, **37**, 1425.

Hearst, J. E., and J. Vinograd (1961), *Proc. Natl. Acad. Sci. U.S.*, **47**, 825, 1005.

Hearst, J. E., J. B. Ifft, and J. Vinograd (1961), *Proc. Natl. Acad. Sci. U.S.*, **47**, 1015.

Heine, S., D. Kratky, G. Porod, and P. J. Schmitz (1961), *Makromol. Chem.*, **44/46**, 682.

Heller, W., and D. D. Fitts (1960), in *Physical Methods of Organic Chemistry* (Technique of Organic Chemistry, Vol. 1) A. Weissberger, ed., Interscience, New York, Part 3, Chap. 33.

Hellfritz, H. (1951), *Makromol. Chem.*, **7**, 191.

Hengstenberg. J., and E. Schuch (1964), *Makromol. Chem.*, **74**, 55.

Henry, D. C. (1931), *Proc. Roy. Soc. (London)*, **A133**, 106.

Hermans, J., Jr., and H. A. Scheraga (1959), *Biochim. Biophys. Acta*, **36**, 534.

Hermans, J. Jr., and H. A. Scheraga (1961), *J. Am. Chem. Soc.*, **83**, 3283.

Hermans, J. J. (1955), *J. Polymer Sci.*, **18**, 527.

Hermans, J. J. (1963), *J. Colloid Sci.*, **18**, 433.

Hermans, J. J., and H. A. Ende (1963a) in *Newer Methods of Polymer Characterization*, B. Ke, ed., Interscience, New York, Chap. 13.

Hermans, J. J., and H. A. Ende (1963b), *J. Polymer Sci.*, **C, No.** 1, 161.

Hermans, J. J., and H. Fujita (1955), *Proc. Roy. Netherland Acad. Sci.*, **B58**, 182.

Hermans, J. J., and J. T. G. Overbeek (1948), *Rec. Trav. Chim.*, **67**, 761.

Herrmann, K., O. Gerngross, and W. Abitz (1930), *Z. Physik. Chem. (Leipzig)*, **B10**, 371.

Hershey, A. D., and E. Burgi (1960), *J. Mol. Biol.*, **2**, 143.

Herskovits, T. T. (1962), *Arch. Biochem. Biophys.*, **97**, 474.

Heymann, E. (1935), *Trans. Faraday Soc.*, **31**, 846.

Higuchi, W. I., M. A. Schwartz, E. G. Rippie, and T. Higuchi (1959), *J. Phys. Chem.*, **63**, 996.

Hijmans, J., and T. Holleman (1962), *J. Chem. Phys.*, **36**, 47.

Hildebrand, J. H. (1953), *Discussions Faraday Soc.*, **15**, 9.

Hildebrand, J. H., and R. L. Scott (1950), *The Solubility of Nonelectrolytes*, Am. Chem. Soc. Monograph No. 17, Reinhold, New York, Chap. 7, 8.

Hildebrand, J. H., and R. L. Scott (1962), *Regular Solutions*, Prentice-Hall, Englewood Cliffs, N.J.

Hill, R. J., and L. C. Craig (1959), *J. Am. Chem. Soc.*, **81**, 2272.

Hill, T. L. (1959), *J. Chem. Phys.*, **30**, 383.

Hirschfelder, J., D. Stevenson, and H. Eyring (1937), *J. Chem. Phys.*, **5**, 896.

Hoeve, C. A. J. (1960), *J. Chem. Phys.*, **32**, 888.

Hofmann, K., F. Finn, W. Haas, M. J. Smithers, Y. Wolman, and N. Yanaihara (1963), *J. Am. Chem. Soc.*, **85**, 833.

Hofmann, T., and P. M. Harrison (1963), *J. Mol. Biol.*, **6**, 256.

Holley, R. W., J. Apgar, G. A. Everett, J. T. Madison, M. Marquisee, S. H. Merrill, J. R. Penswick, and A. Zamir (1965), *Science*, **147**, 1462.

Hollo, J., and J. Szejtli (1958), *Die Stärke*, **10**, 49 (cf. *C. A.*, **53**, 12437).

Holtzer, A. M., H. Benoit, and P. Doty (1954), *J. Phys. Chem.*, **58**, 624.

Holzwarth, G., W. B. Gratzer, and P. Doty (1962), *J. Am. Chem. Soc.*, **84**, 3194.

Horn, P. (1955), *Ann. Phys. (Paris)*, [12], **10**, 386.

Horn, P., H. Benoit, and G. Oster (1951), *J. Chim. Phys.*, **48**, 1.

Hotta, H. (1954), *Bull. Chem. Soc. Japan*, **27**, 80.

Howard, G. J., and D. O. Jordan (1954), *J. Polymer Sci.*, **12**, 209.

Huang, H. T., and C. Niemann (1952), *J. Am. Chem. Soc.*, **74**, 4634.

Hückel, E. (1924), *Physik. Z.*, **25**, 204.

Huggins, M. L. (1942): (a) *J. Phys. Chem.*, **46**, 151; (b) *Ann. N. Y. Acad. Sci.*, **43**, 1; (c) *J. Am. Chem. Soc.*, **64**, 1712.

Huggins, M. L. (1948), *J. Phys. Chem.*, **51**, 248.

Huggins, M. L., G. Natta, V. Desreux, and H. Mark (1962), *J. Polymer Sci.*, **56**, 153.

Huizenga, J. R., P. F. Grieger, and F. T. Wall (1950), *J. Am. Chem. Soc.*, **72**, 2636.

Hunt, M. L., S. Newman, H. A. Scheraga, and P. J. Flory (1956), *J. Phys. Chem.*, **60**, 1278.

Hvidt, A. (1955), *Biochim. Biophys. Acta*, **18**, 306.

Hvidt, A. (1963), *Compt. Rend. Trav. Lab. Carlsberg, Sér. chim.*, **33**, 475.

Hvidt, A. (1964), *Compt. Rend. Trav. Lab. Carlsberg, Sér. chim.*, **34**, 299.

Hvidt, A., and L. Kanarek (1963), *Compt. Rend. Trav. Lab. Carlsberg, Sér. chim.*, **33**, 463.

Hvidt, A., and K. Linderstrøm-Lang (1955a), *Compt. Rend. Trav. Lab. Carlsberg, Sér. chim.*, **29**, 385.

Hvidt, A., and K. Linderstrøm-Lang (1955b), *Biochim. Biophys. Acta*, **16**, 168.

Hyde, A. J., J. H. Ryan, and F. T. Wall (1958), *J. Polymer Sci.*, **33**, 129.

Ifft, J. B., D. H. Voet, and J. Vinograd (1961), *J. Phys. Chem.*, **65**, 1138.

Imahori, K., and J. Tanaka (1959), *J. Mol. Biol.*, **1**, 359.

Imai, K., and M. Matsumoto (1961), *J. Polymer Sci.*, **55**, 335.

Immergut, E. H., B. G. Rånby, and H. F. Mark (1953), *Ind. Eng. Chem.*, **45**, 2483.

Inagaki, H., and M. Hirami (1959), *Z. Elektrochem.*, **63**, 419.

Ingold, C. K. (1930), *J. Chem. Soc.*, 1375.

Ise, N. (1962), *J. Chem. Phys.*, **36**, 3248.

Ise, N. (1963), *J. Phys. Chem.*, **67**, 382.

Isemura, T., and A. Imanishi (1958), *J. Polymer Sci.*, **33**, 337.

Isihara, A. (1950a), *J. Chem. Phys.*, **18**, 1446.

Isihara, A. (1950b), *J. Phys. Soc. Japan*, **5**, 201.

Isihara, A., and R. Koyama (1956), *J. Chem. Phys.*, **25**, 712.

Ito, K. (1953), *J. Am. Chem. Soc.*, **75**, 2430.

Ivin, K. J., and H. A. Ende (1961), *J. Polymer Sci.*, **54**, S17.

Ivin, K. J., H. A. Ende, and G. Meyerhoff (1962), *Polymer*, **3**, 129.

Iyengar, B. R. Y. (1954), *Rec. Trav. Chim.*, **73**, 789.

Jackman, L. M. (1959), *Application of Nuclear Magnetic Resonance Spectroscopy in Organic Chemistry*, Pergamon Press, New York.

Jacobson, A. L. (1964), *Biopolymers*, **2**, 207.

Jacobson, B. (1953), *Rev. Sci. Instr.*, **24**, 949.

Jayme, G., and F. Lang (1955), *Kolloid-Z.*, **144**, 75.

Jayme, G., and K. Neuschäffer (1957), *Makromol. Chem.*, **23**, 71.

Jerrard, H. G. (1959), *Chem. Rev.*, **59**, 345.

Jessup, R. S. (1958), *J. Res. Natl. Bur. Std.*, **60**, 47.

Jirgensons, B. (1961), *Makromol. Chem.*, **44/46**, 123; *Tetrahedron*, **13**, 166.

Joesten, M. D., and R. S. Drago (1962), *J. Am. Chem. Soc.*, **84**, 3817.

Johnsen, U. (1961), *J. Polymer Sci.*, **54**, S6.

Johnston, J. P., and A. G. Ogston (1946), *Trans. Faraday Soc.*, **42**, 789.

Jones, G. (1962), *J. Appl. Polymer Sci.*, **6**, 15.

Joseph, N. R. (1936), *J. Biol. Chem.*, **116**, 353.

Jost, K. (1958), *Rheol. Acta*, **1**, 303.

Kaarsemaker, S., and J. Coops (1952), *Rec. Trav. Chim.*, **71**, 261.

Kägi, J. H. R., and B. L. Vallee (1960), *J. Biol. Chem.*, **235**, 3188.

Kagawa, I., and K. Katsuura (1952), *J. Polymer Sci.*, **9**, 405.

Kandanian, A. Y. (1964), Ph.D. Thesis, Polytechnic Institute of Brooklyn.

Karlson, R. H., K. S. Norland, G. D. Fasman, and E. R. Blout (1960), *J. Am. Chem. Soc.*, **82**, 2268.

Karush, F. (1956), *J. Am. Chem. Soc.*, **78**, 5519.

Katchalski, E. (1951), *Advan. Protein Chem.*, **6**, 123.

Katchalski, E., M. Sela, H. I. Silman, and A. Berger (1964), in *The Proteins*, Vol. 2, H. Neurath, ed., 2nd ed., Academic Press, New York, Chap. 10.

Katchalsky, A., and J. Feitelson (1954), *J. Polymer Sci.*, **13**, 385.

Katchalsky, A., and S. Lifson (1956), *J. Polymer Sci.*, **11**, 409.

Katchalsky, A., and I. R. Miller (1954), *J. Polymer Sci.*, **13**, 57.

Katchalsky, A., and P. Spitnik (1947), *J. Polymer Sci.*, **2**, 432.

Katchalsky, A., O. Künzle, and W. Kuhn (1950), *J. Polymer Sci.*, **5**, 283.

Katchalsky, A., J. Mazur, and P. Spitnik (1957), *J. Polymer Sci.*, **23**, 513.

Katz, J. J. (1954), *Nature*, **173**, 265.

Katz, J. R., and J. C. Derksen (1931), *Rec. Trav. Chim.*, **50**, 149.

Katz, J. R., and J. C. Derksen (1932), *Rec. Trav. Chim.*, **51**, 513.

Katz, J. R., and A. Weidinger (1932), *Rec. Trav. Chim.*, **51**, 847.

Katz, J. R., J. C. Derksen, and W. F. Bon (1931), *Rec. Trav. Chim.*, **50**, 725, 1138.

Kauzmann, W. (1959), *Advan. Protein Chem.*, **14**, 1.

Kauzmann, W., and H. Eyring (1941), *J. Chem. Phys.*, **9**, 41.

Kauzmann, W., and R. B. Simpson (1953), *J. Am. Chem. Soc.*, **75**, 5154.

Kedem, O., and A. Katchalsky (1955), *J. Polymer Sci.*, **15**, 321.

Keller, J. B. (1962), *J. Chem. Phys.*, **37**, 2584.

Keller, J. B., (1963), *J. Chem. Phys.*, **38**, 325.

Kendrew, J. C. (1963), *Science*, **139**, 1259.

Kendrew, J. C., R. E. Dickerson, B. E. Strandberg, R. G. Hart, D. R. Davies, D. C. Phillips, and V. C. Shore (1960), *Nature*, **185**, 422.

Kendrew, J. C., H. C. Watson, B. E. Strandberg, R. E. Dickerson, D. C. Phillips, and V. C. Shore (1961), *Nature*, **190**, 666.

Kennedy, J. P., L. S. Minckler, Jr., G. Wenless, and R. M. Thomas (1964), *J. Polymer Sci.*, **A2**, 1441, 2093.

Kern, R. J. (1956), *J. Polymer Sci.*, **21**, 19.

Kern, R. J. (1958), *J. Polymer Sci.*, **33**, 524.

Kern, R. J., and R. J. Slocombe (1955), *J. Polymer Sci.*, **15**, 183.

Kern, W. (1948), *Makromol. Chem.*, **2**, 279.

Kern, W., W. Herold, and B. Scherlag (1956), *Makromol. Chem.*, **17**, 231.

Kimball, G. E., M. Cutler, and H. Samelson (1952), *J. Phys. Chem.*, **56**, 47.

Kinsinger, J. B., and L. E. Ballard (1964), *J. Polymer Sci.*, **B2**, 879.

Kinsinger, J. B., and R. A. Wessling (1959), *J. Am. Chem. Soc.*, **81**, 2908.

Kirkwood, J. G. (1934), *J. Chem. Phys.*, **2**, 351.

Kirkwood, J. G. (1937), *J. Chem. Phys.*, **5**, 479.

Kirkwood, J. G., and J. Riseman (1948), *J. Chem. Phys.*, **16**, 565.

Kirkwood, J. G., and V. Shumaker (1952), *Proc. Natl. Acad. Sci. U.S.*, **38**, 863.

Kirkwood, J. G., and F. H. Westheimer (1938), *J. Chem. Phys.*, **6**, 506, 513.

Kirste, R., and O. Kratky (1962), *Z. Physik. Chem. (Frankfurt)*, **31**, 363.

Kirste, R., and W. Wunderlich (1964), *Makromol. Chem.*, **73**, 240.

Kisselev, N. A., L. P. Gavrilova, and A. S. Spirin (1961), *J. Mol. Biol.*, **3**, 778.

Kleine, J., and H. H. Kleine (1959), *Makromol. Chem.*, **30**, 23.

Klotz, I. M., and H. A. Fiess (1951), *J. Phys. Colloid Chem.*, **55**, 101.

Kohlrausch, K. W. F. (1932), *Z. Physik. Chem. (Leipzig)*, **B18**, 61.

Koike, M. L., J. Reed, and W. R. Carroll (1963), *J. Biol. Chem.*, **238**, 30.

Kontos, E. (1959), Ph.D. Thesis, Columbia University, New York.

Kornberg, A. (1959), *Rev. Mod. Phys.*, **31**, 200.

Kornberg, A. (1961), *Enzymatic Synthesis of DNA*, Wiley, New York.

Koshland, M. E., and F. M. Englberger (1963), *Proc. Natl. Acad. Sci. U.S.*, **50**, 61.

Kotliar, A. M., and H. Morawetz (1955), *J. Am. Chem. Soc.*, **77**, 3692.

Kowalsky, A. (1962), *J. Biol. Chem.*, **237**, 1807.

Koyama, R. (1957), *J. Chem. Phys.*, **27**, 234.

Kraemer, E. O., and J. R. Fanselow (1928), *J. Phys. Chem.*, **32**, 894.

Krasny-Ergen, W. (1936), *Kolloid-Z.*, **74**, 172.

Kratky, O. (1948), *J. Polymer Sci.*, **3**, 195.

Kratky, O. (1960), *Angew. Chem.*, **72**, 467.

Kratky, O. (1962a), *Kolloid-Z.*, **182**, 7.

Kratky, O. (1962b), *Z. Elektrochem.*, **64**, 880.

Kratky, O., and W. Kreutz (1960), *Z. Elektrochem.*, **64**, 880.

Kratky, O., and G. Porod (1949), *Rec. Trav. Chim.*, **68**, 1106.

Kratky, O., and H. Sand (1960), *Kolloid-Z.*, **172**, 18.

Kratky, O., and W. Worthmann (1947), *Monatsh. Chem.*, **76**, 263.

Kratky, O., G. Porod, and A. Sekora (1948), *Monatsh. Chem.*, **78**, 295.

Kratky, O., G. Porod, A. Sekora, and B. Paletta (1955), *J. Polymer Sci.*, **16**, 163.

Krause, I. M., and K. Linderstrøm-Lang (1955), *Compt. Rend. Trav. Lab. Carlsberg, Sér. chim.*, **29**, 367.

Krause, S. (1961), *J. Phys. Chem.*, **65**, 1618.

Krause, S., and C. T. O'Konski (1959), *J. Am. Chem. Soc.*, **81**, 5082.

Krause, S., and C. T. O'Konski (1963), *Biopolymers*, **1**, 503.

Kraut, J., L. C. Sieker, D. F. High, and S. T. Freer (1962), *Proc. Natl. Acad. Sci. U.S.*, **48**, 1417.

Krigbaum, W. R. (1954), *J. Am. Chem. Soc.*, **76**, 3758.

Krigbaum, W. R. (1955), *J. Chem. Phys.*, **23**, 2113.

Krigbaum, W. R., and D. K. Carpenter (1955), *J. Phys. Chem.*, **59**, 1166.

Krigbaum, W. R., and D. O. Geymer (1959), *J. Am. Chem. Soc.*, **81**, 1859.

Krigbaum, W. R., J. E. Kurz, and P. Smith (1961), *J. Phys. Chem.*, **65**, 1984.

Küster, F. W. (1894), *Ann. Chem.*, **283**, 360.

Kuge, T., and S. Ono (1960), *Bull. Chem. Soc. Japan*, **33**, 1269, 1273.

Kuhn, L. P., and R. E. Bowman (1961), *Spectrochim. Acta*, **17**, 650.

Kuhn, W. (1930), *Trans. Faraday Soc.*, **26**, 293.

Kuhn, W. (1934), *Kolloid-Z.*, **68**, 2.

Kuhn, W. (1958), *Ann. Rev. Phys. Chem.*, **9**, 417.

Kuhn, W., and F. Grün (1942), *Kolloid-Z.*, **101**, 248.

Kuhn, W., and H. Kuhn (1943), *Helv. Chim. Acta*, **26**, 1394.

Kuhn, W., and H. Kuhn (1945a), *Helv. Chim. Acta*, **28**, 97.

Kuhn, W., and H. Kuhn (1945b), *Helv. Chim. Acta*, **28**, 1533.

Kuhn, W., and H. Kuhn (1946), *Helv. Chim. Acta*, **29**, 71.

Kuhn, W., and H. L. Lehmann (1931), *Z. Elektrochem.*, **37**, 549.

Kuhn, W., O. Künzle, and A. Katchalsky (1948), *Helv. Chim. Acta*, **31**, 1994.

Kulkarni, R. K., and E. R. Blout (1962), *J. Am. Chem. Soc.*, **84**, 3971.

Kulkarni, R. K., and H. Morawetz (1961), *J. Polymer Sci.*, **54**, 491.

Kupke, D. W., and K. Linderstrøm-Lang (1954), *Biochim. Biophys. Acta*, **13**, 153.

Kurata, M., and W. H. Stockmayer (1963), *Fortschr. Hoohpolymer. Forsch.*, **3**, 196.

Kurata, M., H. Yamakawa, and H. Utiyama (1959), *Makromol. Chem.*, **34**, 139.

Kurata, M., W. H. Stockmayer, and A. Roig (1960), *J. Chem. Phys.*, **33**, 151.

Kurtz, J., A. Berger, and E. Katchalski (1956), *Nature*, **178**, 1066.

Laar, J. J. van, and R. Lorenz (1925), *Z. Anorg. Allgem. Chem.*, **146**, 42.

Ladenheim, H., and H. Morawetz (1959), *J. Am. Chem. Soc.*, **81**, 4860.

Ladenheim, H., E. M. Loebl, and H. Morawetz (1959), *J. Am. Chem. Soc.*, **81**, 20.

Lamb, Sir H. (1945), *Hydrodynamics*, 1st American ed., Dover, New York, p. 597.

Lando, J. B., and H. Morawetz (1964), *J. Polymer Sci.*, **C4**, 789.

Landsteiner, K. (1946), *The Specificity of Serological Reactions*, 2nd ed., Harvard Univ. Press, Cambridge, Mass.

Langridge, R., H. R. Wilson, C. W. Hooper, M. H. F. Wilkins, and L. D. Hamilton (1960a), *J. Mol. Biol.*, **2**, 19.

Langridge, R., D. A. Marvin, W. E. Seeds, H. R. Wilson, C. W. Hooper, M. H. F. Wilkins, and L. D. Hamilton (1960b), *J. Mol. Biol.*, **2**, 38.

Laskowski, M., and M. Laskowski, Jr. (1954), *Advan. Protein Chem.*, **9**, 203.

Laskowski, M., Jr., S. J. Leach, and H. A. Scheraga (1960), *J. Am. Chem. Soc.*, **82**, 571.

Lauffer, M. A., A. T. Ansevin, T. E. Cartwright, and C. C. Brinton, Jr. (1948), *Nature*, **181**, 1338.

Lazare, L. (1963), *J. Chem. Phys.*, **39**, 727.

Lehrer, S. S., and G. D. Fasman (1964), *Biopolymers*, **2**, 199.

Lemberg, R., and J. W. Legge (1949), *Hematin Compounds and Bile Pigments*, Interscience, New York.

Leng, M., and H. Benoit (1962a), *J. Polymer Sci.*, **57**, 263.

Leng, M., and H. Benoit (1962b), *J. Chim. Phys.*, **59**, 929.

Leng, M., C. Strazielle, and H. Benoit (1963), *J. Chim. Phys.*, **60**, 501.

Leray, J. (1957), *J. Polymer Sci.*, **23**, 167.

Letsinger, R. L., and I. Klaus (1964), *J. Am. Chem. Soc.*, **86**, 3884.

Letsinger, R. L., and T. J. Savereide (1962), *J. Am. Chem. Soc.*, **84**, 3122.

Levi, D. W., P. C. Scherer, and H. T. Lee (1956), *J. Polymer Sci.*, **22**, 184.

Levinthal, C., and P. F. Davison (1961), *J. Mol. Biol.*, **3**, 674.

Lifson, S. (1957a), *J. Polymer Sci.*, **23**, 431.

Lifson, S. (1957b), *J. Chem. Phys.*, **27**, 700.

Lifson, S. (1958), *J. Chem. Phys.*, **29**, 89.

Lifson, S. (1959), *J. Chem. Phys.*, **30**, 964.

Lifson, S. (1963), *Biopolymers*, **1**, 25.

Lifson, S., and I. Oppenheim (1960), *J. Chem. Phys.*, **33**, 109.

Lifson, S., and B. H. Zimm (1963), *Biopolymers*, **1**, 15.

Linderstrøm-Lang, K., and J. A. Schellman (1954), *Biochim. Biophys. Acta*, **15**, 156.

Lindskog, S., and B. G. Malmström (1962), *J. Biol. Chem.*, **237**, 1129.

Lineweaver, H. (1945), *J. Am. Chem. Soc.*, **67**, 1292.

Liquori, A. M. (1955), *Acta Cryst.*, **8**, 345.

Liquori, A. M., G. Anzuino, V. M. Coiro, M. d'Alagni, P. de Santis, and M. Savino (1965), *Nature*, **206**, 358.

Liu, K. J., and R. Ullman (1965), *Polymer*, **6**, 100.

Long, F. A., and W. F. McDevit (1952), *Chem. Rev.*, **51**, 119.

Longsworth, L. G. (1941), *Ann. N. Y. Acad. Sci.*, **41**, 167.

Loucheux, M. H., and A. Banderet (1960), *J. Polymer Sci.*, **48**, 405.

Loucheux, M. H., and A. Banderet (1964), *Bull. Soc. Chim. France*, 1220.

Lovrien, R., and J. C. Waddington (1964), *J. Am. Chem. Soc.*, **86**, 2315.

Low, B. W., and J. R. Einstein (1960), *Nature*, **186**, 470.

Lowe, W. G. (1943), U.S. Patents 2,311,058; 2,311,059.

Lütje, H., and G. Meyerhoff (1963), *Makromol. Chem.*, **68**, 180.

Luzzati, V. (1961), *Acta Cryst.*, **13**, 939.

Luzzati, V., M. Cesari, G. Spach, F. Mason, and J. M. Vincent (1961a), *J. Mol. Biol.* **3**, 566.

Luzzati, V., A. Nicolaieff, and F. Masson (1961b), *J. Mol. Biol.*, **3**, 185.

Luzzati, V., J. Witz, and A. Nicolaieff (1961c), *J. Mol. Biol.*, **3**, 367.

Luzzati, V., J. Witz, and A. Nicolaieff (1961d), *J. Mol. Biol.*, **3**, 373.

Lyons, J. W., and L. Kotin (1964), *J. Am. Chem. Soc.*, **86**, 3634.

McCormick, H. W. (1959a), *J. Polymer Sci.*, **36**, 341.

McCormick, H. W. (1959b), *J. Polymer Sci.*, **41**, 327.

McDowell, W. H., and W. O. Kenyon (1941), U.S. Patents 2,234,186; 2,249,536; 2,249,537; 2,249,538.

McIntyre, D., J. H. O'Mara, and R. C. Konouck (1959), *J. Am. Chem. Soc.*, **81**, 3498.

McMahon, P. E., and W. C. Tincher (1965), *J. Mol. Spectroscopy*, **15**, 180.

Magasanik, B. (1955), in *The Nucleic Acids*, Vol. 1, E. Chargaff and J. Davidson, eds., Academic Press, New York, Chap. 11.

Magasanik, B., and E. Chargaff (1951), *Biochim. Biophys. Acta*, **7**, 396.

Malcolm, G. N., and J. S. Rowlinson (1957), *Trans. Faraday Soc.*, **53**, 921.

Malmström, B. G. (1955), *Arch. Biochem.*, **58**, 381.

Mandel, M., and J. C. Leyte (1964), *J. Polymer Sci.*, **A1**, 2883, 3771.

Mandelkern, L., and P. J. Flory (1952), *J. Chem. Phys.*, **20**, 212.

Mandelkern, L., and T. G Fox (1953), *J. Chem. Phys.*, **21**, 187.

Mandelkern, L., W. R. Krigbaum, H. A. Scheraga, and P. J. Flory (1952), *J. Chem. Phys.*, **20**, 1392.

Mandelkern, L., L. C. Williams, and S. G. Weissberg (1957), *J. Phys. Chem.*, **61**, 271.

Marcker, K. (1960), *Acta Chem. Scand.*, **14**, 194.

Marcus, R. A. (1954), *J. Phys. Chem.*, **58**, 621.

Marcus, R. A. (1955), *J. Chem. Phys.*, **23**, 1057.

Mark, H., and A. V. Tobolsky (1950), *Physical Chemistry of High Polymeric Systems* (High Polymers, Vol. 2), Interscience, New York, p. 289.

Mark, J. E., and P. J. Flory (1964), *J. Am. Chem. Soc.*, **86**, 136.

Marmur, J., and P. Doty (1962), *J. Mol. Biol.*, **5**, 109.

Marmur, J., and D. Lane (1960), *Proc. Natl. Acad. Sci. U.S.*, **46**, 453.

Marmur, J., R. Rownd, and C. L. Schildkraut (1963), in *Progress in Nucleic Acid Research*, Vol. 1, J. N. Davidson and W. E. Cohn, eds., Academic Press, New York, p. 232.

Marvel, C. S., and C. G. Overberger (1946), *J. Am. Chem. Soc.*, **68**, 2106.

Mathieson, A. R., and J. C. J. Thynne (1956), *J. Chem. Soc.*, 3708.

Mathot, V., and D. Desmyter (1953), *J. Chem. Phys.*, **21**, 782.

Mayo, F. R., and F. M. Lewis (1944), *J. Am. Chem. Soc.*, **66**, 1594.

Meselson, M., F. W. Stahl, and J. Vinograd (1957), *Proc. Natl. Acad. Sci. U.S.*, **43**, 581.

Michaelis, L., and H. Pechstein (1914), *Biochem. Z.*, **59**, 77.

Middleton, W. J., and R. V. Lindsey, Jr. (1964), *J. Am. Chem. Soc.*, **86**, 4948.

Mikus, R. F., R. M. Hixon, and R. E. Rundle (1946), *J. Am. Chem. Soc.*, **68**, 1115.

Miller, R. L. (1962), *J. Polymer Sci.*, **56**, 375.

Miller, R. L., and L. E. Nielsen (1960), *J. Polymer Sci.*, **46**, 303.

Miller, R. L., and L. E. Nielsen (1961), *J. Polymer Sci.*, **55**, 643.

Miller, W. L., W. S. Brey, Jr., and G. B. Butler (1961), *J. Polymer Sci.*, **54**, 329.

Minsk, L. M., W. J. Priest, and W. O. Kenyon (1941), *J. Am. Chem. Soc.*, **63**, 2715.

Mitchell, A. G., and W. F. K. Wynne-Jones (1953), *Discussions Faraday Soc.*, **15**, 161.

Mizushima, S., Y. Morino, I. Watanabe, T. Simanouti, and S. Yamaguchi (1949), *J. Chem. Phys.*, **17**, 591.

Mock, R. A. (1960), *J. Polymer Sci.*, **44**, 271.

Mock, R. A., and C. A. Marshall (1954), *J. Polymer Sci.*, **13**, 263.

Mock, R. A., C. A. Marshall, and T. E. Slykhouse (1954), *J. Phys. Chem.*, **58**, 498.

Möller, W. J. H. M., G. A. J. Van Os, and J. T. G. Overbeek (1961), *Trans. Faraday Soc.*, **57**, 312, 325.

Moffitt, W. (1956), *J. Chem. Phys.*, **25**, 467; *Proc. Natl. Acad. Sci. U.S.*, **42**, 736.
Moffitt, W., and J. T. Yang (1956), *Proc. Natl. Acad. Sci. U.S.*, **42**, 596.
Moffitt, W., D. D. Fitts, and J. G. Kirkwood (1957), *Proc. Nat. Acad. Sci. U.S.*, **43**, 723.
Molyneux, P., and H. P. Frank (1961), *J. Am. Chem. Soc.*, **83**, 3169, 3175.
Mommaerts, W. F. H. M. (1952), *J. Biol. Chem.*, **198**, 467.
Monod, J., J. P. Changeux, and F. Jacob (1963), *J. Mol. Biol.*, **6**, 306.
Moore, W. R., and R. Shuttleworth (1963), *J. Polymer Sci.*, **A1**, 733.
Morawetz, H. (1954), *Ind. Chim. Belge*, **19**, 607.
Morawetz, H. (1955), *J. Polymer Sci.*, **17**, 442.
Morawetz, H. (1957), *J. Polymer Sci.*, **23**, 247.
Morawetz, H. (1961), in *Polyelectrolyte Solutions*, by S. A. Rice and M. Nagasawa, eds., Academic Press, New York, Chap. 5.
Morawetz, H., and E. Gaetjens (1958), *J. Polymer Sci.*, **32**, 526.
Morawetz, H., and R. H. Gobran (1954), *J. Polymer Sci.*, **12**, 133.
Morawetz, H., and R. H. Gobran (1955), *J. Polymer Sci.*, **18**, 455.
Morawetz, H., and W. L. Hughes, Jr. (1952), *J. Phys. Chem.*, **56**, 64.
Morawetz, H., and I. Oreskes (1958), *J. Am. Chem. Soc.*, **80**, 2591.
Morawetz, H., and I. D. Rubin (1962), *J. Polymer Sci.*, **57**, 687.
Morawetz, H., and H. Sage (1955), *Arch. Biochem. Biophys.*, **56**, 103.
Morawetz, H., and E. Sammak (1957), *J. Phys. Chem.*, **61**, 1357.
Morawetz, H., and J. A. Shafer (1962), *J. Am. Chem. Soc.*, **84**, 3783.
Morawetz, H., and J. A. Shafer (1963), *J. Phys. Chem.*, **67**, 1293.
Morawetz, H., and E. W. Westhead, Jr. (1955), *J. Polymer Sci.*, **16**, 273.
Morawetz, H., and P. E. Zimmering (1954), *J. Phys. Chem.*, **58**, 753.
Morawetz, H., A. M. Kotliar, and H. Mark (1954), *J. Phys. Chem.*, **58**, 619.
Moscowitz, A. (1962), in *Advances in Chemical Physics*, Vol. 4, I. Prigogine, ed., Interscience, New York, p. 67.
Motomura, K., and R. Matuura (1963), *J. Colloid Sci.*, **18**, 52.
Muirhead, H., and M. F. Perutz (1963), *Nature*, **199**, 633.
Muller, R. H., and H. J. Stolten (1953), *Anal. Chem.*, **25**, 1103.
Myers, C. S. (1954), *J. Polymer Sci.*, **13**, 549.
Myrbäck, K. (1926), *Z. Physiol. Chem.*, **159**, 1.
Nagai, E., and N. Sagane (1955), *Kobunshi Kagaku*, **12**, 195.
Nagai, K. (1959a), *J. Chem. Phys.*, **31**, 1169.
Nagai, K. (1959b), *J. Chem. Phys.*, **37**, 490.
Nagai, K. (1962), *J. Chem. Phys.*, **37**, 490.
Nagasawa, M. (1961), *J. Am. Chem. Soc.*, **83**, 300.
Nagasawa, M., and H. Fujita (1964), *J. Am. Chem. Soc.*, **86**, 3005.
Nagasawa, M., A. Soda, and I. Kagawa (1958), *J. Polymer Sci.*, **31**, 439.
Nagasawa, M., M. Izumi, and I. Kagawa (1959a), *J. Polymer Sci.*, **37**, 375.
Nagasawa, M., A. Takahashi, M. Izumi, and I. Kagawa (1959b), *J. Polymer Sci.*, **38**, 213.
Nair, P. M., and J. D. Roberts (1957), *J. Am. Chem. Soc.*, **79**, 4565.
Natta, G. (1957), *Experientia Suppl.*, **7**, 21.
Natta, G. (1960), *Makromol. Chem.*, **35**, 94.
Natta, G., and P. Corradini (1955), *Makromol. Chem.*, **16**, 77.
Natta, G., and P. Corradini (1956), *J. Polymer Sci.*, **20**, 251.
Natta, G., and F. Danusso (1959), *J. Polymer Sci.*, **34**, 3.
Natta, G., P. Pino, P. Corradini, F. Danusso, E. Mantica, G. Mazzanti, and G. Moraglio (1955), *J. Am. Chem. Soc.*, **77**, 1708.

Natta, G., P. Corradini, and I. W. Bassi (1959), *Gazz. Chim. Ital.*, **89**, 784.

Natta, G., M. Farina, and M. Peraldo (1960), *J. Polymer Sci.*, **43**, 289.

Natta, G., I. Pasquon, and A. Zambelli (1962), *J. Am. Chem. Soc.*, **84**, 1488.

Natta, G., M. Peraldo, and G. Allegra (1964), *Makromol. Chem.*, **75**, 215.

Naylor, R. E., and S. W. Lasoski, Jr. (1960), *J. Polymer Sci.*, **44**, 1.

Néel, J., and B. Sebille (1961), *J. Chim. Phys.*, **58**, 738.

Neely, W. B. (1963), *J. Polymer Sci.*, **A1**, 311.

Nelson, C. A., and J. P. Hummel (1962), *J. Biol. Chem.*, **237**, 1567.

Nemethy, G., and H. A. Scheraga (1962a), *J. Chem. Phys.*, **36**, 3401.

Nemethy, G., and H. A. Scheraga (1962b), *J. Chem. Phys.*, **36**, 3382.

Nemethy, G., and H. A. Scheraga (1962c), *J. Phys. Chem.*, **66**, 1773.

Neugebauer, T. (1942), *Ann. Physik* [5], **42**, 509.

Neurath, H., J. P. Greenstein, F. W. Putnam, and J. O. Erickson (1944), *Chem. Rev.*, **34**, 157.

Neville, D. M., Jr., and D. F. Bradley (1961), *Biochim. Biophys. Acta*, **50**, 397.

Newman, M. S. (1956), *Steric Effects in Organic Chemistry*, Wiley, New York, pp. 4–9.

Newman, S., W. R. Krigbaum, and D. K. Carpenter (1956), *J. Phys. Chem.*, **60**, 648.

Nichol, L. W.., J. L. Bethune, G Kegeles, and E. L. Hess (1964), in *The Proteins*, Vol. II, H. Neurath, ed., 2nd ed., Academic Press, New York, p. 305.

Nielsen, S. O. (1960), *Biochim. Biophys. Acta*, **37**, 146.

Nielsen, S. O., W. P. Bryan, and K. Mikkelsen (1960), *Biochim. Biophys. Acta*, **42**, 550.

Nishijima, Y., and G. Oster (1956), *J. Polymer Sci.*, **19**, 337.

Nisonoff, A., and G. J. Thorbecke (1964), *Ann. Rev. Biochem.*, **33**, 355.

Noda, I., M. Nagasawa, and M. Ota (1964), *J. Am. Chem. Soc.*, **86**, 5075.

Noguchi, H. (1960), *J. Phys. Chem.*, **64**, 185.

Noll, L. A., and S. J. Gill (1963), *J. Phys. Chem.*, **67**, 498.

Nord, F. F., M. Bier, and N. Timasheff (1951), *J. Am. Chem. Soc.*, **73**, 289.

Nozaki, Y., and C. Tanford (1963), *J. Biol. Chem.*, **238**, 4074.

Nozakura, S., S. Takeuchi, H. Yuki, and S. Murahashi (1961), *Bull. Chem. Soc. Japan*, **34**, 1673.

Oka, S. (1942), *Proc. Phys.-Math. Soc. Japan*, **24**, 657.

Okada, R., Y. Toyoshima, and H. Fujita (1963), *Makromol. Chem.*, **59**, 137.

Olson, J. A., and C. B. Anfinsen (1952), *J. Biol. Chem.*, **197**, 67.

Oncley, J. L., D. Gitlin, E. Ellenbogen, and F. R. N. Gurd (1952), *J. Phys. Chem.*, **56**, 85.

O'Neill, J. (1963), Ph.D. Thesis, Polytechnic Institute of Brooklyn.

Ono, S., S. Tsuchihashi, and T. Kuge (1953), *J. Am. Chem. Soc.*, **75**, 3601.

Onsager, L. (1949), *Ann. N.Y. Acad. Sci.*, **51**, 627.

Oosawa, F., and M. Kasai (1962), *J. Mol. Biol.*, **4**, 10.

Oosawa, F., N. Imai, and I. Kagawa (1954), *J. Polymer Sci.*, **13**, 93.

Oosawa, F., S. Asakura, K. Hotta, N. Imai, and T. Ooi (1959), *J. Polymer Sci.*, **37**, 323.

Oparin, A. T. (1957), *The Origin of Life on Earth*, Oliver and Boyd, London, Chap. 7.

Orofino, T. A., and A. Ciferri (1964), *J. Phys. Chem.*, **68**, 3132.

Orofino, T. A., and P. J. Flory (1957), *J. Chem. Phys.*, **26**, 1067.

Orofino, T. A., and P. J. Flory (1959), *J. Phys. Chem.*, **63**, 283.

Orofino, T. A., and J. W. Mickey (1963), *J. Chem. Phys.*, **38**, 2512.

Oster, G. (1948), *Chem. Rev.*, **43**, 319.

Oster, G. (1950), *J. Gen. Physiol.*, **33**, 445.

Oster, G. (1955), *J. Polymer Sci.*, **16**, 235.

Oster, G. (1957), *Trans. Faraday Soc.*, **47**, 660.

Oster, G. (1960), in *Physical Methods of Organic Chemistry*, Part 3 (Technique of Organic Chemistry, Vol. 1), A. Weissberger, ed., Interscience, New York, p. 2107.

Oster, G., and J. S. Bellin (1957), *J. Am. Chem. Soc.*, **79**, 294.

Oster, G., and Y. Nishijima (1964), *Forschr. Hochpolymer. Forsch.*, **3**, 313.

Oster, G., and G. K. Oster (1962), in *Luminescence of Organic and Inorganic Materials*, H. Kallman and G. Spruch eds., Wiley, New York, pp. 186–195.

Oth, A., and P. Doty (1952), *J. Phys. Chem.*, **56**, 43.

Overberger, C. G., and H. Jabloner (1963), *J. Am. Chem. Soc.*, **85**, 3431.

Overberger, C. G., and L. C. Palmer (1956), *J. Am. Chem. Soc.*, **78**, 666.

Overberger, C. G., T. St. Pierre, N. Worchheimer, J. Lee, and S. Yaroslavsky (1965), *J. Am. Chem. Soc.*, **87**, 296.

Painter, T. J. (1962), *J. Chem. Soc.*, 3932.

Pal, M. K., and M. Schubert (1963), *J. Phys. Chem.*, **67**, 1821.

Pals, D. T. F., and J. J. Hermans (1952), *Rec. Trav. Chim.*, **71**, 469.

Parry, D. A. D., and A. Elliott (1965), *Nature*, **206**, 616.

Pauling, L. (1940), *J. Am. Chem. Soc.*, **62**, 2643.

Pauling, L., and R. B. Corey (1951), *Proc. Natl. Acad. Sci. U.S.*, **37**, 235, 241.

Pauling, L., and R. B. Corey (1956), *Arch. Biochem. Biophys.*, **65**, 164.

Pauling, L., R. B. Corey, and H. R. Branson (1951), *Proc. Natl. Acad. Sci. U.S.*, **37**, 205.

Pchelin, V. A., V. N. Izmailova, and V. N. Merzlov (1963), *Dokl. Akad. Nauk SSSR*, **150**, 1307.

Pedersen, K. O. (1958), *J. Phys. Chem.*, **62**, 1282.

Pepe, F. A., and S. J. Singer (1959), *J. Am. Chem. Soc.*, **81**, 3878.

Perrin, F. (1908), *Compt. Rend.*, **146**, 967.

Perrin, F. (1929), *Ann. Phys. (Paris)*, [10], **12**, 169.

Perrin, F. (1934), *J. Phys. Radium*, [7], **5**, 497.

Perrin, F. (1936), *J. Phys. Radium* [7], **7**, 1.

Perutz, M. F. (1962), *Nature*, **194**, 914.

Perutz, M. F., M. G. Rossmann, A. F. Cullis, H. Muirhead, G. Will, and A. C. T. North (1960), *Nature*, **185**, 416.

Peterlin, A. (1938), *Z. Physik*, **111**, 232.

Peterlin, A. (1953), *J. Polymer Sci.*, **10**, 425.

Peterlin, A. (1955), *J. Colloid Sci.*, **10**, 587.

Peterlin, A. (1960a), *J. Polymer Sci.*, **47**, 403.

Peterlin, A. (1960b), *J. Chem. Phys.*, **33**, 1799.

Peterlin, A. (1961a), *Ann. N.Y. Acad. Sci.*, **89**, 578.

Peterlin, A. (1961b), *Makromol. Chem.*, **44/46**, 338.

Peterlin, A. (1963), *J. Chem. Phys.*, **39**, 224.

Peterlin, A., and M. Čopič (1956), *J. Appl. Phys.*, **27**, 434.

Peterlin, A., and H. A. Stuart (1939), *Z. Physik*, **112**, 1.

Peterlin, A., and D. T. Turner (1963), *J. Chem. Phys.*, **38**, 2315.

Phibbs, M. K. (1955), *J. Phys. Chem.*, **59**, 346.

Pinner, S. H. (1953), *J. Polymer Sci.*, **10**, 379.

Pinner, S. H., and T. Alfrey, Jr. (1952), *J. Polymer Sci.*, **9**, 478.

Pino, P., and G. P. Lorenzi (1960), *J. Am. Chem. Soc.*, **82**, 4745.

Pitzer, K. S. (1940), *Chem. Rev.*, **27**, 39; *J. Chem. Phys.*, **8**, 711.

Pool, W. F., and N. Davidson (1962b), *J. Mol. Biol.*, **5**, 479.

Pople, J., W. G. Schneider, and H. J. Bernstein (1959), *High Resolution Nuclear Magnetic Resonance*, McGraw-Hill, New York.

Porod, G. (1953), *J. Polymer Sci.*, **10**, 157.

Porter, R. R. (1959), *Biochem. J.*, **73**, 119.

Potts, J. T., Jr., D. M. Young, and C. B. Anfinsen (1963), *J. Biol. Chem.*, **238**, PC2593.

Price, C. C., and M. Osgan (1956), *J. Am. Chem. Soc.*, **78**, 4787.

Prigogine, I., N. Trappeniers, and V. Mathot (1953), *Discussions Faraday Soc.*, **15**, 93.

Ptitsyn, O. B. (1959), *Vysokomolekul. Soedin.*, **1**, 715 (English transl. *Poly. Sci. USSR* **1**, 259(1961)).

Ptitsyn, O. B., and Yu. E. Eizner (1959), *Zh. Tekhn. Fiz.*, **29**, 1117 (English transl. Soviet Phys. Tech. Phys., **4**, 1020(1960)).

Ptitsyn, O. B., and Yu. A. S. Sharonov (1957), *Zh. Tekhn. Fiz.*, **27**, 2744 (English transl. *Soviet Phys. Tech. Phys.*, **2**, 2544 (1958)).

Pullman, B., and A. Pullman (1959), *Biochim. Biophys. Acta.*, **36**, 343.

Putnam, F. W. (1953), in *The Proteins*, Vol. 18, H. Neurath and K. Bailey, eds., Academic Press, New York, p. 893.

Ray, N. H. (1952), *Trans. Faraday Soc.*, **48**, 809.

Rayleigh, Lord (J. W. Strutt)(1871), *Phil. Mag.*, [4] **41**, 107, 224, 447.

Rayleigh, Lord (J. W. Strutt)(1881), *Phil. Mag.*, [5] **12**, 81.

Rayleigh, Lord (1911), *Proc. Roy. Soc. (London)*, **A84**, 25.

Rayleigh, Lord (1918), *Phil. Mag.*, **35**, 373.

Reddy, J. M., K. Knox, and M. R. Robin (1964), *J. Chem. Phys.*, **40**, 1082.

Rees, E. D., and S. J. Singer (1956), *Arch. Biochem. Biophys.*, **63**, 144.

Reeves, R. E. (1949), *J. Am. Chem. Soc.*, **71**, 212.

Reichmann, M. E., and J. R. Colvin (1956), *Can. J. Chem.*, **34**, 411.

Rein, H. (1938), U. S. Patent 2,140,921.

Reiss, C., and H. Benoit (1961), *Compt. Rend.*, **253**, 268.

Reithel, F. J. (1963), *Advan. Protein Chem.*, **18**, 124.

Rice, R. V., M. A. Stahmann, and R. A. Alberty (1954), *J. Biol. Chem.*, **209**, 105.

Rice, S. A. (1955), *J. Polymer Sci.*, **16**, 94.

Rice, S. A., and F. E. Harris (1954), *J. Phys. Chem.*, **58**, 733.

Rice, S. A., and A. Wada (1958), *J. Chem. Phys.*, **29**, 233.

Rich, A. (1959), *Rev. Mod. Phys.*, **31**, 191.

Richards, F. M. (1963), *Ann. Rev. Biochem.*, **32**, 264.

Richards, F. M., and P. J. Vithayathil (1959), *J. Biol. Chem.*, **234**, 1459.

Richards, M. M. (1938), *J. Biol. Chem.*, **122**, 727.

Riseman, J., and J. G. Kirkwood (1949), *J. Chem. Phys.*, **17**, 442.

Riseman, J., and J. G. Kirkwood (1950), *J. Chem. Phys.*, **18**, 512.

Roberts, J. D. (1959), *Nuclear Magnetic Resonance Applications to Organic Chemistry*, McGraw-Hill, New York.

Robin, M. R. (1964), *J. Chem. Phys.*, **40**, 3369.

Robinson, C. (1956), *Trans. Faraday Soc.*, **52**, 571.

Robinson, C., J. C. Ward, and R. B. Beevers (1958), *Discussions Faraday Soc.*, **25**, 29.

Robinson, D. R., and W. P. Jencks (1963), *J. Biol. Chem.*, **238**, PC1558.

Robinson, E. A., and H. A. Itano (1960), *Nature*, **188**, 798.

Rolfe, R., and M. Meselson (1959), *Proc. Natl. Acad. Sci. U.S.*, **45**, 1039.

Rosen, B., P. Kamath, and F. Eirich (1951), *Discussions Faraday Soc.*, **11**, 135.

Rosenberg, A., and R. Lumry (1964), *Biochemistry*, **3**, 1055.

Rosenheck, K., and P. Doty (1961), *Proc. Natl. Acad. Sci. U.S.*, **47**, 1775.

Rossi, C., U. Bianchi, and E. Bianchi (1960), *Makromol. Chem.*, **41**, 31.

Rowlinson, J. S. (1959), *Liquids and Liquid Mixtures*, Butterworths, London, p. 148.

Rowlinson, J. S., and J. R. Sutton (1955), *Proc. Roy. Soc. (London)*, **A229**, 271.

Rundle, R. E., and R. R. Baldwin (1943), *J. Am. Chem. Soc.*, **65**, 554.

Rundle, R. E., and D. French (1943), *J. Am. Chem. Soc.*, **65**, 1707.

Sadron, C., and P. Rempp (1958), *J. Polymer Sci.*, **29**, 127.

Sage, H. J., and S. J. Singer (1958), *Biochim. Biophys. Acta*, **29**, 663.

Saito, S. (1953), *Kolloid-Z.*, **133**, 12.

Saito, S. (1954), *Kolloid-Z.*, **137**, 98.

Saito, S. (1957), *Kolloid-Z.*, **154**, 19.

de Santis, P., E. Giglio, A. M. Liquori, and A. Ripamonti (1963), *J. Polymer Sci.*, **A1**, 1383.

de Santis, P., E. Giglio, A. M. Liquori, and A. Ripamonti (1965), *Nature*, **206**, 456.

Satoh, S., R. Chujo, T. Ozeki, and E. Nagai (1962), *J. Polymer Sci.*, **61**, 5101.

Saunders, P. R. (1962), *J. Polymer Sci.*, **57**, 131.

Saunders, P. R. (1964), *J. Polymer Sci.*, **A2**, 3755.

Scatchard, G. (1931), *Chem. Rev.*, **8**, 321.

Scatchard, G. (1937), *Trans. Faraday Soc.*, **33**, 160.

Scatchard, G. (1949), *Ann. N.Y. Acad. Sci.*, **51**, 660.

Scatchard, G., S. E. Wood, and J. M. Mochel (1939), *J. Phys. Chem.*, **43**, 119.

Scatchard, G., I. H. Scheinberg, and S. H. Armstrong (1949), *J. Am. Chem. Soc.*, **72**, 535, 540.

Schachman, H. K. (1959), *Ultracentrifugation in Biochemistry*, Academic Press, New York.

Schachman, H. K. (1963), *Biochemistry*, **2**, 887.

Schaefgen, J. R., and P. J. Flory (1948), *J. Am. Chem. Soc.*, **70**, 2709.

Schaefgen, J. R., and C. F. Trivisonno (1952), *J. Am. Chem. Soc.*, **74**, 2715.

Schellman, J. A. (1955), *Compt. Rend. Trav. Lab. Carlsberg, Sér. chim.*, **29**, No. 15.

Schellman, J. A., and C. G. Schellman (1961), *J. Polymer Sci.*, **49**, 129.

Schellman, J. A., R. B. Simpson, and W. Kauzmann (1953), *J. Am. Chem. Soc.*, **75**, 5152.

Scheraga, H. A. (1955), *J. Chem. Phys.*, **23**, 1526.

Scheraga, H. A., and M. Laskowski, Jr. (1957), *Advan. Protein Chem.*, **12**, 1.

Scheraga, H. A., and L. Mandelkern (1953), *J. Am. Chem. Soc.*, **75**, 179.

Scheraga, H. A., J. T. Edsall, and J. O. Gaddy, Jr. (1951), *J. Chem. Phys.*, **19**, 1101.

Scheraga, H. A., G. Nemethy, and I. Z. Steinberg (1962), *J. Biol. Chem.*, **237**, 2506.

Schick, M. J. (1957), *J. Polymer Sci.*, **25**, 465.

Schildkraut, C. L., and S. Lifson (1965), *Biopolymers*, **3**, 195.

Schildkraut, C. L., J. Marmur, and P. Doty (1961), *J. Mol. Biol.*, **3**, 595.

Schildkraut, C. L., J. Marmur, and P. Doty (1962a), *J. Mol. Biol.*, **4**, 430.

Schildkraut, C. L., K. L. Wierzchowski, J. Marmur, D. M. Green, and P. Doty (1962b), *Virology*, **18**, 43.

Schindewolf, U. (1954a), *Z. Physik. Chem. (Frankfurt)*, **1**, 129; *Z. Elektrochem.*, **58**, 697.

Schindewolf, U. (1954b), *Z. Physik. Chem. (Frankfurt)*, **1**, 134.

Schlichting, H. (1960), *Boundary Layer Problem*, 4th ed., McGraw-Hill, New York, p. 16.

Schmier, I., and N. S. Simmons (1962), *J. Am. Chem. Soc.*, **84**, 3193.

Schmitt, G. J., and C. Schuerch (1960), *J. Polymer Sci.*, **45**, 313.

Schneider, N. S., and P. Doty (1954), *J. Phys. Chem.*, **58**, 762.

Schön, K. G., and G. V. Schulz (1954), *Z. Physik. Chem. (Frankfurt)*, **2**, 197.

Scholtan, W. (1953), *Makromol. Chem.*, **11**, 131.

Scholtan, W. and H. Marzolph (1962), *Makromol. Chem.*, **57**, 52.

Schuerch, C. (1952), *J. Am. Chem. Soc.*, **64**, 5061.

Schulz, G. V. (1939), *Z. Physik. Chem.* (*Leipzig*), **B43**, 25.

Schulz, G. V., and H. Baumann (1963), *Makromol. Chem.*, **60**, 120.

Schulz, G. V., and R. Kirste (1961), *Z. Physik. Chem.* (*Frankfurt*), **30**, 171.

Schulz, G. V., and H. Marzolph (1954), *Z. Elektrochem.*, **58**, 211.

Schulz, G. V., K. V. Gunner, and H. Gerrens (1955), *Z. Physik. Chem.* (*Frankfurt*), **4**, 192.

Schulz, G. V., W. Wunderlich, and R. Kirste (1964), *Makromol. Chem.*, **75**, 22.

Schumaker, V. N., and H. K. Schachman (1957), *Biochim. Biophys. Acta*, **23**, 628.

Schwarz, G. (1959), *Z. Physik. Chem.* (*Frankfurt*), **19**, 286.

Scott, R. L., and M. Magat (1949), *J. Polymer Sci.*, **4**, 555.

Sela, M., and A. Berger (1953), *J. Am. Chem. Soc.*, **75**, 6350.

Sela, M., and L. A. Steiner (1963), *Biochemistry*, **2**, 416.

Shashoua, V. E., and R. G. Beaman (1958), *J. Polymer Sci.*, **33**, 101.

Sheppard, N., and J. J. Turner (1959), *Proc. Roy. Soc.* (*London*), **A252**, 506.

Shultz, A. R. (1954), *J. Am. Chem. Soc.*, **76**, 3422.

Shultz, A. R., and P. J. Flory (1952), *J. Am. Chem. Soc.*, **74**, 4760.

Shultz, A. R., and P. J. Flory (1953), *J. Am. Chem. Soc.*, **75**, 3888.

Siddall, III, T. H., and C. A. Prohaska (1962), *J. Am. Chem. Soc.*, **84**, 2502.

Signer, R., and H. Gross (1934), *Helv. Chim. Acta*, **17**, 726.

Silberberg, A., J. Eliassaf, and A. Katchalsky (1957), *J. Polymer Sci.*, **23**, 259.

Simha, R. (1940), *J. Phys. Chem.*, **44**, 25.

Simha, R. (1952), *J. Appl. Phys.*, **23**, 1020.

Simmons, N. S., and E. R. Blout (1960), *Biophys. J.*, **1**, 55.

Simmons, N. S., C. Cohen, A. G. Szent-Györgyi, D. B. Wetlaufer, and E. R. Blout (1961), *J. Am. Chem. Soc.*, **83**, 4706.

Simpson, R. B., and W. Kauzmann (1953), *J. Am. Chem. Soc.*, **75**, 5139.

Singer, S. J. (1948), *J. Chem. Phys.*, **16**, 872.

Singer, S. J. (1962), *Advan. Protein Chem.*, **17**, 1.

Singer, S. J., and D. H. Campbell (1955), *J. Am. Chem. Soc.*, **77**, 3499, 4851.

Singer, S. J., and H. A. Itano (1959), *Proc. Natl. Acad. Sci. U.S.*, **45**, 174.

Sjöberg, B. (1960), *Arkiv. Kemi.*, **15**, 451.

Skeist, I. (1946), *J. Am. Chem. Soc.*, **68**, 1781.

Slater, E. C., and W. D. Bonner, Jr. (1952), *Biochem. J.*, **52**, 185.

Slough, W. (1959), *Trans. Faraday Soc.*, **55**, 1030.

Slough, W. (1962), *Trans. Faraday Soc.*, **58**, 2360.

Small, T. A. (1953), *J. Appl. Chem.*, **3**, 71.

Smets, G., and W. De Loecker (1959), *J. Polymer Sci.*, **41**, 375.

Smets, G., and W. De Loecker (1960), *J. Polymer Sci.*, **45**, 461.

Smets, G., and A. M. Hesbain (1959), *J. Polymer Sci.*, **40**, 217.

Smets, G., and B. Petit (1959), *Makromol. Chem.*, **33**, 41.

Smets, G., and W. Van Humbeeck (1963), *J. Polymer Sci.*, **A1**, 1227.

Smith, K. L., A. E. Winslow, and D. E. Peterson (1959), *Ind. Eng. Chem.*, **51**, 1361.

Smoluchowski, M. v. (1921), in *Handbuch der Elektrizitaet und des Magnetismus*, L. Graetz, ed., J. A. Barth, Leipzig, Vol. II., p. 366.

Smyth, D. G., W. H. Stein, and S. Moore (1963), *J. Biol. Chem.*, **238**, 227.

Sobue, H., T. Uryu, K. Matsuzaki, and Y. Tabata (1963), *J. Polymer Sci.*, **B1**, 409.

Sobue, H., K. Matsuzaki, and S. Nakano (1964), *J. Polymer Sci.*, **A2**, 3339.

Song, W. R. (1965), Ph. D. Thesis, Polytechnic Institute of Brooklyn.

Spanagel, E. W., and W. H. Carothers (1935), *J. Am. Chem. Soc.*, **57**, 929.

Spencer, M., W. Fuller, M. H. F. Wilkins, and G. L. Brown (1962), *Nature*, **194**, 1014.

Spurlin, H. M. (1955), in *Cellulose and Cellulose Derivatives*, Part 3, E. Ott, H. M. Spurlin, and M. W. Graffin, eds. (High Polymers, Vol. 5), Interscience, New York, pp. 1077–1082.

Stacey, K. A. (1956), *Light Scattering in Physical Chemistry*, Butterworths, London.

Stamm, A. J. (1952), in *Wood Chemistry*, L. E. Wise and E. C. Jahn, eds., Am. Chem. Soc. Monograph No. 97, 2nd ed., Reinhold, New York, pp. 226–277.

Stanton, G. W., W. Creek, and T. B. Lefferdink (1953), U. S. Patent 2,648,647.

Starkweather, H. W. (1959), *J. Appl. Polymer Sci.*, **2**, 129.

Staudinger, H. (1932), *Die Hochmolekularen Organischen Verbindungen*, Springer, Berlin, p. 39.

Staudinger, H., K. Frey, and W. Starck (1927), *Ber.*, **60**, 1787.

Staveley, L. A. K., W. I. Tupman, and K. R. Hart (1955), *Trans. Faraday Soc.*, **51**, 323

Staverman, A. J. (1952), *Rec. Trav. Chim.*, **71**, 623.

Stein, R. S., and R. E. Rundle (1948), *J. Chem. Phys.*, **16**, 195.

Steinberg, I. Z., W. F. Harrington, A. Berger, M. Sela, and E. Katchalski (1960), *J. Am. Chem. Soc.*, **82**, 5263.

Steiner, R. F. (1954), *Arch. Biochem. Biophys.*, **49**, 71.

Steiner, R. F., and R. F. Beers, Jr. (1959), *Biochim. Biophys. Acta*, **33**, 470.

Steiner, R. F., and R. F. Beers, Jr. (1961), *Polynucleotides*, Elsevier, Amsterdam.

Steiner, R. F., and H. Edelhoch (1962), *Chem. Rev.*, **62**, 457.

Steiner, R. F., and H. Edelhoch (1963), *Biochim. Biophys. Acta*, **66**, 341.

Steiner, R. F., R. E. Lipoldt, H. Edelhoch, and V. Frattali (1964), *Biopolymers Symp.*, No. **1**, 355.

Stevens, C. L., and G. Felsenfeld (1964), *Biopolymers*, **2**, 293.

Stockmayer, W. H. (1945), *J. Chem. Phys.*, **13**, 199.

Stockmayer, W. H. (1949), *J. Chem. Phys.*, **17**, 588.

Stockmayer, W. H. (1950), *J. Chem. Phys.*, **18**, 58.

Stockmayer, W., and E. F. Casassa (1952), *J. Chem. Phys.*, **20**, 1560.

Stockmayer, W. H., and M. Fixman (1963), *J. Polymer Sci.*, **C, No.** 1, 137.

Stockmayer, W. H., L. D. Moore, Jr., M. Fixman, and B. N. Epstein (1955), *J. Polymer Sci.*, **16**, 517.

Stokes, Sir G. (1880), *Mathematical and Physical Papers*, Cambridge Univ. Press, New York.

Stoll, M., and A. Rouvé (1935), *Helv. Chim. Acta*, **18**, 1087.

Stone, A. L., and D. F. Bradley (1961), *J. Am. Chem. Soc.*, **83**, 3627.

Strauss, U. P., and P. Ander (1958), *J. Am. Chem. Soc.*, **80**, 6494.

Strauss, U. P., and S. Bluestone (1959), *J. Am. Chem. Soc.*, **81**, 5292.

Strauss, U. P., and N. L. Gershfeld (1954), *J. Phys. Chem.*, **58**, 747.

Strauss, U. P., and Y. P. Leung (1965), *J. Am. Chem. Soc.*, **87**, 1476.

Strauss, U. P., and P. D. Ross (1959a), *J. Am. Chem. Soc.*, **81**, 5295.

Strauss, U. P., and P. D. Ross (1959b), *J. Am. Chem. Soc.*, **81**, 5299.

Strauss, U. P., and A. Siegel (1963), *J. Phys. Chem.*, **67**, 2683.

Strauss, U. P., N. L. Gershfeld, and H. Spira (1954), *J. Am. Chem. Soc.*, **76**, 5909.

Strauss, U. P., N. L. Gershfeld, and E. H. Crook (1956), *J. Phys. Chem.*, **60**, 577.

464 MACROMOLECULES IN SOLUTION

Strauss, U. P., D. Woodside, and P. Wineman (1957), *J. Phys. Chem.*, **61**, 1353.
Strazielle, C., and H. Benoit (1961), *J. Chim. Phys.*, **58**, 675, 678.
Stryer, L., and E. R. Blout (1961), *J. Am. Chem. Soc.*, **83**, 1411.
Sueoka, N., J. Marmur, and P. Doty (1959), *Nature*, **183**, 1429.
Svedberg, T. (1926), *Z. Physik. Chem. (Leipzig)*, **121**, 65.
Svedberg, T., and R. Fåhraeus (1926), *J. Am. Chem. Soc.*, **48**, 430.
Svedberg, T., and J. B. Nichols (1926), *J. Am. Chem. Soc.*, **48**, 3081.
Svensson, H. (1939), *Kolloid-Z.*, **87**, 181.
Svensson, H. (1940), *Kolloid-Z.*, **90**, 141.
Swanson, M. A. (1948), *J. Biol. Chem.*, **172**, 825.
Tadokoro, H., T. Yasumoto, S. Murahashi, and I. Nitta (1960), *J. Polymer Sci.*, **44**, 266.
Taft, R., and L. E. Malm (1939), *J. Phys. Chem.*, **43**, 499.
Takeda, M., K. Iimura, A. Yamada, and Y. Imamura (1959), *Bull. Chem. Soc. Japan*, **32**, 1150.
Takenaka, H. (1957), *J. Polymer Sci.*, **24**, 321.
Tanford, C. (1961), *Physical Chemistry of Macromolecules*, Wiley, New York, pp. 554–573.
Tanford, C. (1962), *J. Am. Chem. Soc.*, **84**, 4240.
Tanford, C. (1964), *J. Am. Chem. Soc.*, **84**, 1747.
Tanford, C., and P. K. De (1961), *J. Biol. Chem.*, **236**, 1711.
Tanford, C., and J. D. Hauenstein (1956), *J. Am. Chem. Soc.*, **78**, 5287.
Tanford, C., J. G. Buzzell, D. G. Rands, and S. A. Swanson (1955a), *J. Am. Chem. Soc.*, **77**, 6421.
Tanford, C., J. D. Hauenstein, and D. G. Rands (1955b), *J. Am. Chem. Soc.*, **77**, 6409.
Tanford, C., L. G. Bunville, and Y. Nozaki (1959), *J. Am. Chem. Soc.*, **81**, 1032.
Tanford, C., P. K. De, and V. G. Taggart (1960), *J. Am. Chem. Soc.*, **82**, 6028.
Taylor, G. I. (1932), *Proc. Roy. Soc. (London)*, **A138**, 41.
Taylor, W. J. (1947), *J. Chem. Phys.*, **15**, 412.
Taylor, W. J. (1948), *J. Chem. Phys.*, **16**, 257.
Teale, F. W. J. (1960), *Biochem. J.*, **76**, 381.
Teale, F. W. J., and G. Weber (1957), *Biochem. J.*, **65**, 476.
Terayama, H. (1952), *J. Polymer Sci.*, **8**, 243.
Theorell, H., and B. Chance (1951), *Acta Chem. Scand.*, **5**, 1127.
Thoma, J. A., and D. E. Koshland (1960), *J. Am. Chem. Soc.*, **82**, 3329.
Thurmond, C. D., and B. H. Zimm (1952), *J. Polymer Sci.*, **8**, 477.
Tiers, G. V. D. (1958), *J. Phys. Chem.*, **62**, 1151.
Tiers, G. V. D., and F. A. Bovey (1960), *J. Polymer Sci.*, **47**, 479.
Tiers, G. V. D., and F. A. Bovey (1963), *J. Polymer Sci.*, **A1**, 833.
Timasheff, S. N., J. Witz, and V. Luzzati (1961), *Biophys. J.*, **1**, 525.
Tincher, W. C. (1962), *J. Polymer Sci.*, **62**, S148.
Tincher, W. C. (1965), *Makromol. Chem.*, in press.
Tinoco, I., Jr. (1960), *J. Am. Chem. Soc.*. **82**, 4785,
Tinoco, I., Jr. (1962), in *Advances in Chemical Physics*, Vol. 4, I. Prigogine, ed., Interscience, New York, p. 113.
Tinoco, I., Jr., R. W. Woody, and K. Yamaoka (1961), *Tetrahedron*, **13**, 134.
Tinoco, I., Jr., A. Helpern, and W. I. Simpson (1962), in *Polyaminoacids, Polypeptides and Proteins*, M. A. Stahmann, ed., Univ. of Wisconsin Press, p. 147.
Tiselius, A. (1932), *Kolloid-Z.*, **59**, 306.

Tobolsky, A. V. (1959), *J. Chem. Phys.*, **31**, 387.

Tompa, H. (1952), *J. Polymer Sci.*, **8**, 51.

Tompa, H. (1956), *Polymer Solutions*, Academic Press, New York, p. 42.

Trap, H. J. L., and J. J. Hermans (1954), *J. Phys. Chem.*, **58**, 757.

Treloar, L. D. G. (1949), *The Physics of Rubber Elasticity*, Clarendon Press, Oxford.

Trementozzi, Q. A., R. F. Steiner, and P. Doty (1952), *J. Am. Chem. Soc.*, **74**, 2070.

Tsvetkov, V. N. (1957), *J. Polymer Sci.*, **23**, 151.

Tsvetkov, V. N. (1962), *J. Polymer Sci.*, **51**, 727.

Tvetkov, V. N. (1964), in *Newer Methods of Polymer Characterization*, B. Ke, ed., Interscience, New York, Chap. 14.

Tsvetkov, V. N., and S. I. Klenin (1958), *J. Polymer Sci.*, **30**, 187; *Zh. Tekhn. Fiz.*, **28**, 1019 (English transl. *Soviet Phys. Tech. Phys.*, **3**, 949 (1959)).

Tsvetkov, V. N., and S. I. Klenin (1959), *Zh. Tekhn. Fiz.*, **29**, 1393 (English transl. *Soviet Phys. Tech. Phys.*, **4**, 1283 (1960)).

Tsvetkov, V. N., S. L. Magarik, N. N. Boitsova, and M. G. Okuneva (1961), *J. Polymer Sci.*, **54**, 635.

Uchida, T., Y. Kurita, and M. Kubo (1956), *J. Polymer Sci.*, **19**, 365.

Uda, K., and G. Meyerhoff (1961), *Makromol. Chem.*, **47**, 168.

Ukaji, T., and R. A. Bonham (1962), *J. Am. Chem. Soc.*, **84**, 3631.

Urnes, P., and P. Doty (1961), *Advan. Protein Chem.*, **16**, 401.

Urnes, P. J., K. Imahori, and P. Doty (1961), *Proc. Natl. Acad. Sci. U.S.*, **47**, 1635.

Vallee, B. L. (1955), *Advan. Protein Chem.*, **10**, 317.

Van Amerongen, G. J. (1951), *J. Polymer Sci.*, **6**, 471.

Van Holde, K. E., and R. L. Baldwin (1958), *J. Phys. Chem.*, **62**, 734.

Velick, S. F. (1953), *J. Biol. Chem.*, **203**, 563.

Velick, S. F. (1954), in *The Mechanism of Enzyme Action*, W. D. McElroy and B. Glass, eds., Johns Hopkins Univ. Press, Baltimore p. 491.

Velick, S. F., C. W. Parker, and H. N. Eisen (1960), *Proc. Natl. Acad. Sci. U.S.*, **46**, 1470.

Vinograd, J., and J. E. Hearst (1962), *Fortschr. Chem. Org. Naturstoffe*, **20**, 372–422.

Vinograd, J., and W. D. Hutchinson (1959), *Nature*, **187**, 216.

Vinograd, J., R. Bruner, R. Kent, and J. Weigle (1963), *Proc. Natl. Acad. Sci. U.S.*, **49**, 902.

Volkenstein, M. V. (1963), *Configurational Statistics of Polymer Chains*, Interscience, New York; (a) p. 74 (b) p. 121 (c) pp. 306–331.

Waack, R., A. Rembaum, J. D. Coombes, and M. Szwarc (1957), *J. Am. Chem. Soc.*, **79**, 2026.

Waals, J. H. van der, and J. J. Hermans (1950), *Rec. Trav. Chim.*, **69**, 949, 971.

Wada, A. (1960), *Mol. Phys.*, **3**, 409.

Wales, M., F. T. Adler, and K. E. Van Holde (1951), *J. Phys. Colloid Chem.*, **55**, 145.

Walker, E. E. (1952), *J. Appl. Chem.*, **2**, 470.

Wall, F. T., and J. Berkowitz (1957), *J. Chem. Phys.*, **26**, 114.

Wall, F. T., and J. J. Erpenbeck (1959), *J. Chem. Phys.*, **30**, 634.

Wall, F. T., and P. F. Grieger (1952), *J. Chem. Phys.*, **20**, 1200.

Wall, F. T., P. F. Grieger, J. R. Huizenga, and R. H. Doremus (1952), *J. Chem. Phys.*, **20**, 1206.

Wall, F. T., L. A. Hiller, Jr., and D. J. Wheeler (1954), *J. Chem. Phys.*, **22**, 1036.

Wall, F. T., S. Windwer, and P. J. Gans (1962), *J. Chem. Phys.*, **37**, 1461.

Walter, A. T. (1954), *J. Polymer Sci.*, **13**, 207.

Walters, C., H. Daoust, and H. Rinfret (1960), *Can. J. Chem.*, **38**, 1087

Wang, J. H. (1958), *J. Am. Chem. Soc.*, **80**, 3168.

Wang, J. H., A. Nakahara, and E. B. Fleischer (1958), *J. Am. Chem. Soc.*, **80**, 1109.

Warner, R. C. (1957), *Ann. N.Y. Acad. Sci.*, **69**, 314.

Watanabe, W. H., C. F. Ryan, P. C. Fleischer, Jr., and B. S. Garrett (1961), *J. Phys. Chem.*, **65**, 896.

Watson, H. C., and J. C. Kendrew (1961), *Nature*, **190**, 670.

Watson, J. D. (1963), *Science*, **140**, 17.

Watson, J. D., and F. H. C. Crick (1953), *Nature*, **171**, 737.

Waugh, D. F. (1958), *Discussions Faraday Soc.*, **25**, 186.

Waugh, D. F. (1961), *J. Phys. Chem.*, **65**, 1793.

Weber, F. N., Jr., D. W. Kupke, and J. W. Beams (1963), *Science*, **139**, 837.

Weber, G. (1952), *Biochem. J.*, **51**, 145, 155.

Weber, G. (1953), *Advan. Protein Chem.*, **8**, 416.

Weber, G. (1960), *Biochem. J.*, **75**, 335, 345.

Weber, R. E., and C. Tanford (1959), *J. Am. Chem. Soc.*, **81**, 3255.

Weimarn, P. von (1926), *Kolloid-Z.*, **40**, 120; **41**, 148.

Weissberg, S. G., R. Simha, and S. Rothman (1951), *J. Res. Natl. Bur. Std.*, **47**, 298.

Wenger, F. (1960a), *Makromol. Chem.*, **36**, 200.

Wenger, F. (1960b), *J. Am. Chem. Soc.*, **82**, 4281.

Westgren, A. (1914), *Z. Physik. Chem. (Leipzig)*, **89**, 63.

Westhead, E. W., Jr., and H. Morawetz (1958), *J. Am. Chem. Soc.*, **80**, 237.

Westrum, E. F., Jr., and J. P. McCullough (1963) in *Physics and Chemistry of the Organic Solid State*, Vol. 1, D. Fox, M. M. Labes, and A. Weissberger, eds., Interscience, New York, p. 106.

Wetlaufer, D. B., J. T. Edsall, and B. R. Hallingworth (1958), *J. Biol. Chem.*, **233**, 1421.

White, F. H., Jr. (1960), *J. Biol. Chem.*, **235**, 383.

Wilkins, M. H. F. (1963), *Science*, **140**, 941.

Williams, E. J., and J. F. Foster (1959), *J. Am. Chem. Soc.*, **81**, 865.

Williams, J. W., and W. M. Saunders (1954), *J. Phys. Chem.*, **58**, 854.

Williams, J. W., R. L. Baldwin, W. M. Saunders, and P. G. Squire (1952), *J. Am. Chem. Soc.*, **74**, 1542.

Williams, J. W., K. E. Van Holde, R. L. Baldwin, and H. Fujita (1958), *Chem. Rev.*, **58**, 715.

Williams, R. C., and R. L. Steere (1951), *J. Am. Chem. Soc.*, **73**, 2057.

Wilson, C. W., III (1963), *J. Polymer Sci.*, **A1**, 1305.

Wilson, I. B., and C. Quan (1958), *Arch. Biochem. Biophys.*, **73**, 131.

Wilson, S., G. H. Dixon, and A. C. Wardlaw (1962), *Biochim. Biophys. Acta*, **62**, 483.

Wood, W. W., W. Fickett, and J. G. Kirkwood (1952), *J. Chem. Phys.*, **20**, 561.

Woodbrey, J. C., and Q. A. Trementozzi (1964), paper presented at the Sept. 1964 meeting of the Am. Chemical Society; Polymer Preprints, **5**, 1071.

Yamakawa, H. (1958), *J. Phys. Soc. Japan*, **13**, 87.

Yanari, S., and F. A. Bovey (1960), *J. Biol. Chem.*, **235**, 2818.

Yanari, S. S., F. A. Bovey, and R. Lumry (1963), *Nature*, **200**, 242.

Yang, J. T. (1959), *J. Am. Chem. Soc.*, **81**, 3902.

Yang, J. T. (1961), *Tetrahedron*, **13**, 143.

Yang, J. T., and P. Doty (1957), *J. Am. Chem. Soc.*, **79**, 761.

Yang, J. T., and J. F. Foster (1954), *J. Am. Chem. Soc.*, **76**, 1588.

Yoshino, T., H. Kyogoku, J. Komiyama, and Y. Manabe (1963), *J. Chem. Phys.*, **38**, 1026.

Yoshida, T., S. Sakurai, T. Ukuda, and Y. Takagai (1962), *J. Am. Chem. Soc.*, **84**, 3590.

Yphantis, D. A. (1960), *Ann. N.Y. Acad. Sci.*, **88**, 586.

Zerner, B., and M. L. Bender (1964), *J. Am. Chem. Soc.*, **86**, 3669.

Zimm, B. H. (1946), *J. Chem. Phys.*, **14**, 164.

Zimm, B. H. (1948), *J. Chem. Phys.*, **16**, 1099.

Zimm, B. H. (1956), *J. Chem. Phys.*, **24**, 269.

Zimm, B. H. (1960), *J. Chem. Phys.*, **33**, 1349.

Zimm, B. H., and J. K. Bragg (1959), *J. Chem. Phys.*, **31**, 526.

Zimm, B. H., and S. A. Rice (1960), *Mol. Phys.*, **3**, 391.

Zimm, B. H., and W. H. Stockmayer (1949), *J. Chem. Phys.*, **17**, 1301.

Zimm, B. H., R. S. Stein, and P. Doty (1945), *Polymer Bull.*, **1**, 90.

Zimm, B. H., W. H. Stockmayer, and M. Fixman (1953), *J. Chem. Phys.*, **21**, 1716.

Zimmering, P. E., E. W. Westhead, Jr., and H. Morawetz (1957), *Biochim. Biophys. Acta.* **25**, 376.

Zwick, M. M. (1965), *J. Appl. Polymer Sci.*, **9**, 2393.

AUTHOR INDEX*

A

Abe, A., 240
Abitz, W., 76 (Herrmann)
Adler, F. T., 184 (Wales)
Akkerman, F., 333
d'Alagni, M., 89 (Liquori), 108 (Liquori), 393 (Liquori)
Albertsson, P. A., 82, 85, 86
Alberty, R. A., 396 (Rice)
Alexander, P., 333
Alexandrowicz, Z., 345, 348, 365
Alfrey, T., Jr., 24, 70, 74, 80, 84, 309, 335, 428
Alger, M. S. M., 416
Allegra, G., 108 (Natta), 110, 119
Allred, A. L., 62
Ambrose, E. J., 82, 133, 207, 208, 383
Ander, P., 344, 345
Anderson, E. W., 214 (Bovey), 215 (Bovey), 219 (Bovey)
Andress, K., 82
Anet, F. A. L., 7
Anfinsen, C. B., 156, 158 (Epstein, Potts), 399
Ansevin, A. T., 407
Anzuino, G., 89 (Liquori), 108 (Liquori), 393 (Liquori)
Apgar, J., 147 (Holley)
Archibald, W. J., 282
Arcus, C. L., 426, 436
Arends, C. B., 428, 429
Armstrong, S. H., 385 (Scatchard)
Asadourian, A., 413 (Blout)
Asakura, S., 401
Ashby, C. E., 165

Auer, R. L., 304, 306
Avery, O. T., 143

B

Badger, R. M., 71
Bailey, F. E., Jr., 394
Bailey, W. J., 240
Baker, C. H., 70
Baldwin, R. L., 182, 184 (Williams), 185, 187, 188, 280 (Williams)
Baldwin, R. R., 378, 379
Ballard, L. E., 67
Bamford, C. H., 82 (Ambrose), 133, 383 (Ambrose)
Banderet, A., 433
Barker, J. A., 47, 54
Barkin, S. M., 382
Barnes, B. A., 88 (Cohn)
Barron, E. S. G., 410
Bassi, I. W., 104 (Natta), 106 (Natta), 107 (Natta)
Bates, F. L., 378
Bauer, S. H., 71
Baumann, H., 126
Bawn, C. E. H., 62, 206, 309
Beaman, R. G., 79
Beams, J. W., 189 (Weber)
Bear, R. S., 379
Becker, R. R., 22
Beckmann, C. O., 379
Beers, R. F., Jr., 140, 147, 149
Beevers, R. B., 69 (Robinson)
Beijerinck, M. W., 85
Belford, G. G., 211 (Gutowsky), 219 (Gutowsky)

* Coauthors in references involving three or more persons are not named in the text, but they are cited in this index. For example, the entry "Abitz, W., 76 (Herrmann)" means that W. Abitz is one of the coauthors whose work is referred to on page 76 by the words "Hermann et al." The full citation may be found in the references at the end of the text (pages 441–467) under the name Herrmann.

Bell, R. P., 418
Bellemans, A., 66
Bellin, J. S., 376, 382, 436
Bello, H. R., 77
Bello, J., 77, 158
Bender, M. L., 388, 410, 423
Benesch, R., 391
Benesch, R. E., 391
Benoit, H., 111 (Holtzer), 219, 251, 254, 255, 259, 261, 262, 297
Berdick, M., 88
Beredjick, N., 179, 180, 239
Berg, P. W., 335 (Alfrey)
Berger, A., 21, 98 (Katchalski), 138 (Steinberg), 139 (Steinberg), 235 (Kurtz, Steinberg)
Berkowitz, J., 338
Bernal, J. D., 47, 48, 69, 267
Bernstein, H. J., 209 (Pople)
Berry, K. L., 6
Bersohn, R., 380
Bethune, J. L., 369 (Nichol)
Bevington, J. C., 21
Beychok, S., 235, 238
Bianchi, E., 308 (Rossi)
Bianchi, J. P., 19
Bianchi, U., 126, 127, 308 (Rossi)
Bier, M., 72, 361, 392 (Nord)
Binder, H., 82
Bird, G. R., 208
Birshtein, T. M., 110, 119
Bisschops, J., 76
Bjerrum, N., 339
Björnesjö, K. B., 88
Blake, C. C. F., 27
Blomquist, G., 16, 409
Bloom, S. M., 133 (Blout), 153
Blout, E. R., 133, 135 (Doty), 136, 137 (Doty, Karlson), 139, 153 (Bloom), 207 (Doty), 208, 231, 234–238, 356 (Doty), 413
Bluestone, S., 361
Boardman, F., 234 (Goodman)
Bodemheimer, E., 136 (Fasman), 138 (Fasman)
Bodo, F., 27
Boeder, P., 289
Boedtker, H., 147 (Doty), 205 (Doty), 392

Böhme, D., 70 (Delmas)
Bohak, Z., 82
Bohrer, J. J., 24 (Alfrey)
Boitsova, N. N., 296 (Tsvetkov)
Bon, W. F., 76 (Katz)
Bonham, R. A., 103
Bonner, R. U., 167
Bonner, W. D., Jr., 386
Booth, C., 62
Booth, F., 332
Bothner-By, A. A., 7
Bovey, F. A., 96, 97, 201, 212–216, 218, 219, 221 (Yanari)
Bowman, R. E., 47
Boyer, R. F., 69
Boyer-Kawenoki, F., 85
Bradbury, E. M., 137
Bradbury, J. H., 135 (Doty), 207 (Doty), 311 (Doty)
Bradley, D. F., 376
Brady, G. W., 266
Bragg, J. K., 150
Branson, H. R., 26 (Pauling), 132 (Pauling), 207 (Pauling)
Braun, D., 96
Brause, A. R., 137 (Goodman)
Brechbuhler, T., 298
Breinl, F., 404
Bresler, S. E., 154, 156, 194
Brey, W. S., Jr., 214 (Miller)
Briggs, G. E., 386
Brinton, C. C., Jr., 407 (Lauffer)
Brown, C. P., 47
Brown, G. L., 69 (Spencer), 147 (Spencer)
Brown, I., 47 (Barker)
Brown, R. K., 88 (Cohn)
Brown, W., 126
Brown, W. B., 70 (Baker)
Brownstein, S., 214
Bruice, T. C., 424
Bruner, R., 281 (Vinograd)
Bruschtein, F., 241
Bryan, W. P., 413 (Nielsen)
Buchdahl, R., 195
Buckley, C. E., III, 405
Bueche, A. M., 273, 359
Bueche, F., 116
Bull, H. B., 179
Bungenberg de Jong, H. G., 64, 84, 88

Bunn, C. W., 104, 106, 107
Bunville, L. G., 154 (Tanford)
Burgi, E., 30
Burleigh, P. H., 96 (Fordham)
Bushuk, W., 261
Butler, G. B., 214 (Miller)
Butler, J. A. V., 79
Buzzell, J. G., 154 (Tanford), 156 (Tanford)
Bywater, S., 214 (Brownstein)

C

Cairns, J., 30
Callard, R. W., 394 (Bailey)
Calvin, M., 413
Campbell, D. H., 406
Cann, J. R., 400
Cantoni, G. L., 205
Cantow, H. J., 277, 282
Carothers, W. H., 432
Carpenter, D. K., 72 (Newman), 77 (Newman), 126 (Flory), 127 (Flory), 170, 306, 392 (Newman)
Carroll, W. R., 400 (Koike)
Cartwright, T. E., 407 (Lauffer)
Carver, J. P., 234 (Blout), 236 (Blout)
Casassa, E. F., 172–174, 260, 402
Caspar, D. L. D., 407
Cebra, J. J., 405
Cerf, R., 294, 295
Cesari, M., 135 (Luzzati), 267 (Luzzati)
Chance, B., 386, 388
Chang, S. Y., 208, 392, 395
Changeux, J. P., 389 (Monod)
Chargaff, E., 140, 203, 396
Cheesman, D. F., 179
Chiang, R., 126 (Flory)
Chu, V. H., 340
Chujo, R., 218
Ciferri, A., 126 (Flory), 129
Claesson, S., 310
Cohen, C., 230, 234 (Simmons), 236 (Simmons), 237, 238 (Simmons)
Cohn, E. J., 73, 83, 84, 88
Cohn, M., 391
Cohn-Ginsberg, E., 308
Coiro, V. M., 89 (Liquori), 108 (Liquori), 393 (Liquori)

Coleman, B. D., 96, 416
Coleman, J., 396
Colin, 378
Colin-Naar, C., 66
Colvin, J. R., 400
Coombes, J. D., 18 (Waack), 234
Coops, J., 99
Čopič, M., 310
Copp, J. L., 52
Corbett, J. W., 275
Corey, R. B., 26, 132 (Pauling), 133–135, 144, 207 (Pauling)
Corradini, P., 93 (Natta), 95, 104 (Natta), 106 (Natta), 107, 108, 110 (Allegra), 119 (Allegra)
Cox, H. L., 54
Craig, L. C., 399, 400
Cramer, F., 380
Crammer, J. L., 200
Crawford, I. P., 400
Creek, W., 82 (Stanton)
Crescenzi, V., 127
Creswell, C. J., 62
Cretcher, L. H., 54
Crick, F. H. C., 27, 139, 140, 191
Crisp, D. J., 179
Crook, E. H., 328 (Strauss), 395 (Strauss)
Cullis, A. F., 27 (Perutz), 153
Cutler, M., 326 (Kimball)

D

Daniel, E., 365
Danusso, F., 93 (Natta), 96
Daoust, H., 70 (Walters)
Davern, C. I., 193
Davidson, N., 143
Davies, D. R., 27 (Kendrew), 153 (Kendrew)
Davies, J. T., 179, 180
Davison, P. F., 30
De, P. K., 154, 156 (Tanford)
Deal, W. C., 159
Deber, C. M., 137 (Goodman)
Debye, P., 116, 197, 246, 250, 252, 258 (Ewart), 273, 356, 359
Delmas, G., 70
De Loecker, W., 429
Derksen, J. C., 76, 83

Derouaux, G., 88 (Cohn)
Desmyter, A., 42
Desreux, V., 97 (Huggins)
Deuel, H., 418
De Voe, H., 143, 144
Dickerson, R. E., 27 (Kendrew), 153 (Kendrew)
Dietrich, H. V., 380
DiMarzio, E. A., 152
Dimbat, M., 165, 167 (Bonner)
Dintzis, H. M., 27 (Bodo)
Dixon, G. H., 159 (Wilson)
Djerassi, C., 226–228
Dobry, A., 64, 85
Döller, E., 220
Doi, R. H., 147, 194
Donnan, F. G., 341
Donovan, J. W., 202
Doolittle, A. K., 72, 80
Doremus, R. H., 370 (Wall)
Doty, P., 26, 111 (Holtzer), 135–138, 144, 145 (Schildkraut), 147, 151, 193 (Schildkraut, Sueoka), 197, 203, 205, 207, 231, 234 (Coombes, Holzwarth), 235 (Urnes), 237, 252 (Zimm), 256, 311, 330, 339, 348, 356, 362, 392, 395, 407
Douglass, D. C., 215 (Bovey)
Dove, W. F., 143
Downie, A. R., 137 (Bradbury), 138, 231
Drago, R. S., 75
Dubos, R. J., 221
Dürr, W., 409 (Freudenberg)
Dumpert, G., 378 (Freudenberg)
Dyke, D. E. L., 46

E

Eberson, L., 350
Edelhoch, H., 198, 219 (Steiner), 220, 297, 298, 397, 398
Edelman, G. M., 220
Edsall, J. T., 73, 83, 202 (Wetlaufer), 291 (Scheraga), 292, 398 (Edelhoch), 410
Ehrenpreis, S., 375
Eigen, M., 363
Einstein, A., 181, 246, 275, 299
Einstein, J. R., 399
Eirich, F. R., 363 (Rosen), 382 (Barkin, Frank)

Eisen, H. N., 406 (Velick)
Eisenberg, H., 84, 260, 310, 333, 346
Eisenbraun, E. J., 226 (Djerassi)
Eisner, J., 144 (Doty)
Eizner, Yu. E., 276, 307
Elias, H. G., 125, 127, 178
Eliassaf, J., 72 (Silberberg)
Ellenbogen, E., 399 (Oncley)
Elliott, A., 137 (Bradbury), 207, 208, 231 (Downie), 267, 383 (Ambrose)
Elliott, E., 82 (Ambrose), 133
Emery, A. H., Jr., 170
Ende, H. A., 127, 189, 191, 195
Englberger, F. M., 405
Epstein, B. N., 260 (Stockmayer)
Epstein, C. J., 158
Erickson, J. O., 154 (Neurath)
Ermolenko, J. N., 376
Erpenbeck, J. J., 124
Etter, O., 127
Evans, M. J., 49
Everett, D. H., 47, 52
Everett, G. A., 147 (Holley)
Ewart, R. H., 258
Eyring, H., 225

F

Fåhraeus, R., 181, 182
Fankuchen, I., 69, 267
Fanselow, J. R., 230
Farina, M., 97 (Natta)
Fasman, G. D., 133 (Blout), 136, 137 (Karlson), 138, 139, 153 (Bloom), 220, 235
Feitelson, J., 420
Felix, A. M., 136, 137 (Goodman)
Felsenfeld, G., 149, 205, 376
Ferry, G. V., 370
Ferry, J. D., 31, 76, 77, 84, 328, 356, 402
Fickett, W., 226 (Wood), 241 (Wood)
Fiess, H. A., 383
Filipovich, G., 212 (Bovey), 216 (Bovey), 218 (Bovey)
Finch, J. T., 407 (Franklin)
Finn, F., 158 (Hofmann)
Fischer, E., 385
Fishman, M. M., 375
Fitts, D. D., 222, 234

Fitzgerald, E. B., 360
Fixman, M., 130, 131, 260 (Stockmayer), 308
Flaschner, O., 52
Fleischer, E. B., 412 (Wang)
Fleischer, P. C., Jr., 89 (Watanabe)
Fleischman, J. B., 404
Flory, P. J., 2, 7, 14, 17, 56, 58, 64, 69, 71, 74, 80, 93, 111 (Hunt), 121, 125–128, 129 (Ciferri), 170, 172, 173, 305–307, 314, 326–328, 331, 334, 348, 409, 433, 434
Fock, W., 54
Förster, T., 219, 220
Folt, V. L., 207
Fordham, J. W. L., 96
Fordyce, D. F., 328 (Ferry), 356 (Ferry)
Foster, J. F., 154, 156, 201, 379
Fowler, R. H., 40, 47, 48
Fox, T. G, 95, 126, 176, 308, 314
Fraenkel-Conrat, H., 407
Frank, H. P., 382
Frank, H. S., 49
Franklin, R. E., 407
Frattali, V., 219 (Steiner), 220 (Steiner)
Fredericq, E., 399
Freeman, P. I., 66
Freer, S. T., 27 (Kraut), 28 (Kraut)
French, D., 378
Frenkel, S. Ya., 194 (Bresler)
Fresco, J. R., 147 (Doty), 205 (Doty)
Freudenberg, K., 16, 378, 409
Frey, K., 380 (Staudinger)
Frieden, C., 399
Frisch, H. L., 238, 269
Fujii, K., 96, 426, 429
Fujita, H., 130 (Okada), 184 (Williams), 187 (Williams), 283, 308 (Okada), 359, 361, 366
Fuller, W., 69 (Spencer), 147 (Spencer)
Fuoss, R. M., 74 (Alfrey), 87, 332, 335, 340, 360, 393, 416

G

Gaddy, J. O., Jr., 291 (Scheraga)
Gaetjens, E., 424, 429, 432
Gally, J. A., 220
Ganis, P., 110 (Allegra), 119 (Allegra)
Gans, P. J., 124 (Wall)

Gans, R., 285, 286
Gardner, C. S., 304, 306
Gardon, J. L., 178
Garrett, B. S., 89 (Watanabe), 95 (Fox), 96
Gaultier de Claubry, H., 378
Gavrilova, L. P., 30 (Kisselev)
Gaylord, N. G., 91
Gee, G., 61, 69, 70 (Baker), 80, 81
Geiduschek, E. P., 144, 145
Geller, L. E., 226 (Djerassi)
Germer, H., 207
Gerngross, O., 76
Gerrens, H., 70 (Schulz)
Gershfeld, N. L., 328, 395 (Strauss)
Geymer, D. O., 62, 64
Gibbs, J. H., 152
Gibson, Q. H., 391
Gierer, A., 407, 408
Giglio, E., 104 (de Santis), 108 (de Santis), 133 (de Santis)
Gilbert, G. A., 379
Gill, S. J., 370
Gill, T. J., III, 406, 407
Gillespie, J. M., 88 (Cohn)
Gitlin, D., 399 (Oncley)
Givol, D., 405 (Cebra)
Glavis, F. J., 429
Goates, J. R., 42, 45
Gobran, R. H., 392, 394, 395
Goldberg, A. I., 70 (Alfrey), 309 (Alfrey)
Goldberger, R. F., 158 (Epstein)
Goldfinger, G., 24
Goldstein, M., 254
Goldwasser, E., 396
Goode, W. E., 95 (Fox), 96 (Garrett)
Goodman, D. S., 383
Goodman, M., 136, 137, 203, 207, 232, 234, 240
Gordy, W., 71
Gotlib, Yu. Ya., 119 (Birshtein)
Graham, T., 283
Gratch, S., 95 (Fox), 96 (Garrett)
Gratzer, W. B., 234 (Holzwarth)
Green, D. M., 145 (Schildkraut), 193 (Schildkraut)
Greenstein, J. P., 154 (Neurath), 410
Gregor, H. P., 371

Grieger, P. F., 361 (Huizenga), 362
  (Huizenga), 370
Griffith, J. H., 76
Grimley, T. B., 132
Gross, H., 279
Gross, J., 234 (Blout), 236 (Blout)
Grün, F., 115, 295
Grunberg-Manago, M., 147
Guggenheim, E. A., 40, 341 (Donnan)
Guinier, A., 198
Gunner, K. V., 70 (Schulz)
Gurd, F. R. N., 88 (Cohn), 383, 399
  (Oncky)
Gutfreund, K., 402 (Ferry)
Guth, E., 299
Gutowsky, H. S., 209, 211, 219

H

Haas, W., 158 (Hofmann)
Haber, E., 156 (Anfinsen)
Haldane, J. B. S., 386
Hall, B. D., 193
Hall, C. E., 25, 26, 402
Hallingworth, B. R., 202 (Wetlaufer)
Hamilton, L. D., 140 (Langridge)
Hammer, C. F., 165 (Ashby)
Hanby, W. E., 82 (Ambrose), 133 (Bam-
  ford), 137 (Bradbury), 231 (Downie),
  383 (Ambrose)
Hanes, C. S., 378
Hanson, J., 401
Happey, F., 133 (Bamford)
Harfenist, E. J., 399
Harker, D., 158 (Bello)
Harrington, W. F., 138 (Steinberg), 139
  (Steinberg), 230, 235 (Steinberg)
Harris, F. E., 324, 330
Harrison, P. M., 399
Hart, K. R., 42 (Stavely)
Hart, R. G., 27 (Kendrew), 153 (Kendrew)
Hartmann, H., 296
Haselkorn, R., 147 (Doty), 205 (Doty)
Hauenstein, J. D., 200
Haurowitz, F., 390, 403, 404
Hayes, T. L., 26
Hearst, J. E., 141, 189, 191
Heckler, G. E., 328 (Ferry), 356 (Ferry)
Heine, S., 265

Heller, W., 222
Hellfritz, H., 70
Hellwege, K. H., 207 (Germer)
Helpern, A., 201 (Tinoco)
Hengstenberg, J., 395
Henley, D., 126 (Brown)
Henry, D. C., 358
Hermans, J., Jr., 156, 413
Hermans, J. J., 46, 189, 191, 195, 325, 333
  (Akkerman), 348, 359, 361
Herold, W., 436 (Kern)
Herrmann, K., 76
Hershey, A. D., 30
Herskovits, T. T., 143, 145
Hesbain, A. M., 425
Hess, E. L., 369 (Nichol)
Heymann, E., 72, 77
High, D. F., 27 (Kraut), 28 (Kraut)
Higuchi, T., 165
Higuchi, W. I., 165
Hijmans, J., 118
Hildebrand, J. H., 39, 41–43, 47, 51, 52
Hill, R. J., 400
Hill, T. L., 152
Hiller, L. A., Jr., 124 (Wall)
Hirami, M., 348
Hitch, S. F., 333
Hixon, R. M., 380 (Mikus)
Hoeve, C. A. J., 119, 129 (Ciferri)
Hoffman, C. J., 209
Hofmann, K., 158
Hofmann, T., 399
Holleman, T., 118
Holley, R. W., 147
Hollo, J., 379
Holmes, D. R., 104, 107
Holmes, K. C., 407 (Franklin)
Holtzer, A. M., 111, 135 (Doty), 207
  (Doty), 311 (Doty)
Holzwarth, G., 234
Hood, F. P., 214 (Bovey), 219 (Bovey)
Hooper, C. W., 140 (Langridge)
Horn, P., 251
Hotta, H., 180
Hotta, K., 401 (Oosawa)
Howard, G. J., 363
Howard, T. L., 436 (Arcus)
Howells, E. R., 107

Huang, H. T., 388
Hückel, E., 356, 357
Huggins, M. L., 7, 56, 60, 74, 97, 303
Hughes, W. L., Jr., 88, 396, 398 (Edelhoch)
Huizenga, J. R., 361, 362, 370
Hummel, J. P., 155
Hunt, M. L., 111, 121
Hutchinson, W. D., 400
Hutschnecker, K., 418 (Deuel)
Hvidt, A., 413, 414
Hyde, A. J., 254

I

Ifft, J. B., 190
Iimura, K., 206 (Takeda)
Imahori, K., 203, 235 (Urnes), 237 (Urnes)
Imai, K., 381
Imai, N., 336 (Oosawa), 401 (Oosawa)
Imamura, Y., 206 (Takeda)
Imanishi, A., 381, 382
Immergut, E. H., 5
Imoto, S., 96 (Fujii)
Inagaki, H., 348
Ingold, C. K., 422
Ise, N., 348
Isemura, T., 381, 382
Isenberg, I., 380
Isihara, A., 60, 116, 170, 173
Itano, H. A., 400
Ito, J., 400
Ito, K., 101
Ivin, K. J., 127
Iyengar, B. R. Y., 165
Izmailova, V. N., 230 (Pchelin)
Izumi, M., 344 (Nagasawa), 345 (Nagasawa), 348 (Nagasawa)

J

Jabloner, H., 98
Jackman, L. M., 209
Jacob, F., 389 (Monod)
Jacobson, A. L., 374
Jacobson, B., 363
Jaenicke, R., 296
Jarnette, E. de, 158 (Bello)
Jayme, G., 82
Jencks, W. P., 156
Jerrard, H. G., 288

Jessup, R. S., 62
Jirgensons, B., 237
Joesten, M. D., 75
Johnsen, U., 207 (Germer), 214
Johnston, J. P., 280
Jones, G., 77
Jordan, D. O., 363
Jost, K., 76

K

Kaarsemaker, S., 99
Kägi, J. H. R., 399
Kagawa, I., 336 (Oosawa), 343, 344 (Nagasawa), 345 (Nagasawa), 348 (Nagasawa), 360 (Nagasawa)
Kahnt, F. W., 88 (Cohn)
Kamath, P., 363 (Rosen)
Kanarek, L., 414
Kandanian, A. Y., 374, 375
Karlson, R. H., 137, 235
Karush, F., 404
Kasai, M., 401
Katchalski, E., 82, 98, 138 (Steinberg), 139 (Steinberg), 234 (Coombes), 235 (Kurtz, Steinberg), 398 (Edelhoch), 405 (Cebra)
Katchalsky, A., 72 (Silberberg), 200, 321, 323, 329, 335 (Fuoss), 354, 355, 365, 420
Katibnikov, M. S., 376
Katsuura, K., 343
Katz, J. J., 73
Katz, J. R., 72, 76, 83
Katz, S., 402 (Ferry)
Kauzmann, W., 49, 225, 230
Kedem, O., 365
Kegeles, G., 369 (Nichol)
Keller, J. B., 428
Kellock, M. G., 375
Kendrew, J. C., 27, 153
Kennedy, J. P., 216
Kent, R., 281 (Vinograd)
Kenyon, W. O., 381, 426 (Minsk)
Kern, R. J., 85, 86
Kern, W., 343, 436
Kezdy, F. J., 410
Kimball, G. E., 326
Kincaid, J. F., 95 (Fox), 96 (Garrett)
Kinsinger, J. B., 67, 176 (Fox), 308 (Fox)

Kirkwood, J. G., 83, 84, 224, 226 (Wood), 234, 241 (Wood), 273, 274, 279, 287, 304, 349
Kirste, R., 68 (Schulz), 266, 307
Kisselev, N. A., 30
Klapper, J. A., Jr., 400
Klaus, I., 438
Kleine, H. H., 98
Kleine, J., 98
Klenin, S. I., 276, 277, 282, 314
Klotz, I. M., 383
Klug, A., 407 (Franklin)
Knox, K., 380 (Reddy)
Koenig, D. F., 27 (Blake)
Kohlrausch, K. W. F., 102
Koike, M. L., 400
Konouck, R. C., 173 (McIntyre)
Kontos, E., 379
Kornberg, A., 146
Koshland, D. E., 385
Koshland, M. E., 405
Kotin, L., 374
Kotliar, A. M., 352, 371
Kowalsky, A., 212
Koyama, R., 170, 173, 174
Kraemer, E. O., 230
Krasny-Ergen, W., 332
Kratky, O., 120, 198, 263–266
Krause, I. M., 412
Krause, S., 261, 297
Kraut, J., 27, 28
Kreutz, W., 263, 264
Krigbaum, W. R., 62, 64, 68, 72 (Newman), 77 (Newman), 129, 130, 170, 175, 306, 314 (Mandelkern), 392 (Newman)
Krimm, S., 207 (Folt)
Kruyt, H. R., 64, 88
Kubo, M., 108 (Uchida)
Künzle, O., 321 (Katchalsky, Kuhn)
Küster, F. W., 378
Kuge, T., 379, 380 (Ono)
Kuhn, H., 273, 286, 293, 294, 301, 304
Kuhn, L. P., 47
Kuhn, W., 113, 115, 117, 119, 152, 222, 223, 229, 273, 286, 293–295, 301, 304, 321, 373, 409 (Freudenberg)
Kulkarni, R. K., 136, 241
Kupke, D. W., 189 (Weber), 399

Kurata, M., 117, 125, 130, 306, 307, 314
Kurita, Y., 108 (Uchida)
Kurtz, J., 235
Kurz, J. E., 68 (Krigbaum)

L

Laar, J. J. van, 39, 69
Ladenheim, H., 201, 414, 415, 418, 419, 422
Lamb, Sir H., 271
Lando, J. B., 214
Landsteiner, K., 403
Lane, D., 143, 144
Lang, F., 82
Langridge, R., 140
Laskowski, M., 400
Laskowski, M., Jr., 201, 202 (Donovan), 400, 402
Lasoski, S. W., Jr., 216
Lauffer, M. A., 407
Lazare, L., 428
Leach, S. J., 201 (Laskowski)
Ledwith, A., 206
Lee, H. T., 111 (Levi)
Lee, J., 420 (Overberger), 431 (Overberger)
Lefferdink, T. B., 82 (Stanton)
Legge, J. W., 199
Lehmann, H. L., 229
Lehrer, S. S., 220
Leigh, J. S., 391
Lemberg, R., 199
Leng, M., 261, 262
Leray, J., 295
Letsinger, R. L., 416, 420, 438
Leung, Y. P., 370
Lever, W. F., 88 (Cohn)
Levesque, C. L., 96 (Garrett)
Levi, D. W., 111
Levinthal, C., 30
Lewis, F. M., 24
Leyte, J. C., 371
Lifson, S., 103, 119, 126, 143, 152, 323, 326, 329, 335 (Fuoss), 339
Lindblow, C., 136 (Fasman), 138 (Fasman)
Lindemann, R., 76 (Gerngross)
Linderstrøm-Lang, K., 230, 399, 412, 413
Lindgren, F. T., 26 (Hayes)
Lindsey, R. V., Jr., 75
Lindskog, S., 383

Lineweaver, H., 418
Lipoldt, R. E., 219 (Steiner), 220 (Steiner)
Liquori, A. M., 89, 104 (de Santis), 108, 133 (de Santis), 393
Listowsky, I., 203, 234 (Goodman)
Litt, M., 147 (Doty), 205 (Doty)
Liu, C. H., 88 (Cohn)
Liu, K. J., 218
Llopis, J., 180
Lloyd, W. G., 428
Loebl, E. M., 201 (Ladenheim), 371 (Gregor), 414 (Ladenheim), 419 (Ladenheim), 422 (Ladenheim)
Lohmander, U., 310
Long, F. A., 81
Longsworth, L. G., 359
Lorenz, R., 39, 69
Lorenzi, G. P., 240
Loucheux, M. H., 433
Lovrien, R., 418
Low, B. W., 399
Lowe, W. G., 381
Lowy, J:, 401
Lozé, C. de, 133 (Blout), 153 (Bloom), 238 (Beychok), 413 (Blout)
Lütje, H., 276
Lumry, R., 221 (Yanari), 384
Lundberg, R. D., 394 (Bailey)
Luttinger, L. B., 371 (Gregor)
Luzzati, V., 135, 140, 263, 264, 267
Lyons, J. W., 374

M

McCarthy, M., 143 (Avery)
McCartney, J. M., 258 (Ewart)
McCormick, H. W., 282
McCullough, J. P., 55
McDevit, W. F., 82
McDowell, W. H., 381
McIntyre, D., 173
MacLeod, C. M., 143 (Avery)
McMahon, P. E., 211 (Gutowsky), 215, 219 (Gutowsky)
Madison, J. T., 147 (Holley)
Männer, E., 178
Magarik, S. L., 296 (Tsvetkov)
Magasanik, B., 147, 203
Magat, M., 69, 298
Mair, G. A., 27 (Blake)

Malcolm, B. R., 231 (Downie)
Malcolm, G. N., 51, 66
Malm, L. E., 283
Malmström, B. G., 383
Mandel, M., 371
Mandelkern, L., 184, 312, 314
Mann, H. F., 176 (Fox), 308 (Mann)
Manson, J. A., 215 (Bovey)
Mantica, E., 93 (Natta)
Marcker, K., 399
Marcus, R. A., 343, 354
Mark, H. F., 5 (Immegut), 24 (Alfrey), 91, 97 (Huggins), 306, 371 (Morawetz)
Mark, J. E., 126
Markowitz, H., 174
Marmur, J., 140, 143, 144, 145 (Schildkraut), 193 (Schildkraut, Sueoka)
Marquisee, M., 147 (Holley)
Marriott, J. V. R., 379
Marshall, C. A., 345, 361 (Mock), 362 (Mock)
Marvel, C. S., 238
Marvin, D. A., 140 (Langridge)
Marzolph, H., 165, 282
Mason, H. F., 308 (Cohn-Ginsberg)
Mason, S. G., 178
Masson, F., 135 (Luzzati), 140 (Luzzati), 264 (Luzzati), 267 (Luzzati)
Mathieson, A. R., 47
Mathot, V., 42, 66 (Prigogine)
Matsumoto, M., 96 (Fujii), 381, 426 (Fujii), 429 (Fujii)
Matsuzaki, K., 214 (Sobve), 241 (Sobue)
Matthews, Z. S., 406, 407
Matuura, R., 180
Maybury, R. H., 398 (Edelhoch)
Mayo, F. R., 24
Mazur, J., 355 (Katchalsky)
Mazzanti, G., 93 (Natta)
Melville, H. W., 21 (Bevington)
Merrill, S. H., 147 (Holley)
Merzlov, V. N., 230 (Pchelin)
Meselson, M., 189, 191, 193
Meyerhoff, G., 72, 276
Michaelis, L., 385
Mickey, J. W., 127
Middleton, W. J., 75
Mikkelsen, K., 413 (Nielsen)
Mikus, R. F., 380

Miller, I. R., 200
Miller, R. L., 74, 75, 96
Miller, W. L., 214
Minckler, L. S., Jr., 216 (Kennedy)
Minsk, L. M., 426
Mitchell, A. G., 51
Mittelman, D., 88 (Cohn)
Mizushima, S., 104
Mochel, J. M., 45 (Scatchard)
Mochizuki, T., 96 (Fujii)
Mock, R. A., 343, 345, 361, 362
Möller, W. J. H. M., 358
Moffitt, W., 233, 234
Mohan, G. R., 84, 346
Molyneux, P., 382
Mommaerts, W. F. H. M., 401
Monod, J., 389
Monton, R. F., 88 (Cohn)
Moore, D. H., 396 (Chargaff)
Moore, L. D., Jr., 260 (Stockmayer)
Moore, S., 156 (Smyth)
Moore, W. R., 72
Moraglio, G., 93 (Natta)
Morawetz, H., 74, 80, 88, 201 (Laden-
  heim), 208, 214, 241, 310, 326, 335 (Al-
  frey), 352, 371–374, 392, 394–396, 398,
  414 (Ladenheim), 416, 418, 419 (Laden-
  heim), 422, 424, 426, 427, 429, 431, 432,
  434, 435
Morino, Y., 104 (Mizushima)
Moscowitz, A., 197
Motomura, K., 180
Muirhead, H., 27 (Perutz), 153 (Cullis,
  Perutz), 391
Muller, R. H., 165
Murahashi, S., 108 (Tadokoro), 240 (Noza-
  kura)
Murchio, J. C., 26 (Hayes)
Myers, C. S., 76
Myrbäck, K., 385

N

Naar-Colin, C., 7
Nagai, E., 218 (Chujo)
Nagai, K., 110, 119
Nagasawa, M., 328, 329, 344, 345, 348, 360,
  366
Nair, P. M., 211

Nakahara, A., 412 (Wang)
Nakano, S., 241 (Sobue)
Natta, G., 93, 95–97, 104, 106–108
Naylor, R. E., 216
Néel, J., 382
Neely, W. B., 392, 395
Nelson, C. A., 155
Nemethy, G., 49, 50, 154, 156 (Scheraga)
Neuberger, A., 200
Neugebauer, T., 252
Neurath, H., 154
Neuschäffer, K., 82
Neveu, M. C., 423
Newman, M. S., 100
Newman, S., 72, 77, 111 (Hunt), 121
  (Hunt), 392
Nichol, L. W., 369
Nichols, A. V., 26 (Hayes)
Nichols, J. B., 181, 182
Nicolaieff, A., 140 (Luzzati), 263 (Luzzati),
  264 (Luzzati)
Nielsen, S. O., 413
Nielsen, L. E., 74, 75, 96
Niemann, C., 388
Nishijima, Y., 198, 284, 298
Nisonoff, A., 403
Nitta, I., 108 (Tadokoro)
Noda, I., 360
Noguchi, H., 396
Noll, L. A., 370
Nord, F. F., 72, 392
Norland, K. S., 137 (Karlson), 235 (Karl-
  son)
North, A. C. T., 27 (Blake, Perutz), 153
  (Cullis, Perutz)
Nozaki, Y., 154 (Tanford), 156
Nozakura, S., 240

O

Ochoa, S., 147 (Grunberg-Manago)
Öhman, J., 126 (Brown)
Ogston, A. G., 280
Oka, S., 118
Okada, R., 130, 308
O'Konski, C. T., 297
Okuneva, M. G., 296 (Tsvetkov)
Olson, J. A., 399
O'Mara, J. H., 173 (McIntyre)

Oncley, J. L., 399
O'Neill, J., 374
Ono, S., 379, 380
Onsager, L., 69
Ooi, T., 401 (Oosawa)
Oosawa, F., 336, 401
Oparin, A. T., 88
Oppenheim, I., 126
Oreskes, I., 431
Orofino, T. A., 127, 172, 173, 331, 348
Ortiz, P. J., 147 (Grunberg-Manago)
Orwill, R. A., 71 (Flory)
Osgan, M., 94, 239
Oster, G., 69, 198, 246, 251 (Horn), 284,
   298, 376, 382, 436, 437
Oster, G. K., 437
Osterheld, J. E., 328, 334
Ota, M., 360 (Noda)
Oth, A., 362
Ott, J. B., 42 (Goates), 45 (Goates)
Overbeek, J. T. G., 325, 358 (Möller)
Overberger, C. G., 98, 238, 420, 431
Ozeki, T., 218 (Chujo)

P

Painter, T. J., 436
Pal, M. K., 376
Paletta, B., 264 (Kratky)
Palmer, L. C., 238
Pals, D. T. F., 333 (Akkerman), 348
Pandit, U. K., 424
Parker, C. W., 406 (Velick)
Parry, D. A. D., 267
Pasquon, I., 95 (Natta)
Patterson, D., 70 (Delmas)
Pauling, L., 26, 132–136, 144, 207, 404
Pchelin, V. A., 230
Pechstein, H., 385
Pedersen, K. O., 364
Peebles, L. H., 195 (Buchdahl)
Penswick, J. R., 147 (Holley)
Pepe, F. A., 406
Peraldo, M., 97 (Natta), 108 (Natta)
Perrin, F., 181, 272, 285, 297, 298
Perutz, M. F., 27, 153, 390, 391
Peterlin, A., 125, 254, 265, 276, 289, 291,
   292, 294, 310, 311
Peterson, D. E., 88 (Smith)

Peterson, J. H., 6
Petit, B., 426, 429
Phibbs, M. K., 71
Phillips, D. C., 27 (Blake, Kendrew), 153
   (Kendrew)
Pinner, S. H., 74 (Alfrey), 84, 426
Pino, P., 240
Pitzer, K. S., 99, 100
Ploetz, T., 378 (Freudenberg)
Pople, J., 209
Porod, G., 120, 264–266
Porter, R. R. 404
Potts, J. T., Jr , 158
Pouyet, J., 333
Press, E. M., 404 (Fleischman)
Price, C. C., 94, 239
Price, F. P., 19 (Bianchi)
Price, J. A., 70 (Alfrey), 309 (Alfrey)
Priest, W. J., 426 (Minsk)
Prohaska, C. A., 7
Ptitsyn, O. B., 110, 118, 119, 129, 276, 307
Pullman, A., 144
Pullman, B., 144
Putnam, F. W., 154 (Neurath), 396, 415
Pyrkov, L. M., 194 (Bresler)

Q

Quan, C., 387

R

Rånby, B. G., 5 (Immergut), 76
Randall, A. A., 138
Rands, D. G., 154 (Tanford), 156 (Tan-
   ford), 200 (Tanford)
Rao, V. S. R., 379
Ray, N. H., 165
Rayleigh, Lord, 243, 245, 252
Reddy, J. M., 266 (Brady), 380
Reed, J., 400 (Koike)
Rees, E. D., 73
Reeves, R. E., 82
Reichmann, M. E., 400
Rein, H., 82
Reinhardt, L., 82
Reiss, C., 219
Reitenour, J. S., 165 (Ashby)
Reithel, F. J., 398
Rembaum, A., 18 (Waack)

Rempp, P., 308
Rice, R. V., 396
Rice, S. A., 152, 254, 324, 330, 356
Rich, A., 149, 205
Richards, F. M., 154, 158
Ries, H. E., Jr., 180
Rinfret, H., 70 (Walters)
Ripamonti, A., 104 (de Santis), 108 (de Santis), 133 (de Santis)
Rippie, E. G., 165 (Higuchi)
Riseman, J., 273, 274, 279, 287, 304
Roberts, J. D., 209, 211
Robin, M. R., 380
Robinson, C., 69
Robinson, D. R., 156
Robinson, E. A., 400
Roe, C. P., 258 (Ewart)
Roig, A., 117 (Kurata), 130 (Kurata), 306 (Kurata), 314 (Kurata)
Rolfe, R., 193
Rosen, B., 363
Rosenberg, A., 384
Rosenheck, K., 203
Ross, P. D., 345, 361
Rossi, C., 308
Rossmann, M. G., 27 (Perutz), 153 (Cullis, Perutz)
Rothman, S., 131 (Weissberg), 303 (Weissberg)
Roughton, F. J. W., 391
Rouvé, A., 432
Rowlinson, J. S., 46, 51, 66, 67, 70 (Baker)
Rownd, R., 140 (Marmur)
Rubin, I. D., 214
Rundle, R. E., 378, 379, 380 (Mikus)
Rutter, W. J., 159 (Deal)
Ryan, C. F., 89 (Watanabe)
Ryan, J. H., 254 (Hyde)

S

Sadek, H., 87, 394
Sadron, C., 308
Sage, H. J., 200, 398
St. Pierre, T., 420 (Overberger), 431 (Overberger)
Saito, S., 381, 382

Sakurai, S., 89 (Yoshida)
Salovey, R., 266
Samelson, H., 326 (Kimball)
Sammak, E., 373
Sand, H., 265
Sandeen, G., 205
Santis, P. de, 89 (Liquori), 104, 108, 133, 393 (Liquori)
Sarma, V. A., 27 (Blake)
Satoh, S., 218 (Chujo)
Saunders, P. R., 317
Saunders, W. M., 280 (Williams), 282
Savereide, T. J., 416, 420
Savino, M., 89 (Liquori), 108 (Liquori), 393 (Liquori)
Scatchard, G., 44, 45, 351, 385
Schachman, H. K., 182, 183
Schaefgen, J. R., 121, 317
Schauf, E., 378 (Freudenberg)
Scheinberg, I. H., 385 (Scatchard)
Schellman, C. G., 237
Schellman, J. A., 150, 230, 237
Scheraga, H. A., 49, 50, 111 (Hunt), 121 (Hunt), 154, 156, 201 (Laskowski), 202 (Donovan), 291, 294, 302, 312, 314 (Mandelkern), 402, 413
Schick, M. J., 180
Scherer, P. C., 111 (Levi)
Scherlag, B., 436 (Kern)
Schildkraut, C. L., 140 (Marmur), 143, 144 (Doty), 145, 152, 193
Schindewolf, U., 363
Schlichting, H., 271
Schmid, K., 88 (Cohn)
Schmier, I., 234, 237 (Blout)
Schmitt, E. E., 207 (Goodman), 232
Schmitt, G. J., 239
Schmitz, P. J., 265 (Heine)
Schneider, N. S., 339, 348
Schneider, W. G., 209 (Pople)
Schön, K. G., 165
Scholtan, W., 282, 382
Schubert, M., 376
Schuch, E., 395
Schuele, E. M., 176 (Fox), 308 (Mann)
Schuerch, C., 71, 238 (Frisch), 239
Schulz, G. V., 22, 68, 70, 126, 165, 307
Schumaker, V. N., 182

Schwartz, G., 137 (Goodman), 165 (Higuchi)
Schwarz, G., 363
Scott, R. L., 39, 41, 42, 47, 51, 69
Sébille, B., 382
Seeds, W. E., 140 (Langridge)
Sekora, A., 264 (Kratky), 266 (Kratky)
Sela, M., 21, 98 (Katchalski), 138 (Steinberg), 139 (Steinberg), 156 (Anfinsen), 235 (Steinberg), 397
Shafer, J. A., 431, 434, 435
Sharonov, Yu. A. S., 110, 118
Shashoua, V. E., 79
Sheppard, N., 211, 219
Shipman, J. J., 207 (Folt)
Shore, V. C., 27 (Kendrew), 153 (Kendrew)
Shulman, S., 402 (Ferry)
Shultz, A. R., 64, 80
Shumaker, V., 84
Shuttleworth, R., 72
Siddall, T. H., III, 7
Siegel, A., 374
Sieker, L. C., 27 (Kraut), 28 (Kraut)
Signer, R., 279
Silberberg, A., 72
Silman, H. I., 98 (Katchalski)
Simanouti, T., 104 (Mizushima)
Simha, R., 131 (Weissberg), 269, 299, 300, 302, 303 (Weissberg)
Simmons, N. S., 234, 236–238
Simpson, R. B., 230
Simpson, W. I., 201 (Tinoco)
Singer, S. J , 73, 200, 392 (Doty), 395 (Doty), 400, 406
Sjöberg, B., 228
Skeist, I., 24
Slater, E. C., 386
Slayter, H. S., 402
Slocombe, R. J., 85
Slykhouse, T. E., 361 (Mock), 362 (Mock)
Small, T. A., 70
Smets, G., 425, 426, 429, 431
Smith, F., 47 (Barker)
Smith, K. L., 88
Smith, P., 68 (Krigbaum)
Smithers, M. J., 158 (Hofmann)
Smoluchowski, M. v., 357

Smyth, D. G., 156
Snyder, L. C., 214 (Bovey), 219 (Bovey)
Sobue, H., 214, 241
Soda, A., 360 (Nagasawa)
Solms, J., 418 (Deuel)
Somcynsky, T., 70 (Delmas)
Song, W. R., 437
South, D. S., 436 (Arcus)
Spach, G., 135 (Luzzati), 267 (Luzzati)
Spanagel, E. W., 432
Spell, A., 95 (Fox), 96 (Garrett)
Spencer, M., 69, 147
Spencer, R. S., 69
Spiegelman, S., 147, 193, 194
Spirin, A. S., 30 (Kisselev)
Spitnik, P., 354, 355 (Katchalsky)
Spurlin, H. M., 5
Spurr, O. K., Jr., 126 (Flory), 127 (Flory)
Squire, P. G., 280 (Williams)
Stacey, K. A., 198, 247
Stahl, F. W., 189 (Meselson), 191 (Meselson)
Stahmann, M. A., 22, 396 (Rice)
Stamm, A. J., 82
Stanton, G. W., 82, 83
Starck, W., 380 (Staudinger)
Starkweather, H. W., 73
Staudinger, H., 7, 318, 380
Staveley, L. A. K., 42
Staverman, A. J., 177
Steere, R. L., 292
Stein, R. S., 252 (Zimm), 379
Stein, W. H., 156 (Smyth)
Steinberg, I. Z., 138, 139, 156 (Scheraga), 235
Steinbrunn, G., 409 (Freudenberg)
Steiner, L. A., 397
Steiner, R. F., 140, 147, 149, 198, 219, 220, 256, 297, 298, 330, 392 (Trementozzi), 401
Stevens, C. L., 149
Stockmayer, W. H., 24, 80, 117 (Kurata), 121, 125, 130 (Kurata, Zimm), 141, 172–174, 259, 260, 306, 308, 314 (Kurata)
Stokes, Sir G., 285
Stoll, M., 432
Stolten, H. J., 165
Stone, A. L., 376

Strandberg, B. E., 27 (Kendrew), 153 (Kendrew)
Strauss, U. P., 328, 344, 345, 360, 361, 370, 374, 395
Strazielle, C., 259, 261 (Leng)
Stribley, D., 70 (Baker)
Stross, F. H., 165, 167 (Bonner)
Stroupe, J. D., 95 (Fox), 96 (Garrett)
Stuart, H. A., 291, 292
Sturm, C. L., 96 (Fordham)
Sueoka, N., 193
Sullivan, R. J., 42 (Goates), 45 (Goates)
Surgenor, D. M., 88 (Cohn)
Sutton, J. R., 46
Svedberg, T., 181, 182
Svensson, H., 182
Swanson, M. A., 379
Swanson, S. A., 154 (Tanford), 156 (Tanford)
Swinton, F. L., 47
Szejtli, J., 379
Szent-Györgyi, A. G., 234 (Simmons), 236 (Simmons), 237, 238 (Simmons)
Szwarc, M., 18 (Waack), 238 (Frisch)

Thomas, R. M., 216 (Kennedy)
Thorbecke, G. J., 403
Thurmond, C. D., 311
Thynne, J. C. J., 47
Tiers, G. V. D., 96, 97, 210, 212–215, 216 (Bovey), 218 (Bovey)
Timasheff, S. N., 72, 264, 392 (Nord)
Tincher, W. C., 212, 215
Tinoco, I., Jr., 143, 144, 197, 201, 234
Tiselius, A., 363
Tobolsky, A. V., 118, 306
Tompa, H., 52, 70
Toyoshima, Y., 130 (Okada), 308 (Okada)
Trap, H. J. L., 348
Trappeniers, N., 66 (Prigogine)
Treloar, L. R. G., 62, 92
Trementozzi, Q. A., 215, 392
Trivisonno, C. F., 317
Tsuchihashi, S., 380 (Ono)
Tsvetkov, V. N., 276, 277, 282, 288, 294–296, 314
Tupman, W. I., 42 (Stavely)
Turner, D. T., 311
Turner, J. J., 211, 219

T

Tabata, Y., 214 (Sobue)
Tadokoro, H., 108
Taft, R., 283
Taggart, V. G., 156 (Tanford)
Takagai, Y., 89 (Yoshida)
Takahashi, A., 348 (Nagasawa)
Takeda, M., 206
Takenaka, H., 62
Takeuchi, S., 240 (Nozakura)
Tanaka, J., 203
Tanford, C., 154, 156, 200, 226, 352, 405 (Buckley)
Taylor, G. I., 300
Taylor, R. P., 21 (Bevington)
Taylor, W. J., 102, 118
Teale, F. W. J., 219, 220
Teorell, T., 88
Terayama, H., 87
Thacker, R., 46 (Dyke)
Theorell, H., 388
Thoma, J. A., 385

U

Uchida, T., 108
Uda, K., 72
Udy, D. C., 328 (Ferry), 356 (Ferry)
Ukaji, T., 103
Ukida, J., 96 (Fujii), 426 (Fujii), 429 (Fujii)
Ukuda, T., 89 (Yoshida)
Ullman, R., 218
Urnes, P. J., 197, 231, 235, 237
Uroma, E., 88 (Cohn)
Uryu, T., 214 (Sobue)
Utiyama, H., 307 (Kurata)

V

Vallee, B. L., 399
Van Amerongen, G. J., 76
Van Holde, K. E., 159 (Deal), 182, 184 (Wales, Williams), 185, 187, 188
Van Humbeeck, W., 431

Van Os, G. A. J., 358 (Möller)
Velick, S. F., 388, 406
Vincent, J. M., 135 (Luzzati), 267 (Luzzati)
Vinograd, J., 77, 189, 190 (Ifft), 191, 281, 400
Vithayathil, P. J., 158
Voet, D. H., 190 (Ifft)
Volkenstein, M. V., 102, 103, 109, 118
Von Hippel, P. H., 230
Vrij, A., 71 (Flory), 74

W

Waack, R., 18
Waals, J. H. van der, 42, 46
Wada, A., 152, 356
Wada, S., 136 (Doty), 137 (Doty), 356 (Doty)
Waddington, J. C., 418
Wagner, H., 392 (Doty), 395 (Doty)
Wajid, M. A., 62
Wales, M., 184
Walker, E. E., 70, 71
Wall, F. T., 124, 254 (Hyde), 338, 361 (Huizenga), 362 (Huizenga), 370
Walter, A. T., 76
Walters, C., 70
Wang, J. H., 275, 412
Ward, J. C., 69 (Robinson)
Wardlaw, A. C., 159 (Wilson)
Warner, R. C., 149
Watanabe, I., 104 (Mizushima)
Watanabe, M., 416 (Fuoss)
Watanabe, W. H., 89, 96 (Garrett)
Watson, H. C., 153
Watson, J. D., 27, 139, 140, 191
Waugh, D. F., 402
Weber, F. N., Jr., 189
Weber, G., 219, 221, 297, 298
Weber, R. E., 156
Weidinger, A., 72
Weigle, J., 281 (Vinograd)
Weill, G., 251
Weimarn, P. v., 82
Weissberg, S. G., 131, 184 (Mandelkern), 303
Wen, W. Y., 49

Wenger, F., 18, 22
Wenless, G., 216 (Kennedy)
Wessling, R. A., 67
Westgren, A., 181
Westhead, E. W., Jr., 422 (Zimmering), 426, 427, 431, 434
Westheimer, F. H., 349
Westrum, E. F., Jr., 55
Wetlaufer, D. B., 202, 234 (Simmons), 236–238 (Simmons)
Wheeler, D. J., 124 (Wall)
White, F. H., Jr., 156 (Anfinsen)
Whitney, P. L., 405 (Buckley)
Wierzchowski, K. L., 145 (Schildkraut), 193 (Schildkraut)
Wilkins, M. H. F., 69 (Spencer), 140, 147 (Spencer)
Will, G., 27 (Perutz), 153 (Perutz)
Williams, E. J., 201
Williams, J. W., 184, 187, 280, 282
Williams, L. C., 184 (Mandelkern)
Williams, R. C., 292, 407
Williamson, G. R., 62 (Booth)
Wilson, C. W., III, 216
Wilson, H. R., 140 (Langridge)
Wilson, I. B., 387
Wilson, S., 159
Windwer, S., 124 (Wall)
Wineman, P., 360 (Strauss)
Winslow, A. E., 88 (Smith)
Wippler, C., 261
Witz, J., 263 (Luzzati), 264 (Luzzati, Timasheff)
Wolf, M. K., 376
Wolman, Y., 158 (Hofmann)
Wood, S. E., 45 (Scatchard)
Wood, W. W., 226, 241
Woodbrey, J. C., 215
Woodside, D., 360 (Strauss)
Woody, R. W., 234 (Tinoco)
Worchheimer, N., 420 (Overberger), 431 (Overberger)
Worsfold, D. J., 214 (Brownstein)
Worthmann, W., 266
Wu, F. C., 328 (Ferry), 356 (Ferry)
Wunderlich, W., 68 (Schulz), 266
Wyckoff, H. W., 27 (Bodo)
Wynne-Jones, W. F. K., 51

Y

Yamada, A., 206 (Takeda)
Yamaguchi, S., 104 (Mizushima)
Yamakawa, H., 174, 307 (Kurata)
Yamaoka, K., 234 (Tinoco)
Yanaihara, N., 158 (Hofmann)
Yanari, S., 201, 221
Yang, J. T., 138, 151, 154, 156, 231, 233, 237, 311, 356 (Doty)
Yanofsky, C., 400
Yaroslavsky, S., 420 (Overberger), 431 (Overberger)
Yasumoto, T., 108 (Tadokoro)
Yates, E. T., 240
Yeadon, R. A., 70 (Baker)

Yoshida, T., 89
Young, D. M., 158 (Epstein, Potts)
Yphantis, D. A., 182, 188, 207 (Goodman)
Yuki, H., 240 (Nozakura)

Z

Zambelli, A., 95 (Natta)
Zamir, A., 147 (Holley)
Zerner, B., 388
Ziff, M., 396 (Chargaff)
Zimm, B. H., 19 (Bianchi), 22, 60, 121, 130, 150, 152, 169, 173, 252, 294, 304, 305, 311, 356
Zimmering, P. E., 422
Zwick, M. M., 381

SUBJECT INDEX

A

Acetylcholine esterase, 386–387, 431
Actin, 401–402, 408
Activity coefficients, 35
 ionic, 319, 327–328, 341–346, 348
Activity of solvent, 162–164
Agar-agar, 76, 85
Alcohol dehydrogenase, 399
Aldolase, 159
Alginic acid, 98, 315
Amylase, 385
Amylopectin, 378–379
Amylose, 98, 305, 378–380
Anisotropic solutions, phase equilibria, 68, 69
 x-ray scattering, 266–267
Anisotropy, of dielectric constant, 296
 of electrical conductance, 296, 363
 form, 292, 295
 intrinsic, 292, 295–296
Antibodies, chemical composition, 405
 reaction with antigens, 367–368, 403–407
 specific splitting of, 404
Antigen–antibody reaction, 367–368, 403–407
Antigens, synthetic polypeptide, 406–407
Association, of carboxyl groups in polymers, 208–209, 394–395
 of chain molecules with each other, 212, 367, 392–395
 of detergents with uncharged polymers, 382–383
 of dyes with polyions, 376–377, 436–437
 of dyes with uncharged polymers, 382, 436
 of hemoglobin with oxygen, 390–391, 411
 of iodine with polymers, 378–382
 of isotactic and syndiotactic poly-(methyl methacrylate), 89, 393
 methods of study, 368–369

 of L- and D-poly(benzyl glutamate), 89
 of polynucleotides, 149, 205–206
 rate of, 369
 of ribonuclease fragments, 158
 of small molecules and ions with uncharged polymers, 377–383

B

Benzidine rearrangement, 436
Bond angle, distortion of, 99, 107
Buoyant density, 189–193, 195

C

Carbonic anhydrase, 383
Carboxymethylamylose, 379
Carboxymethylcellulose, 339
Casein, 402
Cellulose, 5, 82, 83, 98, 110
Cellulose acetate, 11, 72, 81
Cellulose derivatives, 127
Cellulose nitrate, 5, 62, 72, 77, 80, 392
Cellulose tricaproate, 305
Cellulose tricaprylate, 65, 305
Chain molecules, branched, 9, 121–122, 311–312
 with catalytic activity, 437–439
 crystalline, 74–76, 93, 96, 104–108
 end-to-end displacement, 112–121
 excess entropy of solution, 55
 excluded volume, 122–132, 169–171, 308, 348
 expansion factor, 128–132, 306–307
 flexibility, 99–112, 117–120, 125–126, 329–330
 free draining, 273, 293, 304, 360–361
 impermeable, 273, 293, 304, 308, 334, 360
 internal viscosity, 31, 293–295
 interpenetration, 170–171, 437–438
 optically active, 107–108

partially permeable, 273–274, 293, 304, 359

pearl necklace model, 130–131, 274, 286–287

persistence length, 121, 141, 265

radius of gyration, 113, 115, 117, 121, 122, 130, 219, 252, 256–258

randomly coiled, 92, 112–132

reaction kinetics, 414–439

segment density distribution, 115–117, 129

statistical chain element, 120–121

statistically equivalent chain, 120

unperturbed dimensions, 124–127

worm-like, 120–121, 265

See also Light scattering; X-ray scattering; Diffusion, linear; Diffusion, rotary; Ultracentrifuge sedimentation; Fluorescence, depolarization of; Surface pressure; Viscosity of solutions; Conformations; Tacticity; Distribution of chain lengths.

Chain transfer, 14

Charge transfer complex, 377

Chondroitin sulfate-A, 375

Chymotrypsin, 220, 410–411

Chymotrypsinogen, 27–28, 79, 220

Coacervation, 64, 88

Cohesive energy density, 41, 66, 70–71, 80–81

Coils. See Chain molecules, randomly coiled.

Collagen, 230

Concentration, effective local, 373, 432–434

Conformation, of butane, 99–101.

of cellulose, 111

of dichloroethane, 104

helical, in amylose, 378–380

in DNA, 139–145, 203, 264, 318

in polynucleotides, 147, 149, 205–206

in polypeptides, 69, 133–139, 149–151, 207–208, 212, 229–238, 266, 267, 311

in proteins, 136, 153, 155, 207

in RNA, 69, 146–148, 264

in vinyl polymers, 104–108, 206, 219, 221, 238, 240

of isotactic polymers, 104, 108, 110–111, 119, 125, 206

of optically active polymers, 107–108

of pentane, 102

of polyethylene, 103, 109, 118

of polyoxymethylene, 108

of polyvinylidene chains, 108–110, 118

of propyl halides, 102–103

of small molecules, NMR studies, 7, 211 and IR spectra, 103–104

Conformational rigidity, and bifunctional catalysis, 430

and optical activity, 241

and specificity of molecular association, 368

Conformational transitions, potential energy barrier in, 101–102, 138, 218, 293

Conformations, of small molecules, from electron diffraction, 103

and optical activity, 226–227

Conformations, of syndiotactic polymers, 105, 108, 110–111, 119, 125, 206

tertiary, of proteins, 153–159

Consolute point, in polymer–solvent systems, 63–68, 70, 79

thermodynamic conditions for, 51–52

Consolute temperature, 52, 66

Copolymers, acrylamide–acrylyl histamine, 437–438

acrylamide–ε-acrylamidocaproic ester, 437–438

acrylic acid–acrylamide, 425

acrylic acid–acrylyl-p-nitrophenylanilide, 426

acrylic acid–ethyl ethacrylate, 431

acrylic acid–p-nitrophenyl methacrylate, 422–425

block, 11, 194, 261–262

distribution of composition, 23–24, 194–195

graft, 11

hexene–1-sulfur dioxide, 127

light scattering by, 260–262

maleic anhydride–acrylic acid, 316–317, 431

maleic anhydride–methylbenzyl vinyl ether, 239

maleic anhydride–methyl methacrylate, 433–434

maleic anhydride–methyl vinyl ether, 315–317, 328
maleic anhydride–styrene, 315–317, 328
methacrylic acid–dimethylaminoethyl methacrylate, 74
methacrylic acid–methacrylamide, 426
methacrylic acid–p-nitrophenyl methacrylate, 422, 424
methacrylic acid–vinylpyridine, 73, 80
methyl methacrylate–dimethylamino-ethyl methacrylate, 309
methyl methacrylate–methacrylic acid, 309, 392–393
optically active, 239–240
styrene with acid comonomers, 80, 208, 394–395
styrene–butadiene, 80, 218
vinyl alcohol–vinyl acetate, 72, 392
Copolypeptides, benzyl glutamate–benzyl aspartate, 235–236
benzyl glutamate–tyrosine, 235
glutamic acid–leucine, 138
glutamic acid–lysine, 407
glutamic acid–lysine–alanine, 406–407
glutamic acid–lysine–leucine, 180
glutamic acid–lysine–phenylalanine, 406–407
glutamic acid–tyrosine, 398
L-leucine–D-leucine, 231–232
proline–sarcosine, 139
Copper binding by polymeric acids, 471–474
Cotton effect, 228–229, 234–238, 377
Cryoscopy, 163–166, 168

D

Debye-Hückel shielding length, 323, 345, 356–357, 359–361
Debye-Hückel theory, 323, 336, 339, 351, 418
Denaturation. *See* Proteins; Deoxyribose nucleic acid.
Density gradient ultracentrifugation, 143, 182, 189–195
of copolymers, 194–195
microgel determination, 195
of nucleic acids, 191–194

resolution in, 190
and stereoregularity, 195
Deoxyribose nucleic acid, autoradiography, 29–30
denaturation, 143–145
density gradient ultracentrifugation, 191–194
double helix, 27, 140–145, 203, 264, 367
dye binding by, 376–377
electrical birefringence, 297
electron microscopy, 29–30
frictional coefficient, 369
hydrodynamic behavior, 141, 369
interaction with proteins, 88, 396–397
as polyelectrolyte, 317–318
replication, 146, 191–192
renaturation, 144–145
structure, 140
theory of helix-coil transition, 152
transforming activity, 143
UV spectrum, 203–205
Dextran, 281
Dialysis equilibrium, 341, 343, 345–346, 348, 368, 371
Dicarboxylic acids, 349
Dichroism. *See* Flow dichroism.
Diffusion, linear, 275–278, 283–284
in gels, 283
combined with intrinsic viscosity, 314
of polyelectrolyte solutions, 365–366
of small molecules in polymer solutions, 283–284
in Θ-solvents, 276–277
rotary, 284–298
from depolarization of fluorescence, 297–298, 376, 401
from flow birefringence, 287–291
combined with intrinsic viscosity, 313
from relaxation of orientation, 296–297
Distribution, of chain segment densities, 115–117, 129
of conformations, 219
of copolymer compositions, 23–24, 261
of counterions, 319, 322, 326, 334–340, 344
of molecular weights, generalized function, 21–23

normal, 13–16, 255, 257–258
Poisson, 17
of sedimentation coefficients, 279, 281
DNA. See Deoxyribose nucleic acid.
Donnan equilibrium, 341, 343, 345–346,
    348, 371
  microscopic, 326–327, 336, 339–340, 435
Donnan potential, 339, 435
Dyes. See Association; Reactivity;
    Photochemical reactions.

E

Ebulliometry, 163–166
Effective local concentration. See Con-
    centration, effective local.
Electrical birefringence, 296–297
Electron microscopy, of F-actin, 401
  of DNA, 30, 141
  of fibrinogen polymer, 402
  helix-coil transition studies, 30
  molecular weights from, 25–26
Electrophoresis, 319, 356–363, 369, 396–
    397
Enolase, 383
Entropy, of melting, 55
  of mixing, excess, 35, 39, 43–47, 55
    ideal, 38
Enzymes, association, with allosteric effec-
    tors, 388–390
  with coenzymes, 367, 387–388, 391
  with inhibitors, 367, 386–387, 396–398,
    400–401
    with ions, 367, 383
    with substrates, 367, 385–387, 389
  denaturation, 154–155
  renaturation, 156, 158–159
Equilibrium ultracentrifugation, 6, 181–
    195
  of associating polymers, 368
  in density gradient, 143, 182, 189–195
  optical methods, 182–183
  with polydisperse polymer solutions,
    185–188
  time required, 188–189
  with two-component systems, 183–185
Excimers, 221
Excluded volume, of chain molecules, 169–
    171

of polyions, 348
of rigid particles, 168–169
Expansion factor, Flory-Fox theory, 127–
    129
  Kurata-Stockmayer theory, 130–131
  in polyelectrolyte solutions, 320–330

F

Ferritin, 399, 408
Fibrinogen, 401–402
Fick's law, 275, 284
Flory-Huggins, interaction parameter, 60–
    62
  theory, 56–59, 61, 179
Flow birefringence, 287–296, 401
Flow dichroism, 208, 378
Fluorescence, depolarization, 221, 297–298,
    376, 401
  and molecular association, 376, 382
  quenching, 376, 406
  spectroscopy, 219–221
Free energy, elastic, 128
  electrostatic, 320–324, 349–352, 420–421
  of mixing, 35–36, 44–47, 50, 59–60, 70–
    71, 127–129
Frictional coefficient, rotary, 285–286
  See also Diffusion, rotary.
Frictional coefficient, translational, 270–
    284
    of association complexes, 368–369
    of chain molecules, 273–275
    of DNA, 369
    of ellipsoids, 271–273
    of polyions, 366
    of rod-like particles, 273
    of spheres, 271
    See also Diffusion, linear.
Fugacity, 34

G

Gelatin, 76–77, 85, 219, 230, 283, 392
Gelation, reversible, 76–77, 367, 393
  effect on diffusion, 283
  effect on optical activity, 230
Glass transition, 70
Glutamic dehydrogenase, 399
Gutta percha, 76

H

Haptens, 403–404, 406
Heat capacity, partial molar, 50–51
Heat of melting, 54, 74, 75
Heat of mixing, Prigogine theory, 66–67, 71
  van Laar theory, 39, 59, 66, 69, 70
Helical conformations. *See* Conformations, helical.
Helix-coil transitions, of DNA, 30, 369
  effect on counterion binding, 374
  effect on titration curve, 355–356
  electron microscopic study, 30
  intermolecular analog, 401
  and intrinsic viscosity, 311
  and isotopic exchange, 412–414
  optical activity study, 230–234
  of polynucleotides, 26, 205–206
  of polypeptides, 26, 135–138, 203, 207, 212, 220, 230–234, 374
  of RNA, 147–149
  spectroscopic study, 203, 205–207, 212, 220
  theory of, 149–152
  in vinyl polymers, 218–219
Helix–helix transition, 138–139, 311, 374
Hemoglobin, 27, 153, 179, 181, 199, 238, 367, 390–391, 397–400, 411
Henry's law, 161, 275
Hexene–1-polysulfone, 127
Huggins constant, 303, 309
Hyaluronic acid, 375
Hydrocarbons, as polymer solvents, 70–71
  thermodynamics of mixing, 46, 71
  vapor pressure, 3
Hydrodynamic shielding length, 274, 359–361
Hydrodynamically equivalent ellipsoid, 269, 313
Hydrodynamically equivalent sphere, 269, 273, 287, 314
Hydrogen bonding, with aromatic nuclei, 62
  of carboxyl groups, 208–209
  in crystalline polymers, 75
  and excess functions, 47
  heat of, 75
  and the α-helix, 133, 135
  intramolecular, in chain polymers, 394–395
  in polymer association, 88, 392, 394
  in polypeptide solutions, 136–137, 212
  and the tertiary protein structure, 156
  in water, 48–49
Hydrolysis, of amides, 425–426
  of esters, 416–420, 422–431
  of proteins, 201–202, 436
Hydrophobic bond, 49, 138, 154, 156, 328, 392, 408

I

Insulin, 157–159, 179, 202, 219, 398–399, 413
Intrinsic viscosity, of branched chains, 311–312
  of chain molecules, 172–173, 304–314
  of charged spheres, 332
  combined with diffusion coefficient, 312–314
  combined with rotary diffusion coefficient, 294, 313
  combined with sedimentation coefficient, 312–314
  of ellipsoids, 301, 302
  of molecular aggregates, 368–369
  of polyelectrolytes, 334
  of polypeptides, 135, 311
  rate of shear dependence, 301–302, 304, 310–311
  and the second virial coefficient, 172
  of spheres, 299–302
Ion pairs, 319, 329, 339–340, 361
Ionization equilibria, of chain molecules, 350, 352–356
  of dibasic acids, 349
  and helix-coil transitions, 355–356
  neighboring group effects, 354–355
  of spherical polyions, 350–351
Isoionic dilution, 333–334
Isotactic poly(acrylic acid), 83, 329
Isotactic poly(1-butene), 68, 106
Isotactic poly(p-fluorostyrene), 104
Isotactic poly(p-iodostyrene), 96, 266
Isotatic polymers, 10, 76, 93, 194–196, 119, 125

Isotactic poly(3-methyl-1-butene), 107
Isotactic poly(4-methyl-1-hexene), 107, 240
Isotactic poly(methyl methacrylate), 68, 69, 108, 180–181, 213–214, 266, 296, 393
Isotactic poly(3-methyl-1-pentene), 107
Isotactic poly(o-methylstyrene), 107
Isotactic poly(1-pentene), 106
Isotactic polypropylene, 67, 106, 107, 215
Isotactic poly(propylene oxide), 94, 239
Isotactic polystyrene, 75, 94, 96, 104, 106–107, 195, 206, 214, 221, 296
Isotactic poly(vinyl acetate), 96
Isotactic poly(vinyl formate), 96
Isotactic poly(vinyl methyl ether), 106
Isotopic exchange, 412–414

L

Lactoglobulin, 413
Light scattering, by anisotropic particles, 245–246, 251
  from associating polymers, 368–369, 395, 401
  and chain branching, 254
  and chain flexibility, 254
  destructive interference in, 198, 249–252
  dissymmetry of, 256–258
  by DNA solutions, 141
  by gases, 243–246
  molecular weights from, 198, 245, 248, 253, 258–261
  and polydispersity of solute, 254
  from polyelectrolyte solutions, 260, 229–230, 348
  by polypeptide solutions, 135
  radius of gyration from, 249–257, 261–262
  by solutes with variable composition, 260–262
  from solutions in mixed solvents, 258–260
  by solutions of small molecules, 246–249
  by solvents, 247
  Zimm plots, 253–255, 257
Lignin, 33
Lysozyme, 27, 397

M

Melting, entropy of, 55, 74
  heat of, 54, 74, 75

Melting point, 54, 74, 75
  of DNA, 143–145
  of gels, 76
Metachromatic effect, 375–376
Methylcellulose, 72, 77, 392
Microgel, determination of, 195
  solutions of, 79
Microstructure of vinyl polymers, determination of, 215–216
Mixing, excess entropy of, 35, 43–47, 49–51, 67, 70–71
  excess volume of, 42, 46, 49, 50, 67, 71
  heat of, 35, 39–47, 49–50, 66–67, 69, 71
  of hydrocarbons, 46, 71
  ideal entropy of, 38
Molecular weight, determination, by the Archibald method, 282–283
  by autoradiography, 29–30
  by ebullioscopy, 3, 163–166
  by electron microscopy, 25–26
  by equilibrium ultracentrifugation, 183–188
  by freezing point depression, 3, 163–166
  of insoluble polymers, 4–6
  from intrinsic viscosity, 303, 305, 306
  by light scattering, 6, 245–249, 253, 258–261
  by osmometry, 7, 164, 166–168, 175–178
  from sedimentation velocity, 278, 282, 314
  by x-ray scattering, 262–263
  distribution, 9, 12–23, 25–26, 185–187, 254, 395
  number average, 19, 163, 188, 255, 395
  weight average, 19, 80, 187, 188, 249, 254–255, 395
  z-average, 20, 80, 188
Myoglobin, 27, 235, 238, 411
Myosin, 237, 410

N

Nuclear magnetic relaxation, 391
Nuclear magnetic resonance. *See* Spectra, NMR.
Nucleophilic catalysis, 416–417, 419–420

Nucleophilic displacement, 415–417, 419–420

Nylon. *See* Polyamides.

O

Optical activity, change on gelatin gelation, 230
  change on protein denaturation, 230, 154–155
  dispersion, 227–229, 233–238
  of dyes bound to helical chains, 376, 377
  of helical chains, 233–234
  and molecular conformation, 197
  of polyelectrolytes, 241–243
  of polyethers, 239–240
  of polypeptides, 230–237
  of proteins, 154–155, 230–231, 237–238
  of vinyl polymers, 238–243
Osmotic pressure, 164–175
  apparent, 175–177
  of associating polymers, 368, 395
  of polyelectrolyte solutions, 341, 346–348
Ovalbumin, 88, 181, 230, 358, 403, 410

P

Pectinic acid. *See* Polygalacturonic acid.
Pepsin, 400
Persistence length, 121, 141, 265
Phase, definition, 77–78
Phase equilibria, binary systems, of small molecules, 51–54
  polyelectrolyte–salt–water, 84–85
  polymer–solvent, 62–69, 79, 82
  solutions of rod-like polymers, 68–69
  solvent with polydisperse polymer, 79–80
  solvent with two polymers, 85–89
Photochemical reactions, 418–419, 436–437
Poly(*O*-acetylhydroxy-L-proline), 139
Polyacrylamide, 72, 438
Poly(acrylic acid), 65, 73, 83, 88, 305, 315–316, 323, 332, 334, 343, 348, 353, 361–362, 370–371, 375, 394, 396–398, 439
Poly(acrylonitrile), 70, 76, 82, 215, 282, 305

Poly(*N*-acrylyl-L-asparagine), 242–243
Polyamides, 31, 73, 75, 98, 317
Poly(β-benzyl-L-aspartate), 137, 235–236
Poly(γ-benzyl-L-glutamate), 69, 89, 133, 135, 137, 138, 151, 235–236, 267, 311, 411
Polybutadiene, 62, 95, 305
Poly(1-butene), 68, 106
Poly(*n*-butyl methacrylate), 305
Poly(*p-tert*-butylphenyl methacrylate), 277
Poly(*p*-carboxyphenyl acrylate), 427–428
Poly(*p*-chloromethylstyrene), 416
Poly(*p*-chlorostyrene), 85–86
Polycondensation, 13, 98
Polydibasic acids, 317
Poly(3,5-dibromotyrosine), 266
Poly(*N,N*-dimethylacrylamide), 438
Polydimethylsiloxane, 65, 126–127, 305
Polydispersity. *See* Distribution of molecular weights.
Polyelectrolyte solutions, binding of bola-form ions, 375
  chelate formation, 371–374
  conductance, 361–363
  counterion distribution, 319, 322, 326, 334–340, 344
  counterion site-binding, 339–340, 345–346, 361–363, 367, 369–377
  electrostatic free energy, 320–324, 349–352, 420–421
  electrostatic potential, 318, 325–326, 335–336, 434–435
  exchange of bound counterions, 370
  ionic activity coefficients, 319, 327, 328, 341–346, 348
  ionic strength, 318, 328
  isoionic dilution, 333–334
  orientation, in electrical field, 296, 363
    by shear gradient, 363
  reactions of two small ions in, 434–437
  See also Osmotic pressure; Ultracentrifuge sedimentation; Diffusion; Electrophoresis; Light scattering; Donnan equilibrium; Polyions.
Polyelectrolytes, optically active, 241–243
  solubility, 83–84
  spectrophotometric titration, 200–201

surface pressure, 180
titration, 350–356
turbidometric titration, 87
Polyesters, 98
Poly(ethyl methacrylate), 305
Polyethylene, 11, 65, 75–76, 118, 126
Poly(ethylene imine), 316–317, 355
Poly(ethylene oxide), 88, 305, 394
Poly(p-fluorostyrene), 104
Polygalacturonic acid, 315, 347–348
Polyglucuronic acid, 98
Poly(α-L-glutamic acid), 136–137, 355–356, 375–376, 398, 407, 413
Poly(δ-hydroxy-α-L-aminovaleric acid), 136
Poly(hydroxy-L-proline), 139
Poly(p-iodostyrene), 96, 266
Polyions, expansion, 320–334
    reactions, with ions, 417–422
    with uncharged molecules, 414–417
Polyisobutene, 62, 65, 66, 70, 108, 119, 172, 305
Poly(isopropyl acrylate), 96
Poly(L-leucine), 133
Poly(L-lysine), 396–397, 407
Poly(L-methyl methacrylate), 241
Polymer degradation, 16
Polymerization, of N-carboxy-α-amino acid anhydrides, 18, 21–22, 98
    free radical, 14–17
    ionic, 18, 21–22, 98
Poly(metaphosphoric acid), 305, 316, 360, 362–363
Polymethacrylamide, 426
Poly(methacrylic acid), 84, 87, 88, 214, 305, 315, 316, 352–354, 356, 371–372, 374–376, 415, 417–418, 430
Poly(methacrylic anhydride), 214
Polymethacrylonitrile, 65, 214, 305
Poly(N-methacrylyl-L-glutamic acid), 241–243
Poly(ε-methacrylyl-L-lysine), 373
Poly(L-methionine), 135
Poly(methyl acrylate), 429
Poly(3-methyl-1-butene), 107, 216
Poly(S-methyl-L-cysteine), 135
Poly(γ-methyl-L-glutamate), 133, 203–204, 207, 232–233
Poly(4-methyl-1-hexene), 107

Poly(methyl methacrylate), 65, 68, 86, 89, 95, 108, 126, 172, 180–181, 213–214, 265–266, 277, 296, 305, 308, 393
Poly(3-methyl-1-pentene), 107
Poly(α-methylstyrene), 214, 305
Poly(β-p-nitrobenzyl-L-aspartate), 137
Polyoxymethylene, 108
Poly(1-pentene), 106
Polypeptides, anisotropic solutions, 69
    antigenic, 406–407
    conformations, 132–139, 203–204, 207–208, 220, 311
    electron microscopy, 26
    as enzyme inhibitors, 397–398
    formation, 18, 21–22
    isotopic exchange in, 413
    solubility, 75
    spectra, fluorescence, 220
      IR, 207–208
      NMR, 212
      UV, 203–204
    stereoisomerism, 98
    relation to protein structure, 153
    theory of helix-coil transition, 149–151
Polyphosphates, 305, 360, 362–363
Poly(L-proline), 138–139, 235–236, 238
Polypropylene, 67, 95, 106–108, 215
Poly(propylene oxide), 94, 239
Polyribonucleotides, 26, 147–149, 205
Poly(L-serine), 82
Polysoaps, 317, 328
Polystyrene, 62, 65, 67, 69, 70, 75, 85, 94, 96, 104, 106–107, 126–127, 172, 191, 195, 206, 214, 216–217, 221, 277, 282, 295–296, 305, 308, 392
Poly(styrene sulfonic acid), 316, 436
Poly(L-tryptophan), 234
Poly(L-tyrosine), 220, 234–235
Poly(L-valine), 133
Poly(vinyl acetal), 426–427
Poly(vinyl acetate), 96, 172, 305, 382, 426–427, 429
Poly(vinyl alcohol), 77, 96, 212, 215, 380–382, 426
Poly(vinyl amine), 88, 316–317, 355
Poly(vinyl bromide), 215, 266
Poly(vinyl chloride), 76, 86, 95–96, 207, 214–215, 367, 392, 395

Poly(vinyl fluoride), 215
Poly(vinyl formal), 382
Poly(vinyl formate), 96
Poly(4(5)vinyl imidazole), 420, 431, 438
Poly(vinyl methyl ether), 106
Poly(α-vinyl naphthalene), 377
Poly(vinyl pyridine), 73, 83, 316–317, 377
    414–417, 419–422, 430
Poly(N-vinyl pyrrolidone), 284, 381–
    382
Poly(vinyl sulfonic acid), 84, 85, 316, 340,
    436
Poly(vinylidene chloride), 76
Poly(vinylidene fluoride), 216
Prigogine theory of solutions, 66, 71
Proteins, association, with chain molecules,
    395–398
    with each other, 367, 398–408
    with small molecules and ions, 383–
      391
    crystalline, 4, 26–28
    denaturation, 154–156, 200–201, 212,
      219–220, 317, 410, 413
    depolarization of fluorescence, 298
    electrical birefringence, 297
    electron microscopy, 25–26
    flow birefringence, 292
    fluorescence spectra, 219–220
    fractionation, 84, 87–88
    helical conformations in, 136, 153, 155
    hydrolysis, 201–202, 436
    ionization, 200, 317, 351–352
    isotopic exchange, 412–414
    light scattering, 320
    optical activity, 154–155, 230–231, 237–
      238
    polymerization, 401–408
    reactivity, 410–412, 415
    renaturation, 156, 158–159
    solubility, 73, 79
    spectra, fluorescence, 219–220
      IR, 207
      NMR, 212
      UV, 200–202
    surface pressure, 179
    ultracentrifuge sedimentation, 364–365,
      388
    x-ray scattering from solutions, 263–264
Pseudoasymmetry, 94, 238

Q

Quasi-chemical equilibrium, 40
Quaternization, 415–416, 419–422

R

Raoult's law, 37, 161–162, 167
Random coils. *See* Chain molecules, ran-
    domly coiled.
Reactivity, bifunctional catalysis, 430–
    432
    of chain molecules, statistics, 427–429
    of chain molecules with each other, 437–
      439
    of chymotrypsin, 410–411
    of dyes, 436–437
    of hemoglobin with oxygen, 411–412
    of ions in polyelectrolyte solutions, 434–
      437
    neighboring group effects, 422–427, 430
    non-neighboring group effects, 432–434
    of polyions, 414–422
    of thiol groups in proteins, 410
Relaxation of orientation, 296–297
Renaturation, of DNA, 144–145
    of proteins, 156, 158–159
Ribonuclease, 155–158, 200, 396, 413
Ribose nucleic acid, 69, 145–148, 193–194,
    264, 396, 407
Rod-like particles, frictional coefficient,
    273
    light scattering, 255–258
    phase separation, 68–69
    from polymerized proteins, 401–402
      407–408
    polypeptide behavior as, 135
    rotational diffusion, 286, 291
Rod-like polyions, 317, 335–337
Rotatory dispersion, 227–229, 233–238
Rubber, crosslinked, 33, 55, 69
    Hevea, 61, 265
Rubber elasticity, 91, 128

S

Salting-out, 81, 84
Self-diffusion, 275
Serum albumin, 87–88, 156, 220, 292, 330,
    358–359, 385, 396–398, 400, 406
Silk fibroin, 82

Solubility, in "active" solvents, 71–72
  in aqueous salts, 81–84
  of crystalline polymers, 74–76
  of crystalline solids, 54
  Hildebrand parameter, 41, 47, 69–70, 80
  of polyamides, 75
  of polydisperse polymers, 79–80
  of proteins, 73, 79, 83–84
Solutions, anisotropic, 68–69
  ideal, 37, 43
  metastable, 76
  Prigogine theory, 66–67, 71
  regular, 43
  of very large particles, 77–79
  in water, 47–51
Solvents, "active," 71, 72
  hydrogen-bonding, 71, 75
  light scattering by, 247
  mixed, 80–81, 258–260
  See also. Theta solvents.
Spectra, fluorescence, 219–221
  infrared, 199, 206–209, 426
  NMR, 7, 200, 209–219
  ultraviolet, 199–205, 372, 374, 382
  visible, 199, 373, 379–382
Spectrophotometric titration, 200–201
Stereoregularity. See Conformation; Isotactic polymers; Syndiotactic polymers; Tacticity.
Surface pressure, 178–181
Suspensions, 78
Syndiotactic poly(acrylic acid), 329
Syndiotactic 1,2-polybutadiene, 95
Syndiotactic poly(isopropyl acrylate), 96
Syndiotactic polymers, 10, 95, 105, 108, 119
Syndiotactic poly(methyl methacrylate), 68, 69, 95, 108, 180–181, 213–214, 266, 393
Syndiotactic polypropylene, 108, 215
Syndiotactic poly(vinyl chloride), 95–96

T

Tacticity, of chain molecules, 10, 93–97
  characterization, by complexation with iodine, 381
    by density gradient ultracentrifugation, 195

  by flow birefringence, 295–296
  by fluorescence spectra, 221
  by IR spectroscopy, 207
  by NMR spectroscopy, 213–215
  by optical activity, 239–240
  by the parameters Θ and Ψ, 67–68
  by reaction kinetics, 424–425, 429
  by surface pressure, 180–181
  by x-ray scattering from solutions, 266
Teflon, 5, 33
Theta (Θ) point, 64–68
Theta (Θ) solvents, ambiguity of definition, 126–127
  definition, 124–125
  diffusion in, 276–277
  dimensions of chain molecules in, 127, 305
  equilibrium ultracentrifugation in, 182
  excluded volume in neighborhood of, 171–172
  frictional coefficient in, 273
  intrinsic viscosity in, 305–307, 309
  reactivity in, 438
  ultracentrifuge sedimentation in, 279, 282
Thrombin, 402
Titration. See Polyelectrolytes; Proteins; Spectrophotometric titration.
Tobacco mosaic virus, 69, 267, 291, 297, 407–408
Trypsin, 201–202, 237, 397–398, 400
Tryptophan synthetase, 400

U

Ultracentrifuge equilibrium. See Equilibrium ultracentrifugation.
Ultracentrifuge sedimentation, 278–283
  Archibald method, 282–283
  of associating molecules, 369, 388
  combined with intrinsic viscosity, 312–314
  concentration dependence, 280–282
  Johnston-Ogston effect, 280
  molecular weight distribution from, 280–283
  of polyelectrolytes, 363–365
  in theta (Θ) solvents, 279
Urease, 383

V

van Laar theory, 39, 59, 66, 69, 70
Vapor pressure, depression of, 163,
      165
   of normal paraffins, 3–4
Virial coefficient, second, 125, 168–175,
      184, 248, 348
   relation to intrinsci viscosity, 172
   third, 62, 64, 168, 174, 184, 248
Viruses, DNA from, 29–30, 193–194
   fractionation, 86
   solutions of, 78
   structure of spherical, 408
   See also Tobacco mosaic virus.
Viscosity, internal, 31, 293–295
   microscopic, 283–284
   Newtonian, 271
   of solutions, of chain molecules, 303–312,
      314
   concentration dependence, 299–303,
      309
   of polyelectrolytes, 332–334

   rate of shear dependence, 301–302, 304,
      310–311, 333
   of rigid particles, 299–302
   See also Intrinsic viscosity

W

Water, as a solvent, 47, 72–73, 77
   statistical mechanics of, 49
   structure, 48

X

X-ray scattering, by anisotropic solutions,
      266–267
   from DNA and RNA solutions, 140, 264
   molecular size from 198, 263
   molecular weight from, 198, 262–263
   from polypeptide solutions, 135, 267
   from protein solutions, 263–264
   from solutions of chain molecules, 264–
      266
   from tobacco mosaic virus solutions,
      266–267
Xylan, 98